Dr. Hyram

(Continued inside back cover)

The Study of ARITHMETIC

The Study of
ARITHMETIC

L. CLARK LAY

Professor of Mathematics, California State College at Fullerton

THE MACMILLAN COMPANY, NEW YORK
COLLIER–MACMILLAN LIMITED, LONDON

THE MACMILLAN COMPANY, NEW YORK

COLLIER-MACMILLAN CANADA, LTD., TORONTO, ONTARIO

Printed in the United States of America

To My Wife

Preface

This book has been developed during the past decade as a text for a course of two semesters for the training of elementary (and secondary) teachers of arithmetic. The Committee on the Undergraduate Program in Mathematics of the Mathematical Association of America has recommended for these teachers a two-course sequence devoted to the structure of the real number system and its subsystems. This text represents the author's convictions about the nature of such a course. All of the material has received a great deal of classroom experimentation and testing, with the goal of making it both attainable and challenging.

Explanations and guidance have been offered wherever experience has shown there are difficulties, even though the topic seems to be considered obvious by others. An example of this is the treatment of substitution in Chapter 6. Although less than usual is taken for granted in the opening chapters, the overall goals are ambitious both in number of mathematical concepts and in the depth to which they are pursued. Many of the developments have been chosen with the anticipation that significant numbers of the students will go on to courses in modern algebra, calculus, and statistics.

A major effort has been made to help the student develop his mathematical intuition. Graphical models have been used extensively, and their treatment here is possibly one of the most comprehensive in the literature. It is also hoped that the students will become familiar with the deductive reasoning that is so characteristic of mathematics. But proofs have been introduced very gradually and are required of students only in the later chapters. The plan is to develop as much mathematical maturity as possible, but to require as little as possible as a prerequisite.

Another feature of the text is the development and use of unary operations. This concept has proved to be very effective in improving student performance with many types of problems. It also provides a novel and direct introduction to the idea of functions.

The contemporary interest in structure is reflected in many places, but not to the exclusion of applications and technical skill. A great deal of emphasis has been given to the rational numbers, with the conviction that mastery of both their theory and use is fundamental to further progress in mathematics.

The number of problems is unusually large. They range in variety from the "of course" type to others that justify the name problem by leaving the student to his own resources. Answers are given to the odd-numbered problems. Answers for the even-numbered problems are included in a detailed Teacher's Manual, which is available from the publisher.

Thousands of persons both want and need to upgrade themselves mathematically, but their only opportunity is to study on their own. It is a particular desire of the author that this book be of help to these students. For this reason the suggestions for further study, given at the ends of the chapters, have been made quite specific. Inevitably this tends also to make them personal and opinionated, and many valuable sources were of necessity omitted in order to keep the list at a reasonable length.

The author is deeply appreciative of the critical reading of much of the manuscript by Professor Paul Johnson of the University of California at Los Angeles. Many rough spots were thereby eliminated; for such that remain the author alone is responsible. Thanks are also due to Miss Rebecca Steel and Mrs. Henrietta Wolf for highly efficient typing. A special measure of gratitude is felt for the students in the author's classes; their enthusiastic response and thoughtful criticisms made the task a most rewarding one.

L. C. L.

Contents

6

7

8

9

18

Some Mathematical Systems   404

19

The Decimal Notation for Rational Numbers   433

20

Computations with Decimal Fractions   445

21

Percentage   470

22

23

The Study of ARITHMETIC

1

Addition and Subtraction of Natural Numbers and Zero

1-1. A Point of View

Few people today would question the importance to everyone of knowing what mathematics is all about. We can broaden our horizon in mathematics by looking ahead to the more accessible parts of unfamiliar and advanced subjects, which can be interesting and stimulating. But mathematical mastery comes from digging deeply, and for this, it is often best to look back to the most elementary topics. Here we can be much more careful and observant than when we first met these ideas. Our approach might be stated this way: To make the hard problems look easy, look hard at the easy problems.

1-2. The Natural Numbers and Zero

For some time we will limit our discussion to those numbers that are represented by these marks: 0, 1, 2, 3, 4, . . . , where the three dots mean "and so on in the same way." This restriction may seem strange at first, since the reader is no doubt familiar with a variety of other kinds of numbers such as those represented by the symbols $\frac{2}{3}$, 3.25, -4, and $\sqrt{7}$. However, by limiting ourselves in this way, we not only achieve simplicity but also give emphasis to the changes that result when we later enlarge our system to include other kinds of numbers.

Considerable attention will be given to arithmetic as a language. All languages make use of symbols. A basic error one must avoid is the confusion of an idea with the symbols that represent it. A symbol for a *number* is called a numeral. Thus the marks 0, 1, 2, . . . , 19, 20, . . . , are called numerals when we wish to speak precisely. Since they represent numbers, it is common practice to speak of them as numbers if no confusion results.

We shall designate the numbers represented by 1, 2, 3, . . . as the natural numbers. Sometimes, but not usually in elementary treatises, zero is included in the class of natural numbers. Hence, the numbers with which we shall work for a while are designated as the natural numbers and zero.

Since the natural numbers are used for counting, they are sometimes called *counting numbers* or *counters*. They are used to count whole objects and hence are sometimes called *whole* numbers. These usages have not been standardized, however. Some authors call the natural numbers counting numbers; and when zero is included, term these the whole numbers. Other authors adopt the opposite convention, using whole numbers as a name for the natural numbers, and using counters when zero is included.

Any collection of symbols that represents uniquely a single number will be called a numeral. Our numeral system is so arranged that any numeral that represents a natural number or zero can be written by the use of just ten marks called *digits*. They are: 0, 1, 2, 3, 4, 5, 6, 7, 8, and 9. Thus 1492 is said to be a numeral of four digits.

*a. Is 7 a numeral, a digit, or both?

The natural numbers may be arranged to follow in a definite one-more-than order, and when arranged in this way they are said to be *consecutive*. Thus 25, 26, 27, 28 are consecutive.

Even numbers are those exactly divisible by two. If a group of objects can be separated into two smaller groups, each of which contains the same number of objects, the original group then contains an even number of objects. 0, 2, 4, 6, . . . are even numbers.

b. Why is zero somewhat a special case as an even number?

An odd number is a number not exactly divisible by two, and hence is one greater (or less) than an even number. The odd numbers are 1, 3, 5, 7, ...

Answers to Exercises

a. Both.   b. Both of the equal groups will have zero objects. Zero is divisible by 2.

Problems (1)

1. Write three consecutive natural numbers, the first of which is 15.
2. Write four consecutive natural numbers, the first of which is 24.
3. Write four consecutive even numbers, the smallest of which is 14. (*Consecutive* continues to refer to next in increasing order of size.)

* Exercises have been inserted in the body of the text as study helps. They are planned to be read and worked out at the time. Answers are given at the ends of the sections.

4. Write three consecutive even numbers, the smallest of which is 8.

5. Write five consecutive odd numbers, the largest of which is 35.

6. Write three consecutive odd numbers, the largest of which is 101.

7. Using each of the digits 1, 2, 3, 4, exactly once, write:

   a. the smallest possible odd number whose numeral has four digits.

   b. the largest possible even number whose numeral has four digits.

8. Using each of the digits 2, 3, 4, 5, exactly once, write:

   a. the smallest possible even number whose numeral has four digits.

   b. the largest possible odd number whose numeral has four digits.

9. Write, in order of increasing size of the numbers represented, all the numbers with three digit numerals that can be formed by using each of the digits 4, 5, and 6 exactly once.

10. Write, in order of increasing size of the numbers represented, all the numbers with three digit numerals that can be formed by using each of the digits 1, 2, and 3 exactly once.

1-3. Different Representations of a Number

If, when we refer to the symbol "8" we call it the "numeral 8," then we can reserve "number 8" as the correct name for an idea we have in mind.   The numeral 8 then is one way by which we can represent our idea of the number eight.

Consider the statement $6 + 2 = 8$.   It has been customary to tell arithmetic students to think of $6 + 2$ as a problem to be done, with 8 being the answer to that problem.   This answer has been called the *sum*.

There is also a different use of the word "sum," more frequently used in algebra than in arithmetic.   We think of "$6 + 2$" as being a sum.   To read $6 + 2 = 8$ as "$6 + 2$ is the same as 8" amounts to agreeing that $6 + 2$ is another way of representing the same number that 8 does; a different way from using the numeral 8. Notice carefully that we are now thinking of $6 + 2$ as being "eight" already.   We are not waiting until we have written down the mark 8.   The word "sum" can now be used to state what $6 + 2$ looks like.   We say $6 + 2$ is a way of writing eight in the form of a sum or, briefly, as a sum.

"Sum" has been used to name a kind of answer or result.

$$\overbrace{6 + 2}_{\uparrow} = \overset{\downarrow}{8}$$

We now see that in algebra, "sum" also refers to a form or pattern.

Later, when we have discussed some uses of letters in mathematics, we shall see what makes this second meaning of the word sum desirable.   When letters are used as placeholders, it is meaningless to think of adding them.   One does not try to add the a and the b in $a + b$.   But it is useful to say that $a + b$ is in the form of a sum, or that $a + b$ is a sum.

A Sum as a Result in Arithmetic
$$6 \quad + \quad 2 \quad = \quad 8$$
(addend) + (addend) = (sum)

A Sum as a Form in Algebra

$$6 \quad + \quad 2 \qquad\qquad a \quad + \quad b$$
(addend) + (addend)   (addend) + (addend)
$$\underbrace{\qquad\qquad}_{\text{sum}} \qquad\qquad \underbrace{\qquad\qquad}_{\text{sum}}$$

(Note: The word "term" can be used for "addend.")

The words used in other operations of arithmetic can be extended in meaning in a similar way.

A Difference as a Result in Arithmetic
$$11 \quad - \quad 3 \quad = \quad 8$$
(minuend) − (subtrahend) = (difference)

A Difference as a Form in Algebra

$$11 \quad - \quad 3 \qquad\qquad a \quad - \quad b$$
(minuend) − (subtrahend)   (term) − (term)
$$\underbrace{\qquad\qquad}_{\text{difference}} \qquad\qquad \underbrace{\qquad\qquad}_{\text{difference}}$$

Notice that the word "term" can be used in both addition and subtraction.

In this section we have indicated some important differences in point of view and practice between traditional arithmetic and algebra, and such considerations will arise a number of times. Many of these arise because arithmetic has in the past been occupied mainly with computation, whereas algebra is more concerned with pattern, form, and logical reasoning.

Let us note the different stages in forming $6 + 2 = 8$, and compare them with $a + b$:

1. 6   1′. a
2. 6   2   2′. $a \quad b$
3. $6 + 2$ 3′. $a + b$
4. $6 + 2 =$
5. $6 + 2 = ?$
6. $6 + 2 = 8$

a. Why is there no 4′., 5′., 6′. to correspond to 4., 5., 6.?

All would agree that when we reach line **6.** an addition has been performed. But there have been two answers as to when this addition took place.

The arithmetic student has on countless occasions been given such as **5.**, told to add, and has then received approval for **6.**   Hence, he can be expected to answer that going from **5.** to **6.** is addition.

However, we shall want to look at the equals sign in **6.** as being correctly used because it stands between two names for the same number.   That is, $6 + 2$ is already "eight" as noted above.   This means that the addition of 6 and 2 was already complete at step **3.**   This point of view brings us into agreement with **3′.** where $a + b$ is accepted as the sum of a and b.

The replacement of $6 + 2$ by 8 is a change of form or appearance only, and not a change of size.   We shall designate this change of form as a *computation*.   In order for $6 + 2$ and 8 to be accepted as truly equivalent (equal in value), there should be practice in moving not only from $6 + 2$ to 8, but also from 8 to $6 + 2$.

> **Example:**
>> *Problem:* What number is the sum of 6 and 2?
>>> *Given:* 6, 2, direction to compute.   *Response:* 8
>> *Problem:* Express 8 as a sum of two addends, the first of which is three times the second.
>>> *Given:* 8, specifications for form.   *Response:* $6 + 2$

ANSWER TO EXERCISE

a. There is for $a + b$ no change of form comparable to replacing $6 + 2$ by 8.

Problems (2)

1. What is the sum of three consecutive natural numbers, the smallest of which is 19?
2. What is the sum of four consecutive natural numbers, the largest of which is 17?
3. What is the sum of four consecutive odd numbers, the largest of which is 25?
4. What is the sum of three consecutive even numbers, the smallest of which is 18?
5. Write 10 as the sum of two natural numbers, in as many ways as possible, if the left-hand number must be larger than the right-hand number.
6. Express 15 as the sum of three odd numbers, in as many ways as possible, if the second number must be larger than the first and the third number larger than the second.
7. Write 12 as the difference of two natural numbers, in as many ways as possible, if the larger number is less than 16.

8. Express 15 as the sum of two natural numbers, in as many ways as possible, if the first number is even and also more than twice the second.
9. What is the difference between the largest possible and the smallest possible natural numbers whose numerals have three digits?
10. What is the largest number whose numeral has two digits with the left-hand digit twice the right-hand digit?
11. What is the difference between 245 and the largest number whose numeral has the same digits as 245?
12. What is the difference between 215 and the smallest even number whose numeral has the same digits as 215?
13. Write 20 as the sum of two odd numbers, in as many ways as possible, if the left-hand number is the smaller.
14. Write 20 as the sum of three odd numbers, as many ways as you can.
15. Express 20 as the sum of four odd numbers, in as many ways as you can, if they increase in size from left to right.
16. Express 20 as a sum of consecutive natural numbers, in as many ways as possible.
17. Express 12 as a sum of an even number of odd numbers, all equal and greater than 1.
18. Express 12 as a sum of an odd number of even numbers, all equal.
19. Express 12 as a sum of an odd number of even numbers, all different and increasing in size.
20. Express 12 as a sum of three different numbers, in as many ways as possible, with any one number less than the sum of the other two.
21. Express 12 as a difference of two nonzero numbers that have the least possible sum.
22. Express 12 as a sum of two odd numbers that have the least possible difference.

1-4. Statements of Addition

$3 + 4 = 7$ is an assertion that $3 + 4$ and 7 are two symbols representing the same number. It is called an *equation*, or *equality*, because of the use of the equals sign. The symbols on the left of the equals sign, in this case $3 + 4$, form the left or first member of the equation. The symbols on the right of the equals sign, in this case the single symbol 7, form the right or second member of the equation.

An important property of an equality is its symmetry. Thus $7 = 3 + 4$ is considered to make the same assertion as $3 + 4 = 7$. Each equation may be obtained from the other by interchanging the first member and the second member.

Sentences are used to write down ideas. If we can decide that a sentence is true or false, but not both, then it is called a *statement*, or a *proposition*. The sentence $3 + 4 = 7$ is a true statement, and the sentence $3 + 4 = 8$ is a false statement.   In these mathematical sentences the equals sign, translated as "equals" or "is," is the verb.

a. Would you call both $3 + 4 = 7$ and $3 + 4 = 8$ equations?

Although the expression $3 + 4 = ?$ has the form of a statement, it is not a statement because it cannot be said to be true or to be false.   This happens because of the question mark, which may be considered as indicating a blank space where a numeral is to be supplied.   If this question mark is replaced by the numeral 7 or any other name for this number, then the statement is true.   If it is replaced by a numeral for a number other than 7, then the statement is false.   If the question mark is replaced by symbols that do not name numbers, the result may be neither true nor false but just meaningless. $3 + 4 = ?$ is an example of a *statement form*, or a *propositional form*, or a *conditional equation*.   It is called conditional because a true statement results only when a certain condition is met.

Which of the following are statements?   **b.** Sugar is sweet.   **c.** Who was that?   **d.** Come here.   **e.** 1900 was a leap year.   **f.** red and black.   **g.** My age is _____.   Which, if any, are statement forms?

Some authors make a further analogy between mathematics and grammar by referring to statements as *closed sentences*, and to statement forms or conditional equations as *open* sentences.   Thus an open sentence leaves open the decision as to truth or falsity, since this cannot be made until the blank (or open) space is filled by an appropriate symbol.

An alternate notation for $3 + 4 = ?$ is $3 + 4 = (\ )$.   This stresses the blank space interpretation that we want.   However, the most common notation of all is to use some letter as a placeholder, and write $3 + 4 = N$, for example.   The problem implied in each case is that we are to find a symbol to replace N or $?$, or to write in $(\ )$, so that a true statement results.   One could use $[\ ]$ or $\{\ \}$ also instead of $(\ )$.   Still other symbols such as $\triangle$, $\square$, $\bigcirc$, are used by some authors.   It may be that some students find it easier to write 7 inside the frame in $3 + 4 = \square$ than to replace the $?$ in $3 + 4 = ?$ or the N in $3 + 4 = N$ with a 7.   This advantage can surely be questioned however, since a standard notation is not attained until the $\boxed{7}$ has been replaced by 7.

ANSWERS TO EXERCISES

a. Both will be considered equations in this text.   This convention may be unexpected, but it allows one to say $a = b$ is an equation without having at hand information to decide whether it is true or false.   **b.** and **e.** are statements.   **g.** is a statement form.

Problems (3)

The following conditional equations each have a blank space (indicated in a variety of ways) where a numeral is to be supplied.   In each case there is exactly one number which will make the resulting statement a true one. Determine this number and write the true statement.

1. $7 + 5 = ?$	7. $8 = ? - 1$	13. $19 + 36 = (\ )$
2. $9 + 1 = ?$	8. $(\ ) - 10 = 4$	14. $y - 20 = 10$
3. $(\ ) = 14 + 6$	9. $N = 21 + 13$	15. $8 = z - 8$
4. $12 = ? - 4$	10. $13 = x - 18$	16. $34 + 27 = [\ ]$
5. $(\ ) - 8 = 7$	11. $7 = x - 30$	17. $y - 10 = 20$
6. $(\ ) = 5 + 11$	12. $N = 6 + 19$	18. $8 = z - 0$

1-5. Explicit and Implicit Statement Forms

The reader will have observed that in all the problems of the preceding set, the missing number was determined by the addition of the two known numbers. This was true even though a minus sign appeared in many places. For this reason we shall refer to all of them as addition problems. There was, nevertheless, considerable variety in the way these problems were expressed. There is an important classification which will divide them all into two groups.

Equations like $4 + 9 = ?$, $(\ ) = 2 + 11$, and $7 + 3 = N$ are said to be *explicit* in form, or to specify addition explicitly. Note that one entire member consists of numerals and a sign of operation, and it represents a number uniquely. The other member is the single symbol that represents the blank space for which a numeral is to be supplied.

Equations like $? - 4 = 7$, $5 = (\ ) - 2$, and $7 = y - 13$ are said to be *implicit* in form, or to specify addition implicitly. Although it is possible to "figure out" or imply what should be done to determine the missing number, the directions are not so clear as in the explicit type. Indeed, a glance at the minus sign might lead to the error of assuming that subtraction is required to determine the correct number. It should also be noted that in the implicit form the question mark or letter is not isolated, so that by itself it forms an entire member of the equation, as was true in the explicit form.

a. If you were to use the terms "direct" and "indirect" to classify statement forms as above, how would you suggest this be done?

ANSWER TO EXERCISE

a. Direct would be equivalent to explicit; indirect to implicit.

Problems (4)

Consider each problem in set (3). If the statement form is explicit, write E; If it is implicit, write I.

1-6. Statements of Subtraction

The sum $7 + 2$ and the sum $2 + 7$ are both equal to 9; but the difference $7 - 2$ does not have the same meaning as $2 - 7$.   The difference $m - n$ does not call for subtracting the smaller from the larger, but rather asks that the second number n be subtracted from the first number m.   Hence $7 - 2$ is equal to 5, but there is no natural number that is represented by $2 - 7$.   Since we are now admitting only natural numbers and zero in our discussion, $2 - 7$ is considered to be meaningless or *undefined*.

This shows that some care must be taken when a minus sign is used.   For example, one must not write $- 5$ to the right of any numerals that stand for a number less than 5.   Thus $9 - 5$ is a representation of 4, and $5 - 5$ represents zero, but $3 - 5$ is undefined at this time.

Problems (5)

For each conditional equation, exactly one number will give a true statement. Determine this number and write the complete statement.

1. $9 - 3 = ?$	**5.** $3 + N = 7$	**9.** $225 - 40 = y$
2. $? = 7 - 5$	**6.** $9 = 2 + N$	**10.** $[\ ] = 729 - 51$
3. $(\ ) = 8 - 4$	**7.** $32 - x = 16$	**11.** $37 = z + 18$
4. $6 - 5 = (\ )$	**8.** $28 = 96 - x$	**12.** $21 = 40 - z$

All the problems in set (5) will be called subtraction problems, since in every case the number that satisfies the statement form is found by subtracting one known number from the other.   Just as for addition, they can be separated into two groups; those problems in which subtraction is called for explicitly, and those for which it is only implied.

Equations like $15 - 10 = ?$ and $N = 17 - 7$ are said to be explicit in form, and to specify subtraction explicitly.   The equals sign separates the equation into two members, one of which consists of numerals and connecting signs of operation, and the other consists solely of the symbol that is to be replaced by a numeral.

Equations like $14 = 4 + x$ and $12 - y = 5$ are said to be implicit in form, and to specify subtraction implicitly.   There is enough information to enable one to decide that subtraction is the correct operation, but the known numbers are not all located in one member of the equation, and the symbol for a blank space does not by itself form an entire member.

    a. $21 - N = 7$ is solved by subtraction and a minus sign appears in the equation.   Is the equation in explicit or implicit form?

Statement forms can be constructed so that neither zero nor any natural number will make the statement true.   For example, there is no number that will replace N

and make $7 = 2 - N$ a true statement. Hence we will regard such problems as impossible to solve at this time. Of course "impossible" is only relative, since later we shall admit another kind of number and then a solution will be possible.

ANSWER TO EXERCISE

a. Implicit. Check the specifications for explicit.

Problems (6)

If, in the following, neither zero nor any natural number can form a true statement as a replacement for N, then write "impossible." In the other problems there is exactly one number that will make the statement true. Determine it and write the complete statement. Both addition and subtraction problems are included. All problems, including those without a solution, can be classified as to form. If the conditional equation is explicit in form, write E, if implicit, write I.

1. $6 + 4 = N$	**13.** $N = 8 + 6$	**25.** $8 - 13 = N$
2. $N - 16 = 25$	**14.** $21 = 15 - N$	**26.** $4 - N = 15$
3. $7 + N = 9$	**15.** $24 = N + 15$	**27.** $50 + N = 20$
4. $42 - N = 18$	**16.** $12 = N - 15$	**28.** $N - 4 = 15$
5. $N + 4 = 7$	**17.** $10 = 6 + N$	**29.** $35 = N + 20$
6. $43 - 25 = N$	**18.** $N = 37 - 18$	**30.** $23 = N + 23$
7. $16 - 6 = N$	**19.** $N = 15 - 4$	**31.** $17 + N = 17$
8. $N + 15 = 17$	**20.** $29 = 13 + N$	**32.** $42 = N + 30$
9. $12 - N = 4$	**21.** $9 = N - 5$	**33.** $31 = N - 16$
10. $3 + N = 13$	**22.** $36 = N + 21$	**34.** $24 + N = 15$
11. $N - 7 = 13$	**23.** $17 = 6 - N$	**35.** $31 = 16 - N$
12. $9 + 13 = N$	**24.** $N = 21 + 34$	**36.** $14 - 18 = N$

1-7. Combined Addition and Subtraction

When a computation involves more than one operation, there must be agreement about "when" as well as "what" to do.

> **Example:** $10 - 6 + 3 = ?$ *Answer:* $10 - 6 + 3 = 7$

The above result follows from the agreement to use these conventions:

- **A.** The plus and minus signs are considered to affect only the numeral directly to their right. Here the minus sign refers to the 6 only, and the plus sign only to the 3.
- **B.** The computations are made one at a time, working left to right. $10 - 6$ is 4, and $4 + 3$ is 7.
- **C.** Any number can be added to any other, but a second number can be subtracted from a first only if it is not greater than the first.

Example: $10 - (6 + 3) = ?$ *Answer:* $10 - (6 + 3) = 1$

Here the agreement to work from left to right has not been followed because of the use of parentheses, which have the effect of requiring; "Do this first." Hence one begins by adding 6 and 3 (as indicated inside the parentheses) and then subtracting 9 from 10.

Another way to look at this is to think of the parentheses as extending the influence of the minus sign. In the first example above, the minus sign refers only to the numeral 6 at its right. In the second example, the minus sign is in front of a parenthesis; hence the number represented within is subtracted.

Problems (7)

Determine the number to replace N that will give a true statement, or write "none" if none is available.

1. $24 + 10 - 7 = N$	**13.** $15 - 12 - 5 = N$	**25.** $30 + 15 + 10 + 2 = N$
2. $N = 32 - (8 - 5)$	**14.** $N = 16 + 8 - 20$	**26.** $N = 40 - (20 - 10) + 3$
3. $N = 24 + (10 - 7)$	**15.** $15 - (12 - 5) = N$	**27.** $30 + (15 + 10 + 2) = N$
4. $N = 32 - 8 - 5$	**16.** $N = 16 - 20 + 8$	**28.** $N = 40 - (20 + 10) + 3$
5. $24 - 10 + 7 = N$	**17.** $N = 12 - 15 - 5$	**29.** $30 - 15 + 10 + 2 = N$
6. $32 - (8 + 5) = N$	**18.** $N = 15 - (18 - 6)$	**30.** $40 - (20 + 10 + 3) = N$
7. $24 - (10 + 7) = N$	**19.** $N = 12 - (15 - 5)$	**31.** $30 - (15 + 10 + 2) = N$
8. $32 - 8 + 5 = N$	**20.** $18 - (15 - 6) = N$	**32.** $40 - 20 + 10 + 3 = N$
9. $N = 24 - 10 - 7$	**21.** $N = 20 - 24 + 6$	**33.** $N = 30 - (15 + 10) + 2$
10. $N = 32 + (8 - 5)$	**22.** $N = 15 - 18 - 6$	**34.** $40 + (20 + 10 + 3) = N$
11. $N = 24 - (10 - 7)$	**23.** $N = 20 + 6 - 24$	**35.** $N = 30 - (15 - 10) + 2$
12. $32 + 8 - 5 = N$	**24.** $18 - 15 - 6 = N$	**36.** $40 + 20 + 10 + 3 = N$

1-8. Verbal Problems

So far we have been working with equations that either stated explicitly, or from which one could imply, how to determine a certain number. The problem had already been "set up" in equation form, and only the computation remained.

We turn now to a skill that must be developed if we are to be prepared to solve problems as they arise in life situations. We must be able to take descriptions of problems as they are given in ordinary language, and construct models for them in mathematical language. These models will be in the form of conditional equations.

> **Example:** Kay received 213 votes in a school election, and Joe received 187. What was the combined vote?

The response expected of the arithmetic student has been that after reading the problem with understanding, he shall proceed immediately to the computation as shown.   We shall emphasize the desirability of first constructing a model of the problem, before proceeding to the computation.

$$
\begin{array}{r}
213 \\
187 \\
\hline
400
\end{array}
$$

$213 + 187 = N$ is an equation that will serve as a model for this problem, for if a number is found that will give a true statement as a replacement for N, it will be the number sought in the verbal problem.   Verbal here refers to problems described in ordinary language, and not by mathematical symbols.   Many advantages follow from analyzing and restating the problem before doing the computation. A reflective attitude is encouraged so that careful planning can precede execution. After the conditional equation has been constructed, one can look back and see if the model does correctly reflect the facts in the verbal problem.

To save time we will not at the present go ahead and compute N, but rather concentrate on building correct mathematical models, and consider our task complete when this is done.   This emphasizes that the formation of the mathematical model is the critical part of the problem solution.   The computation, although important, is much more routine, and indeed is the part we turn over to machines at every opportunity.   We wish to emphasize "programing" of an attack on problems and hence concentrate the practice on this skill.

A variety of correct models can be made for the solution of a given verbal problem.   Thus, for the above example, we might have

$$213 + 187 = N$$
$$\text{or} \quad 187 + 213 = N$$
$$\text{or} \quad N = 213 + 187$$
$$\text{or} \quad N = 187 + 213$$

These are all equivalent in the sense that each correctly reflects the facts and their relation to the problem.   One of the important skills the student should develop is the rapid and accurate recognition of equivalent formulations.   One reason for the variety of models is that it is not possible to predict completely how the reader will respond to the statement of a problem.

> **Example:** How much weight must Albert add to reach 150 pounds if he now weighs 136 pounds?

One correct model is the explicit form, $N = 150 - 136$, but it is also quite logical to use the implicit form $136 + N = 150$.   It is possible to establish criteria for classifying word problems into types, and on this basis to select one model as the most appropriate.   We shall defer such an analysis until later, and emphasize that the first step for each student is to learn how to express his own ideas correctly in mathematical symbols.

It should also be noted that the model for the first example did not have any symbols stating that the numbers were numbers of votes, and the second model made no reference to pounds.   Such references to the *dimensions* of the quantities involved are to be omitted from the statement forms.   Nevertheless, it can be of value to *think* votes + votes = votes, or pounds − pounds = pounds, or possibly write this as a separate statement.   Such dimensional analysis can be a useful tool in problem solving but to be effective on a variety of problems requires ideas we have not discussed as yet (see Section 16-7).

Problems (8)

For each verbal problem, construct a mathematical model in the form of a single conditional equation.   You need not compute the number that is determined by your equation.

1. Albert Jones was born in 1913.   In what year was he 38 years old?
2. Mr. Kell paid $95 for a water heater and also $20 additional for installation. What was the total cost?   (Dollar signs should not be used in your equation.)
3. A coat that had been marked at $60 was bought late in the season for $45. How much was saved?
4. Sixteen members were absent at a meeting of a club of 42 members but there were 5 visitors present.   How many attended the meeting?
5. For lunch Hank bought a hamburger for 35 cents and a glass of milk for 12 cents.   How much did his lunch cost?
6. Mrs. Cook was offered a $5 discount on an electric fan listed at $23.   What was the selling price?
7. The air pressure in one tire was 21 pounds per square inch.   It should have been 30 pounds per square inch.   How much too low was the air pressure?
8. Harry worked 3 hours in the morning, 4 hours after lunch, and 2 hours in the evening.   What was his total time?
9. Sales at a carnival were $12 in the afternoon and $23 in the evening.   If the total expense was $8, what was the net income?
10. A pilot finds that he is at an altitude of 6,400 ft (above sea level).   How many feet must he climb to be able to clear a 10,500 ft mountain by 500 ft?
11. Each day Jean walks 7 blocks to school, then 5 blocks to an after-school job, and then 4 blocks home.   How far does she walk in all?
12. Jane is 15 years of age and her father is 38.   If her father is 2 years older than her mother, Jane's mother is how many years older than Jane?
13. Sam had 8 dollars in his pocket.   He then spent 2 dollars at the beach. Later a friend paid back a dollar he had borrowed.   How much money did Sam have then?
14. How much does the sum of 25 and 17 exceed their difference?
15. Frank wanted to save $300 during his vacation.   He has banked $130 during July, and $75 during the first half of August.   How much has he yet to save?
16. Mr. Jones drove to a town 265 miles away and returned by a route which was 37 miles longer.   If the odometer reading was 37,091 when he left, what would it be upon his return?
17. A 75 ft roll and a 50 ft roll of fencing were purchased.   When the fence was erected, 15 ft was not used.   How many feet were actually needed?

18. A school library contained 2,571 volumes at the beginning of a school year. During the year 245 volumes were added to the library but 67 volumes were lost or discarded. How many volumes were in the library at the close of the year?

19. Tom's new bicycle cost $72 and he was allowed a $10 trade-in on his old bicycle. How much remains to be paid if he made a down payment of $25?

20. Frank made purchases of 21 and 52 cents. How much change should he receive from a dollar bill?

21. A filling station operator put 2,257 gallons of gasoline in an empty tank, and then sold from it 243 gallons during a day. How many gallons are still needed to fill the tank, which has a capacity of 4,000 gallons?

22. On the first day of a trip Mr. Allen drove from 8 to 12 in the morning and from 2 to 5 in the afternoon. How many more hours did he drive in the morning than in the afternoon?

1-9. Some Language of Mathematics

The conditional equation $3 + N = 10$ is true only if $N = 7$. That is, it is only sometimes true. Letters can also be used to form statements that are always true when certain conventions are observed.

The true statement $4 + 6 = 6 + 4$ illustrates that any two numbers have the same sum no matter what the order of addition. This general principle can be written as

$$A + B \equiv B + A$$

To read this sentence, it first must be understood just what are the proper replacements for A and B. Here it is expected that they will be replaced by numerals representing numbers, and at this time our numbers are restricted to the natural numbers and zero. Any one of these may be chosen for A. Note that A is used in more than one place. While any number may be chosen for one of the A's, there is no choice for the replacement of any other A; *all must be the same.* When we select a number for B, the fact that B is different from A does not force a choice different from that for A. Rather, it allows a different choice without denying the choice of the same number for A and B, if so desired. Again the same substitution must be made for all B's. An equals sign with three bars was used in the stronger sense of "always equal."

To repeat, to state that $A + B \equiv B + A$ is to claim that if

1. Any number is chosen and used to replace each and every A,
2. And a different number (or the same) replaces each and every B,
3. Then the resulting statement is always true.

Often we use the usual form of the equals sign to write $A + B = B + A$, and let the statement form itself remind us that it always yields a true statement. Again, for emphasis, one sometimes writes

$$\text{For all } A \text{ and all } B, A + B = B + A.$$

In more advanced discussions the words "For all A and all B" may be replaced by special symbols.

Besides equations that are sometimes true, and those that are always true, we can also construct those that are never true. An example of this is $N = N + 1$. (Remember that both N's must be replaced by the same number.) It can happen that when we make a model of a problem, we shall find that no number meets the conditions as stated. This shows us that the problem has no solution. In practice, with complex problems, the equals sign is often used in a tentative manner without knowledge of whether conditions will allow the statement to be sometimes, always, or never true; and a major task of the problem is to reach this decision.

The always true statements are known as *identities* and are very useful in stating the general principles we assume to hold. The following are some identities.

$A + B \equiv B + A$ is known as the *commutative principle of addition*.

$A - B \neq B - A$, unless $A = B$.

> The sign $\neq$ is read, "is not equal to." If a second number is subtracted from a first, the result is not that obtained by subtracting the first from the second, unless the numbers are equal. Subtraction is, in general, not commutative.

$A + 0 \equiv A,$ and $A - 0 \equiv A$

> The sum of a given number and zero is the given number, or if zero be subtracted from any number, the result is that same number. These are distinctive properties of the number zero.

Such principles as these are of the highest importance in mathematics and can properly be called fundamental. Later on, when we discuss the logical structure of arithmetic, we shall find that it is built on these and similar principles.

The equals relation is of central importance for mathematics and the following principles will be in constant use. The first four of them follow directly from the use of equality in the sense of logical identity; that is, $a = b$ is a true statement if and only if a and b are names for the same object.

1. For all A, $A = A$.
   This is the *reflexive* property of equality.
2. If $A = B$, then $B = A$.
   This *symmetric* property is used when we interchange the members of an equality.
3. If $A = B$ and $B = C$, then $A = C$.
   Equality is *transitive*. The relation is "carried across" from A to C.

4. If $A = B$, then either may replace the other in a statement about the object they name.

    This is known as the *substitution* principle.
5. If $A = B$, then $A + C = B + C$.

    If $A = B$, and $C = D$, then $A + C = B + D$.

    These tell us that addition is *well defined*.
6. If $A + C = B + C$, then $A = B$.

    This is known as the *cancellation* law of addition.

   a. Can the substitution principle be used to justify the transitive property?
   b. Show how the two statements about addition being well defined can be combined into one with the use of the substitution principle.
   c. Why do we not write "If $A = B$, then $A - C = B - C$," and thus state that subtraction is well defined?

Answers to Exercises

a. Yes.   Replace B by C in $A = B$.   **b.** Replace D by C in $A + C = B + D$.   **c.** $A - C$ is not defined at all unless A is greater than or equal to C.   When subtraction is possible, this is covered by the cancellation law for addition.

1-10. The Associative Property of Addition

How should one compute $17 + (13 + 28)$?   The convention that we have agreed to follow would require that one should first add 13 and 28 to obtain 41, and then combine this result with 17 to get a final sum of 58.

A study of the slightly different expression, $(17 + 13) + 28$, shows that this also yields a final sum of 58, although the intermediate steps are different and slightly easier.   (First $17 + 13 = 30$, and then $30 + 28 = 58$.)   In both cases the same numbers were used but there was a difference in the manner in which these addends were associated or grouped together.   Study the example below, which is illustrated with counters.

$$(2 + 3) + 4$$

$$2 + 3$$

* *   *   *   *   *   *   *   *

$$(2 + 3) + 4 = 2 + (3 + 4)$$
$$(A + B) + C = A + (B + C)$$

$$3 + 4$$

$$2 + (3 + 4)$$

These examples are instances of a general property of addition called the *associative* principle.   Since $(A + B) + C = A + B + C$ by the convention of working from left to right, the parentheses can be omitted if desired.   There is, however, a subtle difference between $A + B + C$, and $(A + B) + C$ and $A + (B + C)$, which should not be overlooked.   The first of these three forms is that of the sum of three addends, whereas the latter two express the sum of two addends. Now the commutative principle as given applies only to exactly two addends. Hence, it applies directly only to $(A + B) + C$ and $A + (B + C)$ and not to $A + B + C$.

Problems (9)

The following are first to be computed as given (which means the addition inside the parentheses is done first). Then use the associative property to construct another expression for the same number. Verify that the same sum is determined even though the steps are different.

1. $36 + (14 + 19)$ 3. $(49 + 15) + 25$ 5. $(389 + 77) + 23$
2. $42 + (28 + 5)$ 4. $(37 + 7) + 13$ 6. $286 + (14 + 78)$
7. State the principles used in making the consecutive changes of form; **a.** to **b.**, **b.** to **c.**, etc.

    a. $(x + y) + z$ **e.** $(z + x) + y$ **i.** $x + (z + y)$
    b. $(y + x) + z$ **f.** $z + (x + y)$ **j.** $x + (y + z)$
    c. $y + (x + z)$ **g.** $z + (y + x)$ **k.** $(y + z) + x$
    d. $(x + z) + y$ **h.** $(z + y) + x$ **l.** $y + (z + x)$

8. Follow the same instructions as for problem 7.

    a. $[l + (m + n)] + p$ **e.** $(l + m) + (p + n)$
    b. $l + [(m + n) + p]$ **f.** $(p + n) + (l + m)$
    c. $l + [m + (n + p)]$ **g.** $[(p + n) + l] + m$
    d. $l + [m + (p + n)]$ **h.** $[p + (n + l)] + m$

Another property of addition, closely related to the associative principle, states that the sum of two addends is not changed if whatever is added to one addend is subtracted from the other addend.

```
*  *  *  *  * | *  * |        *  *  *       7 + 3      (5 + 2) + 3
                                                       5 + (2 + 3)
*  *  *  *  *        | *  * | *  *  *       5 + (3 + 2)        5 + 5
              7 + 3 = (7 − 2) + (3 + 2)
```

The general principle may be stated as

$$A + B = (A + C) + (B - C) \qquad \text{or} \qquad A + B = (A - C) + (B + C)$$

We shall refer to this as the *invariant principle for sums*, since it provides a way for changing the addends of a sum without changing the number represented by the sum as a whole. The only limitation on its use is that the subtraction indicated must be defined.

Problem sets (9), (10), and (11) provide an opportunity to practice on an important strategy in problem solving. A problem with some difficulty does not always have to be attacked directly. Perhaps we should look for an easier problem with the same answer.

Problems (10)

Before computing each number, use the invariant principle to replace the problem with a simpler one having the same answer.

1. $69 + 93$	**5.** $157 + 98$	**9.** $19 + 43$	**13.** $199 + 637$
2. $59 + 28$	**6.** $498 + 185$	**10.** $78 + 16$	**14.** $164 + 87$
3. $197 + 65$	**7.** $26 + 47$	**11.** $27 + 44$	**15.** $847 + 989$
4. $224 + 996$	**8.** $512 + 94$	**12.** $657 + 334$	**16.** $18 + 145$

1-11. Subtraction and the Associative Principle

It is not true that $10 - (7 - 2)$ equals $(10 - 7) - 2$, since $5 \neq 1$. The associative principle does not hold for subtraction. We have already observed that subtraction is not commutative and hence subtraction computations require more care than when addition alone is present. A careless reversal of order or a misplaced parenthesis that might do no harm to a sum will most likely introduce an error if subtraction is involved.

Subtraction does have a useful property that corresponds to that above for addition, which we shall term the *invariant principle for differences*. The difference between two numbers is not changed if both are increased or decreased by the same amount.

$$9 - 6 = 3$$
$$(9 - 4) - (6 - 4) = 3$$
$$5 - 2 = 3$$

$$A - B \equiv (A + C) - (B + C) \quad \text{and} \quad A - B = (A - C) - (B - C)$$

Problems (11)

Before doing the computing, replace each difference by one that is simpler to compute but which represents the same number.

1. $25 - 18$	**5.** $103 - 48$	**9.** $37 - 8$	**13.** $43 - 15$
2. $64 - 37$	**6.** $765 - 495$	**10.** $46 - 29$	**14.** $816 - 299$
3. $253 - 98$	**7.** $684 - 287$	**11.** $91 - 16$	**15.** $546 - 98$
4. $83 - 57$	**8.** $162 - 76$	**12.** $262 - 37$	**16.** $461 - 94$

For Further Study

Encouragement and valuable suggestions for the study of mathematics can be found in [S2], particularly Chapters 1, 3, and 4. Reasons for the study of mathematics are placed in an historical and cultural setting in Chapter 1 of [K4]. All students should become acquainted with [N3], a comprehensive anthology of mathematics. (The first article in Vol. 1, by Jourdain, is highly recommended.)

For discussions of "open" sentences and other connections between equations and grammar see [S8], pp. 127–131; [M11], pp. 124–134; and [W3], pp. 159–164. A very good comprehensive study of the symbolism used in mathematics is given in [M5].

Additional discussion of the commutative and associative properties can be found in [A1], pp. 21–25; [K1], pp. 18–19; and [H2], pp. 62–65.

2

Multiplication of Natural Numbers and Zero

2-1. Notations for Multiplication

To indicate multiplication, such as "4 times 5," three notations are in common use: 4×5, $4 \cdot 5$, and $(4)(5)$. We shall use the latter two almost exclusively. One, but not both, of the parentheses may sometimes be omitted as in $4(5)$ or $(4)5$.

If the N in $(3)(8) = N$ is replaced by 24, we have the true statement $(3)(8) = 24$. We say that 24 is the *product*, when it is spoken of as the result of a multiplication computation. However, the word "product" is also used to refer to the appearance of $(3)(8)$. Thus $(3)(8)$ or $3 \cdot 8$ is said to be in the form of a product or, briefly, is called a product. 3 and 8 are the *factors* that form the product.

$\frac{N}{3} = 8$ is a conditional equation that implies multiplication, and it becomes the true statement $\frac{24}{3} = 8$ when N is replaced by 24. The notation of $\frac{24}{3}$ is preferred for "24 divided by 3," rather than the more common $24 \div 3$. Reasons for this choice will appear as the discussion proceeds. The form $3 \overline{)\, 24}$ is also used in computation, but it is not adaptable to equations. Remember that we now have only the natural numbers and zero under consideration so that $\frac{24}{3}$ is at present interpreted only as a quotient or indicated division, and not as a fraction. However, the reading should be "24 divided by 3," and not "3 divided into 24," because the former is in better agreement with later use of this same form for fractions and ratios.

Problems (12)

When the conditional equation is in explicit form, designate it by E; if implicit, by I. Exactly one number will give a true statement as a replacement for N. Determine this number and write $N = $ _____.

1. $(7)(9) = N$ 5. $\dfrac{N}{4} = 7$ 9. $3 \cdot 5 = \dfrac{N}{8}$ 12. $\dfrac{N}{3 \cdot 4} = 5$

2. $\dfrac{N}{15} = 4$ 6. $(8)(11) = N$ 10. $\dfrac{N}{1} = 7$ 13. $N = 0 \cdot 12$

3. $N = 4 \cdot 9$ 7. $N = 6 \cdot 4 \cdot 5$ 11. $15 = \dfrac{N}{15}$ 14. $13 = \dfrac{N}{1}$

4. $3 = \dfrac{N}{2 \cdot 7}$ 8. $\dfrac{N}{6} = 2 \cdot 3$

Problems (13)

1. What is the product of three consecutive natural numbers, the smallest of which is 4?
2. What is the product of three consecutive odd numbers, the largest of which is 9?
3. What is the product of three consecutive even numbers, the largest of which is 8?
4. What is the product of four consecutive natural numbers, the smallest of which is 3?
5. The number 336 is the product of three consecutive natural numbers. What are they?
6. Express 210 as the product of four natural numbers, all different and all greater than 1.
7. Express 1,001 as the product of three factors, each a natural number, all different, and all greater than 1 and less than 15.
8. Express 48, as many ways as you can, as a product of two natural numbers, each greater than 1.
9. Think of each of the following as representing a single number. Express this number as a product of two natural numbers, each greater than 1.
   a. $16 + 5$ b. $48 - 13$ c. $4 + 5 + 6 + 7$ d. $70 - 5$ e. $70 + 7$
10. Find as many pairs of numbers as you can, each less than 5, such that their sum plus their difference equals their product.
11. If a natural number whose numeral has three digits is multiplied by a natural number whose numeral has two digits, what is the least number of digits the product may have? The greatest number of digits it may have?
12. The number 30 can be written as the product of three different natural numbers, each greater than 1. These three factors can be arranged in several different orders. Write all the possible arrangements, using the notation ( ) ( ) ( ).

2-2. Order of Operations

When a computation involves multiplication as well as addition and subtraction, it is still possible to use parentheses to specify the order in which the operations shall be performed. Thus $3 + (4 \cdot 5)$ is computed by first multiplying 4 times 5, and then adding 3. It has been possible to reduce the number of parentheses and thus simplify the notation by the adoption of the following convention: multiplications are done before additions and subtractions, unless there are specific instructions otherwise. Hence $3 + 4 \cdot 5$ is still computed by first multiplying 4 times 5 even though this is an exception to the left-to-right order.

If it is desired that addition or subtraction be done before multiplication, then parentheses are used to establish the priority. The types of parentheses in common use are ( ), [ ], and { }, called respectively parentheses, brackets, and braces.

Examples: $3 + 4 \cdot 5 = 23$, $(3 + 4)5 = 35$, $(3)(4 + 5) = 27$.

Problems (14)

Compute the following:

1. $(4)(3) + 2$	**13.** $50 - 6 \cdot 4$	**25.** $7 \cdot 3 + 8$
2. $(4 + 5)(6)$	**14.** $30 \cdot (7 - 2)$	**26.** $20 + 4 \cdot 3$
3. $(4)(3 + 2)$	**15.** $(50 - 6) \cdot 4$	**27.** $7 \cdot (3 + 8)$
4. $4 + (5)(6)$	**16.** $30 \cdot 7 - 2$	**28.** $20 \cdot (4 + 3)$
5. $4 + (3)(2)$	**17.** $(4)(9) + (3)(7)$	**29.** $7 + 3 \cdot 8$
6. $(4)(5 + 6)$	**18.** $(5)(8 + 4)(6)$	**30.** $20 \cdot 4 + 3$
7. $(4 + 3)(2)$	**19.** $(4)(9 + 3)(7)$	**31.** $(7 + 3) \cdot 8$
8. $(4)(5) + 6$	**20.** $(5)(8) + (4)(6)$	**32.** $(20 + 4) \cdot 3$
9. $50 \cdot 6 - 4$	**21.** $4 \cdot 9 - 3 \cdot 7$	**33.** $5 + 2 \cdot 3 + 6$
10. $(30 - 7) \cdot 2$	**22.** $5(8 - 4)6$	**34.** $4 + 6 \cdot 2 + 5$
11. $50 \cdot (6 - 4)$	**23.** $4(9 - 3)7$	**35.** $(5 + 2)(3 + 6)$
12. $30 - 7 \cdot 2$	**24.** $5 \cdot 8 - 4 \cdot 6$	**36.** $(4 + 6)(2 + 5)$

Whenever a computation involves more than one kind of operation, it is customary to name the form of the expression specifying the computation by the last operation to be performed.

Examples: $2 + (8)(5)$ is a sum, since the multiplication is done first, and the addition is done last.

$(2 + 8)(5)$ is a product, since the addition is done first, and the multiplication is done last.

$2 \cdot 8 - 5$ is a difference, since multiplication is done first, and the subtraction is done last.

Give the name for each form: **a.** $12 + (5 - 3)$. **b.** $(12 + 5) - 3$. **c.** $12 + 5 - 3$.

ANSWERS TO EXERCISES

a. Sum. **b.** Difference. **c.** Difference, because of left-to-right convention.   However, the change to **a.** is immediate.

Problems (15)

Designate each expression in problem set (14) as a sum, a difference, or a product.

2-3. Commutative and Associative Principles

The diagram below shows three 5's, or five 3's, depending on whether we group by rows or by columns.

```
*   *   *   *   *
*   *   *   *   *        (3)(5) = (5)(3)
*   *   *   *   *
```

The general principle, for which $3 \cdot 5 = 5 \cdot 3$ is an example, is assumed to hold for all natural numbers and zero, and is called the *commutative* principle for multiplication.   It may be written as

$$(A)(B) \equiv (B)(A)$$

Since the natural numbers arose out of counting, we may expect that their fundamental properties may be illustrated by arrays of counters.   The next diagram gives an example of the *associative* property of multiplication.

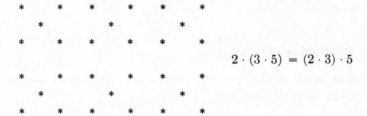

$$2 \cdot (3 \cdot 5) = (2 \cdot 3) \cdot 5$$

There are in each row three groups of 5 each or $3 \cdot 5$.   Hence the entire diagram consists of $2 \cdot (3 \cdot 5)$ counters.

But one may also count $2 \cdot 3$ groups, each of five counters.   Hence there are in all $(2 \cdot 3) \cdot 5$ counters.   Therefore, $2 \cdot (3 \cdot 5) = (2 \cdot 3) \cdot 5$.   It is assumed for all natural numbers and zero that

$$A \cdot (B \cdot C) \equiv (A \cdot B) \cdot C$$

Since $(A \cdot B) \cdot C = A \cdot B \cdot C$ by the convention of working from left to right, the parentheses may be omitted if desired.   Observe, however, that $(A \cdot B) \cdot C$ is a product of two factors, whereas $A \cdot B \cdot C$ is a product of three factors.

Problems (16)

The following are to be computed as given, which means that the multiplication inside the parentheses is done first.   Then use the associative principle to construct an equivalent expression.   Verify that the same final product is obtained even though the steps are different.   Compare with Problems (9).

1. $5 \cdot (2 \cdot 6)$ 3. $25 \cdot (2 \cdot 4)$ 5. $(9 \cdot 5) \cdot 20$ 7. $(7 \cdot 8) \cdot 125$

2. $(8 \cdot 2) \cdot 5$ 4. $2 \cdot (5 \cdot 14)$ 6. $20 \cdot (5 \cdot 13)$ 8. $(13 \cdot 8) \cdot 125$

9. State the principles used in making the consecutive changes of form, **a.** to **b.**, **b.** to **c.**, etc.

    a. $(r \cdot s) \cdot t$ **d.** $(t \cdot s) \cdot r$ **g.** $s \cdot (r \cdot t)$ **j.** $t \cdot (r \cdot s)$

    b. $r \cdot (s \cdot t)$ **e.** $(s \cdot t) \cdot r$ **h.** $(r \cdot t) \cdot s$ **k.** $t \cdot (s \cdot r)$

    c. $r \cdot (t \cdot s)$ **f.** $s \cdot (t \cdot r)$ **i.** $(t \cdot r) \cdot s$ **l.** $(s \cdot r) \cdot t$

10. Follow the same instructions as for problem 9.

    a. $w \cdot [x \cdot (y \cdot z)]$ **d.** $[w \cdot (z \cdot y)] \cdot x$ **g.** $(y \cdot x) \cdot (w \cdot z)$

    b. $w \cdot [(y \cdot z) \cdot x]$ **e.** $[(w \cdot z) \cdot y] \cdot x$ **h.** $y \cdot [x \cdot (w \cdot z)]$

    c. $[w \cdot (y \cdot z)] \cdot x$ **f.** $(w \cdot z) \cdot (y \cdot x)$

11. Follow the same instructions as for problem 9.

    a. $(f \cdot g + h) + i \cdot j$ **c.** $h + (f \cdot g + i \cdot j)$ **e.** $(i \cdot j + f \cdot g) + h$

    b. $(h + f \cdot g) + i \cdot j$ **d.** $(f \cdot g + i \cdot j) + h$ **f.** $i \cdot j + (f \cdot g + h)$

12. Follow the same instructions as for problem 9.

    a. $(l + m) [(n)(o + p)]$ **d.** $(o + p) [(n)(l + m)]$

    b. $[(l + m)(n)] (o + p)$ **e.** $[(o + p)(n)] (l + m)$

    c. $[(n)(l + m)] (o + p)$ **f.** $[(n)(o + p)] (l + m)$

2-4. The Distributive Principle

The number $(5)(3) + (4)(7)$ is illustrated below, each product being represented by a rectangular array of counters.

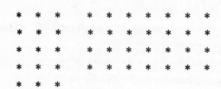

To determine the total number of counters, one would do the two multiplications separately and then add, since $(5)(3) + (4)(7)$ is a sum of two products.

We now change the problem so that one factor in the first product is used again in the second.   One such expression is $(5)(3) + (5)(7)$.

The procedure might be the same as before: multiply twice to obtain 15 and 35; then add to obtain 50.

However, since the factor 5 is the same in both products, the two rectangular patterns will now fit together to form a larger rectangle.   This was not true in the first problem.

An alternate way to compute the total number of counters is now available. Add 3 and 7 to obtain the number of counters in one side of the combined rectangle, and then multiply once by 5.   This computation would be indicated by $(5)(3 + 7)$. Since the last step is now multiplication, this would be called a product.

$$(5)(3) + (5)(7) \qquad \text{is equivalent to} \qquad (5)(3 + 7)$$
$$\text{sum} \qquad\qquad\qquad\qquad\qquad \text{product}$$

The above idea can be considered from the opposite point of view.   Let us begin with a product such as $(3)(12)$ as shown below by a rectangular pattern, which at first is to be thought of as being just one rectangle.

Twelve can be represented as a sum in a variety of ways; for example, as $10 + 2$.   Think of the original rectangle as now divided into two rectangles so that the picture becomes one of $(3)(10) + (3)(2)$.   The multiplication has been broken into two parts, or is, as we say, distributed.   This suggests the name *distributive principle*, which is given to this very useful property.

The second example of this section illustrated the use of the distributive principle in replacing the product $(3)(10 + 2)$ by the equivalent sum $(3)(10) + (3)(2)$.

In the first example the inverse of the distributive principle was used to replace the sum $(5)(3) + (5)(7)$ by the equivalent product $(5)(3 + 7)$.

The full statement of this principle is that *multiplication* is *distributive* with respect to *addition*.   In symbols it is written as

$$(A)(B + C) \equiv (A)(B) + (A)(C)$$

When this is combined with the commutative property of multiplication, which allows a change of order of the factors we get an alternate form,

$$(B + C)(A) \equiv (B)(A) + (C)(A)$$

Multiplication is also distributive with respect to subtraction.

$$(A)(B - C) \equiv (A)(B) - (A)(C) \quad \text{and} \quad (B - C)(A) \equiv (B)(A) - (C)(A)$$

It is hard to overemphasize the importance of these principles in elementary mathematics. We shall meet them many times and in a variety of situations. Remember that the distributive principle refers to a product-to-sum transformation, and the inverse of this principle refers to a sum-to-product transformation.

Problems (17)

For each expression below in the form of a product, use the distributive principle to construct an equivalent sum or difference. The inverse of the distributive principle is to be used to replace sums and differences by equivalent products. Note that no computation is involved. What you are asked to do is to recognize half of a certain pattern. Then as evidence that you have done this, you are to write down the other half of the pattern. For emphasis, you are further asked to avoid any use of the commutative laws.

1. $(6)(5 + 3)$
2. $(8)(5) + (8)(4)$
3. $(4)(7) + (6)(7)$
4. $(100 + 4)(3)$
5. $(9 + 4)(6)$
6. $(7)(10) + (7)(6)$
7. $(6)(8) + (6)(2)$
8. $(5)(7 + 2)$
9. $8 \cdot (10 + 4)$
10. $(13 + 2) \cdot 5$
11. $10 \cdot 15 + 10 \cdot 2$
12. $6 \cdot 12 + 4 \cdot 12$
13. $17 \cdot 5 + 3 \cdot 5$
14. $4 \cdot 8 + 4 \cdot 2$
15. $(7 + 3)5$
16. $6(100 + 7)$
17. $5(200 + 30 + 4)$
18. $(4)(4) + (4)(4)$
19. $9 \cdot 5 + 9 \cdot 3 + 9 \cdot 2$
20. $(2 + 3 + 4) \cdot 5$
21. $(1 + 2 + 3)5$
22. $(8)(14) + (8)(3) + (8)(5)$
23. $(5)(5) + (5)(5)$
24. $2(100 + 40 + 5)$
25. $(4)(13 - 3)$
26. $17 \cdot 4 - 2 \cdot 4$
27. $6(14) - 6(4)$
28. $(8 - 2)15$
29. $(12 - 5) \cdot 7$
30. $(3)24 - (3)4$
31. $9 \cdot 6 - 2 \cdot 6$
32. $7(14 - 3)$
33. $5 \cdot (18 + 7 - 5)$
34. $(10 - 5 + 2)4$
35. $2(3) + 4(3) - 3(3)$
36. $5 \cdot 2 - 3 \cdot 2 + 4 \cdot 2$

For the following, state the principles used in making the consecutive changes of form from **a.** to **b.**, **b.** to **c.**, etc.

37.   a. $(7 + 3)(4 + 6)$
     b. $(7 + 3)(4) + (7 + 3)(6)$
     c. $(7)(4) + (3)(4) + (7)(6) + (3)(6)$
     d. $(7)(4) + (7)(6) + (3)(4) + (3)(6)$
     e. $(7)(4 + 6) + (3)(4 + 6)$
     f. $(7 + 3)(4 + 6)$

38.   a. $[1 + (3 + 6)] \cdot 5$
     b. $1 \cdot 5 + (3 + 6) \cdot 5$
     c. $(3 + 6) \cdot 5 + 1 \cdot 5$
     d. $3 \cdot 5 + 6 \cdot 5 + 1 \cdot 5$
     e. $3 \cdot 5 + 1 \cdot 5 + 6 \cdot 5$
     f. $3 \cdot 5 + (1 + 6) \cdot 5$
     g. $5 \cdot 3 + 5 \cdot (1 + 6)$
     h. $5 \cdot [3 + (1 + 6)]$

2-5. Other Identities for Multiplication

The product $(A)(B)$ may we written more simply as AB, and $(2)(A)$ can be replaced with $2A$, if we agree that multiplication is to be indicated by two letters, or a numeral and a letter, written side by side. With this convention the identities we have just discussed may be written as follows:

$AB \equiv BA$	Multiplication is commutative.
$A(BC) \equiv (AB)C$	Multiplication is associative.
$A(B+C) \equiv AB + AC$	Multiplication is distributive with respect to ad-
$(B+C)A \equiv BA + CA$	dition.
$A(B-C) \equiv AB - AC$	Multiplication is distributive with respect to sub-
$(B-C)A \equiv BA - CA$	traction.

Particular mention should be made of the numbers one and zero when used as factors of a product. For all A it is true that $1 \cdot A = A$, or $1A = A$, and $0 \cdot A = 0$. That is, if we multiply any given number by 1, the result is that same number, but if we multiply by zero, the product is zero.

We might think of 1 as being the weakest sort of multiplier, since no change is produced on the other number. Zero, however, is very dominant, since if it is a factor, then the product is zero, no matter what the other factor is.

a. What number acts in addition as 1 does in multiplication?
b. Justify these changes of form: $4(7) + 7$, to $4(7) + 1(7)$, to $(4+1)(7)$.
c. Justify these changes of form: $ab - b$, to $ab - 1b$, to $(a-1)b$.

Since multiplication by 1 gives a product exactly or identically the same as the other factor, we refer to 1 as being the *identity element* for *multiplication*. Zero is then seen to be the identity element for addition.

In Section 1–9, addition was said to be well defined. This means that addition is consistent; that the sum of two numbers is a unique result, which is independent of the symbols used to name those numbers. In the same way it can be said that *multiplication* is *well defined*.

If $A = B$, then $AC = BC$. If $A = B$, and $C = D$, then $AC = BD$.

There is also a *cancellation law* for *multiplication:*

If $AC = BC$ and $C \neq 0$, then $A = B$.

d. If $x = 11$, then $7x = ?$ What principle supports your result?
e. If $3y = 51$, then $y = ?$ What principle supports your result?

An array of $(4)(6)$ counters can also be arranged as $(2)(12)$ or $(8)(3)$. This suggests an *invariant principle* for *products*, which is closely allied with the associative principle.

$$\left(\frac{4}{2}\right)(2 \cdot 6) = (2)(12)$$

$$(2 \cdot 4)\left(\frac{6}{2}\right) = (8)(3)$$

$$(4)(6) = [(2)(2)][(2)(3)] = (2)\{(2)[(2)(3)]\} = (2)[(2)(2)(3)] = (2)(12)$$
$$= \{[(2)(2)](2)\}(3) = [(2)(2)(2)](3) = (8)(3)$$

$$AB \equiv \left(\frac{A}{C}\right)(CB) \qquad \text{and} \qquad AB \equiv (CA)\left(\frac{B}{C}\right)$$

The application of this principle is sharply limited at present since $\dfrac{A}{C}$ or $\dfrac{B}{C}$ are not defined unless they represent a natural number or zero.

f. Use the invariant principle for products to replace the following products by others which are simpler to compute mentally: $(18)(5)$; $(25)(12)$; $(56)(125)$.

ANSWERS TO EXERCISES

a. Zero.   **b.** The property of 1 in multiplication; the inverse of the distributive principle. **c.** Same as **b.**   **d.** 77, multiplication is well defined.   **e.** 17, cancellation law for multiplication.   **f.** $(9)(10)$; $(100)(3)$; $(7)(1000)$.

2-6. Verbal Problems

The great majority of persons study mathematics principally to acquire a command of mathematical language and methods to be used in the study of the world about them.   The variety of ways in which mathematics can be applied is increasing more rapidly today than at any time in history.   The central task of applied mathematics is the creation of mathematical models of the phenomena we wish to study.   One of the simplest of such models is the single conditional equation as introduced in Section 1–8.

The next problem set will require conditional equations based on combinations of multiplication, addition, and subtraction.   The commutative, associative, distributive, and other principles make possible several ways of describing each problem.   The answer given will be only one of the various correct possibilities.   If you arrive at a different formulation, it is very important to make sure that your equation is indeed equivalent.

Problems (18)

For each verbal problem construct a mathematical model in the form of a single conditional equation.   You need not compute the number determined by the equation.

1. What is the area in square feet of a playing field 140 feet wide and 320 feet long?
2. How far will one travel in 4 hours at a constant speed of 55 miles per hour?
3. Robert has a position that pays $2 per hour.   If he works 35 hours per week for 9 weeks, how much will he earn?
4. Jimmy sold 24 papers in the afternoon and 15 in the evening.   If the price per each was 20 cents, what were his total receipts in cents?
5. A farmer has 30 orange and 25 lemon trees to spray.   How many gallons of insecticide will be required, allowing 2 gallons per tree?

6. Materials for a 65-foot block wall were quoted at $2 per foot. If the labor costs amounted to $190, what was the total cost?

7. A certain brand of canned tuna sells for 36 cents a can regularly. How much is saved by buying ten cans at a special price of 29 cents per can?

8. Mr. and Mrs. Holt bought a home. They paid $3,500 in cash for a down payment, and agreed to pay the rest in monthly payments of $95 for a period of 15 years. By the time they have made all these payments, how much will their home have cost them?

9. A school band raised $1,805 in a campaign to buy new uniforms. How much was left over after buying 39 uniforms at $44 each?

10. How many inches are there in 2 feet and 5 inches?

11. How many minutes are there in 7 hours and 37 minutes?

12. There were 314 boys in a certain school and 38 more boys than girls. How many boys and girls were there altogether?

13. Carol is 16 years old and her brother is 3 years older. How old was her brother 5 years ago?

14. How much will 4 tires and tubes cost at $28 for each tire and $4 for each tube?

15. The product of 21 and 17 is how much greater than their sum?

16. What is the product of the sum and the difference of 21 and 17?

17. If the difference between two numbers is 7 and the larger is 13, what is their product?

18. If the difference between two numbers is 7 and the smaller is 13, what is their sum?

For Further Study

A masterful account of the fundamental ideas of number appears in [C2], which was written over eighty years ago. See Chapter 1 for a discussion of commutativity, associativity, and distributivity. Supplementary discussion of these basic principles is given in [D4], pp. 14–17; [J1], pp. 53–59; [M9], pp. 11–13; and [S8], pp. 81–87.

Reference [W2] has a chapter (10) on problem solving, which includes a discussion of equations used as mathematical models.

3

Division of Natural Numbers and Zero

3-1. Some Limitations on Operations with Natural Numbers

Given any two natural numbers A and B, addition will give a sum that is also a natural number. That is, $A + B$ will always represent a natural number if A and B are such. To make this claim we must assume that we can always construct larger and larger natural numbers without any limit. If this assumption is granted, one can also state that if A and B are any two natural numbers, then they can always be multiplied, and their product AB will be a natural number.

If any two natural numbers are selected, we need not leave the realm of natural numbers to find either a sum or a product for the numbers chosen. Hence, we say the natural numbers are *closed* under the operations of addition and multiplication.

The situation is very different for subtraction. As long as we have only the natural numbers and zero, B can be subtracted from A only if B is not greater than A. If $A = B$, then $A - B = 0$; but if A and B are natural numbers with A less than B, then $A - B$ is not defined and may not be used. Hence we do *not* have closure under subtraction for the natural numbers.

The possibilities for subtraction with the natural numbers and zero are given by the following definition:

Let A and B be selected from the set of natural numbers and zero. Then C is also a member of this set, and we can write $A - B = C$ if and only if $B + C = A$ is true.

> **Examples:** Since $7 + 3 = 10$, we have also $10 - 7 = 3$, and $10 - 3 = 7$.
> But since there is no natural number N such that $7 + N = 3$, neither can we find a natural number N such that $3 - 7 = N$.

Since subtraction is commonly defined this way, by designating its relation to addition, it is often said to be an *indirect* operation. We now discuss another indirect operation, that of division, which is also possible only under certain conditions when the natural numbers and zero are used.

In the statement $\frac{12}{3} = 4$, which is read "12 divided by 3 is 4," 12 is called the *dividend*, 3 the *divisor*, and 4 the *quotient*. The word "quotient" is also used to refer to the form of $\frac{12}{3}$, which is said to represent 4 as a quotient. These same names would be used for the forms $12 \div 3 = 4$, or $3\overline{\smash{\big)}\,12}$ with quotient 4.

$$3\overline{\smash{\big)}\,\begin{array}{r} 4. \\ 12 \\ \underline{12} \end{array}}$$

The possibilities for division, with the natural numbers and zero, are given by the following definition:

Let A be a natural number or zero, and let B be a natural number. Then C is a natural number or zero, and we can write $\frac{A}{B} = C$ if and only if $BC = A$ is true.

Examples: Since $(3)(4) = 12$, we have $\frac{12}{3} = 4$, and $\frac{12}{4} = 3$.

But since there is no natural number N such that $(N)(5) = (12)$, we cannot divide 12 by 5 and $\frac{12}{5}$ is not defined. Furthermore, since $N \cdot 0 = 0$ for every number N, then if A is not equal to zero, there can be no number N such that $\frac{A}{0} = N$.

The difficulty would be of a different kind but just as serious, if in $\frac{A}{0} = N$ we were to consider the possibility of letting A be zero. Since $N \cdot 0 = 0$, no matter what N is, we have $\frac{0}{0} = N$ as a true statement no matter what number replaces N. Hence no particular value can be assigned to N. But this contradicts our requirement that the result of an operation be unique. *Zero cannot be a divisor.*

Zero can be the dividend but even here the situation is unusual. $\frac{0}{A} = 0$, no matter what A is, provided only that A is not zero.

a. $7 \cdot 0 = ?$ **b.** $0 \cdot 0 = ?$ **c.** $\frac{0}{7} = ?$ **d.** $\frac{7}{0} = ?$ **e.** $\frac{0}{0} = ?$

ANSWERS TO EXERCISES

a., b., and **c.** are zero.   **d.** and **e.** are undefined and must not be used.

Problems (19)

The following exercises are direct applications of the definitions for subtraction and division. For every addition statement below there are two related subtraction statements that use the same numerals; and for every difference there is a corresponding sum and also another difference. For every product there are two quotients; and for every quotient there is a product and another quotient. Construct the statements based on these alternate forms:

1. $5 + 7 = 12$

2. $(12)(9) = 108$

3. $13 - 5 = 8$

4. $3 = 11 - 8$

5. $42 = (6)(7)$

6. $12 + 8 = 20$

7. $\dfrac{72}{4} = 18$

8. $11 = 15 - 4$

9. $7 = 16 - 9$

10. $\dfrac{85}{17} = 5$

11. $4 = \dfrac{52}{13}$

12. $(4)(15) = 60$

Problems (20)

If the equation is in explicit form, write E; if implicit, write I. For each there is either no number or exactly one number (natural number or zero) that will give a true statement as a replacement for N. Determine this number, or write "impossible."

1. $\dfrac{12}{3} = N$

2. $4 \cdot N = 36$

3. $(3)(N) = 27$

4. $35 = 7N$

5. $N = \dfrac{1000}{8}$

6. $9 \cdot 8 = N$

7. $49 = 8N$

8. $16 + N = 30$

9. $13N = 0$

10. $30 + N = 16$

11. $6 = \dfrac{N}{42}$

12. $N = \dfrac{101}{5}$

13. $N = \dfrac{3}{15}$

14. $\dfrac{N}{7} = 21$

15. $25 + N = 15$

16. $0 = 9 \cdot N$

17. $17 = \dfrac{51}{N}$

18. $12 - N = 20$

3-2. Division and Remainders

There is no natural number N such that $\dfrac{31}{4} = N$. Hence, we say that 31 is not exactly divisible by 4. (When we are restricted to the natural numbers and zero, 31 is not divisible at all by 4.)

a. What condition must hold if 31 is exactly divisible by 4?

However, it is true that $31 = (7)(4) + 3$. We can study this relation in the following way: Write $31 = (\ )(4) + [\ ]$ and look for two numbers (natural numbers or zero). The number for $(\ )$ should be as large as possible so that the number for $[\ ]$ is less than 4.

The form $31 = (7)(4) + 3$ meets these conditions and shows that if seven 4's are subtracted from 31, there will still be a remainder of 3. The computation may be written as shown below, where 31 is the dividend; 4 is the divisor; 7 is the quotient, or better, the partial quotient; and 3 is the remainder.

$$
\begin{array}{r}
7 \\
4\overline{)31} \\
28 \\
\hline
3
\end{array}
$$

Unfortunately this procedure has been called "division" even though the attempt to divide cannot be completed, with natural numbers. The fact that the division was not accomplished and that something yet remains to be done is suggested by the word "remainder."

The computation by which we determine the two numbers for $31 = (\ )(4) + [\ ]$ might better be called "the division process," "the division computation," or "the division algorithm." The word "division" could then be properly used in those cases where a *single* number can be determined for a quotient.

The use of the form 7 R 3 is definitely to be discouraged. This notation has led to misleading and erroneous statements in elementary texts that have persisted for years. It is not uncommon to encounter such an absurdity as $31 \div 4 = 7$ R 3. This violates completely the convention about the use of the equals sign, since for a true statement this sign must appear only between two representations of the same number. The first member, $31 \div 4$, represents no number at all when only the natural numbers and zero are available, and after the introduction of rational numbers then represents the single number $\frac{31}{4}$. In the other member of the equality we note that 7 R 3 never does represent a single number. At best 7 R 3 could only be considered an abbreviation for 7, 3; or two numbers with no apparent connection between them.

Answer to Exercise

a. There would have to be a natural number N such that $4N = 31$.

Problems (21)

These problems are in the form $A = (\ )B + [\ ]$, where the number for $(\ )$ is to be zero or a natural number, and the number for $[\ ]$ must be zero, or a natural number less than B. Determine these numbers and write the completed statement.

1. $43 = (\ )(5) + [\ ]$	**5.** $2 = (\ )(10) + [\ ]$	**9.** $11 = (\ )(11) + [\ ]$
2. $3 = (\ )(12) + [\ ]$	**6.** $38 = (\ )(7) + [\ ]$	**10.** $9 = (\ )(1) + [\ ]$
3. $15 = (\ )(3) + [\ ]$	**7.** $7 = (\ )(1) + [\ ]$	**11.** $40 = (\ )(7) + [\ ]$
4. $18 = (\ )(6) + [\ ]$	**8.** $28 = (\ )(6) + [\ ]$	**12.** $6 = (\ )(6) + [\ ]$

In all the problems above it may be seen that:

A. The problem is possible; that is, two numbers that meet the requirement can be found.

B. The answers are unique; that is, only one pair of numbers meets the requirements.

If we were to try to use zero as a divisor, as we decided must not be done, the problem cannot be solved. Thus for $3 = (\ )(0) + [\ ]$ there are no numbers that will meet the requirements. Division by zero must be considered as not defined.

Zero can be the dividend, provided that the divisor is different from zero. For $0 = (\ )(3) + [\ ]$, we find that $0 = (0)(3) + [0]$ satisfies the conditions.

> **Summary:** If A is zero, or any natural number, and B is any natural number but may not be zero, then there are unique numbers Q and R, which are natural numbers or zero, such that $A = QB + R$, with R less than B.
>
> If R is zero, then Q is called the quotient. If R is not zero, then Q is called the partial quotient.

Problems (22)

The following are of the form $A = QB + R$ with A and B known and Q and R to be found. R is to be less than B, and Q and R are natural numbers or zero.

1. $72 = Q(8) + R$	**5.** $8 = Q(24) + R$	**9.** $3,724 = 76Q + R$
2. $360 = Q(18) + R$	**6.** $0 = Q(61) + R$	**10.** $5,544 = 37Q + R$
3. $70 = Q(6) + R$	**7.** $0 = Q(1) + R$	**11.** $53,739 = 79Q + R$
4. $41 = Q(15) + R$	**8.** $6 = Q(42) + R$	**12.** $5,561 = 67Q + R$

3-3. Divisors and Multiples

Let A and B be any two natural numbers. Then A is a *multiple* of B, and B is a *divisor* of A, if and only if there is a natural number C such that $A = CB$.

Suppose then there are three natural numbers R, S, and T such that $R = ST$. The following statements can be made:

> S and T are factors of the product R.
> S and T are each divisors of R.
> R is divisible by T, and also S.
> R is a multiple of T, and also of S.

Example: Since $6 = 2 \cdot 3$,
   2 and 3 are factors of 6;
   2 and 3 are divisors of 6;
   6 is divisible by 2, and also by 3;
   6 is a multiple of 2, and also of 3.

a. Is 1 a factor of 6? Why? b. Is 1 a divisor of 6? c. Is 1 a divisor of every natural number? Why? d. Is 6 a multiple of 6? e. What is the smallest divisor of 20? f. What is the smallest divisor of the natural number N? g. Is 6 a factor of 6? Why? h. What is the largest factor or divisor of the natural number N? i. What is the smallest multiple of the natural number N? j. Does the natural number N have a largest multiple?

It is convenient to keep zero out of the discussion of multiples since $0 = (0)(A)$ for all A, and we would then have zero being a multiple of every number. This would not be an advantage and is avoided by the definition given.

ANSWERS TO EXERCISES

a. Yes, $6 = 6 \cdot 1$. b. Yes. c. Yes, $N = N \cdot 1$. d. Yes. e. 1. f. 1. g. Yes, $6 = 6 \cdot 1$. h. N. i. N. j. No.

Problems (23)

1. Express 120 as the product of two factors, one of which is 8.
2. Is 360 a multiple of 48?
3. Is 365 divisible by 4?
4. Express 1,024 as the product of two factors, one of which is 64.
5. Is 13 a divisor of 101? of 1,011?
6. Is 37 a factor of 111? of 1,111?
7. Write 27 as the product of its smallest and its largest divisor.
8. Write 18 as a product of two factors, one of which is its smallest multiple.
9. Write N as a product of two factors, one of which is its largest divisor.
10. Write N as the product of its smallest divisor and its smallest multiple.

3-4. Properties of Division

We have seen that if only the natural numbers and zero are being used, the division of A by B is possible only under quite limited circumstances. In fact $\dfrac{A}{B}$, $A \div B$, and $B\overline{)A}$ make sense only when A is zero or a multiple of B. For this reason, only brief mention will be made at this time of the properties of division.

1. $\dfrac{A}{A} = 1$, if $A \neq 0$. This follows from $A \cdot 1 = A$. A number divided by the same number gives a quotient of 1, if the number is not zero.

> **Example:** $\dfrac{5}{5} = 1$

2. $\dfrac{A}{1} = A$.   If a number is divided by 1, the quotient is the same number.

       Example: $\dfrac{17}{1} = 17$

3. $\dfrac{A}{B} \neq \dfrac{B}{A}$, unless $B = A$.   Division, like subtraction, is not commutative in general.

       Example: $\dfrac{8}{2} \neq \dfrac{2}{8}$

4. $\dfrac{\dfrac{A}{B}}{\dfrac{B}{C}} \neq \dfrac{\dfrac{A}{B}}{C}$, unless $C = 1$.   Division is again like subtraction in failing to be associative in general. The computation on the left is that of dividing B by C, and then A by $\dfrac{B}{C}$.

       Example: $\dfrac{8}{\dfrac{4}{2}} = 4,$

       but $\dfrac{\dfrac{8}{4}}{2} = 1.$ The order of these divisions is controlled by the length of the bar indicating the division.

5. $\dfrac{A + B}{C} \equiv \dfrac{A}{C} + \dfrac{B}{C}$, and $\dfrac{A - B}{C} = \dfrac{A}{C} - \dfrac{B}{C}$.

       Example: $\dfrac{15 + 12}{3} = \dfrac{27}{3} = 9$; $\dfrac{15}{3} + \dfrac{12}{3} = 5 + 4 = 9$

Division is distributive with respect to addition and subtraction. The present usefulness is limited by the requirement that A and B each be zero or multiples of C.

6. $\dfrac{\dfrac{A}{B}}{C} = \dfrac{A}{BC}$, if A is a multiple of B, and also of BC.

       Example: $\dfrac{\dfrac{105}{3}}{5} = \dfrac{35}{5} = 7$ and $\dfrac{105}{3 \cdot 5} = 7$

Problems (24)

For each expression below in the form of a quotient, use the distributive principle to construct an equivalent sum or difference; and use the inverse of this principle to replace sums and differences by equivalent quotients.

1. $\dfrac{16 + 12}{4}$ 5. $\dfrac{40}{8} - \dfrac{16}{8}$ 9. $\dfrac{42}{2 \cdot 3} + \dfrac{24}{2 \cdot 3}$ 13. $\dfrac{4 \cdot 9 + 3 \cdot 16}{7 + 5}$

2. $\dfrac{24}{3} - \dfrac{15}{3}$ 6. $\dfrac{63 - 27}{9}$ 10. $\dfrac{18 - (11 - 2)}{3}$ 14. $\dfrac{49}{9 - 2} - \dfrac{35}{9 - 2}$

3. $\dfrac{35}{5} + \dfrac{15}{5}$ 7. $\dfrac{32 - 20}{4}$ 11. $\dfrac{60 - 20}{3 + 7}$ 15. $\dfrac{27 + 3}{10} - \dfrac{30 - 10}{10}$

4. $\dfrac{28 + 35}{7}$ 8. $\dfrac{91}{13} - \dfrac{52}{13}$ 12. $\dfrac{80 + 20}{8 + 2}$ 16. $\dfrac{4 \cdot 15 + 5 \cdot 18}{2 \cdot 5}$

3-5. Short Division

An analysis of the computations of elementary arithmetic will be made in a later chapter. We now discuss a variation of one of the usual procedures with which some readers may have had little experience.

Shown below is the computation for 356 divided by 2, all the steps being given of the so-called long form. When the divisor is small, it is practical to save time and space by doing more of the work mentally as shown in the second example. Also the quotient has been written below rather than above the dividend. This is convenient if one plans to use this quotient as a dividend for another division. The third example shows 356 divided by 2 to give 178, and then 178 divided by 2 to give 89.

$$
\begin{array}{r}
178 \\
2\,\overline{)\,356} \\
\underline{2} \\
15 \\
\underline{14} \\
16 \\
\underline{16}
\end{array}
\qquad
\begin{array}{r}
2\,\underline{)\,356} \\
178
\end{array}
\qquad
\begin{array}{r}
2\,\underline{)\,356} \\
2\,\underline{)\,178} \\
89
\end{array}
$$

Problems (25)

Use the short form as suggested to divide the first number by the second, then this result by the third number, and so on.

1. 258; 2, 3   3. 846; 2, 3, 3   5. 1,368; 2, 2, 2, 3, 3
2. 255; 3, 5   4. 966; 2, 3, 7   6. 1,836; 2, 2, 3, 3, 3

3-6. Combined Operations

Much of the computation in arithmetic is limited to addition, subtraction, multiplication, and division; hence these are often called the fundamental arithmetic operations.

Suppose a problem involving some or all of these operations is being considered and an expression is desired to indicate both the kind and order for doing these

operations.   The following conventions or rules are a summary of those we have
used so far for the construction and carrying out of such a set of directions.

1. Multiplications and divisions are to be done first, unless there are instructions to the contrary.
2. Additions and subtractions are to be done last, unless there are instructions
   to the contrary.
3. The "instructions to the contrary" can be of several kinds, one of these
   being the several types of parentheses.   These have the effect of requiring
   that the work inside the parentheses be done first.   With nested parentheses
   $\{[( )]\}$, one works from the inside out.   Another priority symbol is the bar
   used in division, which requires that the operations in the dividend and
   divisor first be done separately, before the division.

It should be emphasized that at present we consider $\dfrac{A}{B}$ as a quotient, not as a

fraction.   Hence the words "numerator" and "denominator" are avoided.

Problems (26)

A. Compute, doing the operations in order as specified above, otherwise from
   left to right.
B. Each expression represents a single number.   Is this representation in the
   form of a sum, or a difference, or a product, or a quotient?

1. $\dfrac{23 + 7}{5}$

2. $8 + 2(4 + 3)$

3. $\dfrac{27}{4 + 5}$

4. $\dfrac{75}{3 \cdot 5}$

5. $10 - 2 \cdot 3$

6. $5 + 4 \cdot 5 + 6$

7. $(5 + 7) \cdot 3 + 2$

8. $(30 - 4)(6 - 2)$

9. $50 - 5(7 - 3)$

10. $\dfrac{37 + 3}{4} - 6$

11. $28 - [10 - (5 - 2)]$

12. $\dfrac{37 + 3}{4 + 6}$

13. $(50 - 5)(7 - 3)$

14. $30 - 4(6 - 2)$

15. $\dfrac{19 + 5 - 6}{3}$

16. $32 + [15 - (8 + 2)]$

17. $\left(\dfrac{12}{6}\right)(16 - 4)$

18. $3 + \dfrac{56}{3 + 4} + 4$

3-7. Inverse Operations

In computing $7 + 4 - 4$, one finds that after adding 4 to 7 to obtain 11, the
subtraction of 4 then brings the result back to 7, the original number.   The subtraction of 4 has the effect of undoing the addition of 4.   The operations of addition
and subtraction are said to be *inverse* in kind because each undoes the other, in the

sense that adding and then subtracting (or subtracting and then adding) a number b to a number a produces no change in a.*

$$(a + b) - b = a \qquad (a - b) + b = a$$

a. Which of these two identities is always defined when a and b are natural numbers?

When $\dfrac{4 \cdot 7}{4}$ is computed, one finds that after multiplying 7 by 4 to obtain 28, the division by 4 brings the result back to 7, the original number. Multiplication and division are also called inverse operations, since multiplying and then dividing (or dividing and then multiplying) a number a by a number b leaves a unchanged.

$$\frac{b \cdot a}{b} = a \qquad b\!\left(\frac{a}{b}\right) = a$$

b. Which of these two identities is always defined when a and b are natural numbers?

Sometimes it can be seen that an expression calls for doing some computation, and then immediately undoing it. Where this is the case we can *cancel* the two operations that are inverse to each other; that is, we get the correct result by not doing either.

Cancellation is:

1. A most important simplification when done correctly.

2. A very common error when attempted incorrectly.

These points should be noted particularly:

A. There is more than one kind of cancellation, in fact a different kind for each pair of inverse operations.

B. Different kinds of cancellation do not "mix." Thus, although addition and subtraction of the same number cancel each other, and multiplication and division by the same nonzero number cancel, neither addition nor subtraction will cancel either multiplication or division.

c. $\dfrac{(3)(5)}{3} = 5$ Cancellation is possible.   Why?

d. $(3)(5) - 3 = 12$ Cancellation is not possible.   Why?

e. $\dfrac{3 + 9}{3} = 4$ Cancellation is not possible.   Why?

f. $\dfrac{15 - 3}{3} = 4$ Cancellation is not possible.   Why?

g. $\dfrac{15}{3} + 3 = 8$ Cancellation is not possible.   Why?

* But see Section 10-3.

Cancellation is closely related to the identity element for the operations that are inverse to each other.

$7 + 4 - 4 = 7$ Addition of 4, followed by the subtraction of 4, is equivalent
$7 + 0 = 7$ to the addition of zero.

$\dfrac{4 \cdot 7}{4} = 7$ Multiplication by 4, followed by division by 4, is equivalent
                              to multiplication by 1.
$1 \cdot 7 = 7$

ANSWERS TO EXERCISES

a. The first.   The second is not defined if b is greater than a.   **b.** The first.   The second is not defined unless a is divisible by b.   **c.** Multiplication by 3 is inverse to division by 3.   **d.** Multiplication by 3 is not inverse to subtraction of 3.   **e.** Addition of 3 is not inverse to division by 3.   **f.** Subtraction of 3 is not inverse to division by 3.   **g.** Division by 3 is not inverse to addition of 3.

Problems (27)

Do the computations, carrying out all operations in the specified order.   Then go back and decide whether any cancellation would have been possible, and write "yes" or "no."   Make this decision on the expression as it is given, or on the possibility of using the commutative and associative laws and then cancelling.   In particular, changes based on the distributive principle or its inverse are to be avoided.

1. $5(10) + 5$

2. $5 + 10 - 5$

3. $\dfrac{13 \cdot 6}{6}$

4. $\dfrac{21 - 3}{3}$

5. $17 - 7 + 7$

6. $4\left(\dfrac{36}{4}\right)$

7. $\dfrac{32 + 8}{8}$

8. $3 \cdot 11 - 3$

9. $15 + 2 \cdot 3 - 2 \cdot 3$

10. $\dfrac{35 + 3 \cdot 5}{5}$

11. $\dfrac{12 + 4}{6 - 4}$

12. $\dfrac{(5 + 2)9}{5 + 2}$

3-8. Verbal Problems

Problems (28)

The mathematical models for these problems are to be single conditional equations using the four fundamental operations.   Do no computation.

1. A family budget allows $120 for a five-day vacation.   How much would this be for each day?
2. A grocer bought 12 bags of potatoes weighing 98 pounds each.   How many smaller bags of 14 pounds each could he fill from the lot?
3. Three girls rented a lake cabin for 6 weeks at $30 per week.   What was each girl's share of the total rent?
4. Tim's steps average 24 inches in length.   How many steps would he take in walking a mile (5,280 feet)?

5. Mr. Davis bought a house for $16,500. He spent $2,400 for repairs and then sold it for $21,000. What was his profit?

6. If a bus fare is 20 cents, how much is saved by buying 6 tokens for a dollar? (Each token is good for 1 fare).

7. A ticket sale was organized by distributing 1,500 tickets equally to 6 chairmen, each of whom divided these equally among 10 ticket sellers. How many tickets would each seller receive?

8. Five boys shared equally the car expense of $20 for a weekend trip. The lodging and meals came to $6 for each. What was the total expense of each boy?

9. Three boys picked 24 quarts of cherries. They gave 12 quarts to the owner of the orchard and divided the remainder equally. How many quarts was each boy's share?

10. A car that averages 21 miles per gallon at 30 miles per hour gets only 18 miles per gallon at 60 miles per hour. How much farther will it travel on 15 gallons of gasoline at 30 miles per hour than at 60 miles per hour?

11. Three boys offered to treat at half-time during a game. If they bought 12 drinks at 15 cents each, what was each boy's share?

12. Tom drove to a town 90 miles away in two hours, but he took 3 hours for the return trip. What was his average speed for the whole trip?

13. If candy bars can be purchased at 3 for 10 cents, how many can be bought for 40 cents?

14. What is the product of the sum and the difference of 10 and 3?

15. What is the sum of 10 and the product of 10 and the difference between 10 and 4?

16. What is the quotient, if the sum of 12 and 4 is divided by their difference?

17. By how much does the product of 12 and 5 exceed their difference?

18. What is the sum of 8 and the product of 8 and the sum of 8 and 2?

19. What is the quotient, if the product of 9 and 6 is divided by their difference?

20. What is the quotient, if twice the sum of 20 and 10 is divided by half of their difference?

21. If the product of two factors is 96 and one factor is 8, what is the other factor?

22. If the quotient of two numbers is 9, and the smaller number is 27, what is the larger number?

23. If the quotient of two numbers is 7, and the larger number is 21, what is the smaller number?

24. If the product of two factors is 132, and one factor is 11, what is the other factor?

25. If the quotient of two numbers is 12, and the smaller number is 24, what is the larger number?

26. If the quotient of two numbers is 15, and the larger number is 45, what is the smaller number?

For Further Study

Arithmetic has a rich and fascinating history. For an introduction to this field [S13], [S11], and the early chapters of [D1] and [O3] are recommended. There are sections on arithmetical topics in the standard histories of mathematics such as [E1] and [S12].

4

Powers and Polynomials

4-1. Addition, Multiplication, and Raising to a Power

Multiplication is one of the direct operations and can be defined without reference to the other operations (See Chapter 9). However, it is instructive to interpret the multiplication of two natural numbers as repeated addition with the same addend. Thus, for the product $3 \cdot 5$ we can designate one of the factors, say 5, as the *multiplicand*, and the other factor, 3, as the *multiplier*. The multiplier is then used as a counter or tally; the multiplicand being written as an addend this many times.

$$3 \cdot 5 = 5 + 5 + 5$$

This procedure can be readily extended to larger multipliers.

$$4 \cdot 5 = 5 + 5 + 5 + 5$$
$$5 \cdot 5 = 5 + 5 + 5 + 5 + 5$$

But it is not so clear what should be done with smaller multipliers, since the explanation given in the first paragraph breaks down and does not apply when the multiplier is one or zero.

$$0 \cdot 5 =$$
$$1 \cdot 5 =$$
$$2 \cdot 5 = 5 + 5$$
$$3 \cdot 5 = 5 + 5 + 5$$

Why, then, have we agreed that $1 \cdot N = N$ for all N, so that $1 \cdot 5 = 5$; and further that $0 \cdot N = 0$ for all N so that $0 \cdot 5 = 0$? In effect, multiplications by zero and by one require special definitions, since they are not covered by the repeated addition interpretation. It is important to see why $0 \cdot 5 = 0$ and $1 \cdot 5 = 5$ are, nevertheless, reasonable results.

$$\text{Separately defined} \quad \begin{cases} 0 \cdot 5 = 0 \\ 1 \cdot 5 = 5 \end{cases}$$

$$\text{Repeated addition} \quad \begin{cases} 2 \cdot 5 = 5 + 5 = 10 \\ 3 \cdot 5 = 5 + 5 + 5 = 15 \\ 4 \cdot 5 = 5 + 5 + 5 + 5 = 20 \end{cases}$$
$$\text{etc.}$$

The multiplicand has been held constant at 5, and the final results of 0, 5, 10, 15, 20, ... show a *consistent* increase of 5 every time the multiplier is increased by 1. Also defining $1 \cdot 5$ as 5 brings agreement with the distributive principle since we have, for example,

$$10 = 5 + 5 = 1 \cdot 5 + 1 \cdot 5 = (1 + 1) \cdot 5 = 2 \cdot 5$$
$$5 = 1 \cdot 5$$
$$0 = 5 - 5 = 1 \cdot 5 - 1 \cdot 5 = (1 - 1) \cdot 5 = 0 \cdot 5$$

The diagram below suggests a variation of the above procedure. Study the diagram and then try **a.**

15	10	5	0
$3 \cdot 5$	$2 \cdot 5$	$1 \cdot 5$	$0 \cdot 5$
$0 + 5 + 5 + 5$	$0 + 5 + 5$	$0 + 5$	0

a. Suppose that m and n may be any natural number or zero. Can you define the product $m \cdot n$ in terms of adding n to zero?

In the same way that multiplication was considered as the repeated addition of the same addend, another operation can be developed from repeated multiplication with the same factor.

$$5^3 = 5 \cdot 5 \cdot 5 = 125$$

The 5 in 5^3 is called the *base*. The 3, written at the upper right, is called the *exponent*. The word *power* is used to refer to the result of 125, and also to refer to the form of 5^3, which is said to represent 125 as the third power of 5.

This operation is called *involution* or, more commonly today, *raising to a power*. The extension to larger exponents is again straightforward.

$$5^3 = 5 \cdot 5 \cdot 5$$
$$5^4 = 5 \cdot 5 \cdot 5 \cdot 5$$
$$5^5 = 5 \cdot 5 \cdot 5 \cdot 5 \cdot 5$$

But, just as above for repeated addition, we have trouble with one and zero.

$$\left. \begin{array}{l} 5^0 = \\ 5^1 = \end{array} \right\} \quad \text{Repeated multiplication does not apply.}$$
$$5^2 = 5 \cdot 5$$
$$5^3 = 5 \cdot 5 \cdot 5$$

Separate definitions are given for the use of one and zero as exponents.

$$N^1 = N \qquad \text{for all } N. \quad \text{Hence } 5^1 = 5.$$
$$N^0 = 1 \qquad \text{for all } N \neq 0. \quad \text{Hence } 5^0 = 1.$$

Students sometimes feel these definitions are strange when they meet them for the first time. But experience in their use will demonstrate that they are reasonable. In the sequence below the base of 5 has been kept the same. The final results of $1, 5, 25, 125, \ldots$ show a consistent multiplication by 5 every time the exponent is increased by 1.

$$5^0 = 1$$
$$5^1 = 5$$
$$5^2 = 5 \cdot 5 = 25$$
$$5^3 = 5 \cdot 5 \cdot 5 = 125$$

b. Do you see why defining 5^0 as zero would *not* fit this pattern?

The diagram below is analogous to the one for exercise **a.** and suggests a variation in the way that raising to a power may be defined. Study it and then try **c.**

125	25	5	1
5^3	5^2	5^1	5^0
$5 \cdot 5 \cdot 5 \cdot 1$	$5 \cdot 5 \cdot 1$	$5 \cdot 1$	1

c. Assume that n is a natural number but is not zero, and that m is a natural number or zero. Can you define the power n^m in terms of multiplying 1 by n?

Answers to Exercises

a. To compute $m \cdot n$, start with zero or none. Then add n, m times. In particular, for $1 \cdot n$, add n once to zero; and for $0 \cdot n$, don't add at all. **b.** If 5^0 were to be defined as zero, then 5^1, 5^2, etc. would also be zero. **c.** To compute n^m, start with one. Then multiply 1 by n, m times. In particular for n^1, multiply by n once; and for n^0, don't multiply at all.

The above exercises emphasize the unique role of zero in addition, and of one in multiplication. Zero can serve as a reference number in addition. We can start with none (as designated by zero) and then add to this as required.

It is not possible to use zero this same way with multiplication. If we began with zero, then no matter what number should be the multiplier, we get nowhere. The result is still zero! Hence, we choose one for the reference number, and then multiply as desired.

Problems (29)

The table on the next page has been completed for $n = 1, 2,$ and 3. Continue it to $n = 12$. The products have undoubtedly been memorized in the past. The powers are also useful results and worth memorizing.

n. $n + n = 2n$ $n + n + n = 3n$ $n \cdot n = n^2$ $n \cdot n \cdot n = n^3$

1. $1 + 1 = 2 \cdot 1 = 2$ $1 + 1 + 1 = 3 \cdot 1 = 3$ $1 \cdot 1 = 1^2 = 1$ $1 \cdot 1 \cdot 1 = 1^3 = 1$
2. $2 + 2 = 2 \cdot 2 = 4$ $2 + 2 + 2 = 3 \cdot 2 = 6$ $2 \cdot 2 = 2^2 = 4$ $2 \cdot 2 \cdot 2 = 2^3 = 8$
3. $3 + 3 = 2 \cdot 3 = 6$ $3 + 3 + 3 = 3 \cdot 3 = 9$ $3 \cdot 3 = 3^2 = 9$ $3 \cdot 3 \cdot 3 = 3^3 = 27$

Problems (30)

Compute the following. It will be evident that $AB \equiv BA$, but that it is not always true that $A^B = B^A$.

1. a. $3 \cdot 4$	**b.** $4 \cdot 3$	**c.** 3^4	**d.** 4^3
2. a. $2 \cdot 4$	**b.** $4 \cdot 2$	**c.** 2^4	**d.** 4^2
3. a. $2 \cdot 5$	**b.** $5 \cdot 2$	**c.** 2^5	**d.** 5^2
4. a. $2 \cdot 6$	**b.** $6 \cdot 2$	**c.** 2^6	**d.** 6^2

4-2. Combined Operations

The diagram displayed below is suggestive of a number of concepts that are related to seven operations of elementary mathematics. Five of these operations have been introduced thus far. Evolution, or extracting a root, is deferred to a later chapter and logarithms are not discussed at all. All of these, if limited to their use with natural numbers, can be readily traced back to counting.

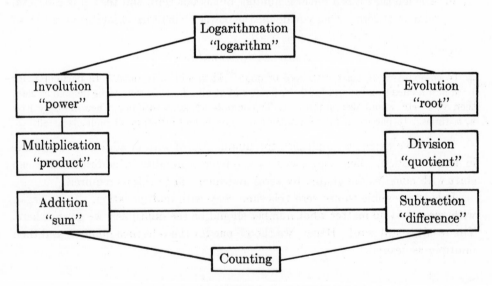

Addition, multiplication, and involution are the direct operations. $A + B$, AB and A^B are defined for the choice of any two natural numbers. The inverse or indirect operations (subtraction and division, thus far) are restricted in their use with natural numbers. Addition is both commutative and associative. Its inverse, subtraction, is neither commutative nor associative. Again, multiplication is both commutative and associative but the inverse operation, division, has neither property.

a. Is raising to a power commutative?

b. Is raising to a power associative?

When the operation of raising to a power is included with the four operations discussed in Section 3–6, it is necessary to revise the conventions stated there. Raising to a power is now done first (unless there are instructions otherwise), then multiplication and division; and finally, addition and subtraction. This means starting at the highest level on the diagram and working down. Parentheses of different kinds and the bar of division are still used to make exceptions to this order and to state what must be done first.

If it becomes necessary to use parentheses within parentheses, it is customary to arrange them in this order: $\{[(\ )]\}$. However, it is perfectly correct, although possibly not so easy to read, if only one style of parentheses is used as in $(\ (\ (\ )\ )\ )$. One of the uses of parentheses is to extend the scope of influence of an exponent.

$$5 \cdot 2^3 = 5 \cdot 8 = 40 \qquad (5 \cdot 2)^3 = 10^3 = 1000$$

In the first example, the exponent 3 is related only to the base number 2, but in the second example the base number $5 \cdot 2$ is determined by the extent of the parentheses. The first example is a product since the multiplication comes last. The second example is in the form of a power.

ANSWERS TO EXERCISES

a. No.   **b.** No.

Problems (31)

Name each form and then compute.

1. $(4 + 1)^4$	**12.** $(10 - 2)^3$	**23.** $(7 - 5)^2$
2. $\left(\dfrac{8}{2}\right)^2$	**13.** $5^3 - 5$	**24.** $(3 + 4 + 5)^2$
3. $(15 - 11)^2$	**14.** $(2 + 7)^2$	**25.** $2 \cdot 3^2 + 2 \cdot 3$
4. $\dfrac{8^2}{2}$	**15.** $(3)^2(3)$	**26.** $3 + (4 + 5)^2$
5. $4^{(3 + 2)}$	**16.** $4^2 + 5^2$	**27.** $2 \cdot 4^2 - 4 \cdot 2$
6. $(3)(4)^3$	**17.** $(4)(2)^3$	**28.** $(3 + 4)^2 + 5$
7. $\dfrac{2^4}{4}$	**18.** $2 \cdot 3 \cdot 5^2$	**29.** $3(1 + 4)^2$
8. $5^2 \cdot 4$	**19.** $2 \cdot 3^2 \cdot 5$	**30.** $5(4 - 1)^2$
9. $\left(\dfrac{12}{4}\right)^3$	**20.** $\dfrac{3^5}{3^2}$	**31.** $[(5)(6)]^2$
10. $12 - 2^3$	**21.** $7^2 - 5^2$	**32.** $4^2 \cdot 7$
11. $7^2 + 7$	**22.** $2^2 \cdot 3 \cdot 5$	**33.** $(3^2)^3$

34. $2 \cdot 5 + 2^2$ **39.** $(3 + 2)(6) - 2$ **44.** $\dfrac{5 \cdot 6^2}{3}$

35. $[(3)(4)]^2 5$ **40.** $(7 + 3 - 2)^2$ **45.** $\dfrac{5^2 \cdot 6}{3}$

36. $2 \cdot (3 \cdot 5)^2$ **41.** $(7 + 3)^2 + 2$ **46.** $3^3 - 2^2 + 3^2$

37. $(3 + 2)(6 - 2)^2$ **42.** $7^2 + (3 - 2)^2$ **47.** $3 \cdot 2^4$

38. $(3 + 2)^2(6 - 2)$ **43.** $1^2 + 2^3 + 3^4$ **48.** $(3^2)^4$

4-3. Properties of Powers

$7^3 \cdot 7^2$ has been defined as $(7 \cdot 7 \cdot 7) \cdot (7 \cdot 7)$. By using the associative property of multiplication we find this is equal to $7 \cdot 7 \cdot 7 \cdot 7 \cdot 7$ or 7^5. Hence, we can conclude that $7^3 \cdot 7^2 = 7^5$. We make the assumption that for all natural numbers A, m, and n that

$$A^m \cdot A^n = A^{m+n}$$

This identity must be studied carefully if a semantic difficulty is to be avoided. The $A^m \cdot A^n$ is in the form of a product and hence suggests *multiplication*. But A^{m+n} has the form of a power with the computation of $m + n$ calling for *addition*. Hence, the transformation of $7^3 \cdot 7^2$ to 7^5 presents the paradox of a problem designated as multiplication (multiply 7^3 by 7^2), while the only computation is addition (2 added to 3). It takes time for some students to accept this, but it is here that the power of later work with exponents and logarithms rests. In effect, when we use this identity to replace a product by an equivalent power, we have stepped our computation difficulty down one level (from multiplication to addition).

$(7^3)^2$ is, by definition, equal to $(7^3)(7^3)$. The principle above can now be applied so that

$$(7^3)^2 = (7^3)(7^3) = 7^{3+3} = 7^{2 \cdot 3} = 7^6$$

This indicates how a power of a power can be simplified by multiplication of exponents. The general principle may be written as

$$(A^m)^n \equiv A^{mn}$$

Thus $(7^3)^2$ calls for raising 7^3 to the second power, but the computation is that of multiplying 3 by 2. So once again the computation is stepped down in difficulty; from raising to a power to multiplication.

$$\frac{7^5}{7^2} = \frac{7 \cdot 7 \cdot 7 \cdot 7 \cdot 7}{7 \cdot 7}$$

To simplify this we use the fact that multiplication and division are inverse operations. To divide by $7 \cdot 7$ is equivalent to dividing by 7, and then dividing again by 7. But these two divisions will "undo" a couple of the multiplications by 7.

Hence $\dfrac{7^5}{7^2} = 7^{5-2} = 7^3$

We assume in general that

$$\frac{A^m}{A^n} \equiv A^{m-n}, \quad \text{if } A \neq 0, \text{ and } m \text{ is greater than } n$$

If m and n are equal, then the dividend and the divisor of $\dfrac{A^m}{A^n}$ are the same and the quotient is 1.   If $\dfrac{A^m}{A^n}$ is to be extended to the case where $m = n$ or $m - n = 0$, it is then required that $A^{m-n} = A^0 = 1$.   This agrees with our definition in Section 4–1.

Since this approach to zero exponents is based on using A as a divisor, the base A may not be zero in A^0, but $A^0 = 1$ for all nonzero A; $\dfrac{7^5}{7^2}$ has the form of a quotient, and we speak of "dividing 7^5 by 7^2."   However, the only computation in obtaining 7^3 is that of subtracting 2 from 5.   By replacing the quotient $\dfrac{7^5}{7^2}$ by 7^{5-2}

we again step down the level of computation, this time from dividing to subtracting.   Each of the three basic identities for powers can therefore be thought of as a procedure for replacing one set of operations by another (simpler) set.

$$A^m \cdot A^n \equiv A^{m+n}$$

a. State, in order of occurrence, the operations specified by $A^m \cdot A^n$.

b. State, in order of occurrence, the operations specified by A^{m+n}.

$$(A^m)^n \equiv A^{mn}$$

c. State, in order of occurrence, the operations specified by $(A^m)^n$.

d. State, in order of occurrence, the operations specified by A^{mn}.

$$\frac{A^m}{A^n} \equiv A^{m-n}$$

e. State, in order of occurrence, the operations specified by $\dfrac{A^m}{A^n}$.

f. State, in order of occurrence, the operations specified by A^{m-n}.

Answers to Exercises

a. Raise to a power, raise to a power, multiply.   **b.** Add, raise to a power.   **c.** Raise to a power, raise to a power.   **d.** Multiply, raise to a power.   **e.** Raise to a power, raise to a power, divide.   **f.** Subtract, raise to a power.

Problems (32)

Make use of the properties of exponents to simplify the following, but do no further computation.

1. $2^3 \cdot 2^3$ 4. $2^2 \cdot 5 \cdot 2$ 7. $\dfrac{2^3 \cdot 11^2}{2}$ 10. $\dfrac{5^4 \cdot 7}{5^2}$

2. $3^4 \cdot 3$ 5. $\dfrac{7^5}{7^2}$ 8. $\dfrac{3^5}{3^5}$ 11. $\dfrac{(4+2)^3}{(4+2)^3}$

3. $5 \cdot 5^3$ 6. $(5^2)^4$ 9. $(7^2)^5$ 12. $3 \cdot 5 \cdot 3^2 \cdot 5$

4-4. Polynomials

Computations such as shown below often arise in elementary mathematics. The expression $(3)(5)^2 - (2)(5) + 4$ is said to be a *polynomial* in powers of 5.

$$(3)(5)^2 - (2)(5) + 4 = (3)(25) - (2)(5) + 4$$
$$= 75 - 10 + 4$$
$$= 69$$

The powers would be more in evidence if we recall that $5 = 5^1$, and that $4 = 4 \cdot 1 = 4(5)^0$, and write

$$3(5)^2 - 2(5)^1 + 4(5)^0$$

For simplicity, we would write the polynomial as first given, unless there was some point in emphasizing the powers. Computation of such polynomials follows the standard convention of first the powers, then the products, and finally the sums and differences.

Problems (33)

Compute:

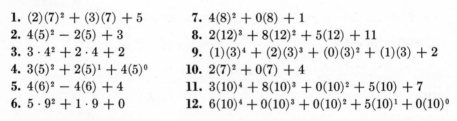

1. $(2)(7)^2 + (3)(7) + 5$ 7. $4(8)^2 + 0(8) + 1$
2. $4(5)^2 - 2(5) + 3$ 8. $2(12)^3 + 8(12)^2 + 5(12) + 11$
3. $3 \cdot 4^2 + 2 \cdot 4 + 2$ 9. $(1)(3)^4 + (2)(3)^3 + (0)(3)^2 + (1)(3) + 2$
4. $3(5)^2 + 2(5)^1 + 4(5)^0$ 10. $2(7)^2 + 0(7) + 4$
5. $4(6)^2 - 4(6) + 4$ 11. $3(10)^4 + 8(10)^3 + 0(10)^2 + 5(10) + 7$
6. $5 \cdot 9^2 + 1 \cdot 9 + 0$ 12. $6(10)^4 + 0(10)^3 + 0(10)^2 + 5(10)^1 + 0(10)^0$

4-5. Natural Numbers Represented by Polynomials

The numeral 1,492 may be read in several ways. When we see it in a history book we think, "fourteen hundred-ninety-two," or just, "fourteen ninety-two." If it were part of a telephone listing, we would say, "one-four-nine-two."

If this number were to be used on a check, the numeral would be replaced with words and written: One thousand four hundred ninety-two.

There is still another way of representing natural numbers, which may be called the *polynomial notation*.   It is valuable for making more evident a certain structure that is somewhat hidden by the usual notation.

We return to 1,492 and replace the words used above by numerals, and insert the plus signs that are now required.

one thousand   four hundred   ninety   two

1,000   +   400   +   90   +   2

A further revision replaces each addend by a product, and this produces a form that gives both the sizes of the groups used and how many of each.

$$(1)(1,000) + (4)(100) + (9)(10) + (2)(1)$$

We now take advantage of exponents and replace 1,000 by 10^3 and 100 by 10^2. We also drop one parenthesis in each product.

$$1(10)^3 + 4(10)^2 + 9(10) + 2(1)$$

The number 1,492 is now said to have been represented as a *polynomial* in powers of 10.   The common notation, 1,492, will be referred to as the *decimal numeral* notation (from the Latin *decem* for ten).

It is now seen that the digits 1, 4, 9, and 2 in the decimal numeral 1,492 have a double usage.   One of these, the *face value*, is unique for that digit and never changes.   The other, its *place value*, depends on the position in the numeral where the digit is placed.

Thus in 1,492,

the digit 2 has a face value of 2, and a place value of 1,
the digit 9 has a face value of 9, and a place value of 10,
the digit 4 has a face value of 4, and a place value of 10^2,
the digit 1 has a face value of 1, and a place value of 10^3.

By contrast, in 4,219,

the digit 9 still has a face value of 9, but a place value of 1,
the digit 1 still has a face value of 1, but a place value of 10,
the digit 2 still has a face value of 2, but a place value of 10^2,
the digit 4 still has a face value of 4, but a place value of 10^3.

The decimal numerals for the natural numbers should be considered as abbreviated forms of polynomials in powers of ten.   These polynomials are sums of products, each product being that of the face value of a digit times its place value.

Examples:

450 is an abbreviation for $4(10)^2 + 5(10) + 0(1)$
1,803 is an abbreviation for $1(10)^3 + 8(10)^2 + 0(10) + 3(1)$

A decimal numeral followed by a number word implies a product of the two numbers stated.

Example: 83 hundreds, $83 \cdot 100$, 8,300, $8(10)^3 + 3(10)^2 + 0(10) + 0(1)$

Problems (34)

Represent each of the following by polynomials in powers of 10.

1. 67	**5.** 840,219	**9.** $7 \cdot 10$	**13.** 19 tens
2. 419	**6.** 50,000	**10.** $10 \cdot 57$	**14.** 46 hundreds
3. 1,483	**7.** 12,345	**11.** $603 \cdot 10$	**15.** 341 hundreds
4. 35,722	**8.** 6,666	**12.** $44 \cdot 10$	**16.** 105 tens

4-6. Some Language Practices in Mathematics

Singular words designate a single object, whereas those that refer to more than one thing are called plural. Such words are of importance in mathematics, but their usage is sometimes unexpected. Suppose someone is overheard to say, "A number of my friends came by last night," we would infer that more than one friend came by, since the word "number" here suggests plurality or more than one. For such reasons "one," which is singular, was not accepted as a number for many centuries. Yet today we accept one and even zero as numbers, thereby admitting the singular as a special case of the plural instead of keeping them separate.

The word "polynomial" suggests more than one, because the prefix "poly" comes from a Greek word meaning "many." The examples we have given of polynomials have been sums of at least two terms, such as $3(10) + 7(1)$.

> **Question:** How shall we designate a single term such as $7(1)$?
> *Answer:* If it is important to call attention to its being a single term, we will say that $7(1)$ is a monomial ("mono" for one). But we will also admit $7(1)$ as being a polynomial and thus once again accept the singular as a special case of the plural.

Symbols with a well-determined meaning that remains unchanged throughout a discussion are called *constants*. Zero, 5, and + are examples of constants. Some symbols have no meaning of their own, but are useful for the substitutions that can be made for them. We have used letters as placeholders; the permissible replacements being the numerals for zero or the natural numbers. Symbols used in this way are called *variables*, and the set of all permissible substitutions is called the *range* of the variable.

The word "variable" strongly suggests more than one; and in $A + B \equiv B + A$, for example, there is no limit to the number of possible choices of numbers for A and B. In $x + 2 = 7$, only one replacement for x will give a true statement. In such cases we often use a singular word for x and call it the *unknown*. However, we would still like to say that x is a variable $x + 2 = 7$, even though there is only one substitution for x that interests us.

Variables are also very important in the construction of mathematical arguments and proofs. They are used at every stage of the following discussion of divisibility. We repeat below a definition previously given, and follow this with a theorem in whose proof this definition plays a key role.   The proof is given in some detail as a model for the proofs asked of the reader in the next problem set.

> **Definition:** *If A and B are natural numbers, then*
> > *A is a divisor of B,*
> > *or A is a factor of B,*
> > *or B is divisible by A,*
> > *or B is a multiple of A,*
>
> *if and only if there exists a natural number N such that $AN = B$.*

Theorem I. *If A is a divisor of B, and B is a divisor of C, then A is a divisor of C.*

Proof:

1. By the above definition, if B is a divisor of C, then there exists a natural number R such that $BR = C$.
2. Again by definition, if A is a divisor of B, then there exists a natural number S such that $AS = B$.
3. If $BR = C$, and $AS = B$ (from steps **1.** and **2.**) then $(AS)R = C$. We want to combine the conditions that are stated by the two equations. This is accomplished by using the substitution principle to replace B by AS in $BR = C$.
4. If $(AS)R = C$, then $A(SR) = C$ by the associative property of multiplication.
5. If S and R are natural numbers, there exists a natural number N such that $N = SR$, since the natural numbers are closed under multiplication.
6. If $A(SR) = C$, and $N = SR$, then $AN = C$ by substitution.
7. Hence A is a divisor of C by definition.

*Comments: Six variables (A, B, C, R, S, and N) are used.   Can you imagine how difficult this argument would be to follow if we depended on words alone? Do you see the reasons for the introduction of R, S, and N?   The substitutions as made in steps **3.** and **6.** are of a very common type.   In fact, they are so much used that the reader is often expected to notice what has happened without his attention being called to it.*

For each variable in the above proof the range was over all the natural numbers. If an argument of this kind seems hard to follow, it is often helpful to think each step through using a particular numerical example.   Suggestion: Go through this proof replacing A by 2, B by 6, and C by 24.

a. What would be the values of R, S, and N in this particular example?

After one is sure of the reasoning in a typical case, one can then replace the example numbers with variables.   This enables one to make statements that apply to any and all natural numbers with scarcely greater mental effort than that required for one numerical example.

The ability to invent such proofs comes only through practice. A systematic study of the logical structure of arithmetic is deferred until later. However, in the next problem set, several theorems are stated whose proofs can be modeled closely upon the one above.

ANSWER TO EXERCISE

a. If $A = 2$, $B = 6$, and $C = 24$, then $R = 4$, $S = 3$, and $N = 12$.

Problems (35)

Write out a proof of each of the following theorems.

1. If A is a divisor of B, and M is any natural number, then A is a divisor of BM.
2. If A is any natural number, then A is a divisor of A.
3. If A is a divisor of B, and A is a divisor of C, then A is a divisor of $B + C$.
4. If A is a divisor of B, and M is any natural number, then AM is a divisor of BM.
5. If A is a divisor of B, and A is a divisor of $B + C$ where C is a natural number, then A is a divisor of C. (You may assume that if XY is a natural number and X is a natural number, then Y is a natural number.)
6. If A is a divisor of B, and A is a divisor of C, then A is a divisor of BC.

4-7. Tests of Divisibility

For some purposes a large or even unlimited number of different variables is required. The usual alphabets of letters would soon be exhausted. One way of meeting this problem is suggested below.

$$N_0, N_1, N_2, N_3, \ldots$$

Some letter, such as N above, is chosen. Numerals, written at the lower right and called subscripts, are used as tags to create as many variables as are needed. Those above would be read as

"N sub-zero, N sub-one, N sub-two, N sub-three, and so on."

This device is used in the formulation of the following statement which is made as an assumption: Zero and every natural number N can be represented in one and only one way by a polynomial of the form

$$\cdots + N_3 \cdot 10^3 + N_2 \cdot 10^2 + N_1 \cdot 10 + N_0$$

where the range of each variable is over the ten digits $0, 1, 2, \ldots, 8, 9$. The three dots are at the left to indicate freedom to extend the pattern as required for larger numbers. For any number N as written in decimal numeral form, we have N_0 as the units digit, N_1 as the tens digit, N_2 as the hundreds digit, N_3 as the thousands digit, ...

Example: If $N = 25{,}308$, then $N_0 = 8$, $N_1 = 0$, $N_2 = 3$, $N_3 = 5$, and $N_4 = 2$.

We are now ready to devise some divisibility tests for natural numbers when they are represented by decimal numerals. The polynomial notation above was introduced so that we can readily make statements that apply to any and all natural numbers. In the example above where $N = 25{,}308$, the units digit N_0 was 8. Now 8 is divisible by 2 and it is claimed that this knowledge is sufficient to guarantee that N, or 25,308, is therefore divisible by 2. Instead of verifying that this is true by carrying out the computation on this one number, the following argument is given as one that applies to every natural number. The strategy is to begin by writing an expression that uses variables to represent any natural number. Identities, or statements that are always true, are then applied to change the form of the statement until the conclusions we want are evident.

For every natural number N,
$$N = \cdots + N_3 \cdot 10^3 + N_2 \cdot 10^2 + N_1 \cdot 10 + N_0$$
$$= (\cdots + N_3 \cdot 10^2 + N_2 \cdot 10 + N_1) \cdot 10 + N_0$$
$$= (\cdots + N_3 \cdot 10^2 + N_2 \cdot 10 + N_1) \cdot 2 \cdot 5 + N_0$$

N is now the sum of two terms, the first of which is certainly divisible by 2. Hence by applying Theorems 3 and 5 in problem set (35) we can conclude that the number N will be divisible by 2 if and only if N_0 is zero or is a multiple of 2.

A natural number is divisible by 2 if and only if the units digit is zero or is a multiple of 2. (We will not mention each time that the number must be written in decimal numeral form.)

The argument above applies equally well to divisibility by 5.

A natural number is divisible by 5 if and only if the units digit is zero or 5.

The next tests will be for 3 and 9. They will also be developed by using the commutative, associative, and distributive principles to change the form of the polynomial representation of N. We first verify that the powers of 10 are each greater, by 1, than some multiple of 9.

$$10 = 1 \cdot 9 + 1$$
$$10^2 = 11 \cdot 9 + 1$$
$$10^3 = 111 \cdot 9 + 1$$

This conclusion can be stated with the use of variables:
If n is a natural number, then there exist natural numbers $M_1, M_2, M_3, \ldots$ such that

$$10^n = M_n \cdot 9 + 1$$

Here M_n is a variable whose range is the set of numbers M_1, M_2, M_3, etc. Thus $M_1 = 1$, $M_2 = 11$, $M_3 = 111$, etc.

For every natural number N,

$$
\begin{aligned}
N &= \cdots + N_3 \cdot 10^3 + N_2 \cdot 10^2 + N_1 \cdot 10 + N_0 \\
&= \cdots + N_3(M_3 \cdot 9 + 1) + N_2(M_2 \cdot 9 + 1) + N_1(M_1 \cdot 9 + 1) + N_0 \\
&= \cdots + N_3 M_3 \cdot 9 + N_3 + N_2 M_2 \cdot 9 + N_2 + N_1 M_1 \cdot 9 + N_1 + N_0 \\
&= (\cdots + N_3 M_3 \cdot 9 + N_2 M_2 \cdot 9 + N_1 M_1 \cdot 9) + (\cdots + N_3 + N_2 + N_1 + N_0) \\
&= (\cdots + N_3 M_3 + N_2 M_2 + N_1 M_1) \cdot 9 + (\cdots + N_3 + N_2 + N_1 + N_0) \\
&= (\cdots + N_3 M_3 + N_2 M_2 + N_1 M_1) \cdot 3 \cdot 3 + (\cdots + N_3 + N_2 + N_1 + N_0)
\end{aligned}
$$

This demonstrates that every natural number (whose decimal numeral has two or more digits) can be written as the sum of two terms such that,

1. One term is some multiple of 9 (and of 3), and
2. The other term is the sum of the digits taken at their face value.

Since the first term is clearly divisible by both 3 and 9, the divisibility of N itself by 3 or 9 depends on whether the sum $\cdots + N_3 + N_2 + N_1 + N_0$ is divisible by 3 or 9, or is not divisible by them.

> **Examples:** $3 + 8 + 5 + 2 = 18$. 18 is divisible by both 3 and 9. 3,852 is divisible by both 3 and 9.
>
> $1 + 4 + 7 = 12$. 12 is a multiple of 3, but not of 9. 147 is a multiple of 3, but not of 9.
>
> $9 + 5 = 14$. 14 is not divisible by either 3 or 9. 95 is not divisible by either 3 or 9.

A natural number is divisible by 3 if and only if the sum of its digits is divisible by 3.
A natural number is divisible by 9 if and only if the sum of its digits is divisible by 9.

The next tests are for 4 and 25. Their development is an extension of the procedure used for the tests for 2 and 5.

For every natural number N, whose decimal numeral has 3 or more digits,

$$
\begin{aligned}
N &= \cdots + N_4 \cdot 10^4 + N_3 \cdot 10^3 + N_2 \cdot 10^2 + N_1 \cdot 10 + N_0 \\
&= (\cdots + N_4 \cdot 10^2 + N_3 \cdot 10 + N_2) \cdot 10^2 + (N_1 \cdot 10 + N_0) \\
&= (\cdots + N_4 \cdot 10^2 + N_3 \cdot 10 + N_2) \cdot 4 \cdot 25 + (N_1 \cdot 10 + N_0)
\end{aligned}
$$

The first term is a multiple of 4 and of 25, and the second term is the number whose decimal numeral is that given by the two digits at the right. Hence inspection of this number will check the divisibility of N by 4 or 25.

> **Examples:** 32 is divisible by 4. 97,532 is divisible by 4.
>
> 15 is not a multiple of 4. 815 is not a multiple of 4.
>
> 75 is a multiple of 25. 1,975 is a multiple of 25.

A natural number whose decimal numeral has 3 or more digits is divisible by 4 if and only if the number formed by the two right-hand digits is divisible by 4.

A natural number whose decimal numeral has 3 or more digits is divisible by 25 if and only if the number formed by the two right-hand digits is divisible by 25.

Problems (36)

1. Give the steps in developing the test for divisibility by 2, but use the number 3,176 instead of variables as in the text above.
2. Give the steps in developing the test for divisibility by 5, but use the number 9,485 instead of variables.
3. Give the steps in developing the test for divisibility by 3, but use the number 673 instead of variables.
4. Give the steps in developing the test for divisibility by 9, but use the number 456 instead of variables.
5. Give the steps in developing the test for divisibility by 4, but use the number 61,712 instead of variables.
6. Give the steps in developing the test for divisibility by 25, but use the number 8,825 instead of variables.
7. Devise a test for divisibility by 8 or 125, which works for a number whose decimal numeral has four or more digits.
8. Give two or more tests, which if all were satisfied would guarantee divisibility by 6; by 12; by 15: by 18; by 24; by 36.
9. Test each number for divisibility by 2, 3, 4, 5, 9, and 10. List such divisors that the number has.

a. 226	**e.** 328	**i.** 306	**m.** 89	**q.** 1,800
b. 291	**f.** 310	**j.** 246	**n.** 625	**r.** 119
c. 747	**g.** 620	**k.** 390	**o.** 729	**s.** 1,234
d. 305	**h.** 171	**l.** 840	**p.** 1,024	**t.** 10,101

10. In each case give the smallest number whose numeral has three digits and meets the divisibility property, if possible.

a. by 2, but not 3	**e.** by 2, but not 5	**i.** by 3 and 5, but not 4
b. by 3, but not 2	**f.** by 5, but not 2	**j.** by 4 and 5, but not 3
c. by 3, but not 9	**g.** by 3, 4, and 5	**k.** by 4 and 9
d. by 9, but not 3	**h.** by 3 and 4, but not 5	**l.** by 3 and 8

4-8. Computation and the Representation of Numbers

The following diagram presents six ways of representing the number eight. It is emphasized that none of these is the number itself.

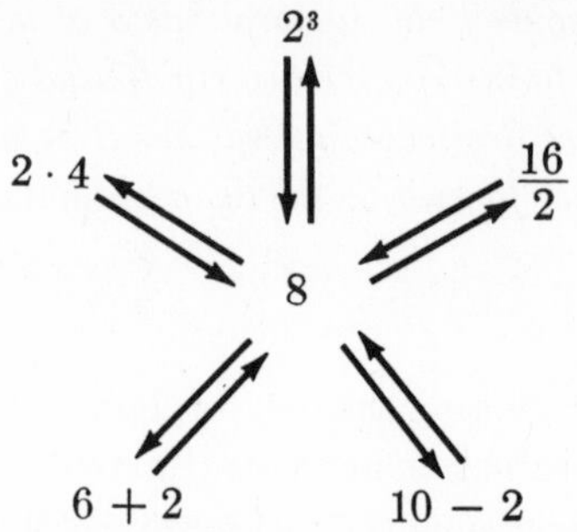

The symbol in the center is the decimal numeral for eight. The expressions on the outside represent eight as a sum, difference, quotient, power, and product, respectively.

Now it is true that the decimal numeral 8 does have special properties that make it unique. Of all the six forms given in the diagram, it is the one most easily recognized as standing for the number 8. It would be the best answer of all to a question asking "How many?" That is, the decimal numerals have become accepted as *basic* numerals for identification of the natural numbers.

This has allowed us to use the word "compute" with the following meaning: Given any set of symbols that determines a number, we are to replace these symbols with the basic numeral for this kind of number. Thus, if asked to compute $6 + 2$, or $10 - 2$, or $2 \cdot 4$, or $\frac{16}{2}$, or 2^3, the result expected in each case is that we write the numeral 8, and nothing else would be acceptable.

But if we were asked to express 8 as a sum, for example, one could write $7 + 1$, or $6 + 2$, or $5 + 3$, or $4 + 4$. There would be no unique answer without further restriction, such as asking for two addends that are consecutive odd numbers. This narrows our choice to $3 + 5$.

So much time has been spent in arithmetic in starting with forms as on the outside of the diagram and working toward the center that it is easy to get the idea that mathematics is mainly computation. This is far from true. A number of problems that have been, and will be proposed, are to help the reader get over any bias toward computation as being the principal activity in mathematics and to become more alert to pattern, form, and structure.

Problems (37)

The number 40 can be represented as a difference of two squares by $7^2 - 3^2$, or by $11^2 - 9^2$. Represent each of the following as a difference of nonzero squares in as many ways as possible. A table of squares (up to at least 20^2) should be available. You are asked to devise a way of determining the required squares, and what may be harder, a way of knowing when you have them all.

1.	3	7.	12	13.	20	19.	28
2.	5	8.	13	14.	21	20.	29
3.	7	9.	15	15.	23	21.	31
4.	8	10.	16	16.	24	22.	32
5.	9	11.	17	17.	25	23.	33
6.	11	12.	19	18.	27	24.	35

The number 13 can be represented as the sum of two squares by $2^2 + 3^2$; it cannot be represented as the sum of three squares; but it can be represented as the sum of four squares by $2^2 + 2^2 + 2^2 + 1^2$. Represent the following numbers as a sum of two, or three, or four squares as many ways as possible. Zero is not to be used.

25.	10	29.	18	33.	61	37.	38
26.	14	30.	29	34.	58	38.	34
27.	37	31.	53	35.	45	39.	52
28.	5	32.	49	36.	41	40.	59

41. For natural numbers n from 2 to 7, write n^2 as the sum of the fewest possible cubes.
42. For $n = 1, 2, 3, 4$, and 5, verify that $n(n + 1)(n + 2)(n + 3) + 1$ is a square.
43. For $n = 1, 2, 3, 4$, and 5, write n^3 as the sum of n consecutive odd numbers.
44. Write each of the following as the sum of consecutive natural numbers in as many ways as possible: a. 30.   b. 31.   c. 32.   d. 33.   e. 34.

Problems (38)

Construct mathematical models for these in the form of a single conditional equation. Do no computation.

1. What is the sum of the squares of 7 and 10?
2. What is the square of the sum of 9 and 5?
3. What is the cube of the difference between 8 and 6?
4. What is the difference of the cubes of 11 and 4?
5. What is the sum of the squares of the three smallest nonzero even numbers?
6. What is the square of the sum of the three smallest odd numbers?
7. What is the square of the product of 6 and 10?
8. What is the sum of the fourth powers of 5 and 3?
9. What is the difference between the square of the sum of 8 and 2, and the sum of their squares?
10. What is the difference between the square of the product of 7 and 3, and the product of their squares?
11. What is the square of the product of the sum and the difference of 6 and 4?
12. What is the product of the sum, and the difference of the squares, of 5 and 3?

For Further Study

Squares, cubes, and higher powers of the natural numbers lend themselves to many mathematical recreations. See [B4], pp. 135–167; [M6], pp. 32–43; and [R1], pp. 17–37.

For further discussion of tests of divisibility refer to [N2], pp. 227–233; [W3], pp. 109–112; [R1], pp. 64–71; and [M6], pp. 1–7. A more complete analysis will be given after Chapter 18.

5

Products and Natural Numbers

5-1. Primes and Composites

We have seen how our decimal numerals emphasize the *additive* structure of the natural numbers by representing them as *sums*. Thus 15 is considered to be an abbreviation for $1(10) + 5(1)$. But this same number may also be designated by the *product* $3 \cdot 5$. The *multiplicative* structure of the natural numbers will be our concern in this chapter.

Since our earliest mathematical experiences grow out of counting, the additive structure of the natural numbers becomes dominant in everyone's mind. By beginning with 1, and repeatedly adding 1, any number may be generated.

$$
\begin{array}{cccccc}
1 & 1+1 & 1+1+1 & 1+1+1+1 & \text{etc.} \\
1 & 2 & 3 & 4
\end{array}
$$

The pattern is very simple—too simple, in fact, to be efficient by itself for many ways that these numbers may be used.

It is evident that the operation of addition and a sufficient stock of 1's would make possible the construction of any natural number. What can be done with 1's and the operation of multiplication?

$$
\begin{array}{cccccc}
1 & 1 \cdot 1 & 1 \cdot 1 \cdot 1 & 1 \cdot 1 \cdot 1 \cdot 1 & \text{etc.} \\
1 & 1 & 1 & 1
\end{array}
$$

Repeated use of 1 as a factor gives only 1 as a product. Because the number 1 has this passive or inactive property as a multiplier, we set it aside in our task of building the natural numbers by multiplication.

By introducing 2, we can obtain 2, 4, 8, 16, . . . by multiplication alone, but a 3 will be needed as well to get, 3, 6, 9, 12, ...   And as the chart below shows, we still need 5, 7, 11, 13, . . . if we are to fill in the gaps.

2	3	4	5	6	7	8	9	10	11	12	13	14
<u>2</u>		2^2				2^3						
	<u>3</u>			$2 \cdot 3$			3^2			$2^2 \cdot 3$		
			<u>5</u>					$2 \cdot 5$				
					<u>7</u>							$2 \cdot 7$
									<u>11</u>		<u>13</u>	

The numbers 2, 3, 5, 7, 11, 13, . . . , called *primes*, are the fundamental building blocks for construction of the natural numbers by multiplication.   The numbers 4, 6, 8, 9, 10, 12, 14, . . . are said to be *composite* and they have a simple geometric interpretation.   A composite number of objects can be placed in a rectangular array, with the same number in each row and the same number in each column, and with more than one row and more than one column.

```
        4         6           8            9
      *  *     *  *  *     *  *  *  *    *  *  *     etc.
      *  *     *  *  *     *  *  *  *    *  *  *
                                        *  *  *
```

Since a rectangular array may be associated with a product, we can state these definitions:

A natural number is said to be composite if it can be expressed as a product of two natural numbers, each greater than 1.
A natural number, greater than 1, which cannot be expressed as the product of two natural numbers, each greater than 1, is a prime.

The number 1 is not classified as either prime or composite, and zero is also not included in this classification.

For every natural number N we have $N = 1 \cdot N$.   If N is greater than 1, the two factors 1 and N are different.   Hence every natural number greater than 1 has at least two divisors; itself, and one.   The number may have only these two divisors, in fact this is an alternate way of defining prime numbers.

Examples: $2 = 1 \cdot 2$, $3 = 1 \cdot 3$, $5 = 1 \cdot 5$, $7 = 1 \cdot 7$, . . .
These show the only way these primes can be expressed as products of natural numbers, and hence reveal their only divisors.

By contrast, every composite number has divisors greater than one, but less than the number itself.

Examples: 4 has the divisors 1, *2*, 4.
6 has the divisors 1, *2*, *3*, 6.
8 has the divisors 1, *2*, *4*, 8.

The number 12 can be written as a product in several ways: $1 \cdot 12$, $2 \cdot 6$, and $3 \cdot 4$. It can be written as a product of prime factors in essentially only one way: $12 = 2 \cdot 2 \cdot 3$. Any other representation of 12 as a product of primes can only be with the same primes in a different order as in $2 \cdot 3 \cdot 2$.

The table in Appendix 1 is based on this important fact: Every natural number greater than 1 either is a prime or, if not, can be expressed as a unique product of primes. Some of the first entries in the table are shown below. The number 1 is omitted, since it is neither prime nor composite. The primes are written in decimal numeral form. The composites are expressed as products of primes. These prime factors are arranged in increasing size, left to right, and exponents are used whenever there is repetition of the same factor.

2	3	2^2	5	$2 \cdot 3$	7	2^3	3^2	$2 \cdot 5$
11	$2^2 \cdot 3$	13	$2 \cdot 7$	$3 \cdot 5$	2^4	17	$2 \cdot 3^2$	19	$2^2 \cdot 5$

We shall consider the directions, "Write these composite numbers in prime factored form," to mean that the conventions above are to be used and hence the form will be as given in the table. Primes are left in decimal numeral form, since their only product form of $1 \cdot N$ is without interest (and 1 is not a prime).

The following are all representations of 36. In what way does each fail to meet the specifications for prime factored form?   **a.** $2^2 \cdot 9$.   **b.** $(2 \cdot 3)^2$.   **c.** $3^2 \cdot 2^2$.   **d.** $2 \cdot 2 \cdot 3^2$.   **e.** What is the correct form?

Example: What is the prime factored form of 420?   of 290?

```
2 | 4 2 0
2 | 2 1 0        420 = 2² · 3 · 5 · 7
3 | 1 0 5
5 |   3 5
        7
```

```
2 | 2 9 0
5 | 1 4 5        290 = 2 · 5 · 29
      2 9
```

The prime factors are found by testing in turn as divisors, the prime numbers in order of increasing size: 2, 3, 5, 7, 11, . . ., until the last quotient is recognized as being prime. The tests for divisibility given in Section 4-7 will be of some help. In the next example the necessary trials are shown that must be made before it can be decided that 181 is a prime number. The remainders are written after a dash ——.

Example:

```
2 | 181              3 | 181              5 | 181
     90 —— 1              60 —— 1              36 —— 1

7 | 181             11 | 181             13 | 181
     25 —— 6              16 —— 5              13 —— 12
```

A trial with 2, 3, 5, 7, 11, and 13 shows that none of these is a factor. The next prime to try would be 17. But $17 \cdot 17 = 189$, which is greater than 181. Hence, if 181 were to be the product of two primes, one of them would have to be less than 17. We have shown by trial that there is no such prime factor. Therefore, 181 is itself a prime.

It is important to see why the testing as above can safely ignore composite divisors or factors. Why, for example, was the number 6 not checked? If 6 actually were a factor of 181, then by definition there would exist a natural number N that would make all of these statements true.

$$181 = 6 \cdot N \qquad 181 = (2 \cdot 3) \cdot N \qquad 181 = 2 \cdot 3N \qquad 181 = 3 \cdot 2N$$

Since $2N$ and $3N$ would then be natural numbers, we conclude that if 6 is a divisor, so also are 2 and 3. Hence, if either 2 or 3 fails to be a factor, then 6 cannot be.

Answers to Exercises

a. 9 is not a prime. **b.** This is a power rather than a product. **c.** The prime 2 should come before the 3. **d.** This should be 2^2 instead of $2 \cdot 2$. **e.** $2^2 \cdot 3^2$.

Problems (39)

Some skill in obtaining the prime factorizations of numbers is required. Practice on numbers up to at least 150, checking your results against the table in the Appendix.

Primes will be found to be of great value in analyzing products, quotients, and powers, but not for sums and differences. Hence, the possibility of expressing even numbers greater than 2 as the sum of two primes may be considered to be a mathematical puzzle, although an interesting one. It was conjectured by Goldbach in 1742 that this was always possible but a proof of the truth (or falsity) for all natural numbers still has not been found.

The following exercise should help you learn to recognize the smaller primes. Each number is to be expressed as a sum of two primes, as many ways as possible.

Example: 18 is $5 + 13$, and $7 + 11$. Remember, 1 is not a prime.

Problems (40)

1. 30	**3.** 32	**5.** 34	**7.** 76	**9.** 78
2. 20	**4.** 22	**6.** 24	**8.** 46	**10.** 50

5-2. Divisors

The decimal numeral is the basic numeral for a natural number because it provides the quickest recognition of which number is being represented. For some other questions the prime factored form is better.

Example: What are all the divisors of 60?   This can be answered very readily if 60 is written as $2^2 \cdot 3 \cdot 5$ or $2 \cdot 2 \cdot 3 \cdot 5$.

    a. Since 1 is not a prime, it is not mentioned in the prime factored form.   But we remember that every natural number has 1 as a divisor.

    b. The divisors 2, 3, and 5 are obtained by choosing, one at a time, from the different prime factors of 60.

    c. The divisors 2^2, $2 \cdot 3$, $2 \cdot 5$, and $3 \cdot 5$, whose decimal numerals are, respectively, 4, 6, 10, and 15, are obtained by multiplying primes chosen two at a time from $2 \cdot 2 \cdot 3 \cdot 5$.

    d. The divisors $2^2 \cdot 3$, $2^2 \cdot 5$, and $2 \cdot 3 \cdot 5$, whose decimal numerals are, respectively, 12, 20, and 30, are obtained by multiplying primes chosen three at a time from $2 \cdot 2 \cdot 3 \cdot 5$.

Hence the list of divisors of 60 is

1, 2, 3, 2^2, 5, $2 \cdot 3$, $2 \cdot 5$, $2^2 \cdot 3$, $3 \cdot 5$, $2^2 \cdot 5$, $2 \cdot 3 \cdot 5$, $2^2 \cdot 3 \cdot 5$, or

1, 2, 3, 4, 5, 6, 10, 12, 15, 20, 30, 60.

Summary: The divisors of a natural number are:

    1; its different prime factors, chosen one at a time; the different possible products of its prime factors, chosen two at a time; and the different possible products of its prime factors, three at a time; and so on until one reaches the product of all the prime factors, which is the number itself.

Problems (41)

List all the divisors of the following, with the composite divisors in prime factored form.

1. $2^4 \cdot 5$	**5.** $2 \cdot 41$	**9.** 84	**13.** 86
2. $2 \cdot 5^3$	**6.** $7 \cdot 19$	**10.** 74	**14.** 76
3. 3^4	**7.** 83	**11.** 85	**15.** 88
4. 2^5	**8.** 73	**12.** 75	**16.** 77

Any divisor of a number N, and the quotient when N is divided by the given divisor, form a pair of divisors whose product is N.   Each divisor is formed by some selection of the prime factors of N ranging from none to all; the quotient is formed from the remaining prime factors.   The divisors of 60 have been arranged in such pairs below.

1	and		$2^2 \cdot 3 \cdot 5$
2	and		$2 \cdot 3 \cdot 5$
3	and		$2^2 \cdot 5$
2^2	and		$3 \cdot 5$
5	and		$2^2 \cdot 3$
$2 \cdot 3$	and		$2 \cdot 5$

1 is not a prime; $2^2 \cdot 3 \cdot 5$ is the product of all the prime factors.

2 is a prime divisor; $2 \cdot 3 \cdot 5$ is the product of the remaining prime factors.

3 is a prime divisor; $2^2 \cdot 5$ is the product of the remaining primes.

2^2 is a product of two primes; $3 \cdot 5$ is the product of the rest.

etc.

$$60 = (1)(2^2 \cdot 3 \cdot 5)$$
$$= (2)(2 \cdot 3 \cdot 5)$$
$$= (3)(2^2 \cdot 5)$$
$$= (2^2)(3 \cdot 5)$$
$$= (5)(2^2 \cdot 3)$$
$$= (2 \cdot 3)(2 \cdot 5)$$

Problems (42)

Express each number as the product of two factors, with each composite factor in prime factored form. Do this in all possible ways, including the trivial factorization of 1 times the number itself.

1. 100   **4.** 107   **7.** 103   **10.** 110

2. 106   **5.** 102   **8.** 109   **11.** 105

3. 101   **6.** 108   **9.** 104   **12.** 111

The divisors of the natural numbers from 2 to 14 are each arranged on a diagram below.

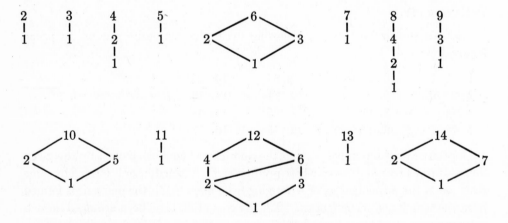

These diagrams show not only the divisors of the number at the top, but also the divisors of its divisors, etc., so that in any diagram all the divisors are shown of every number used in that diagram. Each number is divisible by exactly those numbers to which it is connected by a descending line segment or a chain of such.

a. What is the significance of a single vertical chain?   **b.** What is the signif-

icance of the number of branches at the bottom (or top)?   **c.** What is characteristic of numbers at the same level?   Check the diagram for 12.

ANSWERS TO EXERCISES

a. The number is either a prime, or a power of a single prime.   **b.** The number has this many
distinct prime factors.   **c.** Numbers at the same level are products of the same number of
prime factors (which need not be different).   1 is not a prime, 2 and 3 are single primes,
$4 = 2 \cdot 2$ and $6 = 2 \cdot 3$, $12 = 2 \cdot 2 \cdot 3$.

Problems (43)

Construct diagrams similar to those above for the numbers:

1. 15 to 30   **2.** 31 to 44

The prime factored form reveals the multiplicative structure of a natural number.   It might then be expected that such forms will be of special usefulness in the
operations of multiplication and division.

Examples:

$$\textbf{A.} \quad 12 \overline{)168} = 14 \qquad \textbf{B.} \quad 2^2 \cdot 3 \overline{)2^3 \cdot 3 \cdot 7} = 2 \cdot 7$$

The computation suggested by **A.** where 168 is to be divided by 12 to give a
quotient of 14 is of a kind that has become familiar through much practice.   In
B. each decimal numeral has been replaced by the equivalent prime factored form,
so that each number is now scarcely recognizable.   However, form **B.** does make
very clear relations involving the dividend, divisor, and quotient, that are not at
all obvious in **A.**

Problems (44)

First obtain the prime factored form of the given numbers, using the table in
Appendix 1 if needed.   Then determine N, leaving it also in prime factored form.

1. $\dfrac{170}{34} = N$

2. $14 \overline{)168}$

3. $162 \div 27 = N$

4. $\dfrac{184}{23} = N$

5. $19 \overline{)N}^{\,7}$

6. $\dfrac{N}{14} = 28$

7. $N \div 22 = 8$

8. $\dfrac{154}{N} = 14$

9. $N \overline{)192}^{\,12}$

10. $\dfrac{N}{143} = 9$

11. $172 \div N = 43$

12. $(17)(19) = N$

13. $(4)(N) = 256$

14. $(N)(24) = 192$

15. $\dfrac{N}{21} = 35$

16. $7 \overline{)N}^{\,57}$

17. $\dfrac{204}{N} = 12$

18. $182 \div N = 13$

Problems (45)

Each expression represents a single natural number. Express this number in prime factored form, making sure that all specifications are met. Besides using the basic laws of exponents, there is opportunity to make use of the commutative, associative, and distributive principles.

1. $8 \cdot 18$	**7.** 20^2	**13.** $3^3 \cdot 18^2$	**19.** $19 \cdot 31 - 13 \cdot 31$
2. $12 \cdot 20$	**8.** $(10 \cdot 12)^2$	**14.** $13 + 7 \cdot 13$	**20.** $(17 + 19)18$
3. $21 \cdot 7$	**9.** 28^3	**15.** $17 \cdot 23^2 + 2 \cdot 23^2$	**21.** $17^2 + 17^3$
4. $33 \cdot 22$	**10.** 18^2	**16.** $2^3 \cdot 12^2$	**22.** $23 \cdot 7 - 9 \cdot 7$
5. $15 \cdot 24$	**11.** $(6 \cdot 14)^2$	**17.** $9 \cdot 19 + 19$	**23.** $21(24 + 25)$
6. $8 \cdot 32$	**12.** 34^3	**18.** $2 \cdot 17 + 11 \cdot 17$	**24.** $11^4 - 11^3$

5-3. The Greatest Common Divisor

Sometimes it is useful to know the largest number that is a divisor of two or more numbers. What, for example, is the largest number that is a divisor of both 42 and 48?

$$\begin{cases} 1 \quad 2 \quad 3 \qquad 6 \quad 7 \qquad\qquad 14 \qquad 21 \qquad 42 \\ 1 \quad 2 \quad 3 \quad 4 \quad 6 \qquad 8 \quad 12 \qquad 16 \qquad 24 \qquad 48 \end{cases}$$

After listing the divisors for 42 and 48, we can see that 1, 2, 3, and 6 are divisors of both numbers, and of these divisors which are common to 42 and 48, the largest is 6. Therefore, 6 is the *greatest common divisor* (abbreviated g.c.d.) of 42 and 48. The name highest common factor (h.c.f.) is also used.

The g.c.d. of two or more numbers may be written down at sight if their prime factored forms are available.

Example: $42 = 2 \cdot 3 \cdot 7$

$48 = 2 \cdot 2 \cdot 2 \cdot 2 \cdot 3$

g.c.d.
$2 \cdot 3 = 6$

$42 = 2 \cdot 3 \cdot 7$

$48 = 2^4 \cdot 3$

2 appears as a factor in both numbers. (It is used more than once in one number, but not in the other.)

3 appears as a factor once in both numbers.

The common divisors of 42 and 48 are: 1, which is not mentioned in the prime factored form; 2; 3; and the product $2 \cdot 3$. Their g.c.d., 6, is the largest of these four common divisors.

Example: $48 = 2 \cdot 2 \cdot 2 \cdot 2 \cdot 3$

$84 = 2 \cdot 2 \cdot 3 \cdot 7$

g.c.d.
$2 \cdot 2 \cdot 3 = 12$

$120 = 2 \cdot 2 \cdot 2 \cdot 3 \cdot 5$

$48 = 2^4 \cdot 3$

$84 = 2^2 \cdot 3 \cdot 7$

$120 = 2^3 \cdot 3 \cdot 5$

There are at least two of the 2 factors in all of the numbers.   3 appears once as a factor in all of the numbers.

The common divisors of 48, 84, and 120 are: 1, 2, 3, 2^2, $2 \cdot 3$, $2^2 \cdot 3$. Their g.c.d., 12, is the largest of these six common divisors.

At first the student may prefer to write out the repeated factors without using exponents, and connect the common prime factors in the manner used in the examples.   To work directly with the prime factored form we first observe that a common divisor can have only those prime factors which are factors of *all* the given numbers.   Next, if some prime factor is repeated in some or all of the given numbers, then the exponent of that prime factor (in the g.c.d.) must be the *smallest* used with that factor in any of the given numbers.

Problems (46)

In problems 1 to 12, determine all the common divisors of the two numbers, listing them in order of increasing size so that the final one will be the g.c.d. Write all composite common divisors in prime factored form.

1. $\begin{cases} 2 \cdot 3 \\ 2 \cdot 5 \end{cases}$ 4. $\begin{cases} 3 \cdot 23 \\ 2 \cdot 3 \end{cases}$ 7. $\begin{cases} 2 \cdot 11^2 \\ 2^2 \cdot 11 \end{cases}$ 10. $\begin{cases} 7^3 \\ 7^5 \end{cases}$

2. $\begin{cases} 5 \cdot 7 \\ 3 \cdot 7 \end{cases}$ 5. $\begin{cases} 5^2 \cdot 11 \\ 5^2 \cdot 13 \end{cases}$ 8. $\begin{cases} 2 \cdot 3^2 \cdot 5 \\ 2^2 \cdot 3 \cdot 5 \end{cases}$ 11. $\begin{cases} 294 \\ 126 \end{cases}$

3. $\begin{cases} 5 \cdot 13 \\ 13 \cdot 17 \end{cases}$ 6. $\begin{cases} 2 \cdot 7^2 \\ 3 \cdot 7^2 \end{cases}$ 9. $\begin{cases} 3 \cdot 17 \\ 5 \cdot 11 \end{cases}$ 12. $\begin{cases} 91 \\ 187 \end{cases}$

For problems 13 to 22, N, M_1, and M_2 are to be natural numbers.   List all possible values of N, in order of increasing size, and in prime factored form when composite.

13. $\begin{cases} N \cdot M_1 = 3^2 \cdot 5 \\ N \cdot M_2 = 3^2 \cdot 7 \end{cases}$ 17. $\begin{cases} 11 \cdot 17 \div N = M_1 \\ 2 \cdot 17^2 \div N = M_2 \end{cases}$ 20. $\begin{cases} \dfrac{2 \cdot 5 \cdot 11}{M_1} = N \\ \dfrac{3 \cdot 5 \cdot 11^2}{M_2} = N \end{cases}$

14. $\begin{cases} N \cdot M_1 = 5 \cdot 23 \\ N \cdot M_2 = 5^2 \cdot 29 \end{cases}$ 18. $\begin{cases} 5 \cdot 19 \div N = M_1 \\ 3 \cdot 23 \div N = M_2 \end{cases}$ 21. $\begin{cases} N\,\overline{\smash{\big)}\,\dfrac{M_1}{3^3}} \\ N\,\overline{\smash{\big)}\,\dfrac{M_2}{3^4}} \end{cases}$

15. $\begin{cases} M_1 \cdot N = 2 \cdot 11 \\ M_2 \cdot N = 3 \cdot 13 \end{cases}$ 19. $\begin{cases} \dfrac{3 \cdot 5 \cdot 19}{N} = M_1 \\ \dfrac{3 \cdot 7 \cdot 19}{N} = M_2 \end{cases}$ 22. $\begin{cases} M_1\,\overline{\smash{\big)}\,\dfrac{N}{2^2}} \\ M_2\,\overline{\smash{\big)}\,\dfrac{N}{5^2}} \end{cases}$

16. $\begin{cases} M_1 \cdot N = 2 \cdot 3 \cdot 5 \\ M_2 \cdot N = 3 \cdot 5 \cdot 7 \end{cases}$

For problems 23 to 28, determine the g.c.d. of the set of numbers, writing it in prime factored form when composite.

23. $\begin{cases} 3 \cdot 5 \cdot 7 \\ 3 \cdot 7 \cdot 13 \\ 7 \cdot 13 \cdot 17 \end{cases}$ 25. $\begin{cases} 3 \cdot 5^2 \cdot 11 \\ 3 \cdot 5 \cdot 11 \\ 3 \cdot 5 \cdot 11^2 \end{cases}$ 27. $\begin{cases} 234 \\ 198 \\ 130 \end{cases}$

24. $\begin{cases} 2^5 \\ 2^7 \\ 2^3 \end{cases}$ 26. $\begin{cases} 2 \cdot 3 \\ 3 \cdot 5 \\ 5 \cdot 7 \end{cases}$ 28. $\begin{cases} 42 \\ 63 \\ 105 \end{cases}$

5-4. Relatively Prime Numbers

Since every natural number has 1 as a divisor, then any two natural numbers must always have 1 as a common divisor. They may possibly have no other common divisors except 1 and, if so, the two numbers are said to be *relatively prime*, or prime to each other. Hence, two relatively prime numbers have no common prime factors.

Neither 8 nor 9 is itself a prime, but these two numbers are relatively prime. Because 2^3 and 3^2 have no common prime factors, their only common divisor is 1. Necessarily 1 must be their g.c.d.

"Prime" and "composite" refer to a single natural number. Every natural number greater than 1 is either prime or composite. "Relatively prime" refers to a relation that two numbers may have to each other, but nothing at all is said about each number.

   a. If A is a prime number, to what numbers is A relatively prime?
   b. If A is a composite number, to what numbers is A relatively prime?
   c. The number 1 is relatively prime to what numbers?

ANSWERS TO EXERCISES

a. To all numbers that do not have A as a factor. **b.** To all numbers that are not divisible by any of the prime factors of A. **c.** To every natural number.

Problems (47)

1. Since $18 = 2 \cdot 3^2$, the numbers relatively prime to 18 are those that do not have 2 or 3 as a factor. List the numbers greater than 10 and less than 20 that are relatively prime to 18.
2. List the numbers greater than 20 and less than 30 that are relatively prime to 14.
3. List the numbers less than 10 that are relatively prime to 10.
4. List the numbers less than 9 that are relatively prime to 9.
5. From the following list select all possible pairs of numbers that are relatively prime: 26, 21, 15, 14.

6. What can be said about the relative primality of: **a.** Any two consecutive natural numbers? **b.** Any two consecutive even numbers? **c.** Any two consecutive odd numbers?

7. What is the number, all of whose powers are relatively prime to every odd number?

8. All even numbers that are not relatively prime to 25 must have what rightmost digit in their decimal numeral?

5-5. Multiples

Every natural number has only a limited number of divisors since they cannot be greater than the number itself. There is, however, no limit to the number of multiples of any natural number. Thus, if N is a natural number, then $N \cdot 3$ is by definition a multiple of 3 no matter what natural number replaces N. The multiples of 3 are therefore

$$3, 6, 9, 12, 15, \ldots \text{ as determined by } 1 \cdot 3, 2 \cdot 3, 3 \cdot 3, 4 \cdot 3, 5 \cdot 3, \ldots$$

It is evident that every natural number is its own smallest multiple, but that no natural number has a greatest multiple.

a. How many multiples of 5 are less than 20?

b. For any natural number N, what number is both a multiple of and a divisor of N?

c. Are there any numbers N, such that every multiple of N is odd?

d. Are there any numbers N, such that every multiple of N is even?

For any natural number N, the prime factors of the multiples of N will be all those of N itself, together with the prime factors of the multiplier. This is illustrated below with the first nine multiples of 30. Beneath each multiple is: the product which determines it; then this product with each composite factor in prime factored form; and finally the prime factored form of the multiple.

30	60	90	120	150
$1 \cdot 30$	$2 \cdot 30$	$3 \cdot 30$	$4 \cdot 30$	$5 \cdot 30$
$1 \cdot (2 \cdot 3 \cdot 5)$	$2 \cdot (2 \cdot 3 \cdot 5)$	$3 \cdot (2 \cdot 3 \cdot 5)$	$2^2 \cdot (2 \cdot 3 \cdot 5)$	$5 \cdot (2 \cdot 3 \cdot 5)$
$2 \cdot 3 \cdot 5$	$2^2 \cdot 3 \cdot 5$	$2 \cdot 3^2 \cdot 5$	$2^3 \cdot 3 \cdot 5$	$2 \cdot 3 \cdot 5^2$

180	210	240	270
$6 \cdot 30$	$7 \cdot 30$	$8 \cdot 30$	$9 \cdot 30$
$(2 \cdot 3)(2 \cdot 3 \cdot 5)$	$7 \cdot (2 \cdot 3 \cdot 5)$	$2^3 \cdot (2 \cdot 3 \cdot 5)$	$3^2 \cdot (2 \cdot 3 \cdot 5)$
$2^2 \cdot 3^2 \cdot 5$	$2 \cdot 3 \cdot 5 \cdot 7$	$2^4 \cdot 3 \cdot 5$	$2 \cdot 3^3 \cdot 5$

ANSWERS TO EXERCISES

a. There are three: 5, 10, and 15. **b.** N. **c.** No. **d.** Yes, if N is any even number.

Problems (48)

1. Each of the following is a multiple of 35.   Write each in prime factored form.

    a. $4 \cdot (5 \cdot 7)$ **b.** $5 \cdot (5 \cdot 7)$ **c.** $6 \cdot (5 \cdot 7)$ **d.** $7 \cdot (5 \cdot 7)$ **e.** $8 \cdot (5 \cdot 7)$

2. Each of the following is a multiple of 561.   Write each in prime factored form.

    a. $9 \cdot (3 \cdot 11 \cdot 17)$ **b.** $3 \cdot 11 \cdot (3 \cdot 11 \cdot 17)$ **c.** $51 \cdot (3 \cdot 11 \cdot 17)$ **d.** $121 \cdot 561$

3. When composite, each of the following is to be written in prime factored form. If $N = 2 \cdot 5 \cdot 13^2$

    a. $2N = ?$ **c.** $25N = ?$ **e.** $26N = ?$ **g.** $N^2 = ?$ **i.** $65N = ?$

    b. $10N = ?$ **d.** $30N = ?$ **f.** $\dfrac{N}{5} = ?$ **h.** $\dfrac{N}{10} = ?$ **j.** $\dfrac{N}{65} = ?$

4. Give the five smallest odd multiples of 19, using the prime factored form for the composite numbers.

5-6. Least Common Multiple

For any set of two or more natural numbers it is possible to find a number that is a multiple of each number of the set.   Indeed, there is no limit to how many such common multiples can be found.   The smallest of these common multiples is called the *least common multiple* (l.c.m.) of the set of numbers.

> **Example:** Find the least of the common multiples of 6 and 8.   This can be done by inspection of a list of the multiples of each number.

> 6   12   18   24   30   36   42   48   54   60   66   72
> | | | etc.
> 8   16   24   32   40   48   56   64   72

> Each list could be extended indefinitely.   But already we find 24, 48, and 72 in both lists.   Each of these numbers is a multiple of both 6 and 8, and hence 24 is the l.c.m.

For any natural number N, its multiples are N and then every Nth number following as we count off the natural numbers in turn.   The numbers from 1 to 48 are listed below.   Every sixth number is repeated above, and every eighth number is repeated below.

                            6   12
        1   2   3   4   5   6   7   8   9   10   11   12   13   14   15   16
                                          8   16

                18   24   30
        17   18   19   20   21   22   23   24   25   26   27   28   29   30   31   32
                                          24   32

                            36   42   48
        33   34   35   36   37   38   39   40   41   42   43   44   45   46   47   48
                                          40   48

We begin counting at 1 and are "in step" again at 24, 48, ...   The first time this happens is at 24, the l.c.m.

The l.c.m. of 6 and 8 can be determined readily by making use of their prime factored forms.   Since $6 = 2 \cdot 3$, then any multiple of 6 must include 2 and 3 among its prime factors.   Since $8 = 2^3$, then any multiple of 8 must include in its prime factored form the prime factor 2, repeated at least three times.   Any common multiple of 6 and 8 must meet both requirements.   The smallest number that does this is $2^3 \cdot 3$ or 24.

6	12		18	24
$2 \cdot 3$	$2^2 \cdot 3$		$2 \cdot 3^2$	$2^3 \cdot 3$

8		16		24
2^3		2^4		$2^3 \cdot 3$

The prime factors of the l.c.m. of a set of numbers include every prime factor that is a divisor of any number of the set.   Where there is repetition of any factor in the prime factored form of any number of the set, the exponent required for the l.c.m. is the largest to be found for that prime factor in any of the numbers.   Compare with the g.c.d. (page 69).

Problems (49)

For problems 1 and 2, determine the three smallest common multiples of the two given numbers, writing these in prime factored form.

1. a. $\begin{cases} 5 \\ 3 \cdot 7 \end{cases}$ b. $\begin{cases} 2 \cdot 11 \\ 3 \cdot 5 \end{cases}$ c. $\begin{cases} 3^3 \\ 3 \end{cases}$ d. $\begin{cases} 2 \cdot 5 \\ 2 \cdot 7 \end{cases}$ e. $\begin{cases} 2 \cdot 11^2 \\ 2^3 \cdot 11 \end{cases}$

2. a. $\begin{cases} 2 \\ 3 \cdot 11 \end{cases}$ b. $\begin{cases} 2^4 \\ 2^2 \end{cases}$ c. $\begin{cases} 3 \cdot 7 \\ 5 \cdot 7 \end{cases}$ d. $\begin{cases} 2 \cdot 5 \\ 5 \cdot 11 \end{cases}$ e. $\begin{cases} 2 \cdot 3 \cdot 5 \\ 3 \cdot 5^2 \cdot 7 \end{cases}$

For problems 3 and 4, N, M_1, and M_2 are to be natural numbers.   Only N need be determined. N should be as small as possible, and written in prime factored form when composite.

3. a. $\begin{cases} 2 \cdot 3 \cdot M_1 = N \\ 2^2 \cdot 3 \cdot M_2 = N \end{cases}$ b. $\begin{cases} N \div 5 \cdot 13^2 = M_1 \\ N \div 5^2 \cdot 13 = M_2 \end{cases}$ c. $\begin{cases} N \div M_1 = 5 \cdot 7 \\ N \div M_2 = 2 \cdot 3 \cdot 7 \end{cases}$

   d. $\begin{cases} \dfrac{N}{M_1} = 5 \\ \dfrac{N}{M_2} = 3 \cdot 5^4 \end{cases}$ e. $\begin{cases} \dfrac{N}{2^2} = M_1 \\ \dfrac{N}{2 \cdot 3} = M_2 \end{cases}$ f. $\begin{cases} M_1 \overline{\smash{\big)}\,N}^{\,3 \cdot 7} \\ M_2 \overline{\smash{\big)}\,N}^{\,2 \cdot 7} \end{cases}$

4. a. $\begin{cases} 7 \cdot 19 \cdot M_1 = N \\ 11 \cdot 19^2 \cdot M_2 = N \end{cases}$ b. $\begin{cases} N \div 31 = M_1 \\ N \div 37 = M_2 \end{cases}$ c. $\begin{cases} N \div M_1 = 53 \\ N \div M_2 = 53 \end{cases}$

   d. $\begin{cases} \dfrac{N}{M_1} = 13 \cdot 17^2 \\ \dfrac{N}{M_2} = 13^2 \cdot 17^3 \end{cases}$ e. $\begin{cases} \dfrac{N}{2^3 \cdot 5^2 \cdot 7} = M_1 \\ \dfrac{N}{2 \cdot 5 \cdot 11} = M_2 \end{cases}$ f. $\begin{cases} 2^2 \overline{\smash{\big)}\,N}^{\,M_1} \\ 3^2 \overline{\smash{\big)}\,N}^{\,M_2} \end{cases}$

For problems 5 and 6, determine the l.c.m. of the set of numbers, writing this number in decimal numeral form.

5. a. $\begin{cases} 7 \\ 2{,}401 \\ 49 \end{cases}$ **b.** $\begin{cases} 20 \\ 8 \\ 30 \end{cases}$ **c.** $\begin{cases} 14 \\ 16 \\ 28 \end{cases}$ **d.** $\begin{cases} 60 \\ 90 \\ 150 \end{cases}$

6. a. $\begin{cases} 22 \\ 52 \\ 143 \end{cases}$ **b.** $\begin{cases} 7 \\ 11 \\ 13 \end{cases}$ **c.** $\begin{cases} 1{,}728 \\ 144 \\ 12 \end{cases}$ **d.** $\begin{cases} 57 \\ 209 \\ 190 \end{cases}$

For problems 7 and 8, N, M_1, and M_2 are to be natural numbers. Only N need be determined. If possible, give both the smallest and the largest possible N. If this cannot be done, write "not possible."

7. a. $\begin{cases} 7 \cdot M_1 = N \\ 13 \cdot M_2 = N \end{cases}$
$N \text{ (smallest)} = ?$
$N \text{ (largest)}\ \ = ?$

b. $\begin{cases} N \cdot M_1 = 7 \\ N \cdot M_2 = 13 \end{cases}$
$N \text{ (smallest)} = ?$
$N \text{ (largest)}\ \ = ?$

c. $\begin{cases} N \div 3 \cdot 11^2 = M_1 \\ N \div 3^3 \cdot 11 = M_2 \end{cases}$
$N \text{ (smallest)} = ?$
$N \text{ (largest)}\ \ = ?$

d. $\begin{cases} 7^3 \div N = M_1 \\ 7^2 \div N = M_2 \end{cases}$
$N \text{ (smallest)} = ?$
$N \text{ (largest)}\ \ = ?$

8. a. $\begin{cases} M_1 \cdot 7^2 = N \\ M_2 \cdot 5 \cdot 7 = N \end{cases}$
$N \text{ (smallest)} = ?$
$N \text{ (largest)}\ \ = ?$

b. $\begin{cases} M_1 \cdot N = 7^2 \\ M_2 \cdot N = 5 \cdot 7 \end{cases}$
$N \text{ (smallest)} = ?$
$N \text{ (largest)}\ \ = ?$

c. $\begin{cases} N \div M_1 = 2 \cdot 3 \\ N \div M_2 = 5 \end{cases}$
$N \text{ (smallest)} = ?$
$N \text{ (largest)}\ \ = ?$

d. $\begin{cases} 2 \cdot 3 \div M_1 = N \\ 5 \div M_2\ \ = N \end{cases}$
$N \text{ (smallest)} = ?$
$N \text{ (largest)}\ \ = ?$

When only two or three numbers are involved, effective use can be made of diagrams to display the relationship of their prime factors.

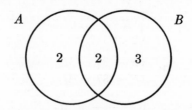

$4 = 2 \cdot 2$ The primes 2 and 2 are inside circle A.
$6 = 2 \cdot 3$ The primes 2 and 3 are inside circle B.

The prime 2 is inside both circles.   The g.c.d. of A and B is 2.   The product of all the primes in the diagram is $2 \cdot 2 \cdot 3$ or 12.   12 is the l.c.m. of 4 and 6.

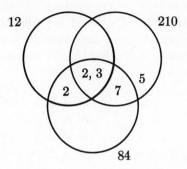

$12 = 2 \cdot 2 \cdot 3$ These factors are inside the circle labeled 12.

$84 = 2 \cdot 2 \cdot 3 \cdot 7$ These factors are inside the circle labeled 84.

$210 = 2 \cdot 3 \cdot 5 \cdot 7$ These factors are inside the circle labeled 210.

It is convenient to think of a blank area as containing the factor 1.

The g.c.d. of 12, 84, and 210 is $2 \cdot 3$ or 6.

The l.c.m. of 12, 84, and 210 is $2 \cdot 2 \cdot 3 \cdot 5 \cdot 7$ or 420.

a. What numbers are divisors of both 84 and 210, but not of 12?

b. What numbers are divisors of both 12 and 84, but not of 210?

c. What numbers are divisors of both 12 and 210, but not of 84?

d. What numbers are divisors of both 84 and 210, and are relatively prime to 12?

e. What numbers divide one, but not more than one, of the three numbers 12, 84, and 210?

f. What numbers divide at least two of the three numbers 12, 84, and 210?

Answers to Exercises

a. 7, 14, 21, 42.   **b.** 4, 12.   **c.** There are none.   **d.** 7.   **e.** 5, 10, 15, 30, 35, 70, 105, 210.
f. 1, 2, 3, 4, 6, 7, 12, 14, 21, 42.

Problems (50)

Use diagrams in the manner suggested above, to illustrate both the g.c.d. and the l.c.m. of each set of numbers.

1. $\begin{cases} 2 \cdot 3 \\ 3 \cdot 5 \end{cases}$ **3.** $\begin{cases} 5^2 \\ 2 \cdot 5 \\ 3 \cdot 5 \end{cases}$ **5.** $\begin{cases} 3 \cdot 5 \\ 5 \cdot 7 \\ 2 \cdot 3 \end{cases}$ **7.** $\begin{cases} 3^3 \cdot 5 \\ 3 \cdot 5 \cdot 7^2 \\ 3 \cdot 5 \cdot 7 \end{cases}$ **9.** $\begin{cases} 2 \cdot 3 \cdot 5 \\ 3 \cdot 5 \cdot 7 \\ 2 \cdot 5 \cdot 7 \end{cases}$ **11.** $\begin{cases} 2 \cdot 3 \\ 3^2 \cdot 5 \\ 3^3 \end{cases}$

2. $\begin{cases} 2 \cdot 5^3 \\ 2^3 \end{cases}$ **4.** $\begin{cases} 2^2 \cdot 5 \\ 2^3 \\ 2 \cdot 3 \cdot 5 \end{cases}$ **6.** $\begin{cases} 2^4 \\ 2 \cdot 7 \\ 2^2 \cdot 7 \end{cases}$ **8.** $\begin{cases} 5^3 \\ 2 \cdot 5^2 \\ 2^2 \cdot 5 \end{cases}$ **10.** $\begin{cases} 2 \cdot 7 \cdot 13 \\ 3 \cdot 7 \cdot 13 \\ 2 \cdot 3 \cdot 17 \end{cases}$ **12.** $\begin{cases} 2 \cdot 3 \cdot 7 \\ 3 \cdot 5 \cdot 11 \\ 7 \cdot 11 \cdot 13 \end{cases}$

5-7. Squares and Cubes

For any natural number N, if there exists a natural number M such that $N = M^2$, then N is said to be a perfect square or, briefly, a square. If there is a natural number R such that $N = R^3$, then N is a cube or third power. In general, if there are natural numbers S and p such that $N = S^p$, then N is a pth power. The structure of the squares and other powers becomes clearer when the prime factored form is used.

$$1^2 = 1 \cdot 1 = 1 \qquad\qquad 5^2 = 5 \cdot 5 = 5^2$$
$$2^2 = 2 \cdot 2 = 2^2 \qquad\qquad 6^2 = (2 \cdot 3)^2 = (2 \cdot 3)(2 \cdot 3) = 2^2 \cdot 3^2$$
$$3^2 = 3 \cdot \, 3 = 3^2 \qquad\qquad 7^2 = 7 \cdot 7 = 7^2$$
$$4^2 = (2^2)^2 = (2 \cdot 2)(2 \cdot 2) = 2^4 \qquad 8^2 = (2^3)^2 = (2 \cdot 2 \cdot 2)(2 \cdot 2 \cdot 2) = 2^6$$

Thus 1 is a square. Zero is also, since $0^2 = 0$. Every natural number, greater than 1, is a square if and only if in its prime factored form every factor has an even exponent.

Example: Is 576 a square?

$576 = N \cdot N$	Since the exponents are both even in
$2^6 \cdot 3^2 = (2^3 \cdot 3)(2^3 \cdot 3)$	$2^6 \cdot 3^2$, half of the 2 factors and half of
$576 = 24 \cdot 24$	the 3's can be used for each N as required.
$\quad = 24^2$	

An identity involving exponents, which follows from the commutative and associative properties of multiplication, is useful at this point.

Example:

$6^2 = (2 \cdot 3)^2$	The numeral 6 was replaced by the prime factored form $2 \cdot 3$. Parentheses are now necessary to extend the reach of the exponent 2.
$= (2 \cdot 3)(2 \cdot 3)$	This follows from the definition of a power.
$= 2 \cdot 2 \cdot 3 \cdot 3$	The commutative and associative property of multiplication permits the rearrangement of the factors.
$= 2^2 \cdot 3^2$	Again the definition of powers is used.

The equality of $(2 \cdot 3)^2$ and $2^2 \cdot 3^2$ is an example of a general principle which may be written as

$$(A \cdot B)^m \equiv A^m \cdot B^m$$

and extended to

$$(A^p \cdot B^q)^m \equiv A^{mp} \cdot B^{mq}$$

The above may be considered to be a statement of a principle by which a power of a product may be replaced by a product of powers; or, inversely, by which a product of powers of a certain kind can be replaced by a power of a product. It also shows that over the natural numbers the operation of raising to a power is distributive over multiplication.

Problems (51)

In problems 1 to 8 make use of the above identity and possibly Table 1 in the Appendix to write each in prime factored form.

1. 18^2 3. 25^2 5. 72^2 7. 112^2
2. 20^2 4. 30^2 6. 96^2 8. 144^2

In problems 9 to 16, replace each power of a product by a product of powers, and each product of powers by a power of a product. Do no further computation.

9. $(2 \cdot 7)^2$ 11. $5^3 \cdot 7^3$ 13. $(3 \cdot 5 \cdot 7)^2$ 15. $5^4 \cdot 7^2 \cdot 13^6$
10. $3^2 \cdot 7^2$ 12. $(3 \cdot 5)^3$ 14. $5^2 \cdot 11^2 \cdot 13^2$ 16. $(3^2 \cdot 5)^2$

If a number is not a square itself, it still may be of interest to know how such numbers are related to squares. In particular, one sometimes needs to know which, if any, of the divisors of a number are squares, and which of its multiples are squares.

The number 24 is not a square, as can be seen from its prime factored form of $2^3 \cdot 3$. However,

$$2^3 \cdot 3 = 2^2 \cdot 2 \cdot 3 = 2^2 \cdot 6$$

Hence, 24 does have a square as a factor, and can be written as the product of a square times a nonsquare. Every natural number, not a square, whose prime factored form shows at least one prime factor that has an exponent of at least two, has a square as a factor and can be expressed as the product of this square times a nonsquare factor.

Sometimes this can be done in more than one way, and one is usually then looking for the largest possible factor that is a square.

> **Example:** $72 = 2^3 \cdot 3^2 = 2^2 \cdot (2 \cdot 3^2) = 2^2 \cdot 18$
> $72 = 3^2 \cdot 2^3 = 3^2 \cdot 8$
> $72 = (2 \cdot 3)^2 \cdot 2 = 6^2 \cdot 8$
> 2^2, 3^2, and 6^2 are all divisors of 72, with 6^2 being the largest divisor which is a square.

Problems (52)

Express each number in the form $A^2 \cdot B$ where A and B are natural numbers in decimal form, and A is as large as possible.

1. $2^3 \cdot 13$ 4. 5^3 7. $2^2 \cdot 3^2 \cdot 5$ 10. 198
2. $2^5 \cdot 5$ 5. $2^2 \cdot 23$ 8. $3^2 \cdot 7^2$ 11. 192
3. $3^3 \cdot 5 \cdot 7$ 6. $2 \cdot 3^3 \cdot 7$ 9. 228   12. 512

While not every natural number has a square (greater than 1) among its divisors, the multiples of every natural number include an unlimited number of squares. The multiples of 24, or $2^3 \cdot 3$, are

$2^3 \cdot 3$	$2^4 \cdot 3$	$2^3 \cdot 3^2$	$2^5 \cdot 3$	$2^3 \cdot 3 \cdot 5$	$2^4 \cdot 3^2$	etc.
24	48	72	96	120	144	
					$(2^2 \cdot 3)^2$	
					12^2	

The smallest multiple of 24 that is a square is $(2 \cdot 3)(2^3 \cdot 3)$ or $2^4 \cdot 3^2$. An extra 2 factor was needed so that 2 would have an even exponent of 4, and an extra 3 factor gave 3 an even exponent of 2.   Given any natural number, one can construct a multiple of it that is a square by adjoining whatever prime factors are necessary to allow every prime factor to have an even exponent.

Recall now that $A \equiv \dfrac{A \cdot B}{B}$, if $B \neq 0$. This allows the possibility of expressing every natural number in the form $\dfrac{A^2}{B}$, that is, as a quotient whose dividend is a square.   This can be done in an unlimited number of ways, and of these that with the smallest possible square for a dividend is usually desired.

$$24 = 2^3 \cdot 3 = \frac{(2^3 \cdot 3)(2 \cdot 3)}{2 \cdot 3} = \frac{2^4 \cdot 3^2}{2 \cdot 3} = \frac{(2^2 \cdot 3)^2}{2 \cdot 3} = \frac{12^2}{6}$$

Problems (53)

For problems 1 to 10, write in prime factored form, and in order of increasing size, the five smallest multiples of the number given that are squares.

1. $2 \cdot 5^2$	**3.** $2 \cdot 3^3$	**5.** $5^2 \cdot 7$	**7.** $2 \cdot 3^3 \cdot 5$	**9.** $2^5 \cdot 3$
2. $3^2 \cdot 7$	**4.** $3 \cdot 11^2$	**6.** $2^2 \cdot 3 \cdot 5$	**8.** $2 \cdot 5 \cdot 7$	**10.** $3 \cdot 7^3$

For problems 11 to 16, express each number in the form $\dfrac{A^2}{B}$, where A and B are natural numbers in decimal numeral form and A is as small as possible.

11. $2^2 \cdot 13$	**12.** $2 \cdot 7^2$	**13.** $2 \cdot 3^3$	**14.** $2 \cdot 3^2 \cdot 5$	**15.** 150	**16.** 162

In problems 17 to 22, p, q, and r represent different primes, whereas M and N are natural numbers.   Only N need be determined, but it should be as small as possible.

17. $p \cdot q^2 \cdot N = M^2$	**19.** $p \cdot q^3 \cdot N = M^2$	**21.** $p \cdot q^5 \cdot r^3 \cdot N = M^2$
18. $p \cdot r \cdot N = M^2$	**20.** $p^3 \cdot r^2 \cdot N = M^2$	**22.** $p \cdot q \cdot r \cdot N = M^2$

The methods used for the study of squares in the previous problems can be readily extended to cubes, and to higher powers.   Zero and 1 are cubes.   A natural number, greater than 1, is a cube if and only if in its prime factored form every factor has an exponent that is a multiple of three.

$$2^3 = 2 \cdot 2 \cdot 2 = 2^3$$
$$4^3 = (2 \cdot 2)^3 = (2 \cdot 2)(2 \cdot 2)(2 \cdot 2) = 2^6$$
$$12^3 = (2^2 \cdot 3)^3 = (2^2 \cdot 3)(2^2 \cdot 3)(2^2 \cdot 3) = 2^6 \cdot 3^3$$

Problems (54)

For problems 1 to 6, try to express each number in the form $A^3 \cdot B$, where A and B are natural numbers in decimal numeral form, and A is as large as possible. Write "no" if this is not possible.

1. $3^4 \cdot 5^2$ **2.** $2^3 \cdot 5$ **3.** 11^2 **4.** 3^7 **5.** $5 \cdot 7^5$ **6.** $2 \cdot 3^5 \cdot 11$

For problems 7 to 12, determine the smallest multiple of the given number that is a cube, writing this number in prime factored form.

7. $3^3 \cdot 7$ **8.** $5^2 \cdot 7^4$ **9.** 11 **10.** 3^5 **11.** 360 **12.** 160

In problems 13 to 18, express each number in the form $\dfrac{A^3}{B}$ where A and B are natural numbers in decimal form, with A as small as possible.

13. 13^2 **14.** 5^4 **15.** $3^2 \cdot 5^3 \cdot 7$ **16.** 7 **17.** 135 **18.** 128

5-8. A Famous Theorem

There are 25 primes between 1 and 100, but only 21 primes between 100 and 200. As we extend our search for primes to larger numbers, we find longer and longer strings of consecutive composite numbers and the primes gradually getting scarcer. In view of this one might ask, "Does the list of primes ever come to an end, so that all numbers larger than this highest prime are composite?" The Greeks found out this cannot be the case, and Euclid gave a proof of this theorem: *There is no largest prime, that is, the number of primes is infinite.* His argument is based on an ingenious method of showing how any supposed largest prime can be used to construct a still larger one.

> **Proof:** Suppose there is a largest prime, which we may call p. This would mean that every number greater than p would then be composite.
> Now consider the number
>
> $$N = (2 \cdot 3 \cdot 5 \cdot 7 \cdot 11 \cdot \ \cdots \ \cdot p) + 1$$
>
> which is formed by multiplying all the primes (beginning with 2 and stopping at p), and then adding 1 to this product. Now N would be an extremely large number, certainly much larger than p. Still, because of the closure property of the natural numbers for multiplication and addition, N would be a natural number and hence either prime or composite. However, N does not have any prime factor from the list

from 2 on up to p, since there would always be a remainder of 1 if N were divided by any of these primes.

If N is prime, we then have a prime larger than p, which is contrary to the assumption that p was the largest possible prime.

The other possibility is that N might be composite. But then it must be a product of primes, each of which must be larger than p, since it does not have p or any smaller prime as a divisor. Hence, in either case the above construction produces a prime larger than p, which establishes that no prime can ever be the largest possible.

Problems (55)

1. If Euclid's method of constructing primes is used with $p = 2$, we have $2 + 1 = 3$. For $p = 3$, $2 \cdot 3 + 1 = 7$. For $p = 5$, $2 \cdot 3 \cdot 5 + 1 = 31$. Continue the pattern as far as you can.
2. Consider the number $(1 \cdot 2 \cdot 3 \cdot 4 \cdot \ \cdots \ \cdot 1000) + 2$, which is 2 more than the product of the first thousand natural numbers. This number is composite since it is a multiple of 2. What can be said about the next 998 consecutive numbers?

5-9. Miscellaneous Problems

Problems (56)

1. Express each number in the form $M + N$, where M and N are natural numbers and M is the largest multiple of 10 that is not greater than the given number.
   a. 27   **b.** 73   **c.** 85   **d.** 236
2. Express each number in the form $M - N$, where M and N are natural numbers and M is the smallest multiple of 10 that is not smaller than the given number.
   a. 27   **b.** 73   **c.** 85   **d.** 236
3. Write each of the following in the form $N \cdot 100$, where N is a natural number.
   a. $16 \cdot 50$ **b.** $25 \cdot 12$ **c.** $45 \cdot 20$ **d.** $50 \cdot 56$ **e.** $36 \cdot 25$
4. Express each number as a sum of products, each product being that of the face value of a digit of the given number times its place value.
   a. 72   **b.** 343   **c.** 2,407
5. Express, as many ways as possible, the number 12 as the sum of two addends, if one addend is a multiple of the other.
6. Express the number 10 as the sum of two addends, one of which is a power of the other. Do this in all possible ways.
7. What is the largest multiple of 5 that is a divisor of 30?
8. What is the smallest divisor of 42 that is a multiple of 3?
9. What is the least multiple of 44 that is a square of a natural number?

10. What number, less than 10, is such that the sum of its divisors is twice the number itself?

11. What is the product of the g.c.d. and the l.c.m. of:
  a. 6 and 8?   **b.** 5 and 7?   **c.** 5 and 10?   **d.** 8 and 12?
  Can you make a conjecture about what might always be true in such problems?

12. If 1 is both a square and a cube, what is the next larger number to have this property?

For problems 13 to 22, construct a mathematical model for each in the form of a conditional equation.   Do no computation.

13. If one of two numbers is 7 more than the other, and the larger is 23, what is the product of the two numbers?

14. If one of two numbers is 5 times the other, and the smaller is 15, what is the sum of the two numbers?

15. If one of two numbers is 7 times the other, and the larger is 35, what is the square of the sum of the two numbers?

16. If one of two numbers is 6 times the other and the larger is 12, what is the difference between the two numbers?

17. If one of two numbers is 5 more than the other, and the larger is 10, what is the difference between the cubes of the numbers?

18. If one of two numbers is 5 less than the other and the smaller is 15, what is the sum of the squares of the two numbers?

19. If a second number is 5 times a first number, and a third number is 3 more than the second, and the largest of the three numbers is 18, what is the sum of the three numbers?

20. If a second number is 4 times a first number, and a third number is 2 less than a second, and the largest of the three numbers is 28, what is the product of the first number and the third?

21. If y is 8 less than x, and z is 3 times y, and the smallest of x, y, and z is 5, what is the sum of x and z?

22. If z is 2 more than y, and y is 2 times x, and the smallest of x, y, and z is 4, then how much greater is z than x?

For Further Study

A vast literature exists concerning prime numbers and their properties.   Supplementary treatments for topics in this chapter can be found in [M11], pp. 192–203; [A1], pp. 94–102; [S17], pp. 192–209; and [H2], pp. 201–214.   An interesting discussion of primes with particularly good problems appears in [S14], pp. 24–38.

Prime numbers are a standard topic in texts on number theory.   Most of these require more algebraic background than has been assumed in this text, but [O3] is reasonably accessible and it includes a good deal of historical information.

6

Formulas

6-1. Substitution

The simple act of substituting one object for another is one of the most fundamental of all mathematical maneuvers. We shall give some examples of substitutions that have arisen thus far and then introduce a notation by which substitutions may be specified formally.

> **Examples:** $2 + 3 = N$ becomes $2 + 3 = 5$, when 5 is substituted for N. To get a true statement, it was necessary to use a name for the number represented by $2 + 3$. To get the best recognition of that number, the decimal numeral 5 was chosen rather than some other name, such as $4 + 1$.
>
> $A + B = B + A$ becomes $4 + 7 = 7 + 4$, when 4 is substituted for each A and 7 is substituted for each B. The 4 and 7 were chosen from the range of permissible substitutions for the variables A and B.
>
> $A + 0 \equiv A$ becomes $X + 0 \equiv X$ when the variable X is substituted for the variable A.

To indicate substitutions, we shall indicate the object to be replaced; follow this with a colon; and then give the substitute, which is then enclosed in parentheses and written after the expression where the substitution is to be performed. If several substitutions are to be made, they are separated by commas. Thus $(L : 50)$ calls for the substitution of "50" for "L"; and $(X : 3, y : 2)$ calls for the substitution of "3" for "X," and of "2" for "y."

Examples: $N^2(N:5)$ gives 5^2, and $(A + B)(A:6, B:4)$ gives $6 + 4$.

The examples at the beginning of this section would be handled as follows:

$(2 + 3 = N)(N:5)$ becomes $2 + 3 = 5$

$(A + B = B + A)(A:4, B:7)$ becomes $4 + 7 = 7 + 4$

$(A + 0 \equiv A)(A:X)$ becomes $X + 0 \equiv X$.

The above substitutions were of a simple type where a single symbol was substituted for a single symbol, but this restriction need not be made. Either the substitute, or that which it replaces, may be a combination of symbols of any degree of complexity just as long as it represents a single object of the proper kind. Thus $(b:4 \cdot 5 - 7)$ indicates that $4 \cdot 5 - 7$ is to be substituted for b. Sometimes, but not always, the substitute must be enclosed in parentheses to ensure its being treated as a single quantity.

Examples: $(A - B)(A:8 + 2, B:5 + 3)$ yields $8 + 2 - (5 + 3)$

It was necessary to enclose $5 + 3$ with parentheses, but they were not needed for $8 + 2$.

$(AB)(A:6 + 4, B:5)$ gives $(6 + 4)5$

Parentheses were required for $6 + 4$, but they could be omitted for 5.

Problems (57)

Make the substitutions indicated, but make no further changes of form or computations. Insert parentheses where required, but omit them where this can be done without change of meaning. To do this properly, one must be aware of the associative and distributive properties and the conventions about the order of operations.

1. $(R + S)\left(R:3 \cdot 7, S:\dfrac{10}{2}\right)$

2. $(X + Y)(X:5 + 4 - 2, Y:8 - 6)$

3. $(U - V)\left(U:\dfrac{45}{3}, V:3^2\right)$

4. $(L - M)(L:12 - 3, M:6 - 1)$

5. $\left(\dfrac{a}{b}\right)(a:17 + 3, b:6 - 2)$

6. $\left(\dfrac{a}{b}\right)(a:3 \cdot 12, b:2 \cdot 6)$

7. $\left(\dfrac{a}{b}\right)\left(a:\dfrac{60}{2}, b:\dfrac{14}{7}\right)$

8. $(mn)(m:8 + 7, n:9 - 4)$

9. $(mn)\left(m:\dfrac{14}{7}, n:3 + 12\right)$

10. $(mn)(m:2^3, n:5 \cdot 7)$

11. $(A^m)(A:3 + 4, m:2)$

12. $(A^m)\left(A:\dfrac{16}{2}, m:4 - 1\right)$

13. $(3a^2)(a:4 + 1)$

14. $(5^n)(n:3 - 1)$

15. $(M_n)(n:5)$

16. $(y_{n+2})(n:2)$

17. $[k(k - 2)](k : x)$ **19.** $\dfrac{(2^{n-1})}{n}(n : 4)$

18. $(2x^2 - x - 5)(x : 3)$ **20.** $(k \cdot 3^k)(k : a + b)$

Problems (58)

The following statements result from substitutions having been made for the variables in certain identities.   State the identity involved, and give the substitution used.

1. $(a + b) + c \equiv c + (a + b)$

2. $x - y - 0 \equiv x - y$

3. $r + 3s \equiv r + 3s$

4. $9 + (5 + 2) = (9 + 5) + 2$

5. $18 + 7 = (18 + 2) + (7 - 2)$

6. $93 - 48 = (93 + 2) - (48 + 2)$

7. $(m + n)(s + t) \equiv (m + n)s + (m + n)t$

8. $(a + b)(c - d) \equiv a(c - d) + b(c - d)$

9. $1(p + q) \equiv p + q$

10. $(a^2 + b^2) \cdot 0 \equiv 0$

11. $16 \cdot 25 = \dfrac{16}{4} \cdot (4 \cdot 25)$

12. $\dfrac{20 + 10 + 5}{5} = \dfrac{20}{5} + \dfrac{10 + 5}{5}$

13. $[t + (x - y)] - (x - y) \equiv t$

14. $(h + k)\left(\dfrac{m}{h + k}\right) \equiv m$

15. $\dfrac{5^9}{5^3} = 5^{9-3}$

16. $(3^2)^5 = 3^{2 \cdot 5}$

17. $M_1 M_2 \equiv M_2 M_1$

18. $(p + q - r) + r \equiv p + q$

19. $(a + b)^x \cdot (a + b)^y \equiv (a + b)^{x+y}$

20. $\dfrac{u + v}{u + v} \equiv 1$

6-2. Substitution in Formulas

Our approach to the solution of verbal problems has been first to construct a mathematical model, using a single conditional equation.   Many problems may also be described by a system of several equations.

> **Example:** An article has a list price of $50.   What will be the selling price if there is a discount of $8?
>
> | *Single equation model* | *System of equations model* |
> |:---:|:---:|
> | $S = 50 - 8$ | $\begin{cases} S = L - D \\ L = 50 \\ D = 8 \end{cases}$ |

Merchants often arrive at a selling price of an article by subtracting a discount from a list price, and the example is seen to be a problem of this kind.   Suppose we think of those numbers that might be selling prices in the sale of some article, and then let the range of a variable S be this set of numbers.   This means that when we replace S by a number, this number is to be the selling price for some particular sale.

In the same way the range of the variable L is such that when L is replaced by a number, this number is to be the list price; and the substitution for D is to be the number that is the discount. The relationship of these three quantities may be stated as $S = L - D$.

Suppose we were to write $(\ ) = [\ ] - \{\ \}$, and then to fill in the blank spaces with three numbers chosen at random. Very likely the resulting statement would be false as it is, for example, with $(3) = [2] - \{7\}$. The letters S, L, and D were chosen to remind us of a particular kind of physical situation, and the assumption is that if we do obtain the numbers for S, L, and D from observation of such a situation then the statement will be true. For this reason $S = L - D$ is said to be a *formula*, for relating selling price, list price, and discount.

We now combine the general statement $S = L - D$, with the equations $L = 50$ and $D = 8$, which state information known about a particular problem of this sort. The resulting system of three equations is then a model of the problem. The brace written at the left indicates that we want all three equations to be true at the same time. Hence, they may be designated as a set of simultaneous equations.

Alternate procedures are available for reducing the system

$$\begin{cases} S = L - D \\ L = 50 \\ D = 8 \end{cases}$$

to the single equation $S = 50 - 8$. The simplest and most common way is to think of substituting for the variables L and D the particular values they are assumed to have in this instance. That is,

$$(S = L - D)(L : 50, D : 8) \qquad \text{gives} \qquad S = 50 - 8$$

However, there is some merit in taking a more general point of view here so that a very important problem solving principle can be emphasized. Let us think of the three equations as being three conditional equations, all of which must be satisfied when choosing replacements for the three variables S, L, and D. Clearly $L = 50$ becomes the true statement of $50 = 50$ only when L is replaced by 50. Similarly $D = 8$ becomes a true statement only if D is replaced by 8. But if a substitution is made for a variable anywhere in the system, the same substitution must be made for that variable throughout the system. If this is done, we have

$$\begin{cases} S = 50 - 8 \\ 50 = 50 \\ 8 = 8 \end{cases}$$

which reduces to $S = 50 - 8$, by ignoring the last two equations, which are without further interest.

The first of these procedures is known simply as *substituting in a formula*. The second may seem forced in this simple example, but it does make possible the observation that there are as many equations in the system as there are variables. We may think of the number of variables as being the number of degrees of freedom for making choices for substitutions for these variables. The number of equations represents the number of conditions or constraints that must be met when making these choices. In our example both of these numbers were the same, or 3. The problem could be solved. We say the system was a *determinate* one.

Now consider the system

$$\begin{cases} S = L - D \\ L = 50 \end{cases}$$

There are here only two equations to control the three variables. This system is underdetermined. One cannot insist on a unique choice of S and D. Thus we might have $S = 49$, $D = 1$; or $S = 48$, $D = 2$; and many other pairs of values will give two true statements.

$$\begin{cases} 49 = 50 - 1 \\ 50 = 50 \end{cases} \qquad \begin{cases} 48 = 50 - 2 \\ 50 = 50 \end{cases}$$

Consider the next system:

$$\begin{cases} S = L - D \\ L = 50 \\ D = 8 \\ S = 41 \end{cases}$$
This system is overdetermined. We now have four constraints with only three degrees of freedom. The information is not consistent and a solution is not possible.

The following criterion will be found to be a useful guide and check for the construction of a system of equations model for the problems we shall consider, even though it is not sufficient to guarantee the model is correct: The number of equations in the system should equal the number of variables.

The models for the problems in the next set are based on some widely used formulas. They are "practical" except for the restriction we have been following of using only the natural numbers and zero. In actual practice we might expect many of the numbers to be given as common or decimal fractions, which we have not yet discussed.

Problems (59)

A verbal statement of a relationship is given. The formula that represents this relationship is one member of a system of equations. Then all but one of the necessary numbers are given. This completes the requirement above for a determinate system.

Substitute in the formula and determine the remaining number.

1. The amount A to be repaid on a loan is equal to the sum of the principal P and the interest I.
$$\begin{cases} A = P + I \\ P = 5,000 \\ I = 250 \end{cases}$$

2. The area A of a rectangle is equal to the product of its base B times the height H.

$$\begin{cases} A = BH \\ B = 25 \\ H = 16 \end{cases}$$

3. The profit P on a transaction is equal to the difference between the sales income S and the sum of the costs C and the overhead costs O.

$$\begin{cases} P = S - (C + O) \\ S = 154{,}000 \\ C = 130{,}000 \\ O = 8{,}300 \end{cases}$$

4. Under certain conditions for an automobile, the stopping distance D in feet is equal to the square of its speed V in miles per hour, divided by 20.

$$\begin{cases} D = \dfrac{V^2}{20} \\ V = 60 \end{cases}$$

5. The area A of a trapezoid is equal to one half the product of the altitude H and the sum of the lower base B and the upper base b.

$$\begin{cases} A = \dfrac{H(B + b)}{2} \\ H = 12 \\ B = 20 \\ b = 14 \end{cases}$$

6. The perimeter of an isosceles triangle is equal to the length of the base increased by twice the length of a leg.

$$\begin{cases} P = b + 2a \\ b = 18 \\ a = 15 \end{cases}$$

In the remaining problems the verbal statement is omitted.

7. $$\begin{cases} V = \dfrac{b^2 h}{3} \\ b = 12 \\ h = 8 \end{cases}$$

10. $$\begin{cases} C = \dfrac{E}{R + r} \\ E = 110 \\ R = 18 \\ r = 4 \end{cases}$$

13. $$\begin{cases} S = 16t^2 \\ t = 15 \end{cases}$$

8. $$\begin{cases} L = a + (n - 1)d \\ a = 7 \\ n = 10 \\ d = 5 \end{cases}$$

11. $$\begin{cases} P = \dfrac{E^2}{R} \\ E = 105 \\ R = 75 \end{cases}$$

14. $$\begin{cases} F = \dfrac{wa}{g} \\ w = 160 \\ g = 32 \\ a = 8 \end{cases}$$

9. $$\begin{cases} S = 180(n - 2) \\ n = 5 \end{cases}$$

12. $$\begin{cases} S = \dfrac{rL - a}{r - 1} \\ r = 3 \\ L = 105 \\ a = 5 \end{cases}$$

6-3. Sequences

Some formulas are introduced in this section that are closely related to the natural numbers. Suppose we have a set of numbers and a rule by which they can be arranged in order and designated as 1st, 2nd, 3rd, ...   When arranged in order by the rule, the numbers form a *sequence*.   The table at the right shows a sequence consisting of ten even numbers.

This table is made up of pairs of numbers that show a correspondence between the natural numbers and the even natural numbers. The left number gives the position in the sequence, and the right number is the even number for that position.

n	$2n$
1	2
2	4
3	6
4	8
5	10
6	12
7	14
8	16
9	18
10	20

The n and the $2n$ at the top of the columns may be used to determine any particular even number of this sequence. What, for example, will be the twelfth even number in this sequence? By choosing $n = 12$, and then substituting 12 for n in $2n$, the twelfth even number is found to be $2 \cdot 12$ or 24.

Again one can show that 34 is the 17th number of sequence by setting $2n = 34$, and obtaining $n = 17$.   It can also be seen that 25 is not a member of the sequence since no natural number n exists such that $2n = 25$.

The numbers in the right-hand column form the sequence itself and it is convenient to have a temporary name for each member.   This may be done as follows:
Set

$$a_1 = 2, \ a_2 = 4, \ a_3 = 6, \ a_4 = 8, \ \dots .$$

The symbols a_1, a_2, a_3, . . . are constants as used here, since they are assigned only one meaning throughout the discussion of this sequence.   This usage should be compared with that in Section 4-7, where the subscript device was used to construct variables.

The formula for this sequence of even numbers can now be written as $a_n = 2n$. A third column could now be added but it is simpler to drop the column for n, and work only with the pairs given by a_n and $2n$.

n	a_n	$2n$
1	a_1	2
2	a_2	4
3	a_3	6
4	a_4	8
	a_5	10

Particular notice should be given to the difference in the results when substitutions are made for the two n's in $a_n = 2n$.   The substitution of a numeral for n in a_n gives a temporary name for a number.   This name is designed to show the position of this number in a sequence.   The substitution of the same numeral for the n in $2n$ enables one to compute this designated number in the sequence.

$$a_n = 2n \qquad \text{For } n = 1, \ a_1 = 2 \cdot 1 = 2$$
$$\text{For } n = 2, \ a_2 = 2 \cdot 2 = 4$$
$$\text{For } n = 3, \ a_3 = 2 \cdot 3 = 6$$

Problems (60)

The following formulas determine sequences.   For each one give the first five terms; that is, a_1, a_2, a_3, a_4, and a_5.

1. $a_n = 2n - 1$ — The sequence of odd numbers.
2. $a_n = n^2$ — The sequence of squares.
3. $a_n = 5n$ — The multiples of five.
4. $a_n = (2n)^2$ — The squares of the even natural numbers.
5. $a_n = (2n - 1)^2$ — The squares of the odd natural numbers.
6. $a_n = 2^n$ — The powers of two.
7. $a_n = 2n + 5$
8. $a_n = 5n - 3$
9. $a_n = n^3$
10. $a_n = n^2 - n + 2$
11. $a_n = (2n - 1)(3n + 1)$
12. $a_n = 3n^2$
13. $a_n = 2^{n+1}$
14. $a_n = n(n + 1)$
15. $a_n = 2^n - 2n$
16. $a_n = (2n)^3$
17. $a_n = n^3 + 3n$
18. $a_n = 3^n - 3n$

Any letter may be used as was "a" in a_n. The first four terms of the sequence given by $y_n = \dfrac{3^{n-1} + 1}{2}$ are given in the table at the right. Check them.

n	y_n	$\dfrac{3^{n-1} + 1}{2}$
1	y_1	1
2	y_2	2
3	y_3	5
4	y_4	14

a. What is y_5? y_6? y_7?

It is possible for two different formulas to yield the same sequence, as is illustrated by the next example.

Example:
$$\begin{cases} y_n = 1, \text{ when } n = 1 \\ y_n = 3y_{n-1} - 1, \text{ when } n \text{ is greater than 1.} \end{cases}$$

These two statements, taken together, give a quite different set of directions for determining a sequence. The first states only that $y_1 = 1$. The second tells how to compute a term of the sequence if we know the one just preceding it. For some choice of n, y_n will be the name assigned to a term of the sequence and y_{n-1} will be the term just before it in the sequence. Hence, for any term after the first, we are directed to compute a desired term by multiplying the one before by 3, and then subtracting 1.

$y_1 = 1$

$y_2 = 3y_{2-1} - 1$
$= 3y_1 - 1$
$= 3 \cdot 1 - 1$
$= 2$

$y_3 = 3y_{3-1} - 1$
$= 3y_2 - 1$
$= 3 \cdot 2 - 1$
$= 5$

$y_4 = 3y_{4-1} - 1$
$= 3y_3 - 1$
$= 3 \cdot 5 - 1$
$= 14$

This example shows the possibility of defining a sequence by giving the first one or more terms, and then supplying a *recursion* formula, which tells how to determine any term (other than those given) if the preceding term or terms are known. The reader should continue as above and compute y_5, y_6, and y_7 and verify that the sequence is the same as that given by

$$y_n = \frac{3^{n-1} + 1}{2} \quad \text{(This checks exercise } \mathbf{a}.\text{)}$$

Problems (61)

In problems 1 to 12, carry out the substitutions as indicated.

1. $(t_n)(n:3)$ **7.** $(x^{n-2})(n:2)$

2. $(c_n)(n:5)$ **8.** $(n^{n+1})(n:3)$

3. $(t^n)(n:3)$ **9.** $(y_n = y_{n-1} + 2)(n:5)$

4. $(c^n)(n:5)$ **10.** $(y_n = y_{n-1} + 2y_{n-2})(n:3)$

5. $(x_{n-1})(n:2)$ **11.** $[y_{n+1} = (y_n)^2 + n](n:1)$

6. $(x_{n-2})(n:4)$ **12.** $[y_n = (y_{n-1})^n](n:2)$

For problems 13 to 22, give the first five terms of each sequence.

13. $\begin{cases} y_n = 1, \text{ for } n = 1. \\ y_n = 2y_{n-1}, \text{ for } n \text{ greater than 1.} \end{cases}$

18. $\begin{cases} a_1 = 0 \\ a_2 = 1 \\ a_n = a_{n-1} + a_{n-2}, \\ \quad \text{for } n \text{ greater than 2.} \end{cases}$

14. $\begin{cases} y_n = 3, \text{ for } n = 1. \\ y_n = 2y_{n-1} + 1, \text{ for } n \text{ greater than 1.} \end{cases}$

19. $\begin{cases} b_1 = 6 \\ b_2 = 4 \\ b_n = 3b_{n-1} + 2b_{n-2}, \\ \quad \text{for } n \text{ greater than 2.} \end{cases}$

15. $\begin{cases} t_n = 6, \text{ for } n = 1. \\ t_n = 3 + t_{n-1}, \text{ for } n \text{ greater than 1.} \end{cases}$

20. $\begin{cases} h_1 = 1 \\ h_n = nh_{n-1}, \\ \quad \text{for } n \text{ greater than 1.} \end{cases}$

16. $\begin{cases} x_n = 1, \text{ for } n = 1. \\ x_n = x_{n-1} + (x_{n-1})^2, \text{ for } n \text{ greater than 1.} \end{cases}$

21. $\begin{cases} h_1 = 2 \\ h_{n+1} = (h_n)^2, \\ \quad \text{for } n \text{ greater than zero.} \end{cases}$

17. $\begin{cases} x_1 = 1 \\ x_n = x_{n-1} + 2n - 1, \text{ for } n \text{ greater than 1.} \end{cases}$

22. $\begin{cases} a_1 = 1 \\ a_2 = 2 \\ a_3 = 3 \\ a_n = a_{n-1} + a_{n-2} + a_{n-3}, \\ \quad \text{for } n \text{ greater than 3.} \end{cases}$

It is not necessary that the first term of a sequence correspond to one, and in particular we often begin a sequence with n equal to zero. If, for example, one sets n equal to zero in $a_n = 2n$, then $a_0 = 2 \cdot 0 = 0$. This allows $a_n = 2n$ to include the full range of the even numbers we have used. However, we must now be aware that the subscript n in a_n now corresponds to the $(n + 1)$st term since a_0 is the first, a_1 the second, and so on.

The formulas used in problem set (60) were all such that any particular term of the sequence could be computed provided only that its position in the sequence was known. That is, y_n depended only on a knowledge of n. In problem set (61) the formulas were such that to compute y_n required more than a choice of n; it was also necessary to have at hand one or more of the previous terms of the sequence. The recursion formulas were less flexible in this respect, but they did give more information about how the terms of the sequence were related to each other.

The terms of the following sequence arise many times in mathematical applications. A recursion formula is used to give a definition of $n!$, which is read "n factorial." It is defined for n equal to zero or any natural number. The value for $0!$ is first specified, and the remaining terms are defined recursively, that is, by relating each term to the previous term.

$$a_0 = 0! = 1$$
$$a_n = n! = n(n-1)!, \text{ for } n \text{ greater than zero.}$$

There is an order of operations convention to the effect that the factorial (as designated by !) is to be computed before the multiplication by n. An alternate notation for the factorial which has some usage is $\lfloor n$.

$$0! = 1$$
$$1! = 1(1-1)! = 1 \cdot 0! = 1 \cdot 1 = 1$$
$$2! = 2(2-1)! = 2 \cdot 1! = 2 \cdot 1 = 2$$
$$3! = 3(3-1)! = 3 \cdot 2! = 3 \cdot 2 \cdot 1 = 6$$
$$4! = 4(4-1)! = 4 \cdot 3! = 4 \cdot 3 \cdot 2 \cdot 1 = 24$$

By reversing the order of the factors, such as $1 \cdot 2 \cdot 3$ instead of $3 \cdot 2 \cdot 1$, it can be observed that for n greater than 1 we have $n! = 1 \cdot 2 \cdot 3 \cdots (n-1) \cdot n$. The definition of $n!$ is often given as being the product of all the natural numbers from 1 up to n. However, this gives only a hint that $1!$ should be 1, and leaves $0!$ undefined. Applications to be given in later chapters will indicate the desirability that both $0!$ and $1!$ equal 1.

Problems (62)

Compute the following:

1. The first ten terms of $a_n = n!$ They increase very rapidly!

2. $\dfrac{5!}{2!3!}$ **7.** $\dfrac{50!}{48!}$ **12.** $1! \cdot 2! \cdot 3!$

3. $\dfrac{5!}{1!4!}$ **8.** $(2!)^2$ **13.** $5! - 4!$

4. $\dfrac{5!}{0!5!}$ **9.** $(2^2)!$ **14.** $1! + 2! + 3!$

5. $\dfrac{6!}{2!4!}$ **10.** $(6-2)!$ **15.** $\dfrac{6!}{1!2!3!}$

6. $\dfrac{100!}{99!}$ **11.** $(3!)!$ **16.** $(1! - 0!)!$

Sometimes we want the sum of all the terms of a sequence, or at least the sum of several consecutive terms.

Example: The odd numbers from 5 to 13 can be obtained from $a_i = 2i - 1$ by setting i equal to 3, 4, 5, 6, and 7 in turn.

$$a_3 = 2 \cdot 3 - 1 \quad a_4 = 2 \cdot 4 - 1 \quad a_5 = 2 \cdot 5 - 1 \quad a_6 = 2 \cdot 6 - 1 \quad a_7 = 2 \cdot 7 - 1$$
$$\quad = 5 \qquad\qquad = 7 \qquad\qquad = 9 \qquad\qquad = 11 \qquad\qquad = 13$$

The sum of these numbers can be specified as follows:

$$\sum_{i=3}^{i=7} 2i - 1 = 5 + 7 + 9 + 11 + 13 = 45$$

The Greek letter Σ (pronounced "sigma") identifies this as the *sigma* notation, or the *summation* notation.   Each term of the sum results from substituting for i in $2i - 1$.   The replacements for i are a set of consecutive natural numbers.   The first number to be substituted for i is written below the sigma, and the last is written above the sigma.

Verify that the same sum is also represented by the following:

a. $\displaystyle\sum_{k=3}^{k=7} 2k - 1$ **b.** $\displaystyle\sum_{r=2}^{r=6} 2r + 1$ **c.** $\displaystyle\sum_{t=4}^{t=8} 2t - 3$ **d.** $\displaystyle\sum_{j=0}^{j=4} 2j + 5$

Any convenient letter may be used as were i, k, r, t, and j above, and hence they are sometimes called dummy variables or dummy indices.   The range of the index may also be shifted, and may begin at zero as in **d.**

Problems (63)

Compute the following:

1. $\displaystyle\sum_{k=1}^{k=3} 2k + 1$ **4.** $\displaystyle\sum_{i=1}^{i=3} i^2 - 1$ **7.** $\displaystyle\sum_{k=0}^{k=3} 3^{k+1}$ **10.** $\displaystyle\sum_{i=0}^{i=5} 5 - i$

2. $\displaystyle\sum_{k=0}^{k=4} 2^k$ **5.** $\displaystyle\sum_{k=0}^{k=4} \frac{k(k+1)}{2}$ **8.** $\displaystyle\sum_{t=1}^{t=5} \frac{60}{t}$ **11.** $\displaystyle\sum_{i=1}^{i=3} a_i,$

                                                                                  where $a_i = 5$
                                                                                     for all i

3. $\displaystyle\sum_{i=1}^{i=4} i^2 + i$ **6.** $\displaystyle\sum_{x=1}^{x=4} x^2 - x + 2$ **9.** $\displaystyle\sum_{j=2}^{=4} j!$ **12.** $\displaystyle\sum_{j=1}^{j=4} (4-j)!$

Express the following in sigma notation (there are many possibilities).

13. $1^3 + 2^3 + 3^3 + 4^3$ **15.** $1 \cdot 2 + 2 \cdot 3 + 3 \cdot 4$ **17.** $2 + 7 + 14 + 23$
14. $2 + 4 + 6 + 8 + 10$ **16.** $5 + 8 + 11 + 14$ **18.** $10 + 7 + 4 + 1$

6-4. Explicit and Implicit Formulas

So far in our work with formulas, the relation of the given numbers to the formula has been such that the problem of determining the remaining number has been explicit in form.   Thus for $d = rt$ we observe that d forms by itself one member of the equation.   Now suppose that numbers are furnished for substitution for the remaining variables; for example, $r = 65$ and $t = 4$.

Substitution then results in $d = 65 \cdot 4$, and the multiplication necessary to compute d is explicitly stated.   Hence the formula $d = rt$ is seen to be an explicit set of directions for determining d when t and r are known.

On the other hand, suppose we have

$$\begin{cases} d = rt \\ d = 260 \\ r = 65 \end{cases}$$

Substitution gives $260 = 65t$.   From this we imply that it is necessary to divide 260 by 65 to obtain $t = 4$.

Problems (64)

Solve each system; that is, determine the remaining numbers or unknowns.

1. $\begin{cases} P = 2a + b \\ P = 30 \\ a = 9 \end{cases}$

2. $\begin{cases} E = IR \\ E = 220 \\ I = 4 \end{cases}$

3. $\begin{cases} r = \dfrac{D}{2} \\ r = 16 \end{cases}$

4. $\begin{cases} M = S - C \\ M = 65 \\ C = 125 \end{cases}$

5. $\begin{cases} s = \dfrac{n(a + L)}{2} \\ s = 150 \\ a = 3 \\ L = 27 \end{cases}$

6. $\begin{cases} P = 6S \\ P = 108 \end{cases}$

7. $\begin{cases} P = \dfrac{E^2}{R} \\ P = 147 \\ E = 105 \end{cases}$

8. $\begin{cases} V = lwh \\ V = 176 \\ l = 11 \\ h = 2 \end{cases}$

6-5. Equivalent Statements

An improved understanding of the number relations expressed by formulas can be gained by studying the various ways in which simple relations may be written.
The diagram

* * *   * *

suggests three equations that not only use the same numbers, but have essentially the same content.

$$5 = 2 + 3$$
$$2 = 5 - 3$$
$$3 = 5 - 2$$

$5 = 2 + 3$ shows how 5 may be obtained from 2 and 3.
$2 = 5 - 3$ shows how 2 may be obtained from 5 and 3.
$3 = 5 - 2$ shows how 3 may be obtained from 5 and 2.

One way to distinguish these equivalent statements is to say that the first is *solved* for 5, the second is solved for 2, and the third is solved for 3.

Later we shall introduce formal rules by which one such form as these can be transformed into another. Such devices are not assumed as known by the reader; rather, an experimental approach is suggested at present. If a certain statement is given, equivalent statements can be constructed provided only that

A. The student can tell a true statement from a false one.
B. There is a willingness to check to see whether the statement is true or false.
C. There is a drive to keep on trying if success has not yet been attained.

If these conditions can be met, it will be possible for the student to get the necessary experience from which he may be able to discover and formulate for himself the laws for the manipulation of equations in this manner.

Problems (65)

Each equality below is to be rewritten in various ways; solve for each number in turn. The new forms of the equality must use exactly the same numerals and no computation is to be done.

1. $15 = 9 + 6$

2. $25 = 32 - 7$

3. $48 = (3)(16)$

4. $15 = \dfrac{60}{4}$

5. $23 = 4 \cdot 7 - 5$

6. $27 = 3 + 4 \cdot 6$

7. $37 - 7 = 5 \cdot 6$

8. $19 - 3 = 11 + 5$

9. $5 = 33 - 4 \cdot 7$

10. $3 \cdot 7 = 19 + 2$

11. $\dfrac{24}{4} = 9 - 3$

12. $\dfrac{80}{2} = 5 \cdot 8$

13. $\dfrac{13 + 17}{6} = 5$

14. $\dfrac{30}{4 + 1} = 6$

15. $\dfrac{48 - 8}{4} = 10$

16. $6 - 2 = \dfrac{32}{8}$

17. $\dfrac{24}{3} = \dfrac{40}{5}$

18. $15 = \dfrac{3 \cdot 25}{5}$

19. $3 \cdot 12 = 4 \cdot 9$

20. $\dfrac{16}{9 - 5} = 4$

21. $3(5 + 2) = 21$

22. $6(8 - 5) = 18$

23. $\dfrac{10 + 2}{8 - 5} = 4$

24. $\dfrac{42}{2} = 3 \cdot 7$

The three equations $r = s + t$, $s = r - t$, and $t = r - s$ are equivalent if and only if both of the following hold:

A. If a choice that is made for substitutions for r, s, and t in one of the equations results in a true statement, then the same substitutions in the other two equations will yield true statements.
B. If a choice for r, s, and t gives a false statement for one of the three equations, it will also give a false statement for the other two equations.

The equivalence of these three particular equations follows directly from the definition in Section 3-1, which relates subtraction to addition.   A choice of three numbers as in problem 1 of set (65) gives opportunity for a single verification of condition **A.** above.   Of course, no amount of repetition of such verifications constitutes a proof of the equivalence.   Nevertheless, such checks with numerical substitutions for the variables do make plausible the conjecture that several equations may indeed be equivalent, and will be useful for the next problem set.

Problems (66)

For each of the following equations, construct a set of equivalent equations, solving for each variable in turn.   Each of the variables r, s, t, and u may be considered to range over the natural numbers, and there is the further restriction that the numerals replacing them must be such as to result in a meaningful (defined) statement.

1. $r = \dfrac{s}{t}$	**7.** $t = rs - u$	**13.** $\dfrac{r}{u} = s - t$
2. $r = s - t$	**8.** $r + s = tu$	**14.** $\dfrac{r}{u} = st$
3. $rs = t + u$	**9.** $\dfrac{r}{s + u} = t$	**15.** $s(t + u) = r$
4. $s = rt$	**10.** $rt = su$	**16.** $r(s - t) = u$
5. $\dfrac{s + t}{r} = u$	**11.** $s = \dfrac{t}{u} + r$	**17.** $\dfrac{r}{s - t} = u$
6. $r = s + tu$	**12.** $r = \dfrac{s}{t} - u$	**18.** $u = r - st$

Since $2 \cdot 3$ and 6 are both names for the same number, the truth or falsity of any statement involving this number will not be changed if either $2 \cdot 3$ or 6 is replaced by the other.

$$\begin{cases} 12 = 2 \cdot 6 \\ 6 = 2 \cdot 3 \end{cases} \quad \text{becomes} \quad 12 = 2 \cdot (2 \cdot 3) \text{ when 6 is replaced by } 2 \cdot 3.$$

By contrast, $s = 24$ is true only for a particular value of s; and $L = 4s$ is not always true, but rather is true only for certain pairs of numbers.   Hence, the substitutions as made below in reducing a system of equations to a single equation amount to incorporating these special conditions in the final equation.

$$\begin{cases} S = L + s \\ L = 4s \\ s = 24 \end{cases} \quad \text{becomes} \quad \begin{cases} S = 4s + s \\ s = 24 \end{cases}$$

and this becomes $S = 4(24) + 24$, provided that all three of the given conditions hold.

Since $s = 24$ is only conditionally true, it was required that 24 be substituted for each s in $S = 4s + s$. In the example below $x = 1 \cdot x$ is an instance of a statement that is true for all x. In this case it is permissible to make the substitution for only one x in $3x + x$, which is desirable to set the stage for the use of the inverse of the distributive principle.

$$\begin{cases} 3x + x = 12 \\ x = 1 \cdot x \end{cases} \quad \text{becomes} \quad 3x + 1 \cdot x = 12 \quad \text{and then} \quad 4x = 12$$

Problems (67)

By using substitution, each of the following can be replaced by a single equation involving only one variable. Since this can be done in more than one way, let this be an equation involving only N. Do no computations.

1. $\begin{cases} N = A - B \\ A = C + D \\ C = 60 \\ D = 20 \\ B = 12 \end{cases}$

4. $\begin{cases} N = RS \\ S = \dfrac{T}{U} \\ T = 18 \\ U = 6 \\ R = 5 \end{cases}$

7. $\begin{cases} E = 4 \\ F = 12 \\ G = 8 \\ N = P + Q \\ P = EF \\ Q = EG \end{cases}$

2. $\begin{cases} N = A - B \\ B = C + D \\ C = 20 \\ D = 16 \\ A = 50 \end{cases}$

5. $\begin{cases} N = \dfrac{X}{Y} \\ Y = UV \\ U = 3 \\ V = 4 \\ X = 36 \end{cases}$

8. $\begin{cases} R = A + B \\ S = A - B \\ A = 18 \\ B = 6 \\ N = \dfrac{R}{S} \end{cases}$

3. $\begin{cases} N = RS \\ S = T - U \\ T = 30 \\ U = 17 \\ R = 2 \end{cases}$

6. $\begin{cases} N = \dfrac{X}{Y} \\ X = \dfrac{U}{V} \\ U = 36 \\ V = 3 \\ Y = 4 \end{cases}$

For problems 9 to 16, it will be necessary to change some of the equations to equivalent ones before making the necessary substitutions. This will be a change from an implicit to an explicit form for the variable involved. Again no computations are to be made.

9. $\begin{cases} N = X - Y \\ X - L = M \\ L = 7 \\ M = 11 \\ Y = 13 \end{cases}$
12. $\begin{cases} N = A - B \\ A - C = E \\ B + C = E \\ E = 8 \\ C = 2 \end{cases}$
15. $\begin{cases} \dfrac{P}{H} = J \\ Q + H = J \\ N = \dfrac{P}{Q} \\ J = 6 \\ H = 2 \end{cases}$

10. $\begin{cases} N = P - Q \\ S + Q = T \\ P = 20 \\ S = 5 \\ T = 10 \end{cases}$
13. $\begin{cases} N = RS \\ RT = U \\ T = 6 \\ U = 12 \\ S = 15 \end{cases}$
16. $\begin{cases} A = ND \\ B = CD \\ A = 16 \\ B = 8 \\ C = 2 \end{cases}$

11. $\begin{cases} N = S - T \\ RS = W \\ R = 3 \\ W = 15 \\ T = 2 \end{cases}$
14. $\begin{cases} N = UV \\ Y = V - X \\ X = 11 \\ Y = 4 \\ U = 3 \end{cases}$

6-6. Systems of Equations Models

We now have the tools at hand so that the attack on a verbal problem can begin with the construction of a mathematical model that is a system of equations. Our first example returns to the problem used in Section 1-8 to introduce the topic of mathematical models.

> **Example 1:** Kay received 213 votes in a school election, and Joe received
> 187. What was the combined vote?
>
> K: number of votes for Kay $\begin{cases} K + J = T \\ K = 213 \\ J = 187 \end{cases}$
> J: number of votes for Joe
> T: total number of votes

The first task was to identify each quantity in the problem by name. Then a suitable variable was assigned to each quantity. The system was then formed by stating, in equation form, the constraints on these variables. A great variety of correct and appropriate models can be made, since the choice of symbols for the variables, and even the form of the equations themselves depends on the judgment of the problem solver.

If T were replaced by N, the above system would reduce to $213 + 187 = N$, which is the result obtained in Section 1-8. Of course, this very simple problem can be easily solved without the detailed analysis we have presented. However, the method, which is quite powerful, can be practiced on simple problems before turning to the more difficult ones.

Example 2: Sally typed 84 invitations by working 3 hours on Friday and 4 hours on Saturday. How many invitations per hour was she able to type, on the average?

Model A

I: number of invitations $I_H = \dfrac{I}{H_T}$

H_F: hours worked on Friday $H_T = H_F + H_S$

H_S: hours worked on Saturday $I = 84$

H_T: total hours worked $H_F = 3$

I_H: number of invitations per hour $H_S = 4$

A subscript notation was used above for the variables, which is both compact and at the same time is suggestive of the range of the variables. These examples are only to illustrate some of the possibilities. The student should use a notation that he finds simple and easy to manipulate and that provides for ready recognition of the quantities being described.

The model designated as A is fully detailed, with each quantity mentioned by name and assigned a variable. Model B is a slightly less elaborate system, and C is a single equation to which the others reduce after substitution.

Model B   *Model C*

$$I_H = \frac{I}{H_F + H_S} \qquad I_H = \frac{84}{3 + 4}$$

$I = 84$

$H_F = 3$

$H_S = 4$

When a problem involves determining only a single number, it has been the traditional practice to suggest to the student that he use only one variable. (Usually this has been "X," called the "unknown" to distinguish it from the other quantities, which are given.) With just one variable, only one equation is then required to relate the unknown to the knowns. This advice to use only one letter is good only for simple problems. If a problem is sufficiently complex so that its solution is giving some difficulty, it is strongly suggested that the student introduce as many variables as will enable him to write down one idea at a time. The reduction of the system to fewer equations can then be attacked in a routine manner.

A comparison of Models A, B, and C reveals that writing the single equation amounts to doing mentally the operations that are written down explicitly in the more detailed systems. The single-variable, single-equation approach may be practical, then, for the simple problems; but more variables (and hence more equations) should be used for the problems that prove to be difficult. By assigning letters as variables to all quantities, both known and unknown, the difficulties of the problems can be analyzed into the smallest possible steps. Also one often finds that the names of the quantities are much more suggestive of the relations between them, than are the numbers associated with them.

Not only are various options possible in the choice of notation but the structure of many problems can be viewed in more than one way.   The next example illustrates this.

> **Example 3:** Harry sold 23 papers in the afternoon and 7 in the evening. If the price of each was 15 cents, what were his total receipts for the day?

Model A   Model B

	Model A	Model B
T: total sales	$R_T = TP$	$R_T = R_A + R_E$
A: afternoon sales	$T = A + E$	$R_A = AP$
E: evening sales	$A = 23$	$R_E = EP$
P: price per paper	$E = 7$	$A = 23$
R_A: afternoon receipts	$P = 15$	$E = 7$
R_E: evening receipts		$P = 15$
R_T: total receipts	or	or

$$R_T = (23 + 7)(15) \qquad R_T = (23)(15) + (7)(15)$$

Problems (68)

Construct systems of equations models for the following problems that give full details.   It is also instructive to experiment with less elaborate models, and in particular, a single equation model should be given.

1. Kitty had \$20.   She spent \$2 in one store and half of the remainder in a second store.   How much did she have left?
2. The students sold 180 tickets for the class play.   Of these, 110 were sold for 90 cents each and the rest for 50 cents each.   What were the total receipts?
3. Six men planned to share the cost of \$60 for a boat for a weekend trip.   Two of the men could not go, but the rest shared the expense equally.   How much more did it cost each man than he had planned?
4. The weight of 7 baskets of fruit was 189 pounds.   Each empty basket weighed 2 pounds, and the selling price was 20 cents per pound of actual fruit.   What were the receipts?
5. Mr. James started on a trip of 255 miles and stopped for gas after driving 120 miles in 3 hours.   How many miles per hour must he increase his average speed for the remainder of the trip in order to complete the trip in 3 more hours?
6. A store prepared 9,600 handbills advertising a sale.   The community was divided into 8 sections, and 2 boys were hired in each section to distribute the handbills.   If each boy was given the same number, how many handbills did each receive?
7. Additional problems for practice are available in problem sets (8), (18), (28), and (38).   A check can be made by reducing your system to a single equation.

For Further Study

The notation for substitution that was introduced in Section 6-1 is that of [M2], pp. 36–40.   Although written at a more advanced level, this text contains very clear treatments of many topics we shall discuss.

There are numerous examples of the use of formulas in giving mathematical descriptions to the world about us in reference [S3], particularly in Chapter VI.

A valuable discussion of the role of induction and generalization in the discovery of formulas can be found in [W2], pp. 2–16, 95–110, and 366–386.   Excellent exercises are included.

For further reading on sequences see [M1], pp. 128–135.

7

Numeration and Computation

7-1. Further Study of Polynomials

In our study of such statements as $2 \cdot 3 \cdot 5 = 30$, the factors 2, 3, and 5 have been designated as divisors of the product 30, while 30 has been termed a multiple of these divisors. The word *coefficient* is used to relate the factors of a product to each other. If in any product of two or more factors we fix our attention on a single factor, then the product of the remaining factors is said to be the coefficient of that factor.

> **Examples:** In the product $2 \cdot 3$, 3 is the coefficient of 2, and 2 is the coefficient of 3.
>
> In the product of $2 \cdot 3 \cdot 5$, $3 \cdot 5$ is the coefficient of 2, $2 \cdot 5$ is the coefficient of 3, and $2 \cdot 3$ is the coefficient of 5.

a. In $2 \cdot 3 \cdot 5$, what are the coefficients of $2 \cdot 3$, $2 \cdot 5$, and $3 \cdot 5$?

The polynomial notation for natural numbers was introduced in Section 4-5, where the decimal numeral 1,492 was considered to be an abbreviation for

$$1(10)^3 + 4(10)^2 + 9(10) + 2(1)$$

which was designated as a polynomial in powers of 10. We now wish to consider a somewhat broader class of polynomials, all of which are of the following form:

$$a_n b^n + a_{n-1} b^{n-1} + a_{n-2} b^{n-2} + \cdots + a_2 b^2 + a_1 b + a_0$$

This is a sum of terms of the form $a_i b^i$, that is, any given term can be obtained by substitutions for the variable i in $a_i b^i$. (The letters i or j are often used in this manner to form a typical or general expression.) Note that the last term, a_0, need not be an exception to this form since $a_0 = a_0 \cdot 1 = a_0 \cdot b^0$.

The powers of b have been arranged in decreasing order of size, for convenience, and b is known as the *base* or *radix* of the polynomial. The a_i, which may differ from term to term, are the coefficients of the powers of b and are called the coefficients of the polynomial.

b. In the polynomial above for 1,492, what are a_0, a_1, a_2, and a_3?

At present the range for b will be natural numbers greater than or equal to 2. The range for the a_i is zero, or any natural number. However, the coefficient of the highest power of b, the so-called *leading* coefficient, should not be zero.

Once b has been chosen, we shall be particularly interested in limiting the choice of the a_0 to the range of zero up to $b - 1$. That is, the largest value that any a_i could have would then be 1 less than the base number. If the coefficients of the polynomial do meet this specification, we shall regard such a polynomial as being in *standard* form.

The example below illustrates the repeated use of the distributive principle and its inverse in transforming a polynomial to standard form. For the base number 10 this can be done mentally after a little practice.

$$9(10)^2 + 13(10) + 4 = 9(10)^2 + (10 + 3)(10) + 4$$
$$= 9(10)^2 + 1(10)^2 + 3(10) + 4$$
$$= (9 + 1)(10)^2 + 3(10) + 4$$
$$= 1(10)^3 + 0(10)^2 + 3(10) + 4$$

ANSWERS TO EXERCISES

a. 5, 3, and 2.   **b.** 2, 9, 4, and 1.

Problems (69)

Each polynomial below represents a natural number, but the specifications for standard form have not been met. Represent this number by a polynomial that retains the same base, but with every coefficient to be not greater than 1 less than the base number. It is necessary at times to insert a zero coefficient to ensure there are no gaps in the descending powers of the base.

1. $6(10)^2 + 15(10) + 7$ 12. $9(7)^2 + 4(7) + 9$
2. $6(10)^2 + 7(10) + 15$ 13. $4(7)^2 + 5(7) + 9$
3. $15(10)^2 + 6(10) + 7$ 14. $2(7)^2 + 6(7) + 8$
4. $3(10)^2 + 9(10) + 17$ 15. $5(5)^2 + 4(5) + 3$
5. $9(10)^2 + 0(10) + 18$ 16. $5(4)^2 + 4(4) + 3$
6. $9(10)^2 + 9(10) + 16$ 17. $5(3)^2 + 4(3) + 3$
7. $9(10)^2 + 9(10) + 10$ 18. $2(3)^2 + 3(3) + 4$
8. $8(10)^2 + 9(10) + 10$ 19. $1(2)^3 + 0(2)^2 + 1(2) + 3$
9. $12(10)^2 + 11(10) + 10$ 20. $1(2)^3 + 1(2)^2 + 2(2) + 2$
10. $9(10)^2 + 10(10) + 11$ 21. $2(2)^3 + 2(2)^2 + 2(2) + 2$
11. $5(7)^2 + 9(7) + 4$ 22. $1(2)^3 + 2(2)^2 + 3(2) + 4$

7-2. Detached Coefficients

Each of the polynomials in the previous problem set represents a certain natural number. To identify just what number this is we need the basic numeral which, for natural numbers, is the decimal numeral form. The computation of this decimal numeral is called computing the *value* of the polynomial. This is immediate when the polynomial is in powers of 10.

$$3(10)^3 + 5(10)^2 + 2(10) + 6 = 3,526$$

If the base is not 10, the computation may follow the usual convention of powers first, then the products, and finally the sum.

$$\begin{aligned}
3(7)^3 + 5(7)^2 + 2(7) + 6 &= 3(343) + 5(49) + 2(7) + 6 \\
&= 1,029 + 245 + 14 + 6 \\
&= 1,294
\end{aligned}$$

This method will always apply and for simple cases would be hard to improve upon. However, another way of computing the value may offer advantages with more complicated polynomials. It also provides an example of an alternate computation, which leads to the same result even though at first sight it seems quite different.

Any systematic way of writing down the numerals in the process of a computation is called an *algorithm*** for that computation. We now present an algorithm for computing the value of a polynomial that is called the method of *detached coefficients*. As a preliminary, we take our example polynomial and break up the polynomial form by repeated use of the inverse of the distributive principle.

$$\begin{aligned}
3(7)^3 + 5(7)^2 + 2(7) + 6 &= 7\{3 \cdot 7^2 + 5 \cdot 7 + 2\} + 6 \\
&= 7\{7\,[3 \cdot 7 + 5] + 2\} + 6 \\
&= 7\{7\,[7(3) + 5] + 2\} + 6
\end{aligned}$$

Before the student decides that the last line above is more complicated than as originally given, let us consider the following algorithm for doing the computation specified in the final line. The first step is to detach the coefficients of the polynomial and arrange them in a row. Then outline the working area, and set down the base number 7 in a convenient spot, say at the right, or at the left as shown.

7	3	5	2	6
		21	182	1,288
	3	26	184	1,294

Next copy the leading coefficient, which is 3 in this example, onto the lower line. Now perform the following computations in order, verifying at each step that they are the ones called for in the modified form.

---

* The term "algorism" is used by some authors.

$$7(3) = 21$$
$$21 + 5 = 26$$
$$7(26) = 182$$
$$182 + 2 = 184$$
$$7(184) = 1,288$$
$$1,288 + 6 = 1,294$$

For small multipliers (base numbers) these computations can be done mentally, writing down the results only. When larger numbers are involved, the multiplications are worked out separately and then recorded as shown above.

To illustrate the generality of this algorithm we set down the steps for the polynomial whose coefficients are a_3, a_2, a_1, and a_0.

b	a_3	a_2	a_1	a_0
		a_3b	$a_3b^2 + a_2b$	$a_3b^3 + a_2b^2 + a_1b$
	a_3	$a_3b + a_2$	$a_3b^2 + a_2b + a_1$	$a_3b^3 + a_2b^2 + a_1b + a_0$

We have already observed that any coefficient, except the leading one, might be zero. Whenever there are zero coefficients, as indicated by some powers of the base being omitted in the decreasing sequence, these zeros must be supplied when using this algorithm.

Example: Compute $2(5)^4 + 3(5)^2$
or $2(5)^4 + 0(5)^3 + 3(5)^2 + 0(5) + 0$

5	2	0	3	0	0
		10	50	265	1,325
	2	10	53	265	1,325

Check:
$$2(5)^4 + 3(5)^2 = 2(625) + 3(25)$$
$$= 1,250 + 75$$
$$= 1,325$$

Problems (70)

Compute the value of these polynomials, using the method of detached coefficients. Check by carrying out the computation with the conventional order of operations.

1. $1(5)^2 + 2(5) + 1$
2. $3(5)^2 + 2(5) + 0$
3. $2(5)^2 + 0(5) + 3$
4. $6(7)^2 + 6(7) + 6$
5. $2(7)^3 + 1(7)^2 + 2(7) + 5$
6. $4(7)^3 + 0(7)^2 + 2(7) + 0$
7. $1(3)^3 + 1(3)^2 + 1(3) + 1$
8. $3(4)^2 + 2(4) + 1$
9. $8(9)^3 + 6(9)^2 + 5(9) + 0$
10. $3(12)^3 + 2(12)^2 + 1(12) + 10$
11. $1(2)^5 + 1(2)^4 + 0(2)^3 + 1(2)^2 + 0(2) + 1$
12. $1(2)^5 + 0(2)^4 + 1(2)^3 + 0(2)^2 + 1(2) + 0$
13. $5(8)^3 + 5(8)$
14. $2(4)^4$
15. $15(20)^2 + 10(20) + 5$
16. $8(60)^2 + 22(60) + 41$

7-3. How Many?

The decimal numerals, each of which is associated with a base ten polynomial, have been accepted as basic numerals for the natural numbers. This means that they are accepted as the preferred answer to the question, "How many is that?" A closer study of this practice will reveal it to be based on arbitrary conventions that have become familiar with long usage, rather than any distinctive property of the number 10.

* *

How many asterisks are in the row above? By forming groups as shown in the next diagram we find there are three groups of ten and a single one. This we may write as $3(10) + 1(1)$ and abbreviate by writing 31.

* *

One could also count by fives as shown; with results that could be recorded as $6(5) + 1(1)$

* *

However, there are enough of the five groups to count them five at a time also. The group of five 5's can be represented by 5^2, and therefore the total number of asterisks can be represented as $1(5)^2 + 1(5) + 1(1)$.

* *

We still keep the same number of asterisks (which happens to be the same as the number of days in the month of January), but this time count by threes, and continue to form larger groups as long as we can.

* *

The diagram shows that the number of days in the month of January can be represented as

$$10(3) + 1$$
or as $$3(3)^2 + 1(3) + 1$$
or as $$1(3)^3 + 0(3)^2 + 1(3) + 1$$

Problems (71)

Complete the grouping, using the base number indicated, and represent the result as a polynomial in powers of the group number. The polynomial will be in standard form, if the grouping is continued as long as possible.

1. *
2. *
3. *
4. *
5. *
6. *

We now introduce a notation by which we can abbreviate the polynomials obtained above. It consists of detaching the coefficients of the polynomial, writing them in the same left-to-right sequence, and then giving the base number. The base number is written in word form and placed in parentheses at the lower right.

Examples: $1(3)^3 + 0(3)^2 + 1(3) + 1$ is written as $1,011_{(three)}$

$1(4)^2 + 3(4) + 3$ is written as $133_{(four)}$

$2(12) + 7$ is written as $27_{(twelve)}$

This convention for writing numerals will be called the *place value notation*. It gives the essential information so that the polynomial that is abbreviated can be written out readily. It is in agreement with, and an extension of, the decimal numeral notation. When the base number is ten, it can be omitted by agreement, or possibly be stated for emphasis.

$$1(10)^3 + 9(10)^2 + 6(10) + 5(1) = 1,965_{(ten)} = 1,965$$

For all bases (ten is now only a special case) the place values are those as given by the following chart:

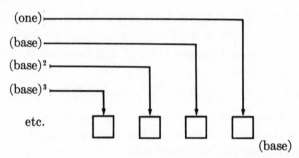

$412_{(five)}$ represents, uniquely, some natural number. Why do we fail to recognize this number? The answer is that it is based on groups of five, whereas our experience has been almost entirely with groups of ten. Hence, the answer to the question, "What number is $412_{(five)}$?" is given by the decimal (base 10) numeral for this number, which is 107.

$$412_{(five)} = 4(5)^2 + 1(5) + 2(1)$$
$$= 100 + 5 + 2$$
$$= 107$$

Alternatively,

5	4	1	2
		20	105
	4	21	107

Man's preference for groups of ten is undoubtedly related to the fact that he has ten fingers. Small groups could be identified by holding up a few fingers, and larger groups by repeatedly using all the fingers on both hands. By doing some work with unfamiliar groupings (other than ten) an appreciation can be gained of the great dependence we have developed on the familiar base of ten.

Problems (72)

1. Give the decimal numeral.

   a. $62_{(eight)}$ d. $10,101_{(three)}$ g. $1,000_{(two)}$
   b. $123_{(four)}$ e. $2,222_{(four)}$ h. $1,221_{(five)}$
   c. $205_{(seven)}$ f. $2,510_{(six)}$

2. Give the decimal numeral.

   a. $34_{(nine)}$ d. $1,101_{(two)}$ g. $10,000_{(three)}$
   b. $432_{(six)}$ e. $4,433_{(five)}$ h. $3,333_{(four)}$
   c. $502_{(seven)}$ f. $1,540_{(seven)}$

3. Give the decimal numeral for the sum of two 81's, one 27, and two 1's.
   Represent this same number in polynomial notation in base three.
   Represent this same number in place value notation in base three.

4. Give the decimal numeral for the sum of three 64's, one 16, two 4's, and
   three 1's.
   Represent this same number in polynomial notation in base four.
   Represent this same number in place value notation in base four.

5. What is the total number of seconds in 2 hours, 7 minutes, and 5 seconds?
   Represent this same number in polynomial notation in base sixty.
   What difficulties arise when using place value notation to record hours,
   minutes, and seconds, or degrees, minutes, and seconds as in problem 6?

6. What is the total number of seconds in 18 degrees, 12 minutes, and 26
   seconds?
   Represent this same number in polynomial notation in base sixty.

7. If a gross is a dozen dozen, give the decimal numeral for 3 gross, 9 dozen,
   and 2.
   Represent this same number in polynomial notation in base twelve.

8. If t represents ten, and e represents eleven, what is the decimal numeral for
   $t6e_{(twelve)}$?
   State this number using gross and dozen.   (See problem 7.)
   Represent this same number in polynomial notation in base twelve.

9. In what base could the number of days in a week be written as $21_{(\quad)}$?

10. In what base could the number of your toes be represented by $13_{(\quad)}$?

11. In what base could the number of states in the U.S. be written as $200_{(\quad)}$?

12. In what base could the number of years in a century be written as $50_{(\quad)}$?

The diagram below has as many asterisks as there are months in the year.

$$* \; * \; * \; * \; * \; * \; * \; * \; * \; * \; * \; *$$

The count below gives the numerals in succession as they would be recorded in
base three place value notation.

1, 2, $10_{(three)}$, $11_{(three)}$, $12_{(three)}$, $20_{(three)}$, $21_{(three)}$, $22_{(three)}$, $100_{(three)}$, $101_{(three)}$,
$102_{(three)}$, $110_{(three)}$.

The first two numerals, 1 and 2, do not need a base designation, and if by agreement the base is omitted from the others, we have:

$$1, 2, 10, 11, 12, 20, 21, 22, 100, 101, 102, 110$$

It would be very confusing if we were to read these numerals the way we do
when they are decimal numerals. If they were to be basic numerals, one could
create new words such as "trio" for 10, and "trio-one" for 11, etc. We shall not do
this, but instead let us read them as we do telephone numbers. We say:

One, two, one-zero (or one-oh), one-one, one-two, two-zero, two-one, two-two,
one-zero-zero, one-zero-one, one-zero-two, one-one-zero.

To get the proper sense, we must keep in mind that we are counting in base three.

A simple device for keeping a record of counting can be designed   Storage
as shown.   Several vertical lines and one horizontal line are drawn.
The spacing should be such that counters (pennies, buttons, etc.)
may be placed on the vertical lines.   Consider as storage space that
part of every vertical line that is above the horizontal line.   The
counters are then moved below as needed.

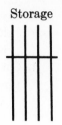

The following conventions are then adopted:

A. To increase any count by one, bring down one counter on the column
farthest to the right.

B. A base, or grouping number of two or more, is chosen.   This amounts to a
decision as to how many counters in any one column are to be equivalent to,
and exchanged for, a single counter in the next column to the left.

C. If such an exchange as in **B.** is possible, it is made before the count is recorded.

With these agreements, counting in base three could proceed as follows:

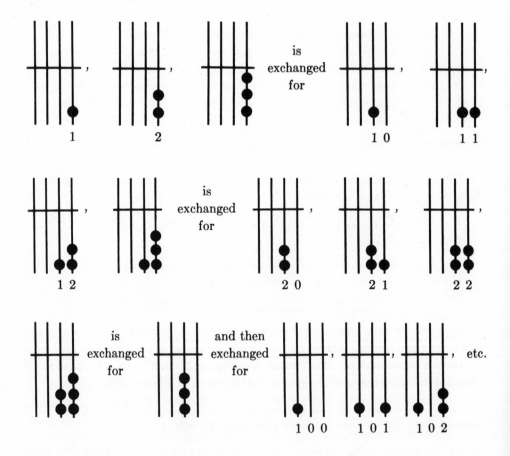

These diagrams serve as a simple type of abacus, a counting and computing device that was used in ancient times and is still used in some parts of the world. Historians have conjectured that the numeral zero may have been invented to represent an empty column on the abacus. Does this seem plausible in the light of the above diagrams?

Problems (73)

This exercise should be worked out with an abacus (or diagrams as suggested), if at all possible. If this cannot be done, one can at least imagine that he is going through the necessary manipulations of the counters.

Complete the chart, using the bases suggested, to count the months in a year. The base names may be omitted from the numerals. For base twelve single symbols (which occupy only one place) must be introduced for ten and eleven. Use t for ten and e for eleven.

ten	two	three	four	five	eight	twelve
1		1				
2		2				
3		10				
.		.				
.		.				
.		.				
12		110				

Problems (74)

An abacus will also be helpful with these exercises.

1. * * * * * * * * * * * * * * * * * *

   Count these asterisks, counting by 2's, but record your result in base five.
   2, 4, 11, _____, _____, etc.
   The numbers represented are all even. Does the usual rule for recognition of even numbers fail in this case? For what bases does the rule hold?

2. * * * * * * * * * * * * * * * * *

   Begin with one, then count by 2's, but record your results in base three.
   1, 10, 12, _____, _____, etc.
   The numbers represented are all odd. What about the rule (for base ten) for recognition of odd numbers?

3. * * * * *   * * * * *   * * * * *   etc.

   Using base six, begin with 5 and add 5 repeatedly. 5, 14, 23, _____, etc.
   What number in base ten shows a similar pattern?

4. * * * *   * * * *   * * * *   etc.

   Using base eight, begin with 4 and add 4 repeatedly. 4, 10, 14, _____,
   etc.
   What number in base ten shows a similar pattern?

5. In base five, begin with 34, and count forward by 1's for ten numbers.
6. In base four, begin with 32, and count backwards by 1's for ten numbers.
7. In base three, begin with 2,012, and count backwards by 1's for ten numbers.
8. In base four, begin with 2,012, and count backwards by 1's for ten numbers.
9. In base four, begin with 203, and count backwards by 2's for ten numbers.
10. In base five, begin with five, and count forward by fives for ten numbers.

    For problems 11 to 16, which are in base twelve, use e for eleven, and t for ten.

11. Begin with 198 and count backwards by 2's for ten numbers.
12. Begin with 198 and count backwards by 4's for ten numbers.
13. Begin with 198 and count backwards by 3's for ten numbers.
14. Begin with 198 and count backwards by 6's for ten numbers.
15. Begin with 198 and count backwards by e's for ten numbers.
16. Begin with 198 and count backwards by $10_{(twelve)}$'s for ten numbers.

Summary: Writing numerals in place value notation for various bases.

   A. In base r, the single symbols 0, 1, ..., $r-1$ are required as digits. That is, r symbols are necessary, the smallest being zero, and the largest has a value one less than the base number.

   B. The numeral 10 (read "one-zero" rather than "ten") will always represent one group, the size of the base number.

   C. Written numeral words are to be interpreted in base ten.

   D. The place value of the rightmost digit is always to be one, and the place value next to the left is that of the base number. If the numeral has n places, the highest place value (which is at the left) will be r^{n-1}.

7-4. Transformation to Unfamiliar Bases

In the previous section the polynomial form served as an intermediate step when transforming the numeral for a number from a base other than ten to the familiar base of ten. For the opposite change, going from the decimal numeral to an unfamiliar base, two algorithms will be given.

   Example: How would the number of weeks in a year be represented in base six?

   First Method. We require a list of powers of 6, so it can be determined which is the highest power of 6 that is not greater than 52.

$$6^0 = 1, \ 6^1 = 6, \ 6^2 = 36, \ 6^3 = 216.$$

It can now be seen that 6^2 or 36 is the desired number, since 6^2 is less than 52, and 6^3 is greater than 52. The problem now becomes that of determining the coefficients of the polynomial

$$A(6)^2 + B(6) + C(1)$$

These can be found by repeated division, using the decreasing powers of 6 in turn.   The usual form of the long division algorithm can be modified slightly to do this.

$$
\begin{array}{ll}
\underline{36\ |\ 52\ |\ 1} & 52 = 1(52) \\
\quad\ 36 & \quad\ = 1(36) + 16 \\
\underline{\ 6\ |\ 16\ |\ 2} & \quad\ = 1(36) + 2(6) + 4 \\
\quad\ 12 & \quad\ = 1(6)^2 + 2(6) + 4(1) \\
\quad\ \ \ \overline{\ 4} &
\end{array}
\qquad
\begin{array}{l}
A = 1 \\
B = 2 \\
C = 4 \\
52 = 124_{(six)}
\end{array}
$$

Second Method.   In the above algorithm the leading coefficient was determined first, then in turn those coefficients associated with smaller powers of the base.   The order can be reversed so that the coefficients are determined in the opposite order.   This computation turns out to be simpler, since all the divisions can be made using a small number (the base) as a divisor.   Hence, the short division algorithm is often practical.

$$
\begin{array}{ll}
6\ |\ 52 & 52(1) = 52 \qquad C = 4 \\
\underline{6\ |\ \ 8 \longrightarrow 4} & 8(6) + 4(1) = 52 \qquad B = 2 \\
\quad\ \ 1 \longrightarrow 2 & 1(6)^2 + 2(6) + 4(1) = 52 \qquad A = 1 \\
& 124_{(six)} = 52
\end{array}
$$

Example: Express the number of days in June in base three.

First Method

$$
\begin{array}{l}
3^0 = 1 \\
3^1 = 3 \\
3^2 = 9 \\
3^3 = 27 \\
3^4 = 81
\end{array}
\qquad
\begin{array}{l}
\underline{27\ |\ 30\ |\ 1} \\
\quad\ \ 27 \\
\underline{\ 9\ |\ \ 3\ |\ 0} \\
\underline{\ 3\ |\ \ 3\ |\ 1} \\
\quad\ \ 3 \\
\quad\ \ \overline{0}
\end{array}
\qquad
30 = 1{,}010_{(three)}
$$

Second Method

$$
\begin{array}{ll}
3\ |\ 30 & 30 = 1{,}010_{(three)} \\
\underline{3\ |\ 10 \longrightarrow 0} & \\
\underline{3\ |\ \ 3 \longrightarrow 1} & \\
\quad\ \ 1 \longrightarrow 0 &
\end{array}
$$

Problems (75)

1. How would the number of days in a leap year be represented in base three?
2. How would the number of states in the United States be represented in binary (base two) notation?

3. Represent 1,964 in duodecimal (base twelve) notation.

4. Represent 1,000 in octal (base eight) notation.

5. Consider a collection of 1,000 individual objects. It is desired to package these in packages of these sizes: 1, 3, 9, 27, 81, 243, or 729. There should be as few packages as possible and not more than two of any one size. How is this to be done?

6. From a collection of weights in pounds of 1, 2, 2^2, 2^3, 2^4, 2^5, and 2^6 make a selection whose total weight is 116 pounds, with not more than one weight of each size being used.

7. a. $15_{(six)} = ($ $)_{(ten)} = ($ $)_{(four)}$

   b. $23_{(five)} = ($ $)_{(ten)} = ($ $)_{(two)}$

8. a. $101_{(seven)} = ($ $)_{(ten)} = ($ $)_{(five)}$

   b. $203_{(four)} = ($ $)_{(ten)} = ($ $)_{(six)}$

9. a. If a number has five digits when represented in base four, what is the place value of the digit at the left?

   b. If a number has four digits when represented in base five, what is the place value of the digit at the left?

   c. In the base r, the number r is represented by 10, r^2 by _____, and r^3 by _____.

10. $7^4 = ($ $)_{(seven)}$

11. What is the smallest number that can be represented by $123_{(base)}$?

12. Compute the decimal numeral for $121_{(r)}$ for several values of r. Do you find a common property?

7-5. Addition and Subtraction Computations

Much practice with such computations as adding 435 and 278 has made the routine seem quite simple. Our purpose now is to take a closer look at the rationale or "why" of each step. This will be more apparent if we write out in full the polynomials for which each numeral is an abbreviation.

Add:

435
278
───
713

$$435 + 278 = 4(10)^2 + 3(10) + 5(1) + 2(10)^2 + 7(10) + 8(1)$$

Each polynomial is a sum of three terms. The sum of the two polynomials will be the total of all six terms and we want this finally to be a polynomial in standard form.

The commutative and associative principles allow us to group and combine these terms in any manner we choose. The vertical arrangement with one polynomial beneath the other is used for this purpose.

Add:

$$4(10)^2 + 3(10) + 5(1)$$
$$2(10)^2 + 7(10) + 8(1)$$

This brings the coefficients of like powers of ten into vertical columns so that the inverse of the distributive principle can be readily applied.

Add: Note that

$$4(10)^2 + 3(10) + 5(1)$$ $5(1) + 8(1) \quad = (5 + 8)(1) \quad = 13(1)$

$$\underline{2(10)^2 + 7(10) + 8(1)}$$ $3(10) + 7(10) \quad = (3 + 7)(10) \quad = 10(10)$

$$6(10)^2 + 10(10) + 13(1)$$ $4(10)^2 + 2(10)^2 = (4 + 2)(10)^2 = 6(10)^2$

The above result does represent the required sum but we cannot immediately detach the coefficients and write the decimal numeral, since the polynomial is not yet in standard form.

$$6(10)^2 + 10(10) + 13(1) = 7(10)^2 + 1(10) + 3(1) = 713$$

In practice it is found to be simpler to do the required regrouping for each coefficient at a time, working right to left, and "carrying" when necessary.

Add:

$$4(10)^2 + 3(10) + 5(1) \qquad 435$$
$$\underline{2(10)^2 + 7(10) + 8(1)} \qquad \underline{278}$$
$$7(10)^2 + 1(10) + 3(1) \qquad 713$$

Experience teaches us that one of the best ways to appreciate the value of a tool in a given task is to try to get along without it. This is our motivation for introducing some computations with numerals written in bases other than ten. The algorithm for addition is seen to be a process by which the required sum is broken up into a number of smaller sums so that advantage can be taken of previously memorized results. Hence, for efficient computation in any base there is required to be at hand a certain stock of memorized answers.

For addition (in base five) these basic combinations can be listed in a table as at the right. For example, we read from this table that $3 + 4 = 12$, which is read as "three plus four equals one-two."

Since we are working in base five, what we are saying is that three plus four makes one group of five, and two left over. For proficiency in addition in base five (which we do *not* require), these results would need to be memorized to the point of auto-

+	0	1	2	3	4
0	0	1	2	3	4
1	1	2	3	4	10
2	2	3	4	10	11
3	3	4	10	11	12
4	4	10	11	12	13

matic response. With this done, a computation such as that below would be as routine as the ones we now do in base ten.

$$30142$$
$$\underline{32344}$$
$$113041_{\text{(five)}}$$

Our analysis of the algorithm for subtraction again begins by writing out the corresponding polynomials.

Subtract: **Subtract:**

435                              $4(10)^2 + 3(10) + 5(1)$
278                              $2(10)^2 + 7(10) + 8(1)$

In spite of the fact that 435 is greater than 278, which makes the subtraction possible, there is difficulty evident when we try to subtract the coefficients of like powers.   There are, in common use, two ways of transforming the polynomials so that this difficulty can be avoided.   One of these makes no change in the lower polynomial but regroups the upper one into nonstandard form.

Subtract:

$$3(10)^2 + 12(10) + 15(1)$$
$$2(10)^2 + 7(10) + 8(1)$$
$$1(10)^2 + 5(10) + 7(1)$$

This maneuver is commonly referred to as the method of *decomposition* or *regrouping*.   It is the one most widely taught at the present time in the U.S. elementary schools.   The difference between the two numbers is broken up into a series of differences, "borrowing" as required to make this possible.   Note that in subtraction the regrouping comes before the individual computations, rather than after, as in addition.

However, it is just as feasible to set the stage for the subtraction by changing both the upper and the lower polynomials.   Moreover, these changes are not just changes of form but actually replace the two given numbers by two different numbers.   We recall from the invariant principle for subtraction that the difference between two numbers is not changed if both numbers are increased by the same amount and this is the principle used here.

Both the polynomials are changed by the same amount but they are not changed in the same way.   In this example the upper number is increased by ten 1's.   To compensate for this the lower number is increased by one 10.   Then the upper number is increased by ten 10's, and corresponding to this the lower number is increased by one 100 or 10^2.   This is the method of "equal additions."

Subtract:

$4(10)^2 + 3(10) + 5(1)$ is changed to $4(10)^2 + 13(10) + 15(1)$
$2(10)^2 + 7(10) + 8(1)$ $3(10)^2 + 8(10) + 8(1)$
                                                  $1(10)^2 + 5(10) + 7(1)$

Problems (76)

1. Perform these computations, all of which are additions, interpreting the numerals in the base designated.

a. 5	**b.** 5	**c.** 35	**d.** 65
2	3	6	19
(eight)	(seven)	(eight)	(twelve)

e. 327	**f.** 23	**g.** 1011
664	12	1101
(nine)	33	1001
	22	(two)
	(four)	

2. Follow the same directions as given in problem 1.

a. 2	**b.** 30	**c.** 412	**d.** 20202
22	10	253	40413
(three)	(four)	(seven)	(five)

Each of the subtraction computations for problems 3 and 4 is to be written out with polynomials. Give two solutions for each, using the method of regrouping and the method of equal additions.

3.

a. 456	**b.** 231	**c.** 1011010
279	122	110111
	(four)	(two)

4.

a. 504	**b.** 1000	**c.** 2345
136	11	1638
	(three)	(nine)

5. Subtract in the base indicated.

a. 4231	**b.** 5203	**c.** 7020	**d.** 73096
3414	1025	6888	2e7t8
(five)	(six)	(nine)	(twelve)

6. Subtract in the base indicated.

a. 6045	**b.** 3000	**c.** 4444	**d.** 1021
5261	1023	1655	222
(eight)	(four)	(seven)	(three)

7. In what bases have the following additions been performed?

a. 3421	**b.** 3421	**c.** 3421
2234	2234	2234
11210( )	10055( )	5655( )

8. In what bases have the following subtractions been performed?

a. 2400	b. 1435	c. 8042	d. 7654
333	461	3521	889
2023( )	644( )	4521( )	6987( )

9. Assume there is exactly one error in this subtraction. Determine the base and the error.

$$\begin{array}{r} 52432 \\ 3434 \\ \hline 45664_{(\ \ )} \end{array}$$

10. Add in the smallest base for which this could be a correct notation.

$$\begin{array}{r} 4325 \\ 5041 \\ \hline _{(\ \ )} \end{array}$$

7-6. Multiplication Computations

Again we find that the usual algorithms for manipulation of decimal numerals should be considered as abbreviated forms (using the detached coefficients) for working with the polynomials associated with these numerals. The multiplication of polynomials involves extensive use of the distributive property of multiplication with respect to addition. If the product of two sums is expanded by the distributive principle, the result is the sum of all possible products of two factors that can be formed by selecting one factor from the terms of the first sum, and selecting the other factor from the terms of the second sum.

Example:
$$(2 + 4)(3 + 5 + 7) = (2)(3 + 5 + 7) + (4)(3 + 5 + 7)$$
$$= (2)(3) + (2)(5) + (2)(7) + (4)(3) + (4)(5) + (4)(7)$$

or $(2 + 4)(3 + 5 + 7) = (2 + 4)(3) + (2 + 4)(5) + (2 + 4)(7)$
$$= (2)(3) + (4)(3) + (2)(5) + (4)(5) + (2)(7) + (4)(7)$$

If one sum has m terms and the other has n terms, then the expanded sum will have mn terms.

The common algorithms for multiplication are designed to expedite the calculation of the separate products, together with combining them as we proceed if this is convenient.

Example:

$Multiply:$
$$\begin{array}{r} 342 \\ 2 \\ \hline 684 \end{array}$$
$$[3(10)^2 + 4(10) + 2(1)]\ (2)$$
$$6(10)^2 + 8(10) + 4(1) \qquad = 684$$

The product polynomial is in standard form, so no regrouping or "carrying" is required.

Example:
$$[3(10)^2 + 4(10) + 2(1)]\ (5)$$

$15(10)^2 + 20(10) + 10(1) = 1(10)^3 + 7(10)^2 + 1(10) + 0(1) = 1710$

$300 + 40 + 2$	342	342
$\underline{\hspace{3em}5}$	$\underline{\hspace{1.5em}5}$	$\underline{\hspace{1.5em}5}$
$1500 + 200 + 10 = 1710$	10 or $5(2)$	1710
	200 or $5(40)$	
	$\underline{1500 \text{ or } 5(300)}$	
	1710 or $\overline{5(300 + 40 + 2)}$	

The usual algorithm is seen to be an abbreviated form for working with the coefficients of the polynomial. By beginning with the smallest product and working to the left, it becomes possible to reduce one term at a time and "carry" mentally as required.

If the multiplier has more than one digit, then the distribution of the multiplier requires a repetition of the above procedure for each digit of the multiplier.

Example:

1734	$1(10)^3 + 7(10)^2 + 3(10) + 4(1)$
$\underline{\ 586}$	$\underline{\qquad\qquad\quad 5(10)^2 + 8(10) + 6(1)}$
10404	$1(10)^4 + 0(10)^3 + 4(10)^2 + 0(10) + 4(1)$
13872	$1(10)^5 + 3(10)^4 + 8(10)^3 + 7(10)^2 + 2(10)$
$\underline{\ 8670}$	$\underline{8(10)^5 + 6(10)^4 + 7(10)^3 + 0(10)^2}$
1016124	$1(10)^6 + 0(10)^5 + 1(10)^4 + 6(10)^3 + 1(10)^2 + 2(10) + 4(1)$

In the last example the distributive principle yields $3 \cdot 4$ or 12 separate products since one polynomial has three terms and the other has four terms. However, this can be shortened to writing down only three so-called "partial products" since one is able to combine and reduce four products at a time. Again if one does some of this with an unfamiliar base, it serves to emphasize the central role of the base number.

Problems (77)

Use the polynomial form for the multiplication computations in problems 1 and 2.

1.
a. 32	**b.** 72	**c.** 123	**d.** 23	**e.** 42	**f.** 342
$\underline{\ \ 3}$	$\underline{\ \ 4}$	$\underline{\ \ \ 7}$	$\underline{\ \ 2}$	$\underline{\ \ 3}$	$\underline{\ \ \ 4}$
			(nine)	(eight)	(five)

2.
a. 103	**b.** 60	**c.** 458	**d.** 76	**e.** 32	**f.** 212
$\underline{\ \ \ 2}$	$\underline{\ \ 5}$	$\underline{\ \ \ 6}$	$\underline{\ \ 2}$	$\underline{\ \ 3}$	$\underline{\ \ \ 2}$
			(twelve)	(four)	(three)

3. Multiply in the base indicated.

   a. 102   **b.** 234   **c.** 64   **d.** 134

        3   2   37   52

      (four)   (five)   (eight)   (six)

   e. 4t2   **f.** 21012   **g.** 1101011   **h.** 645

      93   201   1101   100

    (twelve)   (three)   (two)   (seven)

4. Multiply in the base indicated.

   a. 112   **b.** 130   **c.** 427   **d.** 142

      6   2   5   34

     (eight)   (four)   (nine)   (five)

   e. 222   **f.** 2e4   **g.** 1011101   **h.** 500

     22   t3   1011   500

    (three)   (twelve)   (two)   (six)

7-7. Division Computations

In the computations considered thus far the overall strategy has been to break up the problem into a number of simpler tasks, which can be approached one at a time in succession. In particular, one hopes to break the job down sufficiently so that the individual steps can make use of results that have been memorized. Thus the multiplication of two natural numbers, whose decimal numerals may have a large number of digits, can always be accomplished by adding a number of products. Furthermore, these products will have only two factors, with neither being larger than nine. For any base, these basic products need involve only factors that are less than the base number.

One might hope that division computations could be handled in a similar manner, that is, by breaking the main problem up into a series of simple divisions. Unfortunately difficulties arise when this is attempted because one does not have as much freedom for division as for multiplication, in the use of the distributive principle.

In $A(B + C) = AB + AC$, the multiplier A is on the left, and the multiplier is distributed over the other factor which has the form of a sum. We say that multiplication is *left distributive* with respect to addition.

But multiplication is commutative, and we have then another identity $(B + C)A = BA + CA$. Here the multiplier A is on the right, and the multiplier is again distributed over the other factor. Hence, multiplication is also *right distributive* with respect to addition.

   a. Can you prove that the right distributive law follows logically from commutativity and the left distributive law?

By checking the first example in Section 7-6 it may be verified that both right and left distributivity were used in expanding a product having both factors in the form of sums.   This was essential and could be avoided only by repeated use of the commutativity principle.

In Section 3-4, it was stated that division was distributive with respect to addition and subtraction.   Strictly speaking, division is only right distributive with respect to addition and subtraction, and the left distributive law does not hold.

Examples:

$$(15 + 12) \div 3 = (15 \div 3) + (12 \div 3) \qquad \frac{15 + 12}{3} = \frac{15}{3} + \frac{12}{3}$$

The divisor, which is on the right, can be distributed over the dividend which is in the form of a sum.

$$12 \div (4 + 2) \neq (12 \div 4) + (12 \div 2) \qquad \frac{12}{4 + 2} \neq \frac{12}{4} + \frac{12}{2}$$

The dividend, at the left, cannot be distributed over the divisor which is in the form of a sum.

In other words, there may be profit in splitting up the dividend into a sum of several addends, but this maneuver is not permissible for the divisor.   For this reason the majority of the cases where a given division computation is replaced directly by a sum of simple divisions will occur when the divisor is not greater than the base number.

Examples:

$$\frac{824}{2} = \frac{8(10)^2 + 2(10) + 4(1)}{2} = \frac{8(10)^2}{2} + \frac{2(10)}{2} + \frac{4(1)}{2}$$

$$= 4(10)^2 + 1(10) + 2(1) = 412$$

$$\frac{825}{3} = \frac{8(10)^2 + 2(10) + 5(1)}{3} = \frac{6(10)^2 + 21(10) + 15(1)}{3}$$

$$= \frac{6(10)^2}{3} + \frac{21(10)}{3} + \frac{15(1)}{3} = 2(10)^2 + 7(10) + 5(1) = 275$$

The second example shows the transformation of the polynomials for which the short division algorithm is an abbreviation.

$$3 \,\big|\, \underline{825}$$
$$275$$

The coefficient 6 is the largest multiple of 3 that is not greater than 8.
6 divided by 3 is 2, and 8 minus 6 is 2.
$2(10)^2 + 2(10)$ is then regrouped as $22(10)$.
21 is the largest multiple of 3 that is not greater than 22.
21 divided by 3 is 7, and 22 minus 21 is 1.
Finally, $1(10) + 5$ is 15, and 15 divided by 3 is 5.

Answer to Exercise

a. $A(B + C) = (B + C)A$, $AB = BA$, and $AC = CA$, all by the commutative principle. Hence, by substitution, if $A(B + C) = AB + AC$, then $(B + C)A = BA + CA$.

Problems (78)

In problems 1 to 10, analyze the division by writing out the polynomials in the manner of the above examples.

1. $\dfrac{28}{2}$ **3.** $\dfrac{116}{4}$ **5.** $\dfrac{3210}{6}$ **7.** $\dfrac{44}{3}$ (five)   **9.** $\dfrac{2202}{3}$ (four)

2. $\dfrac{63}{3}$ **4.** $\dfrac{252}{9}$ **6.** $\dfrac{1467}{3}$ **8.** $\dfrac{32}{4}$ (six)   **10.** $\dfrac{1770}{4}$ (eight)

For problems 11 to 14, use the short division algorithm for the computation.

11. $2\,\lfloor 1201$ **12.** $3\,\lfloor 1560$ **13.** $t\,\lfloor 47e8$ **14.** $4\,\lfloor 2344$
   (three)   (nine)   (twelve)   (six)

The technique used in problem set (78) becomes impractical whenever the divisor is larger than the base number. In this instance we adopt an indirect approach to division computations, which is essentially that of repeatedly subtracting multiples of the divisor. The central concept was introduced in Section 3-2, and a summary of the ideas discussed there is given for reference.

If A is zero, or any natural number, and B is any natural number but may not be zero, then there are unique numbers Q and R, which may be zero or natural numbers, such that

$$A = (Q)(B) + R \qquad \text{with } R \text{ less than } B$$

To compute Q and R for a given A and B, we first observe that if A is less than B, then Q is zero and $R = A$. When A is greater than or equal to B, which is the case of practical interest, we can begin by subtracting B from A. The subtraction of B is done repeatedly until a remainder R is obtained which is less than B. Q is the count of the number of times that B has been subtracted, and is termed the incomplete quotient when $R \neq 0$. In the case where $R = 0$, we have $A = QB$, and then by the definition of division in terms of multiplication, $\dfrac{A}{B} = Q$. Q is now known as the quotient.

Example:

$$25 = (Q)(7) + R \qquad 25 - 7 = 18 \qquad 25 = 1(7) + 18$$
$$Q = 3, R = 4 \qquad 18 - 7 = 11 \qquad 25 = 2(7) + 11$$
$$11 - 7 = 4 \qquad 25 = 3(7) + 4$$

```
A.       3      B. 7 ) 25        C.       3
         ─          7 │ 1           7 ) 25
         1         ──                    21
         1         18                   ──
         1          7 │ 1                 4
   7 ) 25          ──
        7          11
       ──           7 │ 1
       18          ──
        7           4 │ 3
       ──
       11
        7
       ──
        4
```

A. and **B.** are suggestions of the various ways that one can make a systematic record of the number of times that 7 must be subtracted. Of course, there is no need to subtract the 7's, one at a time. Algorithm **C.** saves time by subtracting all three 7's at one time. However, to be sure this is the correct thing to do, we need to know the largest multiple of the divisor 7 that is not greater than the dividend 25. It is this decision that becomes critical when the divisor is large.

Example:
$$259 = (Q)(37) + R$$
$$Q = 7, R = 0 \qquad 259 = (7)(37) \qquad \frac{259}{7} = 37$$

```
A.  37 ) 259          B.           7
        185 │ 5          37 ) 259
        ──               259
         74
         74 │ 2
        ──
          │ 7
```

A. is a somewhat cautious approach which opens by subtracting five 37's and then two more for a total of seven. **B.** is shorter but again the difficulty lies in determining (mentally) the largest multiple of 37 that is not greater than 259. Note that it is not good enough to compare multiples of 3 with 25.

When the dividend is a large multiple of the divisor, as in the next example, the procedure is to use the multiples of the divisor that are most easily calculated.

$10(37) = 370$	The base times the divisor.
$100(37) = 3700$	The square of the base times the divisor.
$1000(37) = 37000$	The cube of the base times the divisor.
etc.	

Example:
$$8559 = (Q)(37) + R$$
$$Q = 231, R = 12 \qquad 8559 = (231)(37) + 12$$

```
A. 37 | 8,559 |              B.            231
      | 3,700 | 100       37 | 8,559
      | 4,859 |                 74
      | 3,700 | 100             115
      | 1,159 |                 111
      |   370 | 10               49
      |   789 |                  37
      |   370 | 10               12
      |   419 |
      |   370 | 10
      |    49 |
      |    37 | 1
      |    12 | 231
```

Again **A.** is slow, but possibly sure, as compared with the usual highly condensed form in **B.** To be successful consistently in getting the "best multiple" at each stage the student must be able to mentally compute the product of any one-digit number (for the quotient) by any two-digit number (two left hand digits of the divisor).

If one uses only the single left-hand digit of the divisor the estimates are often wrong because of the carry-over from the next digit. Hence, in base ten one must be able to mentally compute products such as $(6)(38)$, and on up to $(9)(99)$, in order to estimate digits for the quotient. For this reason it has become customary in recent arithmetic texts to introduce the division algorithm with some form such as **A.** and then modify it to **B.** by stages as proficiency is acquired. An inspection of **A.** soon reveals the possibility of leaving out a considerable number of zeros, and of devising rules for "bringing down" digits as necessary.

Problems (79)

Compute Q and R. The student is urged to experiment with the more extended algorithms as suggested in **A.** of the examples. This eases the strain of estimating the best multiple, particularly when working with an unfamiliar base. Check these results by changing all the numbers to their decimal numeral representation, and then comparing the dividend with the sum of the remainder plus the divisor times the quotient. For example, problem 1 then becomes $47 = (3)(15) + 2$.

1. $65 = (Q)21 + R_{\text{(seven)}}$

2. $389 = (Q)32 + R_{\text{(twelve)}}$

3. $1763 = (Q)41 + R_{\text{(eight)}}$

4. $1200 = (Q)15 + R_{\text{(six)}}$

5. $2251 = (Q)26 + R_{\text{(seven)}}$

6. $15,477 = (Q)231 + R_{\text{(eight)}}$

7. $29,0e5 = (Q)57 + R_{\text{(twelve)}}$

8. $10001111 = (Q)1011 + R_{\text{(two)}}$

9. $1010010000 = (Q)11010 + R_{\text{(two)}}$

10. $52,342 = (Q)53 + R_{\text{(six)}}$

7-8. Memory and Computation

With any of the algorithms for computing the decimal numerals for sums, differences, products, etc., one needs to recall certain basic facts. The principal results of this kind can be arranged in table form as shown below. These, when completed, give the decimal numerals for $N_1 + N_2$ and $N_1 \cdot N_2$ where the range of substitutions for each variable is over the ten digits, 0, 1, 2, 3, . . ., 9.

	Sums						*Products*				
	0	1	2	$\cdots$	9		0	1	2	$\cdots$	9
0	0	1	2		9	0	0	0	0		0
1	1	2	3		10	1	0	1	2		9
2	2	3	4		11	2	0	2	4		18
.				.	.				.		.
.				.	.				.		.
.				.	.				.		.
9	9	10	11	$\cdots$	18	9	0	9	18	$\cdots$	81

The memorization of these facts amounts to a task of considerable magnitude in the elementary schools. Great effort has been expended to find ways for motivation, and to bring mastery within reach of a larger proportion of the population. One suggestion that should not be overlooked is that of making the greatest possible use of the structural relations that the natural numbers possess.

There are, for example, an equal number of facts for differences and quotients that correspond to the sums and products to be learned. But this need not be a heavy burden on the memory. What is required is recognition of the inverse character of addition and subtraction, and of multiplication and division; together with familiarity with explicit and implicit forms, and then this information becomes available to the student.

Knowledge of the commutative property reveals a large number of cases where $A + B$ and $A \cdot B$ can be related to $B + A$ and $B \cdot A$ so that these do not have to be learned separately.

a. Both the addition and the multiplication tables have 100 entries. How much is the memory load reduced by using the commutative property?

There are many opportunities to use the associative property in analyzing sums.

Example:

$$8 + 7 = 8 + (2 + 5) \qquad \text{or} \qquad 8 + 7 = (5 + 3) + 7$$
$$= (8 + 2) + 5 \qquad\qquad\qquad = 5 + (3 + 7)$$
$$= 10 + 5 \qquad\qquad\qquad\quad = 5 + 10$$
$$= 15 \qquad\qquad\qquad\qquad = 15$$

b. What is the relation of the first example to $8 + 7 = 7 - (10 - 8) + 10$? Give a similar statement for the second example.

Example: $8 + 7 = (3 + 5) + (5 + 2) = 3 + (5 + 5) + 2 = 5 + 10 = 15$

If one factor of a product is composite, then the associative property allows one to replace the product by a succession of products but with smaller factors.

Example: $6 \cdot 7 = (2 \cdot 3) \cdot 7 = 2 \cdot (3 \cdot 7) = 2 \cdot 21 = 42$

c. What principle is used in $8 + 7 = (8 + 2) + (7 - 2) = 10 + 5 = 15$?
In $6 \cdot 7 = \dfrac{6}{3}(3 \cdot 7)$?

d. Discuss the "why" of $15 - 7 = 5 + (10 - 7) = 5 + 3 = 8$.
e. Discuss $15 - 7 = 10 - (7 - 5) = 10 - 2 = 8$
f. Discuss $15 - 7 = 15 + (10 - 7) - 10 = 18 - 10 = 8$

The distributive principle can be used in a variety of ways to break a product up into a sum of smaller products.

Example: $(7)(8) = (5 + 2)(8) = (5)(8) + (2)(8) = 40 + 16 = 56$

The following question is sometimes asked regarding the use of devices such as those suggested above.   Do they not tend to become fixed in the mind as "crutches" and thus form a barrier to the ultimate goal of an instantaneous response?   This danger might very well be present if too much emphasis were placed on a single method.   The suggestion made here is that every fundamental fact to be memorized should be "figured out" as many ways as possible.   We have given here only a hint of the almost endless variety of ways of doing this.

Furthermore, it is most important that these devices not be imposed by the teacher as rules to be learned, but rather that the student be encouraged to experiment so that he may discover or invent them by himself.   The insights acquired in this manner build a number sense which greatly reduces the strain on the memory.

Answers to Exercises

a. There are 45 duplicates in each table.   **b.** Starting with 8, we need $10 - 8$, or 2, to make 10.   This 2, or $10 - 8$, is subtracted from 7 to find how much goes with the 10.   **c.** The invariant principles for sums and products were used.   **d.** 15 is the sum of 10 and 5.   Take 7 from 10 to get $10 - 7$, or 3, which is then added to the 5 that remains.   **e.** We have 15 or $10 + 5$, and want to take away 7.   We first take away 5, but need $7 - 5$, or 2 more.   This is subtracted from the 10.   Alternatively, this could be considered as $15 - 7 = (15 - 5) - (7 - 5)$, which makes use of the invariant principle for differences.   **f.** $15 - 7 = 18 - 10$ by the invariant principle for differences.   To find out how much to add to each number first get $10 - 7$, or 3, which is then added to 15, and then 10 is subtracted.

Problems (80)

An excellent way to become familiar with some of the ideas that have been suggested is to assume the task of extending one's mastery of elementary products on beyond the usual 10 times 10 table, up to 15 times 15, or more.   All products are to be computed mentally.   Try to avoid imitating the usual pencil and paper algorithm.   Instead, try to analyze each product in as many ways as you can that will bring it within your capacity to compute it mentally.

For Further Study

A large number of books in the bibliography have chapters on nondecimal systems of numeration.   Extensive treatments can be found in [C4], pp. 118–168; [H2], pp. 22–52; [O1], pp. 112–149; [P1], pp. 59–80; [S17], pp. 29–53; and [W3], pp. 12–21.   All of these include discussions of alogrithms for computations, and comprehensive analyses of these extend over several chapters in [L1] and [M11].

For historical comments on systems of numeration see [L1], pp. 1–14; [P1], pp. 1–19; [S6], pp. 128–135; [S17], pp. 1–27; and [W9], pp. 23–31.   See also the books on the history of mathematics cited earlier.

Short methods for computation appear in [L1], pp. 95–99, 118–120; and [M7] and [S15] are full texts on this subject.

8

Sets

8-1. Sets and Members

Mathematics is abstract in the sense that its investigations do not concern physical objects directly, but rather have to do with relations among the objects. But these abstractions, or at least the simpler and more fundamental of them, have arisen from the consideration of objects. We need a precise language for the statement of those mathematical concepts that are derived from the study of collections of objects.

Any collection of definite distinguishable objects of which we may think, and which is to be conceived as a whole, is called a *set*. This statement is to be considered as descriptive of sets rather than as a definition. The idea of a set is so basic that it is difficult to find simpler words with which to define it.

The concept of set enables one to treat a collection of objects as though it were an individual thing. There are many other words in our language, besides "set" and "collection," which direct our attention from the individual object to the group as a whole. Some of these are "groups," "bunch," and "class." Still others commonly refer to sets of a certain kind like "flock of sheep," "herd of cattle," and "family of persons."

Someone has said that mathematics is the subject that "uses easy words for hard ideas." This observation refers to a widespread practice in mathematics of choosing a commonplace term for a new idea, rather than coining a new word for it. However, the apparent simplicity to be gained can be deceptive, for words in common use often acquire a number of quite different meanings. For mathematical use it is required that words have a unique meaning, at least in a particular context. Definitions of terms are therefore of very great importance in mathematics, and must be particularly kept in mind when the word defined is a familiar one in its nonmathematical usage. Though it may be true that "everyone knows what a set

126

is," we cannot always depend on intuition and common sense to decide how the word should be used in mathematics.

The objects that make up a set are said to be in the set, or to belong to it, and are called *members* or *elements* of the set.   One might expect that the members of a set should have something significant in common to justify their being together in a set, but it may not be apparent at first just what this property may be.   Hence, no prior knowledge of any such property is demanded and a set can be assembled by arbitrary choice of any elements whatever.

One way to identify a set is simply to list the names of the members, as in {apple, 3, Mars}.   This *roster* notation is widely used when the set has only a small number of elements; the names being separated by commas, and enclosed by braces. The three objects named are accepted as forming a set even though they seem to have little in common except their listing together.

The word "set" and its synonyms all suggest plurality or many, yet we do allow sets with only one member.   Thus the set of all even primes has only one member, the number two.   The manner in which this set, {2}, was determined is fundamental.   A test condition was announced, and the members of the set were those objects, and only those, that met the condition.

A notation for specifying $S = \{2\}$ by the defining property above is

$$S = \{x \mid x \text{ is an even prime}\}$$

This is called the *set-builder* or the *set-selector* notation, and may be read as "S is the set of those elements x, such that x is an even prime."   The vertical bar is read "such that" or "for which." S is a convenient short name for the set.

This method of specifying sets influences us to extend the idea of a set even more, so that we accept as sets those that have no members at all.   Such a set is termed an *empty* set or a *null* set.   As an example, consider the set

$$N = \{x \mid x \text{ is a natural number, and } \frac{241}{17} = x\}$$

Upon checking the division, we find there is no such number as demanded. Some might now want to argue that the set N referred to is now known not to exist. This is not the position taken.   Rather the accepted convention is that since we have a workable procedure for deciding whether any natural number is a member of N, we therefore have a set $N = \{\ \ \}$, even though it is empty.

This assumption amounts to accepting the decision rule for determining whether any object is, or is not, a member of the set as being of paramount importance to the set; actually of equal importance with the members themselves.   Mathematics deals only with *well-defined* sets, where there is no question whether any given object is, or is not, a member.   Much of the power and effectiveness of set theory rests on being able to give a clear-cut decision on the issue of membership.

A strong requirement is made for the equality of sets; if $A = B$, then A and B are sets that have the same elements.   This need not mean that the statement

$S = M$ is trivial when S and M are sets, since the same set may have a variety of defining rules.   Thus $S = M$ if

$$S = \{x \mid x \text{ is an even prime}\}$$
$$\text{and } M = \{x \mid x \text{ is a natural number, and } x + x = x \cdot x\}$$

The order of listing is not important when giving the roster of members of a set. If $S_1 = \{a, b, c\}$, $S_2 = \{b, a, c\}$, and $S_3 = \{c, b, a\}$, then $S_1 = S_2 = S_3$.

However, the members of a given set must all be distinguishable one from another.   Hence $\{1, 2, 3, 2\} = \{1, 2, 3\}$.   We avoid listing the name of a member more than once; but if for any reason this occurs, the notation is revised to avoid the duplication.

It is desired that any two sets A and B be either equal, or not equal.   If A does not equal B, we write $A \neq B$.   Since two sets are equal if and only if they have the same elements, we can prove that two sets are unequal only by finding an element in one that is not in the other.

Let S_1 be an empty set, and S_2 be any other empty set.   Now S_1 and S_2 must either be equal (the same set), or not equal.   It is not possible to show that S_1 and S_2 are unequal, for there is no element in either, and hence one cannot produce the required element in one that is not in the other.   But if it is impossible to prove S_1 and S_2 unequal, we then accept the other alternative, which is $S_1 = S_2$.

Since two empty or null sets cannot be distinguished from each other, there is essentially only one empty set.   Being unique, we assign it the symbol $\varnothing$ for a name and speak of *the* empty set, or *the* null set.   At times we shall also designate the empty set by $\{\ \}$.

One other set merits special attention.   In any discussion it is well to have in mind just those things that are considered appropriate for mention, in order to satisfactorily limit the agenda for the discussion.   Such a fixed set of objects for use in a given discussion is known as the *universe of discourse*, or the *universal set* for this discussion.

Sometimes when considering numbers our universal set has been zero and all the natural numbers.   (See Section 1-2.)   At other times it has been the set of all primes, the set of even numbers, etc.   The set of natural numbers, the set of prime numbers, and the set of even numbers are alike in that none of these sets can be listed completely.   The list of candidates for each set can never be exhausted.   All three are examples of *infinite* sets.   (Recall the proof in Section 5-8 that all the primes constitute such a set.)

One can suggest the set of natural numbers with the notation

$$\{1, 2, 3, 4, \ldots\}$$

or the set of even numbers by

$$\{0, 2, 4, 6, 8, \ldots\}$$

but if any doubt is likely, the defining condition should be clearly stated.

Problems (81)

1. Each of the following words can be associated with a certain set. Refer to a dictionary to identify this set. More than one answer may be possible.
   a. bevy **b.** clutch **c.** legal code **d.** army **e.** pride **f.** brace.
2. Give the roster of the set of letters in the word "Mississippi."
3. Consider the set $A = \{1, 2, 3\}$. State in roster notation all the sets that can be constructed by selecting at least one element of A.
4. The set $S = \{2, 4, 6\}$ may also be given as $\{2, 6, 4\}$. Give all possible orders for listing this set.

For problems 5 to 16, give the roster of each set.

5. $\{x \mid x$ is a prime number less than 10$\}$.
6. $\{x \mid x$ is a divisor of 12$\}$.
7. $\{x \mid x$ is a multiple of 4, and x is less than 20$\}$.
8. $\{x \mid x$ is a digit used in base five notation$\}$.
9. $\{y \mid y$ is a coefficient of the polynomial $a_2x^2 + a_1x + a_0\}$.
10. $\{z \mid z$ is a common divisor of 12 and 18$\}$.
11. $\{x \mid x$ is both a square and a cube, and its decimal numeral has two digits$\}$.
12. $\{x \mid x$ is a natural number, greater than 5 but less than 10$\}$.
13. $\{x \mid 2x = x$ is a true statement$\}$.
14. $\{x \mid x$ can never be a divisor$\}$.
15. $\{x \mid x$ is a set having no members$\}$.
16. $\{x \mid x$ is the set of primes that are multiples of 3$\}$.
17. Let U consist of all numbers inside the rectangle, and let A and B have as members all the numbers inside the circles so marked. Thus $U = \{1, 2, 3, 4\}$, $A = \{1, 2\}$, and $B = \{2, 3\}$.

    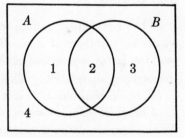

    Give the roster of the sets whose elements are the numbers meeting the following conditions:

   a. In both A and B.
   b. In either A or B, or both.
   c. In A, but not in B.
   d. In B, but not in A.
   e. Not in both A and B.
   f. In neither A nor B.
   g. In exactly one circle.
   h. In exactly two circles.
   i. In at least two circles.

   j. In at least one circle.
   k. In not more than one circle.
   l. In not more than two circles.
   m. Not in exactly one circle.
   n. Not in exactly two circles.
   o. Not in at least one circle.
   p. Not in more than one circle.
   q. Not in more than two circles.
   r. In three circles.

18. $U = \{1, 2, 3, 4, 5, 6, 7, 8\}$, as in the diagram.

$A = \{1, 2, 4, 5\}$.

$B = \{2, 3, 5, 6\}$.

$C = \{4, 5, 6, 7\}$.

Give the roster of the sets whose elements are the numbers meeting the following conditions:

a. In all three of A, B, and C.
b. In both A and B.
c. In both B and C.
d. In both A and C.
e. In either A or B, or both.
f. In either B or C, or both.
g. In either A or C, or both.
h. In A, but not in B.
i. In A, but not in both B and C.
j. In A, but in neither B nor C.
k. In neither A, B, nor C.
l. In exactly one circle.
m. In exactly two circles.
n. In exactly three circles.

o. In not more than one circle.
p. In not more than two circles.
q. In not more than three circles.
r. In at least three circles.
s. In at least two circles.
t. In at least one circle.
u. Not in exactly two circles.
v. Not in at least two circles.
w. Not in either A or C.
x. Not in both A and C.

8-2. Subsets

When convenient, capital letters will be used as names for sets, and lowercase letters for members of sets. Since we have sets whose members are themselves sets, the latter convention cannot always be observed. The symbol $\in$ represents the membership relation. Thus $x \in S$ can be read, "x is a member of S," "x belongs to S," or "S contains x." If x is not a member of S, we write $x \notin S$.

A baseball team is a set of players, and a league is a set of such teams (or sets). As an alternate usage to a set of sets, we sometimes speak of a family or class of sets. It is very difficult to think of a set as ever being a member of itself. Hence, we shall assume always that $A \notin A$ for any set A.

If A and B are sets such that every member of A is also a member of B, then we call A a *subset* of B, or say that A is *included* in B. This will be written $A \subseteq B$. This definition of subset allows every set to be a subset of itself, since every element of A is clearly an element of A for every set A. That is, $A \subseteq A$, for every set A.

If every element of A is an element of B, but B has at least one element that is not an element of A, then A is called a *proper* subset of B and we write $A \subset B$. Thus the pitcher and catcher form a subset that is a proper subset of the baseball team (set of players) on the field. Some authors do not distinguish proper subsets, and use the notation $A \subset B$ for all subsets, proper or not.

At times it is convenient to write $B \supseteq A$ rather than $A \subseteq B$ since they have the same meaning, and $A \subset B$ can also be written as $B \supset A$. If it should happen that $A \subseteq B$ and $B \subseteq A$, then $A = B$, which means they are the same set. This provides an alternate definition for equality of sets: Two sets are equal, if and only if, the subset relation holds both ways.

The following example displays all of the subsets of $\{x, y\}$.

Example:

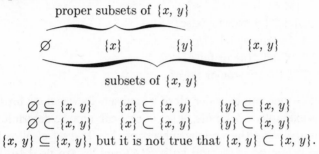

$$\varnothing \subseteq \{x, y\} \qquad \{x\} \subseteq \{x, y\} \qquad \{y\} \subseteq \{x, y\}$$
$$\varnothing \subset \{x, y\} \qquad \{x\} \subset \{x, y\} \qquad \{y\} \subset \{x, y\}$$
$\{x, y\} \subseteq \{x, y\}$, but it is not true that $\{x, y\} \subset \{x, y\}$.

The empty set is included in the listing above because we want the empty set to be either a subset or not a subset. (One other possibility might be to refuse to talk about the empty set whenever the subject of subsets comes up, but this is awkward.) But we cannot show that $\varnothing$ is not a subset of $\{x, y\}$, since this would require that $\varnothing$ have a member that $\{x, y\}$ does not have, and actually $\varnothing$ has none at all. Hence, the other alternative is accepted and $\varnothing$ is counted as a subset of $\{x, y\}$. Similar reasoning supports the argument that the empty set be considered a subset of every set, and a proper subset of every set except itself.

One reason for introducing set language is to provide tools for precise discussion of some simple ideas. But to gain this advantage we must choose and use words with great care. Students sometimes regard "is a member of" and "is a subset of" as being quite similar. A closer look will reveal that they are quite different.

The subset relation is reflexive, like equality (see Section 1-9), but membership is not.

For all sets A, $A \subseteq A$ but $A \notin A$

The subset relation is transitive, as is equality, but membership is not.

If $A \subseteq B$ and $B \subseteq C$, then $A \subseteq C$
If $A \in B$ and $B \in C$, then it need not be true that $A \in C$.

Neither of these relations is symmetric. However, it may be, as noted previously, that both $A \subseteq B$ and $B \subseteq A$ are true. But we shall not discuss sets such that both $A \in B$ and $B \in A$ are true.

We must also carefully distinguish between any object represented by a, and the set $\{a\}$ whose only member is a. Thus if a is an apple, it may be red, juicy, and edible. But a set never has such properties, since it is an idea, a construct of the mind.   Again the set $\{a\}$ has one member, but we do not speak of apples as having members.   If x is an object, then the set $\{x\}$, which has x as its only member, is sometimes called *singleton x*.

    a. How many elements does $\varnothing$ have?
    b. $\{\varnothing\}$ has one element.   What is it?
    c. $\{\,\{\varnothing\}\,\}$ has one element.   What is it?
    d. Is $\varnothing \in \{\varnothing\}$ true or false?
    e. Is $\varnothing \in \{\,\{\varnothing\}\,\}$ true or false?
    f. Is $\{\varnothing\} \in \{\,\{\varnothing\}\,\}$ true or false?
    g. Is $\varnothing \subseteq \{\varnothing\}$ true or false?
    h. Is $\varnothing \subseteq \{\,\{\varnothing\}\,\}$ true or false?
    i. Is $\{\varnothing\} \subseteq \{\,\{\varnothing\}\,\}$ true or false?

Given a set A, one can consider all of its subsets as was done for the set $\{x, y\}$ in the previous example.   A family or set of sets can now be determined, the members of this family being the various subsets of A.   The set of all subsets of a set A is called the *power* set of A, and both $P(A)$ and 2^A are used to designate this power set.

If $A = \{x, y\}$ as above, then $P(A) = \{\varnothing, \{x\}, \{y\}, \{x, y\}\,\}$.

Note that in this example A has 2 members while the power set $P(A)$ has 2^2 or 4 members.   This gives a hint as to why 2^A is appropriate as a name for the power set of A.   The diagram below displays a systematic procedure for determining the subsets of A, which we need for $P(A)$.   It is called a *tree* diagram, with the branches of each stage showing the possible choices.

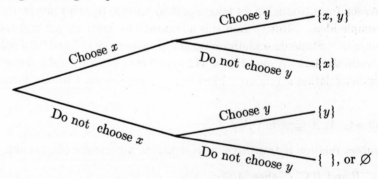

The subsets of A are constructed using only elements that are selected from the elements of A.   For each element of A, there are two choices: take it, or leave it. The tree diagram shows all possible ways of making the choices, and the number of its branches doubles at each choice point.   For a set A having n elements there are

$$\underbrace{2 \cdot 2 \cdot 2 \cdots 2}_{n \text{ factors}} = 2^n \text{ different possible choices.}$$

Hence, set A has a total of 2^n subsets.

If at each decision point we always decide to choose the element for the subset, then we end up with the subset having the largest possible number of elements, and that is the set A itself.   If we never choose the element in question, then our subset is the empty set.   The other subsets of A include at least one, but not all, of the elements of A.

 j. If the empty set was not counted as a subset, how many subsets would A have if A has n members?   How many subsets if A itself was also not counted as a subset?
 k. A set having 3 members has how many subsets?   Having 4 members? Having 1 member?   Having no members?
 l. What is the power set of $\{x\}$?
 m. What is the power set of $\{\ \}$?

ANSWERS TO EXERCISES

a. None.   **b.** The singleton $\{\varnothing\}$ has one element, the empty set $\varnothing$.   **c.** The singleton $\{\{\varnothing\}\}$ has one element $\{\varnothing\}$, which is *not* the same as $\varnothing$.   **d.** True.   **e.** False; check answer **c.**   **f.** True.   **g.** True.   **h.** True; $\varnothing$ is a subset of *every* set.   **i.** False; the one member that the first set has is not a member of the second set.   **j.** $2^n - 1, 2^n - 2$.   The formula is simpler if both the empty set and the set itself are counted as subsets.   **k.** $2^3 = 8$, $2^4 = 16$, $2^1 = 2$, $2^0 = 1$.   **l.** $\{\varnothing, \{x\}\}$.   **m.** $\{\{\}\}$ or $\{\varnothing\}$.

Problems (82)

 1. Assume $S = \{0, 1, 2, 3, 4, 5, 6, 7, 8\}$.   Give the following sets in roster notation.
   a. $\{x \mid x \in S, x \text{ is even}\}$ **e.** $\{x \mid x \in S, x - 5 \in S\}$
   b. $\{x \mid x \in S, x \text{ is prime}\}$ **f.** $\{x \mid x \in S, x + 5 \notin S\}$
   c. $\{x \mid x \in S, 3x \in S\}$ **g.** $\{x \mid x \in S, 2x + 5 \in S\}$
   d. $\{x \mid x \in S, x = 3y, y \text{ is a natural number}\}$ **h.** $\{x \mid x - 2 \in S\}$
 2. Assume $A = \{c, \{c\}\}$.
   a. How many elements does A have?
   b. What is the power set of A?
   c. What element of 2^A is not a proper subset of A?
 3. If one of the following statements is always true, no matter what the set S is, then label it true.   If there is even one choice of a set S such that the statement is not true, then label it false.
   a. For each set S, $\varnothing \in S$.
   b. For each set S, $\varnothing \subset S$.
   c. For each set S, $S \subseteq S$.
   d. For each set S, $S \in \{S\}$.
   e. For each set S, $S \in 2^S$.
   f. For each set S, $S \subset 2^S$.
   g. For each set S, $\{S\} \subset 2^S$.
   h. For each set S, $\varnothing \in 2^S$.
   i. For each set S, $\varnothing \subset 2^S$.

4. Assume $A = \{r\}$; $B = \{r, s\}$. Designate the following as true or false:

  a. $A \in A$ **c.** $A \subset A$ **e.** $A \subseteq B$ **g.** $A \in 2^B$ **i.** $\{A\} \in 2^B$
  b. $A \subseteq A$ **d.** $A \in B$ **f.** $A \subset B$ **h.** $A \subseteq 2^B$ **j.** $\{A\} \subseteq 2^B$

8-3. Intersection

Once the decision has been made on the universal set U for a particular discussion, we can if desired limit the discussion to subsets of U. Let A and B be any two such sets. A third set, corresponding to A and B, can be determined by the following rule. The *intersection (product, meet)* of sets A and B is the set whose elements are elements of both A and B.

The symbol $\cap$ is used to designate the operation of intersection; $A \cap B$ represents the set formed by the intersection of A and B. It may be read "A intersection B," or "A cap B." In the set builder notation the definition can be stated as

$$A \cap B = \{x \mid x \in A \text{ and } x \in B\}$$

The use of the word "and" is to demand that both conditions hold.

  Example: $\{1, 3, 4\} \cap \{1, 2, 3\} = \{1, 3\}$.

Effective use can be made of diagrams when considering sets and operations on them. The interior of a rectangle can be used to represent the universal set U. Then a subset A is represented by the region within a circle or other closed figure drawn inside the rectangle. Such diagrams, called Venn diagrams, cannot be used to illustrate every possible situation. In no sense do they constitute a proof of the concepts they illustrate, but they are helpful in many ways. The points inside the various figures are thought of as corresponding to the members of the sets being represented.

$A \cap B$ is shaded in each diagram.

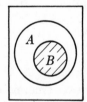 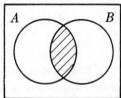 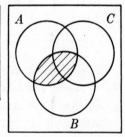

When two sets A and B have no members in common, it is still possible to form their intersection and in this case we have $A \cap B = \varnothing$. Two sets whose intersection is the empty set are said to be *disjoint* or *mutually exclusive*. Two sets are said to intersect or overlap whenever $A \cap B \neq \varnothing$.

The following statements are fundamental properties of the operation of intersection. Translate them into English. An appropriate diagram will help to "visualize" them.

a. $A \cap A = A$ **b.** $A \cap B = B \cap A$ **c.** $A \cap (B \cap C) = (A \cap B) \cap C$
d. $A \cap B \subseteq A, A \cap B \subseteq B$ **e.** $A \cap \varnothing = \varnothing$ **f.** $A \cap U = A$

ANSWERS TO EXERCISES

a. The intersection of any set with itself gives the same set.   **b.** Intersection is commutative.   The elements that are in both A and B are those that are in both B and A.   **c.** Intersection is associative.   The members of A that are also in both B and C are those elements that are members of both A and B and also of C.   **d.** The intersection of two sets is a subset of each of the sets.   The elements that are members of both A and B are members of A, and also of B.   **e.** The intersection of any set and the empty set gives the empty set.   The empty set dominates the operation of intersection.   **f.** The intersection of any set with the universal set is the given set.   The universal set is the identity for intersection.

Problems (83)

1. Let $A = \{1, 2, 3\}$, $B = \{2, 3, 4\}$, $C = \{3, 4\}$, $D = \{4, 5\}$.
   Give the roster, and when available, the letter name of:
   a. $B \cap B$ **d.** $A \cap (B \cap C)$ **g.** $(A \cap B) \cap D$ **j.** $(B \cap C) \cap D$
   b. $A \cap B$ **e.** $(A \cap B) \cap C$ **h.** $C \cap B$ **k.** $B \cap (C \cap D)$
   c. $B \cap A$ **f.** $A \cap (B \cap D)$ **i.** $B \cap C$ **l.** $D \cap \varnothing$

2. Assume U is the student body of a certain school, that the members of S are the sophomores, that the members of G are all of the girls, that R consists of those students having red hair.   Represent the following symbolically:
   a. Sophomore girls   **b.** Girls with red hair   **c.** red-headed sophomore girls

3. Let $S = \{a, b\}$, $A = \{a\}$, and $B = \{b\}$.   Then the power set of 2^S is $\{\varnothing, A, B, S\}$.   This power set is an example of a set that is closed under the operation of intersection.   That is, the intersection $P \cap Q$ is always a member of the power set, for any choice of P and Q from the power set.   Verify this by filling in the following table, using the letter name for the set that is the intersection of the sets assigned to that row and column.   For example, $A \cap S = A$.

$\cap$	$\varnothing$	A	B	S
$\varnothing$				
A				A
B				
S				

Note that the word "product" was given as one of the synonyms for intersection.   Assume that this table is a "multiplication" table.

   a. Which set is suggestive of the number 1?   How is this recognized in the table?
   b. Which set is suggestive of the number 0?   How is this recognized in the table?
   c. How does one recognize from the table that intersection is commutative?
   d. Give an example from the table showing that this "multiplication" does not have a cancellation law that always holds.

4. If $A = \varnothing$, then
   a. $\{A\} \cap A = ?$ **c.** $\{A\} \cap \{A, \{A\}\} = ?$
   b. $\{A\} \cap \{A\} = ?$ **d.** $\{\{A\}\} \cap \{A, \{A\}\} = ?$

5. Draw a Venn diagram with three overlapping circles inside the rectangle. Then place numerals in the various regions so that *all* of the following statements are true:

$U = \{1, 2, 3, 4, 5, 6, 7, 8\}, A = \{1, 5, 6, 7\}, B = \{2, 4, 6, 7\}, C = \{3, 4, 5, 7\}, A \cap B = \{6, 7\}, B \cap C = \{4, 7\}, A \cap C = \{5, 7\}, A \cap B \cap C = \{7\}$. The last four equations are hints that could be omitted.

6. Draw a diagram as in problem 5 so that all the following statements are true:

$U = \{2, 3, 4\}, A = \{4\}, B = \{3, 4\}, B \subset C, A \subset (B \cap C)$.

8-4. Union

Again let A and B be any subsets of a universal set U. Then the *union* (*sum, join*) of sets A and B is the set whose elements are those that belong to A or to B, or both. In mathematical use the word "or" is always given in the inclusive sense. Hence, the "or both" could be dropped from the definition, since it would be implied anyway. This is in contrast to the usage outside mathematics where the exclusive "or" is sometimes meant, that is, A or B, but not both.

An equivalent definition for the union of A and B is that its elements belong to at least one of A and B. The symbol $\cup$, which is suggestive of the first letter of the word union, is used to designate the operation of union. $A \cup B$ is read as "A union B," or "A cup B."

$$A \cup B = \{x \mid x \in A \text{ or } x \in B\}$$

Example: $\{1, 3, 4\} \cup \{1, 2, 3\} = \{1, 2, 3, 4\}$

It is also useful to think of $A \cap B$ as being the "and" combination, and $A \cup B$ as being the "or" combination of the two sets. Both union and intersection may be extended to operations on more than two sets.

The union of two or more sets is the set each of whose elements is a member of *at least one* of the given sets. The intersection of two or more sets is the set each of whose elements is a member of *all* the given sets.

The exercises below give some of the basic properties of union. They should be compared with the similar exercises on intersection in Section 8-3. Diagrams are again a useful visual aid.

$A \cup B$ is shaded in each diagram.

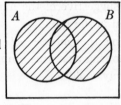 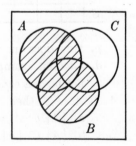

Translate the following into English, and check with diagrams.

a. $A \cup A = A$ **b.** $A \cup B = B \cup A$
c. $A \cup (B \cup C) = (A \cup B) \cup C$
d. $A \subseteq A \cup B$, $B \subseteq A \cup B$
e. $A \cup \varnothing = A$ **f.** $A \cup U = U$

The diagram at the right is an illustration of $A \cup B$ if we consider those areas that have any shading, either single *or* double. It also shows $A \cap B$ if we consider the area that is doubly shaded, both as in A *and* as in B.

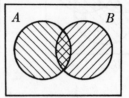

This optional interpretation is used in the following examples:

Example:

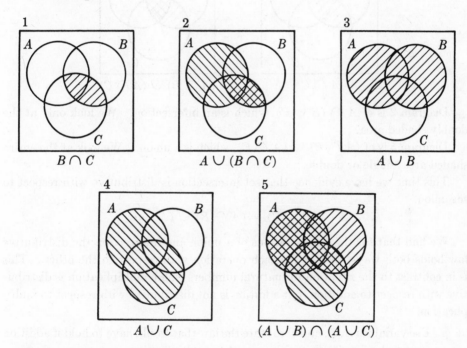

1    $B \cap C$

2    $A \cup (B \cap C)$

3    $A \cup B$

4    $A \cup C$

5    $(A \cup B) \cap (A \cup C)$

Diagram 2 is of a union (the last operation performed). Hence, we look at all shaded areas, single or double.

Diagram 5 is of an intersection (the last operation performed). Hence, we look only at the doubly shaded area.

Since these areas are the same, when viewed in this manner, we have evidence that set union is distributive with respect to set intersection.

$$A \cup (B \cap C) = (A \cup B) \cap (A \cup C)$$

Example:

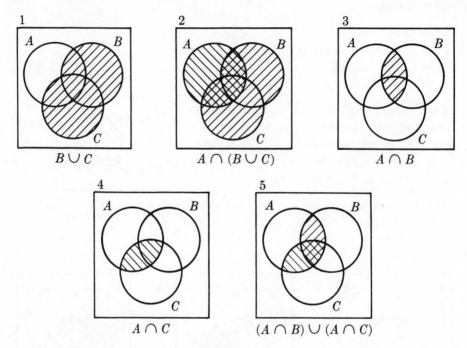

Diagram 2 is of $A \cap (B \cup C)$, which is an intersection. We look only at the doubly shaded area.

Diagram 5 is of $(A \cap B) \cup (A \cap C)$, which is a union. We look at the entire shaded area, single or double.

This time we have evidence that set intersection is distributive with respect to set union.

$$A \cap (B \cup C) = (A \cap B) \cup (A \cap C)$$

We find that for the set operations of a union and intersection the distributive law holds both ways, that is, for each operation with respect to the other. This is in contrast to the situation for natural numbers where multiplication is distributive with respect to addition, but addition is not distributive with respect to multiplication.

  g. Use variables A, B, and C to state the law that would have to hold if addition were to be distributive with respect to multiplication.

  h. Let $A = 2$, $B = 3$, and $C = 4$ to give an example where the law in **g.** is false.

Answers to Exercises

a. The union of any set with itself is the same set. **b.** Union is commutative. The elements that are members of at least one of A and B are members of at least one of B and A. **c.** Union is associative. The elements that are members of at least one of A or B, or of C, are members of at least one of A, or of B or C. **d.** Each of two sets is a subset of their union.

e. The union of any given set with the empty set is that given set.   The empty set is the identity for union.   **f.** The union of any set with the universal set gives the universal set. The universal set dominates the operation of union.   **g.** $A + (B)(C) = (A + B)(A + C)$. **h.** $2 + 3 \cdot 4 \neq (2 + 3)(2 + 4)$.

Problems (84)

1. Let $A = \{1, 2, 3\}$, $B = \{2, 3, 4\}$, $C = \{3, 4\}$, $D = \{4, 5\}$.
   Give the roster, and when available, the letter name of:

   a. $C \cup C$ **e.** $A \cup (B \cup D)$ **i.** $(B \cup A) \cap D$

   b. $A \cup B$ **f.** $A \cap (B \cup D)$ **j.** $(A \cap B) \cup (A \cap D)$

   c. $B \cup A$ **g.** $B \cup C$ **k.** $(B \cup A) \cap (B \cup D)$

   d. $(A \cup B) \cup D$ **h.** $B \cup (A \cap D)$ **l.** $(B \cap D) \cup (A \cap D)$

2. What can be said about $A \cup B$ and $A \cap B$ under these conditions?

   a. A and B are disjoint   **d.** B is a subset of A

   b. A and B are equal   **e.** A and B intersect

   c. A is a subset of B

3. Let $S = \{a, b\}$, $A = \{a\}$, and $B = \{b\}$.   Show that 2^S is closed under the operation of union, by filling in the table below.   See problem 1 of set (83).

$\cup$	$\varnothing$	A	B	S
$\varnothing$				
A				
B				
S				

   The word "sum" was given as one of the synonyms for union.   Assume the table at the left is an "addition" table.

   a. Which set is suggestive of the number zero?   How is this recognized in the table?

   b. How does the table show that union is commutative?

   c. Give an example from the table showing that this "addition" does not have a cancellation law that always holds.

4. Translate into English, and illustrate with a diagram.

   a. If $A \subseteq B$, then $(A \cup C) \subseteq (B \cup C)$

   b. If $A \subseteq B$, then $(A \cap C) \subseteq (B \cap C)$

5. Construct a diagram where A, B, and C are subsets of U such that:
   $U = \{1, 2, 3, 4, 5, 6, 7, 8\}$, $A = \{1, 2, 3, 6\}$, $B = \{1, 3, 4, 7\}$, $C = \{1, 2, 4, 5\}$.

6. Construct a diagram where A, B, and C are subsets of U such that:
   $U = \{1, 2, 3, 4, 5, 6, 7, 8\}$, $A \cup B \cup C = \{1, 2, 3, 4, 5, 6, 7\}$, $A \cup B = \{2, 3, 4, 5, 6, 7\}$, $B \cup C = \{1, 2, 3, 5, 6, 7\}$, $A \cup C = \{1, 2, 4, 5, 6, 7\}$, $A \cap (B \cup C) = \{5, 6, 7\}$, $B \cap (A \cup C) = \{2, 6, 7\}$, $C \cap (A \cup B) = \{2, 5, 6\}$.

   In problems 7 to 10 A, B, and C are subsets of $U = \{1, 2, 3, 4, 5\}$. $B = \{1, 2\}$, $A \neq \varnothing$, $C \neq \varnothing$, and the additional given conditions hold.

7. $A \cup C = U$, $A \cap C = \varnothing$, and $C = \{1\}$

8. $A \subset C$, $A \cup C = \{4, 5\}$, $A \cap C = \{4\}$

9. $A \cap C = \{2\}$, $A \cup C = \{2, 3, 4\}$, $B \cup C = \{1, 2, 3\}$

10. $A \cap C = \varnothing$, $B \cap C = \varnothing$, $A \cup C = \{1, 3\}$

8-5. Complementation

If A and B are subsets of U, we represent by $A - B$ the set of those elements that are members of A but not of B.

$$A - B = \{x \mid x \in A \text{ and } x \in B\}$$

$A - B$ may be read "A minus B" and is known as the *relative complement of B in (or with respect to) A*. If A is the universal set U, then $U - B$ is then represented by the shorter notation of B' and referred to simply as the *complement* of B. The notations $\widetilde{B}$ and B^c are also in use for the complement of B. The definition of relative complement may be written as

$$A - B = A \cap B'$$

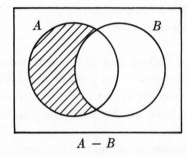

$A - B$

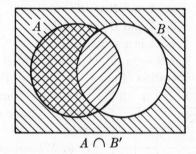

$A \cap B'$

Some of the fundamental properties of complementation are given below. Translate them into English, and check with diagrams.

a. $A \cap A' = \varnothing$ **b.** $A \subseteq B$ if and only if $B' \subseteq A'$ **c.** $(A')' = A$
d. $\varnothing' = U$ **e.** $U' = \varnothing$ **f.** $A - A = \varnothing$ **g.** $A - \varnothing = A$
h. $\varnothing - A = \varnothing$ **i.** $A - B = \varnothing$ if and only if $A \subseteq B$
j. $(A - B) \cap (B - A) = \varnothing$ **k.** $A = B$, if and only if $A' = B'$

> **Examples:** If $U = \{1, 2, 3, 4, 5\}$, $A = \{1, 2, 3\}$, $B = \{3, 4, 5\}$, and $C = \{4, 5\}$, then
> $$
> \begin{array}{lll}
> A - B = \{1, 2\} & C - A = \{4, 5\} & A' = \{4, 5\} \\
> B - A = \{4, 5\} & B - C = \{3\} & B' = \{1, 2\} \\
> A - C = \{1, 2, 3\} & C - B = \varnothing & C' = \{1, 2, 3\}
> \end{array}
> $$

ANSWERS TO EXERCISES

a. The intersection of any set with its complement is the empty set. **b.** A is a subset of B if and only if the complement of B is a subset of the complement of A. **c.** For any set, the complement of its complement is the set itself. **d.** and **e.** The empty set and the universal set are complements of each other. **f.** The relative complement of any set with respect to itself is the empty set. **g.** The relative complement of any set with respect to the empty set is the set itself. **h.** The relative complement of the empty set with respect to any set is the empty set. **i.** The relative complement of set A with respect to set B is the empty set if and only if A is a subset of B. **j.** The intersection of the relative complement of A with respect to B with the relative complement of B with respect to A is the empty set. **k.** Two sets are equal if and only if their complements are equal.

Problems (85)

1. Verify the following by drawing a Venn diagram for each member of the equality.   State the principle in English.   These are known as De Morgan's Laws.
   - **a.** $(A \cup B)' = A' \cap B'$ **b.** $(A \cap B)' = A' \cup B'$

2. State the conditions under which the following are true:
   - **a.** $\{x \mid x = a\} = \{b\}$ **e.** $A = \{x \mid x \in B\}$ **i.** $A - B = A$
   - **b.** $\{a, b\} = \{c\}$ **f.** $A \subseteq \varnothing$ **j.** $\{b, c\} \subseteq \{a\}$
   - **c.** $s \notin \{t\}$ **g.** $A \cup B = A \cap B$ **k.** $\{a\} \subseteq \{b, c\}$
   - **d.** $C = \{x \mid x \neq x\}$ **h.** $A - B = \varnothing$ **l.** $(A - B) \cup B = A$

3. Let $A = \{1\}$, $B = \{1, \{1\}\}$, $C = \{1, 2\}$, $D = \{1, 2, \{1\}\}$, and $E = \{1, \{1, \{1\}\}\}$.   Determine:
   - **a.** $A \cap B$ **c.** $(A \cup B) \cap C$ **e.** $(C \cup D) - B$ **g.** $\{B\} \cap E$
   - **b.** $A \cup B$ **d.** $\{A\} \cap B$ **f.** $(A \cap D) - E$ **h.** $(\{A\} \cup D) \cap (E - C)$

   Which of the following are true?
   - **i.** $A \in B$ **k.** $B \in E$ **m.** $C \in D$ **o.** $(B - A) \in D$
   - **j.** $A \subseteq B$ **l.** $B \subseteq E$ **n.** $C \subseteq C$ **p.** $(E - B) \subseteq A$

4. What can be said about A, B, and C if
   - **a.** $(A \cup B) - B = A$?   **c.** $A \cap (B - C)$
   - **b.** $A \cup (B - C) = (A \cup B) - C$? $= (A \cap B) - (A \cap C)$?
   - **d.** $(A \cup B) \subseteq C'$ and $A \cup C \subseteq B$?

5. Give the number, or numbers, which identify the regions associated with these sets.
   - **a.** P **i.** $P \cup Q'$
   - **b.** P' **j.** $P' \cup Q$
   - **c.** Q **k.** $P' \cap Q$
   - **d.** Q' **l.** $P \cap Q'$
   - **e.** $P \cap Q$ **m.** $P \cup P'$
   - **f.** $(P \cap Q)'$ **n.** $Q \cap Q'$
   - **g.** $P \cup Q$ **o.** $(P - Q) \cup (Q - P)$
   - **h.** $(P \cup Q)'$ **p.** $(P \cap Q) \cup (P \cup Q)'$

6. Give the number, or numbers, which identify the regions associated with these sets.

   - **a.** $P \cap Q \cap R$ **g.** $P \cap (Q \cup R)'$
   - **b.** $P' \cap Q \cap R$ **h.** $P \cup (Q \cap R)$
   - **c.** $P' \cap Q' \cap R$ **i.** $P' \cup (Q \cap R)$
   - **d.** $P' \cap Q' \cap R'$ **j.** $P \cup (Q \cap R')$
   - **e.** $P \cap (Q \cup R)$ **k.** $Q' \cup R' \cup P'$
   - **f.** $P' \cap (Q \cup R)$ **l.** $(Q - R) - P$

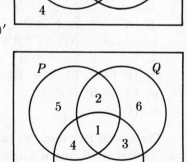

8-6. Partitions

One of the important applications of the theory of sets is to the problem of classification, and the problem sets thus far in this chapter have indicated some of the possibilities. Often we wish to break up a set into nonempty subsets in such a way that every element of the set belongs to one and only one of the subsets. A *partition* of a nonempty set S is a set of nonempty subsets of S, $\{S_1, S_2, \ldots, S_n\}$, with these properties:

   i. $S_i \cap S_j = \emptyset$ for $i \neq j$
   ii. $S_1 \cup S_2 \cup \cdots \cup S_n = S$

A partition of a set S is therefore a set of subsets that are disjoint by property **i.**, and exhaustive by property **ii.**

> **Example:** If $A = \{1, 2, 3, 4, 5\}$, then $\{\ \{1, 2\}, \{3\}, \{4, 5\}\ \}$ is a partition of A.

In the diagram at the right, A and B are subsets of U, with members as given on the diagram. The following are partitions of S. Give the roster of each set.

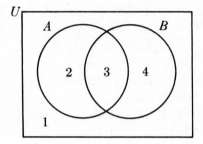

   a. $\{A' \cap B', A \cup B\}$
   b. $\{A \cap B', A' \cup B\}$
   c. $\{A \cap B, A' \cup B'\}$
   d. $\{A' \cap B, A \cup B'\}$
   e. $\{B', B\}$
   f. $\{(A - B) \cup (B - A), (A \cap B) \cup (A \cup B)'\}$
   g. $\{A', A\}$
   h. $\{B', A \cap B, B - A\}$
   i. $\{(A \cap B) \cup (A \cup B)', A - B, B - A\}$
   j. $\{A', A - B, A \cap B\}$
   k. $\{A, (A \cup B)', B \cap A'\}$
   l. $\{(A - B) \cup (B - A), A' \cap B', A \cap B\}$
   m. $\{B, (A \cup B)', A - B\}$
   n. $\{A' \cap B', A \cap B', A \cap B, A' \cap B\}$
   o. $\{U\}$

The subsets that form the partition are known as *cells*. Any nonempty set is a partition of itself into a single cell (see exercise **o.** above). The next simplest partition of a set U is that of any proper subset as one cell, and its complement as the other cell. Such a partition is called a *dichotomy*.

p. Which of the partitions in **a.** to **n.** in the above exercise are dichotomies?

A partition $\{A_1, A_2, \ldots, A_n\}$ is said to be a refinement of the partition $\{B_1, B_2, \ldots, B_m\}$ if every A_i is a subset of some B_j.

Example: Assume $U = \{1, 2, 3, 4, 5\}$
  Then $B = \{\ \{1, 2\}, \{3, 4, 5\}\ \}$ is a partition of U.

$A_1 = \{\ \{1, 2\}, \{3\}, \{4, 5\}\ \}$
$A_2 = \{\ \{1\}, \{2\}, \{3, 4, 5\}\ \}$ and
$A_3 = \{\ \{1\}, \{2\}, \{3, 4\}, \{5\}\ \}$ are some of the possible refinements of B.

Each of the refinements in the above example was formed by making a partition of one or more of the cells of partition B. However, one can also set up two partitions independently, and by considering them simultaneously, arrive at a refinement of each by what is termed a *cross-partition*.

Example: Let the universe be represented by an entire rectangle as in the diagram at the right. The dichotomy of A and A' is shown by the upper and lower halves, and the partition into the dichotomy B and B' by the left and right halves of the rectangle.

	B	B'
A	$A \cap B$	$A \cap B'$
A'	$A' \cap B$	$A' \cap B'$

$\{A \cap B, A \cap B', A' \cap B, A' \cap B'\}$ is the cross-partition. This should be compared with exercise **n.** above, and a Venn diagram.

A tree diagram can also portray this structure, with each branching stage associated with a partition.

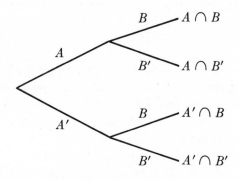

ANSWERS TO EXERCISES

a. $\{\{1\}, \{2, 3, 4\}\}$. **b.** $\{\{2\}, \{1, 3, 4\}\}$. **c.** $\{\{3\}, \{1, 2, 4\}\}$. **d.** $\{\{4\}, \{1, 2, 3\}\}$. **e.** $\{\{1, 2\}, \{3, 4\}\}$. **f.** $\{\{2, 4\}, \{1, 3\}\}$. **g.** $\{\{1, 4\}, \{2, 3\}\}$. **h.** $\{\{1, 2\} \{3\}, \{4\}\}$. **i.** $\{\{1, 3\}, \{2\}, \{4\}\}$. **j.** $\{\{1, 4\}, \{2\}, \{3\}\}$. **k.** $\{\{2, 3\}, \{1\}, \{4\}\}$. **l.** $\{\{2, 4\}, \{1\}, \{3\}\}$. **m.** $\{\{3, 4\}, \{1\}, \{2\}\}$. **n.** $\{\{1\}, \{2\}, \{3\}, \{4\}\}$. **o.** $\{\{1, 2, 3, 4\}\}$. **p.** Partitions **a.** through **g.** are dichotomies.

Problems (86)

1. Give, in roster form, the set of all partitions of $\{x, y, z\}$.
2. A cross-partition is formed from partition A, which has m cells, and a partition B, which has n cells. Both A and B are partitions of a set S.
   a. What is the maximum number of cells in the cross-partition?
   b. What is the minimum number of cells in the cross-partition?
   c. What is the maximum number of cells in n successive dichotomies?
3. Assume $U = \{1, 2, 3, 4, 5, 6, 7, 8, 9, 10\}$. Give the following partitions.
   a. The dichotomy of the even and the odd numbers.
   b. The trichotomy of the unit, the prime numbers, and the composite numbers.
   c. The trichotomy based on multiples of 3, one less than a multiple of 3, and two less than a multiple of 3.
   d. The dichotomy of the square and the nonsquare numbers.
   e. The cross-partition of **a.** and **d.**
   f. The cross-partition of **a.** and **b.**
   g. The cross-partition of **b.** and **c.**
   h. The cross-partition of **c.** and **e.**
4. a. Verify that the numbers from 1 to 8 can be identified by "yes" or "no" answers to all of these three questions.
      i. Is the number a member of $\{2, 3, 5, 6\}$?
      ii. Is the number a member of $\{3, 4, 6, 7\}$?
      iii. Is the number a member of $\{5, 6, 7, 8\}$?
      Hint: Try a Venn diagram.
   b. Devise another set of three questions (there are many) that will also identify each number in the same manner.

8-7. Mappings

Suppose a person is checking over a map of California. The map involves a correspondence between points of the region and points on the map itself. Such correspondences between the members of two sets are very important in mathematics. We say that this correspondence is a mapping of the points of California into the points of the map.

More generally, let S and T be any two sets. Then a *mapping* of the first set S *into* the second set T is a rule that associates each element of S with *one and only one* element of T. The set S is called the *domain of definition* of the mapping. If a is an element of S, and b is the element of T assigned to a by the mapping, then b is called the *image* of a. The set whose elements are all those members of T that are images of the elements of S is called the *range* or *image set* of the mapping. The image set will always be a subset of the set T but it does not necessarily include all the elements of T. Whenever the range is equal to the set T, then the mapping is said to be of S *onto* T.

a. Is an onto mapping also an into mapping?

Mappings can sometimes be illustrated by displaying members of the sets S and T and then drawing arrows to point out the associations that are to be made.

A mapping of S into T

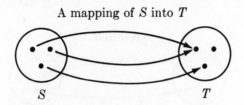

S T

> **Example:** Each element of S is linked to exactly one element of T. This mapping is not onto, since there is an element of T that is not an image of an element of S.
>
> Arrows are used, rather than simple line segments, to point out that it may not be possible to interchange the roles of the sets S and T and still have a mapping.
>
> There are two reasons the next diagram does not show a mapping. First, the set T is now the domain, but one of its members fails to have an image as required. Second, a member of the domain T has been assigned more than one image in the range, and this is not permitted by the definition of mapping.

This is *not* a mapping of T into S

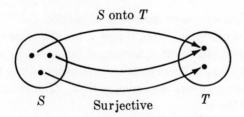

S T

The next example shows an onto mapping, where each element of the set T is an image of at least one element of S.

> **Example:** Onto mappings are also known as *surjective* mappings (from the French *sur* for "on").

S onto T

S Surjective T

We may require the condition that the elements of the range be images of only one member of the domain.   The mapping is then said to be *one to one*, written 1:1.

> **Example:** One-to-one mappings are also known as *injective* mappings. Distinct elements of domain have distinct images in the range.

S into T

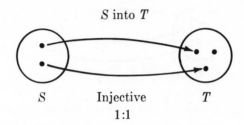

S   Injective   T
1:1

If the mapping is both 1:1 and onto, then the mapping is said to be *biunique*, or *bijective*.   Still more commonly, it is referred to as being a 1:1 *correspondence*.

> **Example:** By checking over the diagrams for the previous examples we find this is the first case where there is also a mapping from T back onto S.   This mapping would be the *inverse* of the one shown.

S onto T

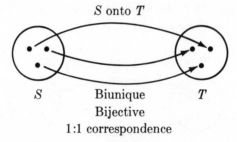

S   Biunique   T
Bijective
1:1 correspondence

b. If S is a set of boys and T is a set of girls, and the mapping of S into T is to be based on the brother-sister relationship, what conditions must hold?
c. What would also be true if the mapping were to be onto?
d. What would be true if the mapping were to be 1:1?
e. What would be required for a 1:1 correspondence?
f. In which of **b., c., d.,** and **e.** could we be sure there is a sister-brother mapping?

Formulas for sequences were discussed in Section 6-3.   These provide some simple examples of mappings.   Often S and T are the same set and we then say that the set is mapped into itself.   Assume S (and also T) is the set of natural numbers.   The formula $a_n = 2n$ determines a correspondence between the natural numbers and the even numbers beginning with 2.   The notation we shall use for this mapping is $n \rightarrow 2n$.

The substitutions for n are from S, the set of natural numbers. The number chosen is also substituted in $2n$ to get the image. This mapping is into, but not onto, since the range (the even numbers which are 2 or more) is a proper subset of the set of natural numbers. The arrows shown would not usually be drawn, since the two vertical columns give the pairs of numbers which show the correspondence.

n	$2n$
1	2
2	4
3	6
.	.
.	.
.	.

ANSWERS TO EXERCISES

a. Yes.   **b.** Every boy in S must have exactly one sister in T.   **c.** Every girl in T must be a sister of some boy in S.   **d.** No girl in S can be a sister of more than one boy in T.   **e.** Each boy in S has exactly one sister in T, and each girl in T has exactly one brother in S.   **f.** Only in **e.**

Problems (87)

In problems 1 and 2, the boys Elmer, Frank, Grant, and Henry are represented by the set $S = \{E, F, G, H\}$ and the girls Alice, Betty, Carol, and Donna by $T = \{A, B, C, D\}$. If the correspondences shown are not mappings of $S \to T$, state why they fail to be. If they are mappings, classify them as into, onto, 1:1, or 1:1 correspondences.

1.

2.

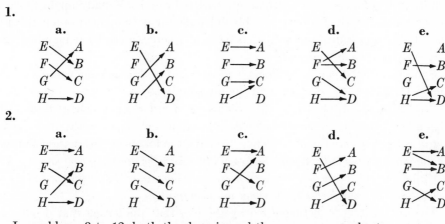

In problems 3 to 12, both the domain and the range are a subset of the natural numbers. The domain set S is given first, followed by the mapping rule. List on a diagram, as at the right, the pairs of numbers given by this mapping. The left-hand number is a member of the domain and the right-hand number is its image.

3. $\{10, 20, 30\}$, $n \to 2n + 3$

4. $\{2, 4, 6\}$, $n \to 3n - 2$

5. $\{1, 3, 5\}$, $n \to 2n^3$

6. $\{1, 2, 3\}$, $n \to 3^{n-1}$

7. $\{2, 3, 4, 5\}$, $n \to n! - (n - 1)!$

8. $\{1, 4\}$, $n \to \dfrac{5^{n-1} + 1}{2}$

9. $\{1, 2\}, n \to \sum\limits_{k=0}^{k=n} 2k$
 11. $\{5\}, n \to \sum\limits_{k=4}^{k=n} (k-3)!$

10. $\{2, 3\}, n \to \sum\limits_{k=2}^{k=n} (k^2 - k)$
 12. $\{4, 5, 6\}, n \to \dfrac{n(n-1)(n-2)}{3!}$

8-8. Ordered Sets

The sets $\{a, b, c\}$ and $\{b, a, c\}$ are said to be equal, or the same set, because they have the same elements; and we ignore the order in which the elements are listed in the roster. The notation (a, b, c), in which the braces have been replaced by parentheses, is used to designate an *ordered* set. That is, this notation specifies that order is now to be taken into account. Two equal ordered sets must not only have the same elements, but they must appear in the same order in the listing of the members. Hence (a, b, c) does not equal (b, a, c), for they are different ordered sets.

An ordered set with two elements is called an *ordered pair*, one with three elements is called an *ordered triple*, and in general an ordered set with n elements is called an *ordered n-tuple*.

For the ordered set given by the n-tuple $(x_1, x_2, \ldots, x_n)$ we call x_1 the *first component* or the *first coordinate*, x_2 is the second component or coordinate, $\ldots$, and x_n is the nth component or coordinate. Ordered sets have many applications in mathematics. By their use we are able to handle the development of a number of ideas at the same time, and still keep track of where we are by demanding that things stay in their proper places.

By using ordered pairs we can get a restatement of the mapping concept. The domain $\{1, 2, 3, 4, 5\}$ together with the mapping $n \to 2n$ yields the ordered pairs $\{(1, 2), (2, 4), (3, 6), (4, 8), (5, 10)\}$. This set of ordered pairs characterizes this domain and mapping so completely that it is often convenient to say that a mapping *is* a set of ordered pairs. Hence, we have the following alternate definition: *A mapping is a set of ordered pairs no two of which have the same first component. The set of all first components of the ordered pairs is the domain of the mapping, and the set of all the second components is the range of the mapping.*

The set (p, q, r) is distinguished by the fact that the letters that denote the elements appear in alphabetical order. Stated below are some significant properties of the ordered set of all 26 letters of the English alphabet as written in alphabetical order, or alphabetical succession.

$$(a, b, c, d, e, f, g, h, i, j, k, l, m, n, o, p, q, r, s, t, u, v, w, x, y, z)$$

1. Every letter, except z, has associated with it one and only one letter called its *successor*. A child who can "say the alphabet" can always state what comes next.

2. No two different letters have the same successor. This prevents us from writing, for example: $a, b, c, d, e, f, c, \ldots$ where now both b and f have the same successor. If this were allowed, then property **1.** would force us to keep repeating the cycle, $c, d, e, f, c, d, e, f, \ldots$, endlessly.

3. There is no letter whose successor is a. Without this restriction one could write $a, b, c, d, a, \ldots$, for example, and thus get into the same difficulty as in **2**. We now have two distinctive letters; a, a first one, which is not itself a successor; and z, a last one, which has no successor.

4. Any set of letters that contains the letter a, and that also contains the successor of every member of the set (except z) contains all the letters of the alphabet.

Let us check for these properties in another familiar ordered set, the natural numbers as written in their "natural" order. The similarity is striking except there is no last number to correspond to z of the alphabet.

$$(1, 2, 3, 4, 5, \ldots)$$

1. Every natural number has a unique successor.

2. No two different natural numbers have the same successor.

3. There is a natural number 1, which is not itself a successor.

4. Any set of natural numbers that contains 1, and that also contains the successor of every member of the set, contains all the natural numbers.

Since the natural numbers have the above properties, they can be used as components to create some standard ordered sets for reference. Let us call these *counting* sets, for reasons to be given later.

$$(1), (1, 2), (1, 2, 3), (1, 2, 3, 4), \ldots$$

We now want to consider the number of different ordered sets that can be formed by arranging n objects in different orders. An arrangement of n different objects in a certain order is called a *permutation* of the n objects. If these objects are the letters a, b, and c, we have the following six possible ordered triples:

$$(a, b, c) \quad (b, a, c) \quad (c, a, b)$$
$$(a, c, b) \quad (b, c, a) \quad (c, b, a)$$

A tree diagram provides a useful analysis from which we can see how to compute the possible number of permutations of n objects.

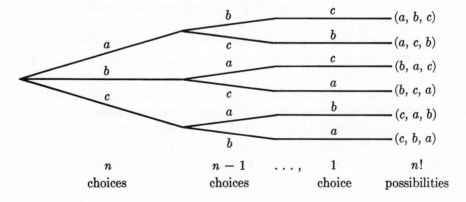

| n | $n-1$ | $\ldots,$ | 1 | $n!$ |
| choices | choices | | choice | possibilities |

There are available n choices for the first position or component.   There remains one less or $n - 1$ choices for the second position, and for each successive choice there will be available one less object from which to choose.   Finally, there will remain only one object to choose for the last position.   Hence, the tree diagram will have n branches at the first stage; each of these will branch $n - 1$ ways at the next stage and so on.   The number of permutations is then

$$n \cdot (n - 1) \cdot (n - 2) \ldots 3 \cdot 2 \cdot 1 = n!$$

"Permutation" can also be used to name a 1:1 correspondence between a set and itself.

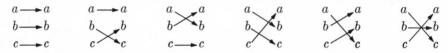

We shall write $A \sim B$ for "set A is in one-to-one correspondence to set B," but many words are in use for this very important relation between sets.   Thus $A \sim B$ is often written with the notation $A \approx B$, and the following translations are all in use by various authors:

Set A matches set B.
Sets A and B are similar, or equivalent, or equinumerous, or equipollent, or have the same power.

There are, of course, an unlimited quantity of sets that can be placed in 1:1 correspondence with the set $\{a, b, c\}$.   For example:

$$\{\text{Tom, Dick, Harry}\}, \qquad \{\text{land, sea, air}\},$$
$$\begin{array}{ccc} | & | & | \\ \{a, & b, & c\} \end{array} \qquad \begin{array}{ccc} | & | & | \\ \{a, & b, & c\} \end{array}$$

But there is also no limit to the sets that cannot be placed in 1:1 correspondence with $\{a, b, c\}$ such as

$$\{\text{North, South, East, West}\} \qquad \text{or} \qquad \{\text{Right, Wrong}\}$$
$$\{a, \quad b, \quad c\} \qquad\qquad\qquad \{a, \quad b, \quad c\}$$

This property of sets, of either matching or not matching, enables us to speak of all the sets that can be placed in 1:1 correspondence with such a set as $\{a, b, c\}$ and to say that each of the sets has the same *cardinal number*.   Note that this is not an attempt to explain what we mean by a number, but rather what is meant by "having the same number."

The next question is what this number shall be that we assign to each of these sets that are in 1:1 correspondence, and here is where our standard counting sets (1), (1, 2), (1, 2, 3), (1, 2, 3, 4), ... are used.   We find by trial that $\{a, b, c\}$ can be placed in 1:1 correspondence only with (1, 2, 3).   In this case there are 3! ways to set up the correspondence but if we first find a correspondent for 1, then one for 2, etc., the last pair will always have a first component of 3.   Hence, we say that $\{a, b, c\}$ has 3 elements:

$$n(A) = n(\{a, b, c\}) = 3,$$

and read this, "The number of elements in A or $\{a, b, c\}$ is 3."

Hence to "count," or determine the number of elements in a set S, we use the ordered set of natural numbers $N = (1, 2, 3, \ldots)$, of which each of our standard counting sets is a subset.   We then seek a 1:1 correspondence between S and a subset of N.   For this correspondence the elements of S are selected in any order, but those selected from N are taken in their fixed "natural" order.   If this pairing uses up all the members of S, then the last used member of N is said to be the number of elements in S.   Thus if the last paired element of N is k, then $n(S) = k$. In this case we say that S is finite and has k elements.

Problems (88)

1.   **a.** $n(\{a, a\}) = ?$
     b. If $S = \{a, e, i, o, u\}$, then $n(2^S) = ?$
     c. If $S = \{a, e, i, o, u\}$ how many 1:1 correspondences does S have with itself?
2.   **a.** If $(x, y) = (2, 4)$, what can be said about x?   about y?
     b. If $\{x, y\} = \{2, 4\}$, what can be said about x and y?
3. Given that $n(U) = 17$, $n(A) = 10$, $n(B) = 8$, and $n(A \cap B) = 3$.
   Determine:
     a. $n(A' \cap B)$ **b.** $n(A - B)$ **c.** $n(A \cup B)$ **d.** $n(B')$ **e.** $n(A' \cup B)$
4. Given that $n(U) = 11$, $n(A - B) = 4$, $n(B) = 5$, and $n(A') = 6$.
   Determine:
     a. $n(A \cap B)$ **b.** $n(A' \cup B')$
5. Given that $n(U) = 14$, $n(A \cap B') = 7$, $n(A' \cap B) = 3$, $n(B') = 9$.
   Determine:
     a. $n(A')$ **b.** $n[(A \cap B)']$
6. Given that $n(U) = 11$, $n(A) = 5$, $n(B) = 7$, $n(A' \cap B') = 2$.
   Determine:
     a. $n(A \cap B)$ **b.** $n[(A - B) \cup (B - A)]$
7. How may $n(A \cup B)$ be computed if $n(A)$, $n(B)$, and $n(A \cap B)$ are known?
8. How may $n(A \cup B \cup C)$ be computed if $n(A)$, $n(B)$, $n(C)$, $n(A \cap B)$, $n(A \cap C)$, $n(B \cap C)$, and $n(A \cap B \cap C)$ are known?

In problems 9 and 10 a domain set is given first, followed by a mapping rule. List the ordered pairs thus determined.   (The first component is from the domain, the second is the image under the mapping.)

9. **a.** Domain $\{1, 2, 3\}$ **b.** Domain $\{3, 4\}$ **c.** Domain $\{1, 2\}$

$$n \to \sum_{k=n}^{k=3} 3k \qquad n \to \sum_{k=n}^{k=n+2} (6 - k) \qquad n \to \sum_{k=0}^{k=n} (kn)!$$

10. a. Domain $\{1, 2, 3\}$ **b.** Domain $\{2, 3\}$ **c.** Domain $\{1, 2, 3\}$

$$n \to \sum_{k=n}^{k=4} \frac{12}{k} \qquad n \to \sum_{k=n-1}^{k=n+1} k! \qquad n \to \sum_{k=n}^{k=3} k^{n-1}$$

11. A school requires that all students take either physics, biology, or chemistry. In a graduating class of 300, 220 have taken biology, 180 have taken chemistry, and 70 have taken physics. If 100 have taken both biology and chemistry, 50 have taken chemistry and physics, and 30 have taken both biology and physics, how many have taken all three subjects?

12. On a chair car on a train there were 27 boys, 15 American children, 27 men, 21 foreign boys, 42 Americans, 18 American males, and 21 foreign females. What was the number of people on the chair car? *Hint:* Consider a cross-partition {American, foreign} of the partition {men, women, boys, girls}.

13. In a survey of 100 students the numbers studying various languages were found to be: German only, 20; German but not Spanish, 26; German and French, 8; German, 28; French, 43; French and Spanish, 7; no language, 29.
   a. How many students took Spanish?
   b. How many students took two languages but not three?

14. In an elementary school district having 100 teachers there are 60 who are women and 70 who are married.
   a. What is the greatest possible number of married women teachers?
   b. What is the least possible number of married women teachers?
   If 75 of the 100 teachers are blond,
   c. What is the greatest possible number of blond, married, women teachers?
   d. What is the least possible number of blond, married, women teachers?

8-9. Cartesian Products

Let A and B be any two given sets. Then if a is any member of A, and b is any member of B, we have (a, b) as an ordered pair with its first component selected from A and its second component selected from B. The set of all possible such ordered pairs is called the *Cartesian product* of sets A and B and will be denoted by $A \otimes B$.

$$A \otimes B = \{(a, b) \mid a \in A \text{ and } b \in B\}$$

Example: Let $A = \{X, Y, Z\}$ and $B = \{s, t\}$.
$$A \otimes B = \{(X, s), (X, t), (Y, s), (Y, t), (Z, s), (Z, t)\}$$
$$B \otimes A = \{(s, X), (s, Y), (s, Z), (t, X), (t, Y), (t, Z)\}$$

The diagram shown gives one method of exhibiting the possible pairs. The possible choices of the first and second components for the ordered pairs can also be set forth on a tree diagram.

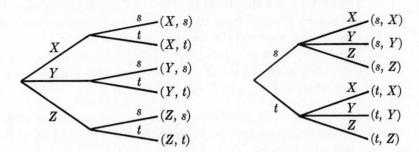

In this example each ordered pair in $A \otimes B$ is different from every ordered pair in $B \otimes A$. Hence $A \otimes B \neq B \otimes A$ and the Cartesian product of two sets is not a commutative operation on sets. However, we do observe in the example that

$$n(A \otimes B) = 6 = n(B \otimes A)$$

The reasons these two numbers should be the same should become more evident in the following discussion. Let us study those tasks where one can select one of m alternate courses of action, and then independently make a choice from n alternatives. The m times n different ordered pairs of successive choices could be classified on a tree diagram, and also by means of a rectangular array.

Example: Let the problem be that of using subscripts to identify each one of the a's uniquely, and in such a way that it can be readily located in the array.

$$
\begin{array}{ccccc}
a & a & a & a & a \\
a & a & a & a & a \\
a & a & a & a & a \\
a & a & a & a & a \\
\end{array}
$$

We begin at the upper left, and number the rows down and the columns to the right. The double subscripts are then used in the row-column order.

Columns

		1	2	3	4	5
	1	$a_{1,1}$	$a_{1,2}$	$a_{1,3}$	$a_{1,4}$	$a_{1,5}$
R	2	$a_{2,1}$	$a_{2,2}$	$a_{2,3}$	$a_{2,4}$	$a_{2,5}$
o						
w	3	$a_{3,1}$	$a_{3,2}$	$a_{3,3}$	$\boxed{a_{3,4}}$	$a_{3,5}$
s	4	$a_{4,1}$	$a_{4,2}$	$a_{4,3}$	$a_{4,4}$	$a_{4,5}$

The notation $a_{3,4}$ appears in the third row and in the fourth column. With a small number of rows and columns, the comma is often omitted between the two subscripts so that $a_{3,4}$ is written as a_{34}.

This is read as "a sub-three, four." The complete list of $4 \cdot 5 = 20$ subscripts can be recognized as the ordered pairs determined by $A \otimes B$ where $A = \{1, 2, 3, 4\}$, and $B = \{1, 2, 3, 4, 5\}$.

Example: The problem is to identify and give the position of each individual asterisk. This time we begin at the lower left and count first to the right, and then up.

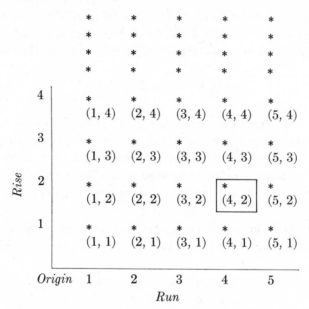

To avoid confusion with the previous example we use the carpenter's terms of *run* and *rise*. This time the standard notation for ordered pairs is used. The asterisk (or position) marked (4, 2) can then be located with respect to the origin by counting 4 to the right and then up to 2.

Again we find that if $n(A) = m$ and $n(B) = n$, then $n(A \otimes B) = mn$.

The reader is no doubt familiar with the second example in another context where the "run" numbers are assigned to points on the x axis, and the "rise" numbers are assigned to points on the y axis. Such Cartesian coordinates are fundamental in the study of analytic geometry. The Cartesian product gets its name from René Descartes, one of the pioneers of analytic geometry.

There is nothing in the definition of $A \otimes B$ that prevents A and B from having elements in common, and one set may be a subset of the other. If $A = B$ and A has n members, then $A \otimes A$ will have n^2 ordered pairs and the rectangular array of these pairs will become a square.

By using n-tuples the Cartesian product can be extended to an operation on n sets. The Cartesian product of the sets $A_1, A_2, \ldots, A_n$ is the set of all possible ordered n-tuples $(a_1, a_2, \ldots, a_n)$ such that a_1 belongs to A_1, a_2 belongs to $A_2, \ldots, a_n$ belongs to A_n.

$$A_1 \otimes A_2 \otimes \cdots \otimes A_n = \{(a_1, a_2, \ldots, a_n) \mid a_j \in A_j \text{ for } j = 1, 2, \ldots, n\}$$

A tree diagram can still be used to display these n-tuples with each branching stage having as many alternatives as the set associated with that stage has members. This makes it evident that

$$n(A_1 \otimes A_2 \otimes \cdots \otimes A_r = n(A_1) \cdot n(A_2) \cdots n(A_r)$$

In this formula all the sets are assumed to be finite, although the definition of Cartesian product does extend to infinite sets.

Problems (89)

1. Write out the Cartesian product of each of the following pairs of sets.
   a. $A = \{\text{Dodge, Ford, Chevrolet}\}$, $B = \{\text{sedan, truck}\}$.
   b. $A = \{\text{box 1, box 2, box 3}\}$, $B = \{\text{black ball, white ball, red ball}\}$.
   c. $A = B = \{\text{true, false}\}$.
   d. $A = \{0, 1\}$, $B = \{1, 2, 3\}$.
   e. $A = \{a, b, c\}$, $B = \varnothing$.

2. Write out the Cartesian product of each of the following pairs of sets.
   a. $A = \{\text{dime, nickel, penny}\}$, $B = \{\text{head, tail}\}$.
   b. $A = \{\text{game 1, game 2}\}$, $B = \{\text{win, lose, draw}\}$.

3. Illustrate $A \otimes A \otimes A$ with a tree diagram if $A = \{0, 1\}$. Compare your result with the numbers 0 to 7 written in place value notation in base two.

4. Find three conditions such that $A \otimes B = B \otimes A$.

5. Determine the following subsets of $A \otimes A$ where $A = \{1, 2, 3, 4\}$. Each subset is of the form $\{t \mid t = (x, y), (x, y) \in A \otimes A, x \text{ and } y \text{ meet the further conditions listed below}\}$.

a. $x = y$	**d.** $x - y = 1$	**g.** $y = 2x$
b. $y = x^2$	**e.** $x = 3$	**h.** y is less than x
c. $x + y = 5$	**f.** $y = 2$	**i.** $y \neq x$

6. A mapping from A into B is a subset of $A \otimes B$ with the condition that no two distinct ordered pairs have the same first component.
   Assume $A = \{a, b, c\}$ and $B = \{x, y\}$.
   a. List all mappings from A into B.
   b. List all mappings from B into A.

7. Let $A = \{1, 2\}$, $B = \{1, 2, 3\}$, and $C = \{1\}$.
   a. b. Write out $(A \otimes B) \otimes C$, and $A \otimes (B \otimes C)$.
   c. Parts **a.** and **b.** show that the Cartesian product is not associative. Each member of $(A \otimes B) \otimes C$ is an ordered pair, with each first component being an ordered pair. Each member of $A \otimes (B \otimes C)$ is an ordered pair, with each second component being an ordered pair. Now write out $A \otimes B \otimes C$ and compare these ordered triples with part **a.**

8. Let $A = \{a, b\}$, $B = \{1, 2\}$, and $C = \{2, 3\}$.   Verify the following:
   a. $A \otimes (B \cap C) = (A \otimes B) \cap (A \otimes C)$
   b. $A \otimes (B \cup C) = (A \otimes B) \cup (A \otimes C)$

8-10. Counting of Sets and Subsets

The branch of mathematics called *combinatorial analysis* is largely concerned with counting the number of ways there are of doing some well-defined act.   Several problems of this type have already been discussed in this chapter, and are listed below.

1. If $n(A) = k$, then $n(2^A) = 2^k$.   If a set has k elements, then there are 2^k different subsets of this set.
2. If $n(A) = k$, then the number of permutations of the members of A is $k!$
3. If $n(A) = a$, and $n(B) = b$, then $n(A \otimes B) = ab$.

In such problems it is very important to observe whether one is working with ordered sets or unordered sets.   Thus in example 1 above the power set 2^A is a set of sets.   The elements of 2^A need not be listed in a specified order, and the elements themselves are also unordered sets.

In example 2 the set of all permutations is not ordered and these may be listed in any order, but the elements of this set (which are the permutations) are ordered k-tuples.   Hence, in this problem we count the number of members in an unordered set of ordered sets, and the same is true of example 3.

Our next counting problem will be that of counting the number of subsets of two elements (unordered pairs) that can be selected from a set of n elements.   One method is based on first counting the ordered pairs, and then eliminating certain pairs to get a count of the unordered pairs.

Listed below are all the ordered pairs in $A \otimes A$ where $A = \{1, 2, 3, 4\}$.

(1, 4)	(2, 4)	(3, 4)	$\boxed{(4, 4)}$
(1, 3)	(2, 3)	$\boxed{(3, 3)}$	(4, 3)
(1, 2)	$\boxed{(2, 2)}$	(3, 2)	(4, 2)
$\boxed{(1, 1)}$	(2, 1)	(3, 1)	(4, 1)

There are 4^2 or 16 such ordered pairs, and when $n(A) = n$, there would be n^2 of them.   Along the diagonal are 4 pairs whose first and second components are the same.   If these are omitted, we have an example of what may be called the *deleted Cartesian product*, where we insist that the first and second components be different.   There now remain

$$4^2 - 4 = 4(4 - 1) = 4 \cdot 3 = 12 \text{ ordered pairs}$$

In the general case there would be $n^2 - n = n(n - 1)$ members of the deleted Cartesian product.   We now observe that those pairs above the diagonal can be matched in one-to-one correspondence with those below the diagonal by associating any one ordered pair with that ordered pair which has the same numbers for components but in the opposite order.

Thus $(1, 2)$ is matched with $(2, 1)$

$(2, 3)$ is matched with $(3, 2)$, etc.

But while $(2, 4)$ and $(4, 2)$, for example, count as two different ordered pairs, they can be constructed from a single set $\{2, 4\}$ by permutation of the elements. Hence, there are only half as many unordered pairs, or sets, which can be distinguished. From a set of 4 elements there are $\dfrac{4 \cdot 3}{2} = 6$ subsets that have two elements. For $A = \{1, 2, 3, 4\}$ they are

$$\{1, 2\}, \{1, 3\}, \{1, 4\}, \{2, 3\}, \{2, 4\}, \text{ and } \{3, 4\}$$

We infer that if A has n elements, $\dfrac{n(n - 1)}{2}$ subsets can be selected that have two elements.

The reasoning that supports this formula can be checked out on a tree diagram. If A has n elements, there will be n choices for the first component of the ordered pairs, and hence n branches at the first stage. But we want the second component to be different so there are only $n - 1$ choices for the second component, and therefore $n - 1$ branches for the second stage.

So far we are counting ordered pairs, so if we wish to count sets (whose members are not ordered), we must ignore the duplicates that come from the permutations. A set of 2 elements has 2! permutations of its elements. Hence, we write $\dfrac{n(n - 1)}{2!}$, for this suggests how to extend our analysis.

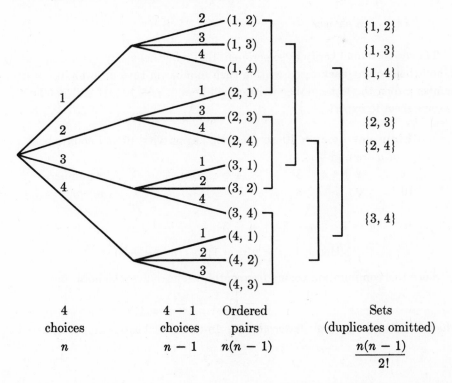

4	4 − 1	Ordered	Sets
choices	choices	pairs	(duplicates omitted)
n	$n - 1$	$n(n - 1)$	$\dfrac{n(n - 1)}{2!}$

The same strategy can be used to count the number of subsets of size r, where r is less than or equal to n. It consists of first counting the ordered sets or r-tuples, and then dividing by $r!$, which is the number of permutations possible with the members of an r-tuple (provided these members are all different).

Given a set of n different objects, the ordered sets of r different objects chosen in any manner from the n given objects will be called the *variations* of n objects taken r at a time. The notation for this will be $V_{n,r}$.

The number $V_{n,r}$ can be readily determined by analysis of a tree diagram. All that is required is the extension of the previous pattern for ordered pairs to include more branching stages with the number of alternatives continuing to decrease by one at each stage. Thus from a set of five objects we can select an ordered set of three objects in $V_{5,3} = 5 \cdot 4 \cdot 3$, or 60 ways. Part of the tree diagram is shown below.

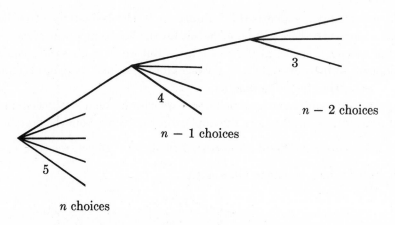

The reader should verify by experiment that if one begins by writing the number n, and then counts backwards writing each number in turn until he has written r numbers, then the last number written will be $n - r + 1$. (It will not be $n - r$ as some seem to expect.)

> **Example:** Let $n = 10$, so that one begins with 10 and counts back for 1 or more numbers.
>
> | 1 | 2 | 3 | 4 | . | . | . | r numbers |
> |----|----|-------|-------|---|---|---|----------------|
> | 10 | 9 | 8 | 7 | . | . | . | $n - r + 1$ |
> | | | | | | | | or |
> | n | $n-1$ | $n-2$ | $n-3$ | . | . | . | $n - (r-1)$ |
>
> Hence $V_{n,r} = n(n-1) \cdots (n - r + 1)$

Since this computation occurs frequently, we introduce the notation

$$(n)_r = n(n-1) \cdots (n - r + 1)$$

which is called the *falling r factorial* of n. In the special case where $r = n$ we have

$$V_{n,n} = n(n-1) \cdots 2 \cdot 1 = n!$$

This corresponds to the case of choosing an ordered n-tuple of objects from a set of n objects so that the last choice is of the single remaining object.

The permutations of n objects constitute a special case of the variations of n objects taken r at a time.   For this reason some authors use the term r permutations where we have used variation, and they write $P(n, r)$ or $_nP_r$ where we have used $V_{n,r}$.

Instead of using the falling factorial notation it is often convenient to "build up" to where the factorial notation can be used.

$$V_{5,2} = 5 \cdot 4 = \frac{5 \cdot 4 \cdot 3 \cdot 2 \cdot 1}{3 \cdot 2 \cdot 1} = \frac{5!}{3!} = \frac{5!}{(5-2)!}$$

$$V_{n,r} = (n)_r = n(n-1) \cdots (n-r+1) = \frac{n(n-1) \cdots (n-r+1)(n-r) \cdots 2 \cdot 1}{(n-r) \cdots 2 \cdot 1}$$

$$= \frac{n!}{(n-r)!}$$

In order to get the complete $n!$ it is necessary to fill in the missing $(n-r)!$, and having introduced this factor we must compensate by dividing by the same number.

Although the latter form of this result may seem to have been obtained by a rather arbitrary manipulation, it can also be arrived at by reasoning directly with the sets involved.   In the particular example above of $V_{5,2}$ let us assume that the $5! = 120$ permutations of the five objects have been listed.   We can now obtain our desired ordered pairs by selecting the first and second components from each of the 120 five-tuples.   Of course, whenever we select two out of the five, we have rejected three for this choice.

Now every possible ordered pair will appear in our list, but there will be many duplications.   For example, the following will appear somewhere in the total list of the 5! permutations.   The particular ordered pair of $(4, 2)$ that we are choosing will be listed six times because of the 3! permutations of the remaining objects that are not selected.

Select	Reject
4 2	1 3 5
4 2	1 5 3
4 2	3 1 5
4 2	3 5 1
4 2	5 1 3
4 2	5 3 1

Hence again,

$$V_{5,2} = \frac{5!}{3!} = \frac{5!}{(5-2)!}$$

Problems (90)

1. Write as a product: **a.** $(6)_2$ **b.** $(7)_3$ **c.** $(5)_5$ **d.** 5^5
2. Write as a product: **a.** $(5)_3$ **b.** $(8)_2$ **c.** $(4)_4$ **d.** 4^4

3. Represent with a more compact notation:

    a. $8 \cdot 7 \cdot 6 \cdot 5$ **b.** $8 \cdot 8 \cdot 8 \cdot 8$ **c.** $6 \cdot 5 \cdot 4 \cdot 3 \cdot 2 \cdot 1$ **d.** $\dfrac{7!}{2!}$

4. Represent with a more compact notation:

    a. $30 \cdot 29 \cdot 28$ **b.** $25 \cdot 26 \cdot 27 \cdot 28$ **c.** $25 \cdot 25 \cdot 25$ **d.** $\dfrac{25!}{22!}$

5. Write as a quotient of two factorials:
    a. $(6)_2$ **b.** $(7)_3$ **c.** $(5)_5$ **d.** $(100)_{12}$ **e.** $25 \cdot 24$ **f.** 9

6. Write as a quotient of two factorials:
    a. $(5)_3$ **b.** $(8)_2$ **c.** $(4)_4$ **d.** $(50)_{31}$ **e.** $12 \cdot 11 \cdot 10$ **f.** 17

7. Compute: **a.** $V_{6,4}$ **b.** $V_{6,2}$ **c.** $V_{7,3}$ **d.** $V_{7,4}$ **e.** $V_{4,4}$

8. Compute: **a.** $V_{7,2}$ **b.** $V_{7,5}$ **c.** $V_{6,3}$ **d.** $V_{6,1}$ **e.** $V_{6,6}$

After we have computed the number of ordered sets that make up the variations of n objects taken r at a time, we are but one step from determining the number of subsets (which are unordered) or size r that are contained in a set of n elements. All that remains is to divide by $r!$ to remove the duplicates that we do not want when order is ignored. The notation $\binom{n}{r}$ will be used to denote the number of subsets having r elements that are contained in a set of n elements.

$$\binom{n}{r} = \frac{(n)_r}{r!} = \frac{n(n-1) \cdots (n-r+1)}{1 \cdot 2 \cdot 3 \cdots r}$$

$$= \frac{n(n-1) \cdots (n-r+1)(n-r) \cdots 2 \cdot 1}{1 \cdot 2 \cdot 3 \cdots r \cdot (n-r) \cdots 2 \cdot 1} = \frac{n!}{r!(n-r)!}$$

Again the final form could be found directly from the $n!$ permutations by

1. Dividing by $(n-r)!$ to eliminate the duplicates of the subsets not selected, as on the previous page.

2. Dividing by $r!$ to eliminate the duplicates of the subsets that are selected.

    Example:

$$\binom{5}{2} = \frac{(5)_2}{2!} = \frac{5 \cdot 4}{1 \cdot 2} = 10 \qquad \text{or} \qquad \binom{5}{2} = \frac{5!}{2!3!} = \frac{5 \cdot 4 \cdot 3 \cdot 2 \cdot 1}{1 \cdot 2 \cdot 1 \cdot 2 \cdot 3} = 10$$

The first computation is clearly the shortest, but the second is often better in the theory since it preserves some patterns that are "cancelled out" in the first.

Despite the appearance of these formulas as fractions, we have not violated our restriction of using only zero and the natural numbers. No fractions can arise from these computations, since we are counting the number of ways some act can, or cannot, be done.

The ability to compute the number of subsets of various sizes that can be formed for any given finite set is fundamental for a great variety of counting problems. The possibilities for subsets of sets which have zero, one, two, three, or four members are arranged below in the form of a triangle.

$$\binom{0}{0} \text{-------------------- subsets of the empty set}$$

$$\binom{1}{0} \quad \binom{1}{1} \text{----------------- of a singleton set}$$

$$\binom{2}{0} \quad \binom{2}{1} \quad \binom{2}{2} \text{------------- of a set of 2 elements}$$

$$\binom{3}{0} \quad \binom{3}{1} \quad \binom{3}{2} \quad \binom{3}{3} \text{---------- of a set of 3 elements}$$

$$\binom{4}{0} \quad \binom{4}{1} \quad \binom{4}{2} \quad \binom{4}{3} \quad \binom{4}{4} \text{------- of a set of 4 elements}$$

The numbers of subsets having (none, 1, 2, . . . , all) of the elements of the set.

The reader should compute the numbers and verify that they are as given at the right.

It will be found that $0! = 1$, and $1! = 1$ allow

the formula $\binom{n}{r} = \dfrac{n!}{r!(n-r)!}$ to extend to all cases.

Indeed this is a principal reason the definition of factorial includes $0!$ and $1!$. If we are to avoid

exceptional cases for $\binom{n}{r} = \dfrac{(n)_r}{r!}$ it is also necessary to define $(n)_0 = 1$ for n equal to zero or any natural number.

			1					Row 0
		1		1				Row 1
	1		2		1			Row 2
1		3		3		1		Row 3
1	4		6		4		1	Row 4

Each row of the triangle begins and ends with 1. For any set of n elements there is just one way to form the empty set and hence $\binom{n}{0} = 1$ for all n. Also there is just one way to consider the set itself as one of the subsets and therefore $\binom{n}{n} = 1$, for all n.

When n is even, there are an odd number of possible sizes of subsets, and the entries in a row show symmetry with respect to the middle number. When n is odd, there are an even number of entries and the symmetry is with respect to the two equal central terms. This happens because the selection of any subset also leaves the complementary subset, which is rejected, and hence there must be the same number of ways of obtaining the sets of these two sizes.

For example, there are n ways to pick a subset of 1 element and hence $\binom{n}{1} = n$ for all n greater than zero. But there must be an equal number of ways to select subsets that lack one element and therefore $\binom{n}{n-1} = n$ for all n greater than zero. In general,

$$\binom{n}{r} = \binom{n}{n-r}$$

If all the entries in any one row are added the sum will be found to be 2^n. This checks our previous conclusion that for a set having n members there are 2^n elements in the power set, or set of all subsets.

The numbers $\binom{n}{r}$ are also called *binomial coefficients* because of their occurrence in certain algebraic formulas. The triangle array is often called Pascal's triangle in honor of the French mathematician who studied certain properties of these numbers. We shall mention only one more of these properties, which is the relation that the entries in one row have to those of the next row. This is a relation that the subsets of a set of n elements have to the subsets of a set of $n + 1$ elements.

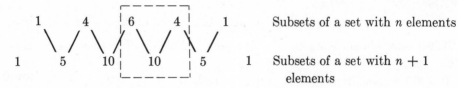

1	4	6	4	1		Subsets of a set with n elements
1	5	10	10	5	1	Subsets of a set with $n + 1$ elements

The next row begins and ends with 1, and the remaining terms are sums of two terms from the row above. This means that the nonempty proper subsets from a set of $n + 1$ elements can be associated with two sizes of subsets from a set of n elements.

Example:

$$\binom{5}{3} = \binom{4}{2} + \binom{4}{3}$$

$$10 = 6 + 4$$

contain a ⟍ ⟋ do not contain a

$$\binom{4}{0} \quad \binom{4}{1} \quad \binom{4}{2} \quad \binom{4}{3} \quad \binom{4}{4}$$

$$\binom{5}{0} \quad \binom{5}{1} \quad \binom{5}{2} \quad \binom{5}{3} \quad \binom{5}{4} \quad \binom{5}{5}$$

To see why this is true, select one member of the set of five elements and call it a. There are $\binom{5}{3}$ of the subsets that have three members and they can be partitioned into the sets that contain a and those that do not. Those that do not contain a are the $\binom{4}{3}$ subsets of three elements formed from the four remaining elements. For those that do contain a we find there are $\binom{4}{2}$ subsets of two elements to put with a, to make a subset of three elements. Since this reasoning is general, we have

$$\binom{n+1}{j} = \binom{n}{j-1} + \binom{n}{j}$$ where j is greater than zero, and less than or equal to n.

In the verbal problems in set (91) the numbers have been kept small so that it is not too time-consuming to list all of the possibilities. If this is done systematically, it may then be possible to identify formulas that would enable one to compute the result directly without having to count the possibilities one at a time. This is recommended as a strategy for attacking combinatorial problems. There is such a bewildering variety of these problems that it is rather futile to try to classify them all and then to remember a particular formula for a given type. If, as in most cases, the listing is too long to complete, nevertheless an analysis of just how this might be planned is an excellent way to get insight into the problem. One of the most critical decisions is whether one is counting sets (whose members are not ordered) or n-tuples (whose components are ordered).

Problems (91)

1. Compute: **a.** $\binom{6}{2}$ **b.** $\binom{6}{4}$ **c.** $\binom{100}{98}$ **d.** $\sum_{k=0}^{k=5} \binom{5}{k}$

2. Compute: **a.** $(7)_4$ **b.** 7^4 **c.** $\binom{7}{4}$ **d.** $(7)_0$ **e.** 7^0 **f.** $\binom{7}{0}$

3. How many numerals of two digits, and no repeated digit, can be written with the digits 4, 5, 6, 7?

4. In a room are four chairs designated as 1, 2, 3, and 4. There are also two people whose temporary names are A and B. In how many ways can they be seated? (one person to a chair)

5. A room has four doors. In how many ways should one person be able to enter the room by one door and leave by another?

6. Assume there are five points in a plane, no three of which lie on a straight line. How many triangles can be constructed, using only these points as vertices?

7. Three coins are tossed simultaneously, each of which may land either heads or tails. How many possibilities are there?

8. In a certain physics course, there are three lecture sessions A, B, and C; and two laboratory sections M and N. A student must select one of each. How many choices are possible?

9. In how many ways can five people be divided into two groups, each having one or more persons in it?

10. How many committees of two persons can be selected from a group of five students?

11. How many different sums of money can be formed by selecting sets of two coins from a cent, a nickel, a dime, a quarter, and a half dollar?

12. In how many ways can a red ball and a black ball be placed in three boxes labeled 1, 2, and 3?

For Further Study

The following references are a selection of texts for teachers of mathematics that give considerable emphasis to the elements of sets: [C4], pp. 27–43; [O1], pp.

41–67; [P1], pp. 20–36; and [W2], pp. 17–43.   Detailed discussions are also to be found in [D6], pp. 1–54; and [S9], pp. 1–40.

A discussion of partitions that leads to a number of interesting applications appears in [K3], pp. 79–87.   See also [C3], pp. 50–55.

Reference [H3], pp. 52–61, gives a detailed introduction to mappings, and a shorter account is given in [S6], pp. 20–24.

A study of [K3], pp. 88–112, and [C3], pp. 33–66, is recommended for help on the counting problems in Section 8-10.

Chapter 2 of [G1] gives a history of the use of diagrams as an aid in problems of logic.

9

Meanings and Diagrams

9-1. Graphic Models for Numbers

In our work thus far it has been assumed that the student's past experience has provided him with considerable familiarity with the natural numbers and operations on them. In this chapter we will consider certain of these ideas more critically. Some of the concepts of set theory will make possible some sharper definitions, even though a complete logical development will not be attempted.

However, the user of arithmetic must have more at hand than a command of the definitions and skill in computation. Thus, he might be able to state an exact definition of multiplication, be able to execute any multiplication computation without error, and still be helpless, unless he "knows a multiplication problem when he sees one." One must be able to identify a considerable variety of physical situations to construct the appropriate mathematical description. Particular attention will be given to diagrams and such graphic models that can be of aid in the visualization of these situations, since they help to form a link between the physical phenomena and the symbolic mathematical model.

The first question to be considered is basic. How does one "picture" a number? The only numbers we have so far considered are those represented by the numerals $0, 1, 2, 3, \ldots$. In Chapter 8 a method was given of setting up a 1:1 correspondence between these numbers and certain sets. This can be illustrated with a collection of separate objects used as "counters," as is shown here for the number 5:

$$* \quad * \quad * \quad * \quad *$$

This works nicely for small natural numbers, but zero is troublesome because there are then no objects to represent. Nevertheless, essentially all the concepts that we have developed with the natural numbers can be illustrated by an appropriate array of such counters.   To produce such a display we need only enough time and space.

This way of thinking about numbers is related to the question of "How many?" But numbers can also be used to answer the question of "How much?" and this leads to the idea of measurement, and then to the introduction of a new kind of number (Chapter 11).   Hence, another objective for our current discussion is to provide some foundation for an extension of our number system.   There were five objects in the row above.   The number 5 can also be associated with the length of a line segment.

Do you see why a person who is thinking of counting might mistake the above for a picture of 6 instead of 5 as intended?   Many difficulties arise when we assign numbers to magnitude rather than to multitude.   For example, we have assumed that the above diagram has five smaller line segments, which are all of the same length.   But a little thought should convince one that this equality is impossible to attain.   Certainly these shown above are not of equal length as careful measurement, under a microscope if necessary, would show.   What do we mean, then, by assuming that they are of the same length?   Roughly this: the differences in length are so small that we shall ignore them.

When we assign a number to a finite set, our one-to-one correspondence is based on a clear-cut decision rule and no question of approximation arises.   This is not the case when we say that a line segment is five units in length.   Already we have substituted an idealized situation for the actual one.   We shall try not to belabor this point, but it must be admitted at the outset that measuring is a far more sophisticated task than counting.

The diagram shown above provides a representation for each of the following amounts:

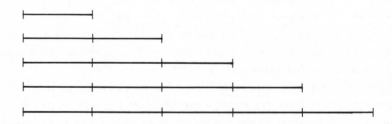

A scale is constructed by placing a numeral at the extreme right end of the line segment to which it refers.   This convention can be a bit unexpected to a child learning to use a scale.   Since the number is assigned to the entire magnitude, why shouldn't the numeral be located nearer the center rather than at the extreme end?   However, we find the usual practice is the only convenient one to follow. Furthermore, we now have a natural way to introduce the number zero.   There is no magnitude to assign to this number, but it does occupy a unique position or place.   It is used to identify the origin, to mark the point at which each measurement begins (the left end of each of the designated line segments).

One can also identify the numbers 1, 2, 3, 4, and 5 with unique points on the scale.   This one-to-one correspondence between numbers and points on a line is in fact indispensable when later extensions of the number system are made.   We shall defer such discussions for two reasons.   The situations in elementary arithmetic for which there is an advantage in thinking of a number as a point are quite rare, but there are many situations where the insistence on this model confuses the issues quite completely.   Hence, for a time we will use counters, or scales and the associated magnitudes, to picture our ideas.

The following exercises are a review of some graphical models that have been introduced in prior chapters.   The reader is challenged to see how many of these he can reproduce before looking back at the references.

a. Use a pattern of counters to verify that addition is associative, using the sum $2 + 3 + 4$.   (p. 16)

b. Use a pattern of counters to verify that $7 + 3 = 5 + 5$, as an example of the invariant principle for sums.   (p. 17)

c. Use a pattern of counters to verify that $9 - 6 = 5 - 2$, as an example of the invariant principle for differences.   (p. 18)

d. Use a pattern of counters to verify that multiplication is associative, using the product $2 \cdot 3 \cdot 5$.   (p. 23)

e. Use a pattern of counters to verify that multiplication is distributive with respect to addition, using the product $5(3 + 7)$.   (p. 25)

f. Use a pattern of counters to verify that $4 \cdot 6 = 2 \cdot 12$, as an example of the invariant principle for products.   (p. 27)

g. How can arrays of counters be used to distinguish between primes and composite numbers?   (p. 62)

h. Use a tree diagram to illustrate the product $4 \cdot 3$.   (p. 157)

9-2. Addition and Subtraction of the Natural Numbers and Zero

Discussions of operations such as addition may be carried on at different levels of abstraction, which we might designate as the object, numeral, and number levels. If we are to speak of the addition of numbers, let us begin by assuming that our universe is the set of natural numbers and zero.   Addition is called a *binary operation* on this set, because it is a rule of correspondence by which if an ordered pair of numbers from this set be chosen, then a uniquely determined third number can be assigned to this ordered pair.   Thus to the ordered pair (3, 4), addition assigns the number $3 + 4$.

The replacement of $3 + 4$ by the basic numeral 7 has long been called *addition*.

Strictly speaking, however, this is a manipulation of numerals, since $3 + 4$ and 7 are numerals for the same number. Hence, this replacement of $3 + 4$ by 7 has been referred to in this text as an *addition computation* rather than as addition. In practice neither the author nor anyone else is likely to find it convenient or desirable to always maintain this distinction in language.

Addition problems, such as the example above, can be "explained" by manipulations of sets of actual objects, and the language of sets enables us to be more precise in our accounts than has been the former practice in arithmetic. However, old habits are hard to break, and no one wants mathematics to be mainly an exercise in semantics. Therefore, we may expect to still hear of students "adding 3 rabbits to 4 rabbits," even though this is meaningless if we enforce the strict standards that addition shall refer only to numbers or to numerals.

A correspondence can be shown between the addition of numbers and the union of sets. To add 3 and 4, or as we say, to find their sum, we can begin by choosing two disjoint sets such that A has 3 members and B has 4 members. The union $A \cup B$ will then be a set of $3 + 4$ or 7 members. The condition of disjointness or nonoverlapping is necessary to avoid counting some elements more than once.

$$A \cap B = \varnothing \qquad\qquad\qquad A \cap B \neq \varnothing$$

$n(A) = 3$ [diagram: set A with a, b, c; set B with d, e, f, g] $n(B) = 4$ $n(A) = 3$ [diagram: set A with a, b; intersection c; set B with d, e, f] $n(B) = 4$

$$n(A \cup B) = n(A) + n(B) - n(A \cap B) \qquad n(A \cup B) = n(A) + n(B) - n(A \cap B)$$
$$= 3 + 4 \qquad\qquad\qquad\qquad\qquad = 3 + 4 - 1$$
$$= 7 \qquad\qquad\qquad\qquad\qquad\qquad = 6$$

If A and B are finite sets and if $n(A) = x$, $n(B) = y$, and $A \cap B = \varnothing$, then $x + y = n(A \cup B)$.

The union of disjoint sets thus provides a very satisfactory definition of addition (for the natural numbers and zero) from the logical point of view. Part of the advantage stems from the direct analogies between union and addition for such properties as are noted in problem 1 of problem set (92). The definition guarantees the possibility of counting out the sum, but gives no specific direction as to the manner of doing this.

To illustrate the sum of 3 and 4 with counters, we first count out each group (members of each set) separately, then bring the groups together (union of the sets), and count the combined groups.

```
    *  *  *   ⎞
    1  2  3   ⎟      1  2  3  4  5  6  7
    *  *  *  * ⎬     *  *  *  *  *  *  *  *
    1  2  3  4 ⎠     1  2  3,  1  2  3  4
```

One has more freedom when he is working with actual objects, than when using the language of sets to write or talk about the process. Thus the objects, while separate, may look alike as can be seen with the asterisks above. But {*, *, *} and {*, *, *, *} would not be an acceptable notation for the sets, since the names listed in the roster must provide for identifying and thus distinguishing the elements. One would require something like {a, b, c} and {d, e, f, g}, as were used in the set union example. Also with objects the problem of overlapping sets, as in the second Venn diagram, is much less likely to arise. For such reasons there is some question as to how much formal set notation and language should be used with the primary student who is learning to count and to add. It may take much classroom experimentation before the decision can be made as to whether set language is an asset or an added burden to the young learner.

Let $A = \{x \mid x$ is zero, or a natural number$\}$. Then the binary operation of addition on the set A is a mapping from the Cartesian product set $A \otimes A$ into the set A. This mapping is also onto since every element of A is an image of at least one ordered pair in $A \otimes A$.

Examples: $(0, 0) \rightarrow 0$, $(0, 1) \rightarrow 1$, $(1, 1) \rightarrow 2$, etc.

But it is not one-to-one, but rather many-to-one, since many ordered pairs may correspond to the same image.

Examples: $(0, 2) \rightarrow 2$, $(1, 1) \rightarrow 2$, $(2, 0) \rightarrow 2$.

It also is possible to use the mapping idea to actually compute sums. For this we could use the ordered set $(0, 1, 2, 3, \ldots)$ whose components are first zero, and then the natural numbers in order. The inclusion of zero makes this set different from the ordered set $(1, 2, 3, \ldots)$, which was used for counting in Section 8-8. In particular it should be observed that in $(0, 1, 2, 3, \ldots)$ the number n is the $n + 1$st component. Since mapping has been defined only for unordered sets, the domain and range sets are formed by selecting their members as shown from the two ordered sets.

$$
\begin{array}{cc}
 & b \quad\; a + b \\
(0, 1, 2, 3, 4, 5, 6, 7, \ldots) & \text{2nd set} \\
\text{range} \quad \{4, 5, 6, 7\} & \\
\mid \;\; \mid \;\; \mid \;\; \mid & \\
\text{domain} \quad \{0, 1, 2, 3\} & \\
a = 3 \quad (0, 1, 2, 3, \ldots) & \text{1st set} \\
b = 4 \qquad\qquad a & \\
a + b = 7 &
\end{array}
$$

This can be simplified considerably by omitting the set notation and working directly with two sequences; $0, 1, 2, 3, \ldots$.

$$
\begin{array}{c}
 b \quad\; a + b \\
0, 1, 2, 3, 4, 5, 6, 7, \ldots \text{2nd sequence} \\
\mid \;\; \mid \;\; \mid \;\; \mid \\
0, 1, 2, 3, \ldots \text{1st sequence} \\
a
\end{array}
$$

To obtain the sum $a + b$, of a first number a and a second number b, let zero of the first sequence correspond to b of the second sequence. Then the successor of zero corresponds to the successor of b, and so on. These correspondences are continued until we reach a in the first sequence, which will correspond to $a + b$ in the second sequence.

It would have been possible to have left off the zeros and thus to begin each of the sequences with the number one. In this case the beginning correspondence would be between 1 in the first sequence and the successor of b in the second sequence. The next correspondence would relate the successor of 1 to the successor of the successor b, and so on.

   a. The matching process, without the zeros, is exactly that used by those who have taught themselves to compute small sums by counting on their fingers. Describe this process.

There are several reasons we want to include the zeros in the sequences. First of all, we are *not* counting objects (which requires that we begin with 1). By including zero we can compute sums where one or both of the addends are zero, which otherwise could not be done.

   b. Verify that the method given enables one to compute $0 + 4$, and $4 + 0$.

Furthermore the sequences that begin with zero allow a simple and direct transition to the next model to be given for the computation of sums.

If 3 and 4 are each the measure of a line segment, then the sequences 0, 1, 2, 3 and 0, 1, 2, 3, 4 are used in constructing the scales as shown below. The computation of the sum $3 + 4$ requires that we determine the basic numeral (in this case, the decimal numeral) that represents the same number that $3 + 4$ does. This can be done by placing the line segments end to end and then measuring their combined length.

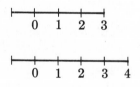

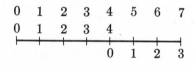

If actual rules are used, one gets a "slide rule" for addition, which shows a direct analogy with the example using sequences. Zero is shown although it is usually left off ordinary rulers.

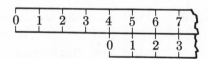

The sum $3 + 4$ could have been suggested by such a question as "Three (objects) and four (objects) are how many (objects) altogether?" This could be represented by the conditional equation $3 + 4 = N$, which is explicit in form. The cue words here for addition are "and" and "altogether." But one cannot depend on cue words alone, since addition can be implied by sentences using words, which by themselves suggest subtraction. Such possibilities will be discussed after consideration of some models for subtraction.

ANSWERS TO EXERCISES

a. Name each finger on both hands using the numbers 1 to 10 in order. To add 4 to 3, begin with the finger whose name is the successor to 3, and count 1, 2, 3, 4. The four will correspond to the finger whose name is 7. In this counting, finger 1 follows finger 10 and the cycle is repeated if necessary. Such finger computation can be reliable, but it is much too slow. **b.** For $0 + 4$, the correspondence $0 \rightarrow 4$ is the only one required. For $4 + 0$ we have $0 \rightarrow 0$, and $4 \rightarrow 4$.

Problems (92)

1. The following are identities in the theory of sets. In each case give an analogy for the operation of addition on zero and the natural numbers, and state whether it is also an identity.
   a. $A \cup B = B \cup A$ **d.** $A \cup A = A$
   b. $A \cup (B \cup C) = (A \cup B) \cup C$ **e.** $A \cup U = U$
   c. $A \cup \emptyset = A$
2. Assume $n(A) = 5$, $n(B) = 3$.
   Show by Venn diagrams all the possibilities for $n(A \cup B)$.
3. Illustrate $x + y$, with $x = 5$ and $y = 2$.
   a. By showing a correspondence between two sequences.
   b. By a diagram of two rulers.
4. Illustrate $x + y$, with $x = 4$ and $y = 7$.
   a. By showing a correspondence between two sequences.
   b. By a diagram of two rulers.

Some authors state that subtraction is not a binary operation over the set A of zero and the natural numbers, since it is true that there is no mapping $A \otimes A \rightarrow A$ with subtraction as the rule of correspondence. If $a \in A$ and $b \in A$, and $(a, b) \in A \otimes A$, then (a, b) will have a unique image in A if a is greater than or equal to b, but will fail to have an image in A if a is less than b, if (a, b) is to have $a - b$ as an image.

However, in most elementary treatises it is common to refer to subtraction as being a binary operation over A, under the appropriate restrictions. But because of these limitations the operation is said to be not closed. This was the practice followed in Section 3-1. Subtraction is further limited by the failure of the commutative and associative laws to hold. Nevertheless the variety of physical situations for which subtraction is an appropriate model is greater than for addition.

The mathematical operation of addition has been derived by abstraction from the physical act of combining two groups to make one. The physical act that undoes this is the separation of one group into two groups. This suggests that we look for a model in the partitioning of sets, and in particular to the dichotomy of a set into two subsets. The problem of zero could be handled by extending the definition of a partition, as previously given, to include the possibility of one set being the empty set.

Let us recall at this point that the dichotomy of a set begins with one set and produces two sets. But a binary operation starts with two objects and from this determines one object. Hence we look elsewhere for a model of subtraction as a binary operation on numbers. For this, the closest analog we have with sets is the binary operation of set difference, but again the two sets must meet a certain condition.

To subtract 3 from 7, or to find the difference $7 - 3$, we select two sets A and B, with $B \subseteq A$, and with $n(A) = 7$, and $n(B) = 3$. The relative complement of B with respect to A, or $A - B$, will be a set having $7 - 3$ or 4 members. The necessity that $B \subseteq A$ is evident in the following examples:

Examples:

$$n(A) - n(B) = 7 - 3$$
$$n(A - B) = 4$$

$$n(A) - n(B) = 7 - 3$$
$$n(A - B) = 5$$

If A and B are finite sets and if $n(A) = x$, $n(B) = y$, and $B \subseteq A$, then $x - y = n(A - B)$.

The difference $7 - 3$ can be illustrated with counters by using a diagram similar to that for addition but proceeding in the reverse order. Starting with a group of 7, a subgroup of 3 is counted out, isolated, and possibly taken away. Those counters that remain are then counted to determine $7 - 3$.

In this case the word "remainder" is a natural one to use for $7 - 3$. Since we have already decided on the word "difference" for the form $a - b$, we shall continue this practice and use the word "remainder" only when this particular physical model of subtraction is to be inferred. When speaking of the mathematical operation of subtraction, apart from any physical model, the word "difference" is standard.

There is a quite different way of looking at subtraction, which requires two distinct groups of counters.   In this case we make a *difference comparison* to find out how many more, or how many less.   No separation is involved but rather an attempt to complete a 1:1 correspondence between two sets.

If two finite sets can be placed in 1:1 correspondence, then there is no (or zero) difference between the numbers of their elements.   If there is a correspondence between set A and set B that associates every element of B with one and only one element of A, but that leaves at least one element of A that is not an image of an element of B, then we have a mapping from B into A, which is 1:1 but not onto. In this case the number of elements in A is *greater than* the number of elements in B.   An equivalent assertion is that the number of elements in B is *less than* the number of elements in A.   Assume $n(A) = a$, and $n(B) = b$.   We write $a > b$ as a notation for "a is greater than b," or $b < a$ as a notation for "b is less than a."

$$A = \{a, b, c, d, e, f, g\} \qquad n(A) = 7, n(B) = 3$$
$$B = \{x, y, z\}$$

The mapping from B into A is 1:1, but not onto; $7 > 3, 3 < 7$.

The difference between a and b is then the number of elements in A that are not images of elements in B.   In the above example, let A_1 be the range of the mapping.   Then A_1 is a subset of A, formed by those elements that are images of elements in B.

$$A_1 = \{a, b, c\} \qquad \text{and} \qquad n(A_1) = n(B) = 3$$
$$A - A_1 = \{d, e, f, g\}$$
$$n(A - A_1) = n(A) - n(A_1) \qquad \text{since } A_1 \subseteq A$$
$$= n(A) - n(B)$$
$$= 7 - 3$$
$$= 4$$

This shows why the remainder when 3 is subtracted from 7, based on a set difference model, is the same number as the difference between 7 and 3, as derived from a difference comparison model.

If in a sequence, a term x has a successor y, then x is said to be the predecessor of y (that which precedes).   Just as every term but the last term of a finite sequence has a unique successor, so does every term but the first have a unique predecessor. This concept will be useful in a mapping rule for matching sequences as we construct a computation model for subtraction.

$$a - b \qquad a$$
$$0, 1, 2, 3, 4, 5, 6, 7, \ldots \text{2nd sequence}$$
$$0, 1, 2, 3, \ldots \text{1st sequence}$$
$$b$$

The number b in the first sequence is matched with a in the second sequence. Then the predecessor of b corresponds to the predecessor of a, and so on, until we find zero of the first sequence paired with $a - b$ of the second. Clearly this correspondence can be completed only when b is not greater than a. Two rulers may be placed as shown.

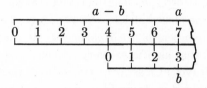

It was necessary to count backwards when matching the two sequences above for computing the difference comparison. This suggests that we reverse the left to right order of one of the sequences (or rulers).

$$a - b \qquad a$$

0, 1, 2, 3, 4, 5, 6, 7, . . . 2nd sequence

$$| \quad | \quad | \quad |$$

. . . 3, 2, 1, 0 . . . 1st sequence

$$b$$

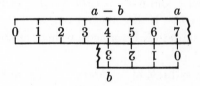

One might adopt the convention that a difference comparison is always that of a first number minus a second. Then the difference between a and b would be $a - b$, provided that $a - b$ was defined, that is, that a was not less than b. Hence, if a were less than b one could then not represent the difference between a and b by $a - b$ when the universe consisted of zero and the natural numbers.

We shall defer such a convention until we have extended the number system in such a way as to remove this restriction on $a - b$. At present we shall follow the practice, which has been common in elementary arithmetic, of making a difference comparison between a large number and a small without regard to order. One can then assert that any two numbers have a difference (possibly zero) and that this difference can be computed by subtracting the smaller from the larger when the numbers are unequal. The disadvantage of this is that in sentences containing the variables a and b, we cannot choose between $a - b$ and $b - a$ for representing their difference, unless it is known which, if any, is the larger.

Another way of thinking about subtraction is the following: If $b < a$, we can ask for the number x, which added to b gives a, as represented by the conditional equation $b + x = a$. We return to the sets A and B in the example on page 173 and now seek a set B_1, disjoint from B, such that $B \cup B_1$ can be placed in one-to-one correspondence with A.

$$\{d, e, f, g\} = A - A_1 \qquad n(A) = 7$$

$$A_1 = \{a, b, c\} \qquad\qquad\qquad n(B) = 3$$

$$\begin{bmatrix} A &= \{a, b, c, d, e, f, g\} \\ B &= \{x, y, z\} \end{bmatrix} \qquad\qquad n(A_1) = 3$$

$$n(A - A_1) = 7 - 3 = 4$$

$$\{l, m, n, o\} = B_1 \qquad\qquad n(B_1) = 4$$

It is required to determine a set B_1 such that $n(B) + n(B_1) = n(A)$. Let A_1 be a subset of A (as introduced in the model for a difference) such that

$$n(A_1) = n(B) \qquad \text{and} \qquad n(A_1) + n(A - A_1) = n(A)$$

Then, by substitution, if $n(B) + n(B_1)$ is to equal $n(A)$, it is necessary that

$$n(A_1) + n(B_1) = n(A_1) + n(A - A_1)$$

Then, by the cancellation property,

$$n(B_1) = n(A - A_1)$$

Therefore, the number of elements in B_1 is the same number previously determined as a remainder and as a difference. This provides us with a model for the "how many more needed" subtraction situation.

```
                    *   *   *   *   *   *   *      Larger collection
                    |   |   |
Smaller collection  *   *   *   ↑   ↑   ↑   ↑
                            *   *   *   *      Objects needed to make
                                              the collections equal in
                                              number
```

This way of looking at subtraction provides the most satisfactory logical definition of this operation. In the set whose members consist of zero and the natural numbers, the difference $a - b$ exists and $a - b = x$, if and only if, there is a number x in the set such that $b + x = a$ (see Section 3-1). When subtraction is defined in this manner, there is no need to go back to set models to establish the properties of subtraction. Instead one can reason directly from the corresponding addition problem and appeal to the already established properties of addition. In this sense addition is often designated as a direct operation and subtraction as an indirect one (Section 3-1). A third method of matching sequences is to compute $a - b$ as given below. It determines the number $a - b$, which added to b, gives a. $b + (a - b) = a$.

$$a - b$$

```
        0, 1, 2, 3, 4, . . . 2nd sequence
        |  |  |  |  |
  0, 1, 2, 3, 4, 5, 6, 7, . . . 1st sequence
        b        a
```

Here b in the first sequence matches zero in the second sequence. Then the successor of b corresponds to the successor of zero, and so on until a corresponds to $a - b$. The ordered pairs that are established in turn are $(3, 0)$, $(4, 1)$, $(5, 2)$, $(6, 3)$, and $(7, 4)$. Note that in each the second component (from the second sequence) is three less than the first component.

 a. Give, in turn, the ordered pairs that were determined by the two preceding methods for matching sequences to compute $7 - 3$.

This is the model with two rulers for the above matching sequences. It is of course arbitrary which sequence is written above or below, but we have shown only those where the number being computed appears in the upper sequence (or on the top ruler).

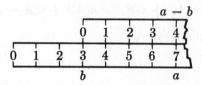

In the explicit form of $a - b = x$, a is called the *minuend*, b the *subtrahend*, and x is the *difference* (or remainder). In the equivalent but implicit form of $b + x = a$, a would be the sum, b the known addend, and x is the missing addend. Since addition is commutative, one could also write $x + b = a$, and ask for the number x, which if increased by the number b, would yield the sum a.

 Again if x is to be determined, then subtraction is also implied by $a - x = b$, and this can be given a verbal translation using either the language of a difference comparison or a remainder. Addition is implied by $x - b = a$ if x is to be determined. If to all the possibilities we have indicated for varieties of descriptions of addition and subtraction problems we include the variations of word order in English sentences, such changes as from active to passive voice, and the use of synonyms, we arrive at a list of some length. A wealth of experience is necessary before there can be accuracy and confidence in identifying all of these.

 One possible classification is that based on the number of counters needed to make a model of the physical situation.

  Examples:

   $3 + 4 = x$ 7 counters needed for the addends and sum

   $7 - 3 = x$ 7 counters needed for a separation and remainder problem; 10 counters for a difference comparison

   $3 + x = 7$ 14 counters for "how many needed," or only 7 if the reference collection is only imagined as for the missing addend problem

ANSWER TO EXERCISE

a. $(3, 7)$, $(2, 6)$, $(1, 5)$, $(0, 4)$; and $(0, 7)$, $(1, 6)$, $(2, 5)$, $(3, 4)$.

Problems (93)

1. Let $n(A) = 6$ and $n(B) = 3$. What are all the possibilities for $n(A - B)$?
2. **a.** What is true about numbers p and q if $p - q = q - p$?
   b. What is true about sets P and Q if $n(P - Q) = n(Q - P)$?
3. Illustrate the computation of $x - y$ with $x = 8$ and $y = 5$:
   a. In three ways by a correspondence between two sequences. Label x, y, and $x - y$.
   b. In three ways by a diagram of two rulers. Label x, y, and $x - y$.
4. Follow the same as instructions for problem 3 with $x = 9$ and $y = 4$.
5. For each of the following construct mathematical models in the form of a single conditional equation. Some should be explicit and some should be implicit. Make this choice to agree with your decision as to whether the English form should be termed explicit or implicit. Supply meaningful numbers for the blanks.
   a. What is the sum of ( ) and [ ]?
   b. What must be added to ( ) to give a sum of [ ]?
   c. What is the remainder when ( ) is subtracted from [ ]?
   d. ( ) is how many more than [ ]?
   e. From what number can ( ) be subtracted with a remainder of [ ]?
   f. What number can be subtracted from ( ) and leave a remainder of [ ]?
   g. To what number can ( ) be added to give a total of [ ]?
   h. The difference between two numbers is ( ), and the larger number is [ ]. What is the smaller number?
   i. The difference between two numbers is ( ), and the smaller number is [ ]. What is the larger number?
   j. What is the excess of ( ) over [ ]?
6. These twelve conditional equations are based on addition and subtraction and the numbers 2, 3, and 5. Twelve more would result from symmetric property of equality.

   a. $x + 3 = 5$ **d.** $x + 2 = 5$ **g.** $x - 2 = 3$ **j.** $x - 3 = 2$
   b. $2 + x = 5$ **e.** $3 + x = 5$ **h.** $5 - x = 3$ **k.** $5 - x = 2$
   c. $2 + 3 = x$ **f.** $3 + 2 = x$ **i.** $5 - 2 = x$ **l.** $5 - 3 = x$

   A. Classify each as involving addition or subtraction for its solution, and also whether it is explicit or implicit in form.
   B. When subtraction is defined in terms of addition, then **a.** and **h.** are equivalent. Determine the remaining equivalent pairs resulting from this definition.
   C. By the commutative property of addition, **a.** and **e.** are equivalent. Determine the other equivalent pairs of this type.
   D. Because of **B.** and **C.**, we find **a.**, **h.**, **e.**, and **l.**, are equivalent. Determine the two other groups of four equivalent equations.

9-3. Multiplication and Division of the Natural Numbers and Zero

In Section 4-1, the multiplication of two natural numbers was related to repeated addition. This suggests the possibility of developing a model for multiplication by extending the model for addition, which was based on union of disjoint sets. When $a + b$ is defined by the binary operation of set union, there is a symmetry with respect to a and b. Each is assigned a like role, with $a = n(A)$ and $b = n(B)$. This symmetry is lost when the extension is made to multiplication. In the product ab we shall distinguish the factors a and b, calling one the *multiplier* and the other the *multiplicand* and interpret them quite differently.

Let 3 be the multiplier and 5 the multiplicand in the product $3 \cdot 5$. We then choose three sets S_1, S_2, and S_3, each having five elements, making sure that these sets are mutually disjoint (no element to be a member of more than one set). We then form the union of these sets, and the number of elements in this union is the desired product. A Venn diagram can be used effectively only if there are not more than three of the sets.

$$n(S_1 \cup S_2 \cup S_3) = n(S_1) + n(S_2) + n(S_3)$$
$$- n(S_1 \cap S_2) - n(S_2 \cap S_3)$$
$$- n(S_1 \cap S_3)$$
$$+ n(S_1 \cap S_2 \cap S_3)$$
$$= 5 + 5 + 5$$
$$3 \cdot 5 = 15$$

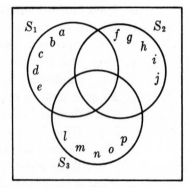

Let $S_1, S_2, \ldots, S_a$ be sets such that $n(S_i) = b$ for $i = 1, 2, \ldots, a$ and such that $S_i \cap S_j = \varnothing$ for $i \neq j$. Then $ab = n(S_1 \cup S_2 \cup \cdots \cup S_a)$.

The discussion in Section 4-1 indicated an inadequacy of repeated addition when seeking interpretations for multipliers of one and zero. Let us test the above definition in this respect.

$n \cdot 1 = n$ The number of elements in n mutually disjoint sets each having one member.

$1 \cdot n = n$ The number of elements in one set of n elements.

$n \cdot 0 = 0$ The number of elements in n empty sets.

$0 \cdot n = 0$ The number of elements in no (or zero) sets each having n elements.

The first three go smoothly enough but the last statement leaves something to be desired. Also the lack of symmetry in this definition means that the commutative property of multiplication is not obvious.

The members of the sets (when they have any) can be arranged in a rectangular

array as in Section 2-3, and the commutative property then becomes evident upon the interchange of rows and columns.

The use of rectangular arrays for the visualization of products
of natural numbers can be extended to more than two factors.
Some compactness can be achieved by alternation between horizontal and vertical
for the successive repetition of the design.

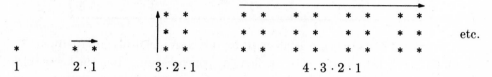

$$1 \qquad 2 \cdot 1 \qquad 3 \cdot 2 \cdot 1 \qquad\qquad 4 \cdot 3 \cdot 2 \cdot 1 \qquad \text{etc.}$$

Such a device was used in Section 2-3 in a diagram giving intuitive support to
the associative property of multiplication.

The product xy with $x = 3$ and $y = 5$ can be computed by establishing a correspondence between two sequences of the form 0, 1, 2, 3, ... The terms of the
first sequence will be used in the succession, but their images will be a selection of
only certain terms of the second sequence.

$$
\begin{array}{llllllllllllllllll}
 & & & x & & & & & & & & & & & & xy & & \\
\text{2nd:} & 0 & 1 & 2 & 3 & 4 & 5 & 6 & 7 & 8 & 9 & 10 & 11 & 12 & 13 & 14 & 15 & 16 & \cdots \\
 & | & & & | & & & | & & & | & & & | & & & | & & \\
\text{1st:} & 0 & & & 1 & & & 2 & & & 3 & & & 4 & & & 5 & & \cdots \\
 & & & & & & & & & & & & & & & & y & &
\end{array}
$$

The zeros of each sequence are matched with each other. The successor of
zero in the first sequence corresponds to the 3rd (or xth) in succession after zero in
the second sequence.   A similar procedure matches 2 to 6, and finally 5 (or y) to 15
(or xy).   Since multiplication is commutative, the product is not disturbed if the
roles of x and y are interchanged so that y is the multiplier and x is the multiplicand.
The next diagram verifies this but in neither case is it particularly obvious that
multiplication is indeed commutative.

$$
\begin{array}{llllllllllllllllll}
 & & & & y & & & & & & & & & & & & xy & \\
\text{2nd:} & 0 & 1 & 2 & 3 & 4 & 5 & 6 & 7 & 8 & 9 & 10 & 11 & 12 & 13 & 14 & 15 & 16 & \cdots \\
 & | & & & & & | & & & & & | & & & & & | & \\
\text{1st:} & 0 & & & & & 1 & & & & & 2 & & & & & 3 & \\
 & & & & & & & & & & & & & & & & x &
\end{array}
$$

Again the sequences suggest how to move directly from a counting to a measurement model.   However, in contrast to addition and subtraction, we find that
multiplication and division require an unlimited variety of scales or rulers.   For
sums and differences the number 1 was assigned to the same length on both scales,
so that the scales were of identical appearance.   Then the zero points were sepa-

rated by a specified amount by shifting one scale along the other. For products and quotients the scales will be placed so that the zero points of each correspond, but in general the two scales will be quite different, since the number 1 will now be assigned to different magnitudes on each scale as required for a particular product.

The ordered pairs that are established by this correspondence are (0, 0), (1, 3), (2, 6), (3, 9), (4, 12), (5, 15); with the first component coming from the lower ruler (or sequence), and the second component from the upper ruler (or sequence). In each ordered pair the second component is three times the first component.

In the second method above of setting up the correspondence, the ordered pairs would be (0, 0), (1, 5), (2, 10), and (3, 15). Two scales could be constructed to illustrate them.

a. Which one of these sets of ordered pairs relates best to repeatedly adding 5?
b. To repeatedly adding 3?

The rulers needed for such demonstrations are not available commercially, but for a given product or quotient to be studied the necessary scales can be constructed in a few moments on squared paper or on a blackboard ruled in squares. The design of such scales would present problems if it was mandatory to select a line segment such as AB, designate it as of length 1, and then to divide it, for example, into seven parts of equal length.

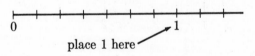

However, in measurement the assignment of the number 1 to a magnitude is an arbitrary decision. The difficulties above can be avoided by beginning with a diagram with equal segments as given below and then placing 1 at the right point to get seven equal segments.

0 |—+—+—+—+—+—+—+—+—| 1

place 1 here

The emphasis that we are giving to the use of scales is partly in anticipation of the invaluable role they assume as models for the rational numbers, which will be our first extension of the number system (Chapter 11).

A rectangular array can be readily extended to a measurement model. If the counters are square blocks, they can be pushed together to form a rectangle or a larger square. A scale may then be constructed along two sides as shown.

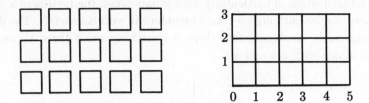

This is still a rectangular array for which the number of rows, the number of columns, and the total number of small squares can be determined by counting. We also now have a measure for the length and width of the rectangle. A number called the *area* can be assigned to the rectangle, this number being the total number of squares that cover the rectangle in the manner shown. The area of a rectangle is thereby defined as the product of the number which measures the length, by the number which measures the width. The area of a rectangle and the lengths of two adjacent sides thus make a useful model for the relation of a product to its factors. For example, composite numbers can measure the area of rectangles, each of whose sides is measured by natural numbers greater than one; the prime numbers cannot.

The product of three natural numbers can be illustrated by the volume of a rectangular solid constructed with cubes of unit volume. Extension horizontally, vertically, and in depth exhausts the three dimensions of physical space. Hence, for a model involving four or more factors, there will be some repetition of the direction of the extensions. The product $2 \cdot (4 \cdot 3)$, which is illustrated here, can be multiplied by n by arranging n of such solids end to end, or vertically, and so on.

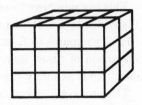

In Chapter 8 a binary operation on sets was introduced that provides a good model for a definition of multiplication with the natural numbers and zero. This is the Cartesian product of two sets. The symmetry of the formation of the ordered pairs which are the elements of $A \otimes B$ ensures that $n(A \otimes B) = n(B \otimes A)$ even though the Cartesian product itself was found to be neither commutative nor associative. It can be easily verified that zero and one give no special difficulty when the empty set or a singleton set is used as one of the factors of the Cartesian product.

However, the variety of physical situations that suggest the formation of a Cartesian product is quite small compared to those for which repeated addition would be a closer analogy, and this reduces its intuitive appeal for beginning instruction. Also, this definition is not one that generalizes readily when we extend the number system beyond the natural numbers and zero. We found in Chapter 8 that many multiplicative situations based on a Cartesian product can be illustrated effectively by a tree diagram. But such diagrams are strongly associated with counting and do not readily generalize to measurement.

We now consider a quite different way of thinking about multiplication, which emphasizes the very important role the number 1 has in this operation. This model for multiplication is particularly appropriate when the factors of a product represent magnitudes, although we shall introduce it with counters.   The diagram below is designed to emphasize that there is something about three 5's and one 5 that can be shown with a 3 and a 1.

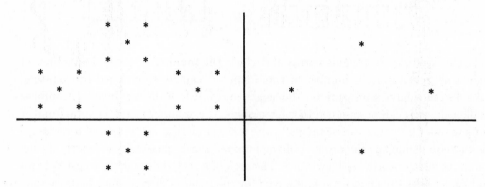

We say that "15 has the same ratio to 5 that 3 has to 1."   This may be written as $\frac{15}{5} = \frac{3}{1}$.

This is a new way to read this equality, as formerly we would have read this as "15 divided by 5 is the same as 3 divided by 1."   One can also say that 15 compares to 5 as 3 compares to 1, but here it must be remembered that this is not a difference comparison of "how many more," but rather a ratio comparison of "how many times": 15 is as many times 5 as 3 is times 1.

The product $3 \cdot 5$ can then be determined by finding a number that has the same ratio to 5 that 3 has to 1.   This would be an implicit form, written as

$$\frac{N}{5} = \frac{3}{1}$$

By referring back to the diagram we can further observe that 15 has the same ratio to 3 that 5 has to 1, which can be written

$$\frac{15}{3} = \frac{5}{1}$$

We shall defer a more logical treatment of the ratio concept to a later chapter and emphasize at present some diagrams that help to achieve an intuitive grasp for what is meant by "having the same ratio."   If the counters for the four numbers in the previous diagram are arranged in the manner below, there is a suggestion of how line segments may be used to picture the ratio idea.

```
        *
      *  *  *

    *  *  *  *  *
    *  *  *  *  *      *  *  *  *  *      *  *  *  *  *
```

or

```
        *
    *   *   *   *
    *   *   *
    *  *  *    *  *  *    *  *  *    *  *  *    *  *  *
```

become

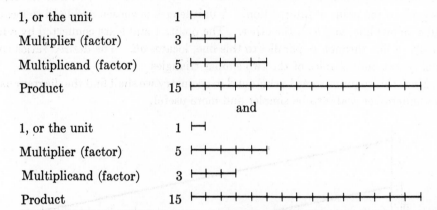

1, or the unit	1	
Multiplier (factor)	3	
Multiplicand (factor)	5	
Product	15	

and

1, or the unit	1	
Multiplier (factor)	5	
Multiplicand (factor)	3	
Product	15	

Such diagrams help one to "see" something that is harder to grasp through words; that the ratio of 15 to 5 is the same as the ratio of 3 to 1, and that the ratio of 15 to 3 is the same as the ratio of 5 to 1.

A ratio interpretation can also be found for the two scales that were in the under-over position in the diagram on page 180.   Consider now the length of the line segment extending from A to C, and also the length of the line segment extending from A to B.

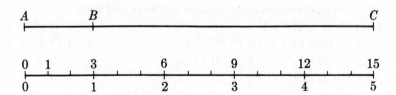

The ratio of these lengths is 15 to 3 as measured by upper scale, and 5 to 1 measured by the lower scale.

$$\frac{\text{Distance from } A \text{ to } C}{\text{Distance from } A \text{ to } B} \quad = \quad \frac{15}{3} \quad = \quad \frac{5}{1}$$

$$\underset{\text{scale}}{\text{upper}} \quad \underset{\text{scale}}{\text{lower}}$$

But we want these ratios to be equal.   This is an instance of a very important assumption about ratios: *The ratio of two magnitudes is independent of (does not depend on) the scale used to measure them.* By contrast, the difference comparison does vary with the scale used. Thus the distance from A to C is 12 more than that from A to B if measured with the upper scale, but only 4 more if measured with the lower scale.

Ratio is a highly geometrical concept and there are a variety of constructions for determining the product of two numbers that have been represented by lengths of line segments. One of these can be shown by drawing two intersecting lines. They are shown as perpendicular here but this is not necessary. The number zero is assigned to the point of intersection. A unit length is chosen and used to locate 1 and a on one line, and b on the other. The points 1 and b are connected by a line. Finally, a line through a, parallel to this line, locates ab. The desired ratios come from corresponding sides of the two similar triangles.

Since this requires some background in geometry we shall find the diagram using two under-over scales to be simpler and more useful.

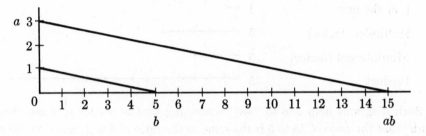

ANSWERS TO EXERCISES

a. The second. **b.** The first.

Problems (94)

1. The following are identities in the theory of sets. Where possible, give an analogy for operations on the natural numbers and zero.
   a. $A \cap B = B \cap A$ e. $A \cap \varnothing = \varnothing$
   b. $A \cap (B \cap C) = (A \cap B) \cap C$ f. $A \cap U = A$
   c. $A \cap (B \cup C) = (A \cap B) \cup (A \cap C)$ g. $A \cap A = A$
   d. $A \cup (B \cap C) = (A \cup B) \cap (A \cup C)$
2. The following are identities in the theory of sets. Construct the analogous equation for operations on the natural numbers and zero. Give a numerical example for which the statement is true, and one for which it is false.
   a. $(A - B) \cap B = \varnothing$ b. $A \cap (A - B) = A - B$
3. Illustrate the product xy where $x = 4$ and $y = 3$ in the following ways:
   a. By a rectangular array of counters.
   b. By matching two sequences. Do this in two ways.
   c. With two scales, one over the other. Do this in two ways.
   d. By the length, width, and area of a rectangle.

    e. With a rectangular solid.

    f. By a tree diagram.   Do this in two ways.

    g. With a Cartesian product.   Display members three different ways.

    h. With a ratio model, using counters.

    i. With four line segments.   Do this in two ways.

    j. With two similar triangles.   Do this in two ways.

4. Follow directions for problem 3 with $x = 2$ and $y = 6$.

5. Follow directions for problem 3 with $x = 0$ and $y = 5$.   When some model cannot be used, discuss the difficulties.

6. Follow directions for problem 3 for xyz with $x = 2$, $y = 3$, $z = 5$.   Indicate which models are not practical for more than two or three factors.

Division, like subtraction, is said to be an indirect operation.   The best logical definition proves to be one that defines division in terms of multiplication rather than directly by abstraction from sets or magnitudes.   Division is limited, as was subtraction, by the lack of closure over the set of zero and the natural numbers, and by the lack of commutativity and associativity.   But there is a wealth of physical situations for which a division model is an appropriate description.

The two scales below have four magnitudes designated that correspond to the determination of a product when the multiplier and the multiplicand are known. Since multiplication is commutative, there is sometimes no reason to distinguish between the multiplier and the multiplicand and in this case both are called factors.

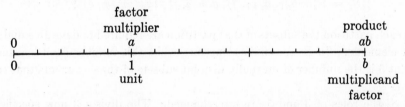

If the product and only one of the factors are known, the missing factor is determined by a division computation.   The definition for division given in Section 3-1 is repeated here for reference:

If A is zero or a natural number, and if B is a natural number, then we can divide A by B, and write $\dfrac{A}{B} = C$, if and only if, there exists a number C, which is zero or a natural number, such that $BC = A$.

We now rename the magnitudes on the above diagram, using the language of division, and showing the two cases that arise.   There is little reason to distinguish these two cases logically, since multiplication is commutative.   However, the corresponding physical models are often clearly different, since different roles for the multiplier and multiplicand are reflected in differences in the interpretation of divisor and dividend.

1.

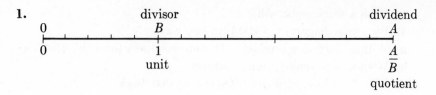

2.

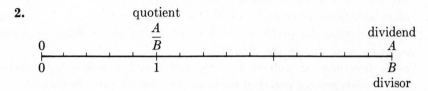

These suggest that it may be possible to take other multiplication models, and by changing the point of view, reinterpret them in the language of division. This will indeed be the case.

Let S be a set with $n(S) = 15$. Two models for the division, $\dfrac{15}{3} = 5$, are shown, both based on the partition of S into disjoint subsets. They should be compared with the set theoretic model of multiplication based on the union of disjoint sets.

$$S = \{a, b, c, d, e, f, g, h, i, j, k, l, m, n, o\}$$
$$S_1 = \{ \{a, b, c\}, \{d, e, f\}, \{g, h, i\}, \{j, k, l\}, \{m, n, o\} \}$$
$$S_2 = \{ \{a, b, c, d, e\}, \{f, g, h, i, j\}, \{k, l, m, n, o\} \}$$

In each partition the subsets of that partition are required to have an equal number of elements. In S_1 the divisor specifies what this number shall be, and the quotient 5 is the number of mutually disjoint subsets of three elements that can be formed.

In S_2 the roles of 3 and 5 are interchanged. The divisor 3 now specifies the required number of subsets, and the quotient 5 is the resulting number of elements in each of the subsets.

An analysis of partition S_1 suggests that each of the problems

$$\frac{15}{3}, \qquad 15 \div 3, \qquad \text{and} \qquad 3\overline{)15}$$

may be read as "How many 3's in 15?" To find out, we may subtract 3 from 15 as many times as possible and keep a record of how many times this can be done. Thus corresponding to multiplication interpreted as repeated addition we have division interpreted as repeated subtraction.

15	12	9	6	3
3	3	3	3	3
12	9	6	3	0

If we have a group of 15 counters, we can set 3 aside, and then 3 more, and so on until we have five groups of 3's.

1	2	3	4	5
* * *	* * *	* * *	* * *	* * *
1 2 3	4 5 6	7 8 9	10 11 12	13 14 15

This in turn suggests how we may compute the quotient by matching sequences. The zeros of the two sequences are first paired.   Then the divisor (the Bth element in succession after zero of the first sequence) is matched to the successor of zero in the second sequence.   This method of matching is continued until the dividend A in the first sequence is paired with the quotient $\frac{A}{B}$ in the second sequence.

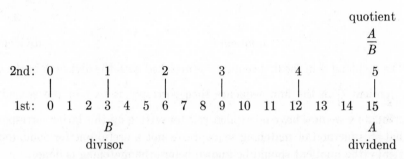

When these two sequences are used on two scales, we find we have a record of how many times a length of 3 units can be "measured off" on a length of 15 units.

In the literature of arithmetic a division model corresponding to the partition S_1 is usually called a *repeated subtraction*, or a *measurement* model.   It is evident that matching of the two sequences above can be completed only when the dividend is a multiple of the divisor, or when the dividend is zero.

We now consider partition S_2.   Here we can use counters with the problems

$$\frac{15}{3}, \qquad 15 \div 3, \qquad \text{and} \qquad 3\overline{)15}$$

to answer the question, "How many will there be in each group, if 15 counters be divided into 3 groups each having the same number?"

1	2	3
* * * * *	* * * * *	* * * * *
1 2 3 4 5	6 7 8 9 10	11 12 13 14 15

The word "share" is useful in thinking about division in this way.   The expression $\frac{15}{3}$ = ? can be read as, "If 15 is to be divided into 3 shares, what will 1 share

be?" Note the use of the number 1 in this question. The equation shows this bet-

ter when written as $\frac{15}{3} = \frac{?}{1}$. This suggests the following matching of two se-

quences.

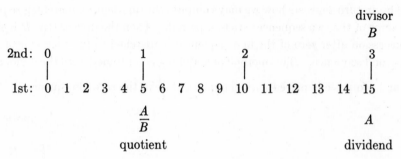

The dividend A in the first sequence is matched with the divisor B in the second.

The quotient $\frac{A}{B}$ in the first sequence then corresponds to 1 in the second. But

unfortunately we now have no explicit rule for setting up this latter correspondence
so that this method of matching sequences is not a useful one for computation of
quotients (the quotient should be known before the matching is done).

A division model based on the S_2 partition is usually called a *partition* because of
the requirement that the multitude or magnitude be divided into equal parts. If
we observe what is actually done in rearranging a set of fifteen objects into either
form S_1 or S_2, it is likely that the procedure will be much the same no matter which
partition is the final goal. Thus one might select three elements from S and then
form a single group with them if form S_1 is sought, or distribute one each to three
groups if S_2 is wanted. This is then repeated with three more elements of S, and
so on until S is exhausted. That is, one can follow the S_1 pattern for the selection of
the elements of S no matter whether S_1 or S_2 is to be the final result. This suggests
that regardless of the interpretation used to set up a division problem, the *division
computation* can likely be best rationalized by regarding the process to be one of
repeated subtraction. This was confirmed above in the two methods of matching
sequences where only the first, which grew out of repeated subtraction, was effective
for computing the quotient. This is also in agreement with the analysis of division
computations in Section 7-7.

In many division problems, particularly those involving measurement in the
sciences, the information sought would be the response to a question we have not as
yet considered for division. Thus the problems

$$\frac{30}{6}, \qquad 30 \div 6, \qquad \text{or} \qquad 6\overline{)30}$$

could arise in the study of magnitudes A and B below.

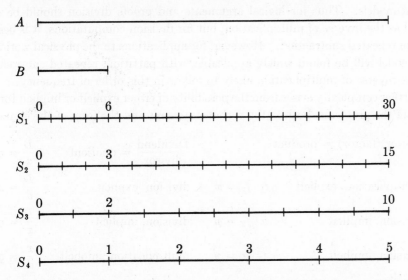

If A and B are measured with scale S_1, we could report that the ratio of length A to length B is 30 to 6.   If measured with scale S_2, it would be 15 to 3.   For scale S_3 it would be 10 to 2.   If measured with S_4, the ratio would be 5 to 1.   Recall now that the ratio is not to depend on the scale used.   Hence, we accept all these statements as representing the same ratio and ask this question, "Which of these is the simplest statement?"

The ratio of 5 to 1 is the accepted answer to this question.   This is not due alone to the smaller numbers used, but is true in particular because 1, the identity for multiplication, is the best reference number as a standard for ratio comparisons. Thus one may divide 30 by 6 to answer this question, "What number has the same ratio to 1 (the standard) as 30 has to 6?"

$$\frac{30}{6} = \frac{?}{1} \qquad \frac{30}{6} = \frac{5}{1} \qquad \frac{30}{6} = 5$$

To say that 30 is 5 times 6 is equivalent to the assertion that 30 has the same ratio to 6 that 5 has to 1.

An older notation for ratio, which still has some usage, represents the ratio of a to b by $a:b$.   Division is not commutative, and when a and b are natural numbers, the ratio $a:b$ is not that of $b:a$ unless a and b are the same number.   Hence, one speaks of the ratio of a first number a to a second number b, or of the *antecedent* a to the *consequent* b.   It is evident that the ratio interpretation, and all other models for division, are of quite limited application when we are restricted to zero and the natural numbers, since $\frac{a}{b}$ is defined only when b is not zero and a is zero or a multiple of b.

Division is the most difficult operation to master in elementary arithmetic and one reason for this lies in the necessity to be familiar with such a wide range of con-

ceptual models. Thus for logical arguments and proofs division should be considered as the inverse of multiplication, but for division computations, it is best to
think of repeated subtraction. However, for applications to the physical world the
ratio model will be found widely applicable, with partition, repeated subtraction,
and the inverse of multiplication likely to follow in this order of frequency.

Further complexity arises from the possibility of either explicit or implicit formulation of the problems, both in the verbal statement and the form of the equation.

(factor)(factor) = product		$\dfrac{\text{Dividend}}{\text{divisor}}$ = quotient	$\dfrac{D}{d} = q$
$f_1 \cdot f_2 \qquad = p$			
multiplication, explicit	$f_1 \cdot f_2 = x$	division, explicit	$\dfrac{D}{d} = x$
division, implicit	$x \cdot f_2 = p$	division, implicit	$\dfrac{D}{x} = q$
division, implicit	$f_1 \cdot x = p$	multiplication, implicit	$\dfrac{x}{d} = q$

Several of the diagrams and graphic models for multiplication have a less useful
counterpart for division, since for them it would be necessary to know the answer
before the diagram could be constructed. For example, if the area and width of a
rectangle are known, the length can be found by division but the area illustration
cannot be drawn until this number is known.

Problems (95)

1. Illustrate the quotient $\dfrac{x}{y}$ where $x = 12$ and $y = 4$ in the following ways:

    a. Partition of a set into subsets having an equal number of elements.
    (Two ways.)

    b. By matching two sequences. Label x, y, and $\dfrac{x}{y}$. (Two ways.)

    c. With two scales, one over the other. Label x, y, and $\dfrac{x}{y}$. (Two ways.)

    d. By the ratio of two lengths as measured by two different scales.

    e. With four line segments. Label x, y, and $\dfrac{x}{y}$. (Two ways.)

    f. With two similar triangles. Label x, y, and $\dfrac{x}{y}$. (Two ways.)

2. Follow the directions for problem 1 with $x = 10$, $y = 2$.

3. For each of the following construct mathematical models in the form of a single
conditional equation. Some should be explicit and some implicit. Make this
choice to agree with your decision as to whether the English form should be
termed explicit or implicit. Supply meaningful numbers for the blanks.

    a. What is the product of ( ) and [ ]?

b. By what number must ( ) be multiplied to give a product of [ ]?

c. What is the quotient, if ( ) is divided by [ ]?

d. What number, when divided by ( ), gives a quotient of [ ]?

e. If the product is ( ), and one of two factors is [ ], what is the other factor?

f. How many ( )'s in [ ]?

g. If the quotient is ( ), and the divisor is [ ], what is the dividend?

h. If the ratio of a larger number to a smaller number is ( ) to 1, and the smaller number is [ ], what is the larger number?

i. If the ratio of a larger number to a smaller number is ( ) to 1, and the larger number is [ ], what is the smaller number?

j. If ( ) is divided into [ ] equal shares, what will 1 share be?

k. What number can be divided into ( ) equal shares of [ ] each?

l. If a rectangle has an area of ( ) and a width of [ ], what is its length?

m. What number has the same ratio to 1, that ( ) has to [ ]?

n. What number has the same ratio to ( ) that [ ] has to 1?

4. These twelve conditional equations are based on multiplication and division and the numbers 2, 3, and 6. Twelve more would result from the symmetric property of equality.

a. $x \cdot 3 = 6$ **d.** $x \cdot 2 = 6$ **g.** $\frac{x}{2} = 3$ **j.** $\frac{x}{3} = 2$

b. $2 \cdot x = 6$ **e.** $3 \cdot x = 6$ **h.** $\frac{6}{x} = 3$ **k.** $\frac{6}{x} = 2$

c. $2 \cdot 3 = x$ **f.** $3 \cdot 2 = x$ **i.** $\frac{6}{2} = x$ **l.** $\frac{6}{3} = x$

A. Classify each as involving multiplication or division for its solution, and also whether it is explicit or implicit in form.

B. By the definition of division **a.** and **h.** are equivalent. Determine the remaining equivalent pairs resulting from this definition.

C. By the commutative property of multiplication, **a.** and **e.** are equivalent. Determine the other equivalent pairs of this type.

D. Because of **B.** and **C.** we find that **a.**, **e.**, **h.**, and **l.** are equivalent. Determine the other two groups of four equivalent equations.

9-4. Raising to a Power with the Natural Numbers and Zero

The operation of raising to a power was introduced in Section 4-1 as repeated multiplication by the same factor, by analogy to multiplication considered as repeated addition of the same addend. If n and m are not both zero, we have

$$n^m = 1 \cdot \underbrace{n \cdot n \cdots n}_{m \text{ factors}}$$

Hence, any model for multiplication that extends to m factors can be used to illustrate raising to a power. A tree diagram for n^m would have m branching stages, with each branch splitting into n branches at each stage.

The powers of any natural number could be computed by matching sequences in the manner shown below for powers of 2.

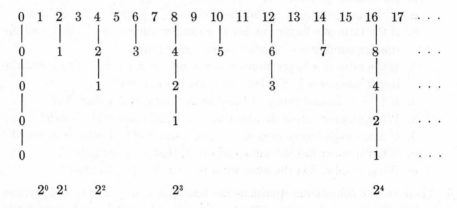

A diagram for n^m based on arrays of counters can be made as follows. Begin with one counter, which represents n^0 if $n \neq 0$. Then arrange n of these counters in some specific pattern. This group of n counters is then treated as a unit (corresponding to one counter in the first pattern) to form the pattern for n^2. This cycle is repeated m times, with the entire array at the kth stage becoming the unit for the $k + 1$st stage.

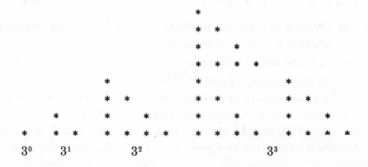

The expression n^2 is commonly read as "n squared," and n^3 as "n cubed" because of the association of these numbers with the area of a square and the volume of a cube. Since the space of our senses is three-dimensional, there are no corresponding names for n^4 and higher powers. Ancient mathematicians tended to rely so much on the length, area, volume analogy that they were handicapped in thinking of powers of a number if a factor was repeated more than three times. We have indicated on page 181 a systematic, but nonsymmetrical, way of extending the volume analogy to higher powers.

The powers of 2 are used below as an example of how n^m may be constructed geometrically. It is evident that such diagrams soon become too large to be practical because of the explosive growth of n^m for $n > 1$.

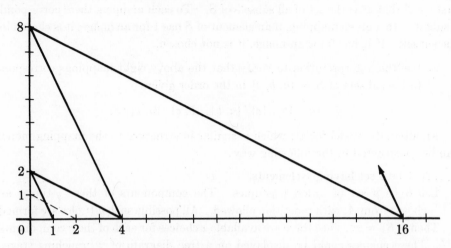

Raising to a power is considered to be a direct operation and it can be defined directly in terms of sets. The corresponding binary operation on sets is known as *exponentiation*.

Let S be a set with $n(S) = y$, and let T be a set with $n(T) = x$. Now consider all possible mappings of the set S into the set T, and represent the set of all such mappings by T^S. Each of these mappings is a set of ordered pairs (Section 8-7) of the form (s, t) *with* $s \in S$ and $t \in T$. T^S is a family (or set) of sets of ordered pairs. (This is to be distinguished from 2^S; T is a set, 2 is not.)

Example: Let $S = \{a, b, c\}$ and $T = \{0, 1\}$. There are $2^3 = 8$ possible mappings of S into T as shown.

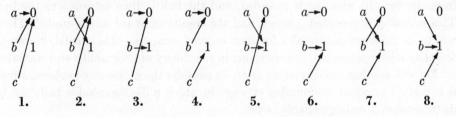

$$T^S = \{ \{(a, 0), (b, 0), (c, 0)\}, \{(a, 1), (b, 0), (c, 0)\},$$
$$(c, 0)\}, \{(a, 0), (b, 0), (c, 1)\}, \{(a, 1), (b, 1), (c, 0)\}, \{(a, 0),$$
$$(b, 1), (c, 1)\}, \{(a, 1), (b, 0), (c, 1)\}, \{(a, 1), (b, 1), (c, 1)\} \}$$

For each member of S there were $n(T)$ or $x = 2$ ways to choose its image in T. These choices were available for each of the $n(S)$ or $y = 3$ elements of S. Hence, there were $2 \cdot 2 \cdot 2$ or 2^3 possible mappings. In general there are $\underbrace{x \cdot x \cdots x}_{(y \text{ factors})}$ or x^y of such mappings.

If $n(S) = y$ and $n(T) = x$, then $n(T^S) = x^y$.

For any set S the power set 2^S furnishes an example of exponentiation where the elements of S are mapped into a two-element set such as $(0, 1)$. To verify this, first recall that 2^S is the set of all subsets of S. To each mapping there corresponds a subset. In a given mapping, if an element of S has 1 for an image, it is chosen for the subset. If it has 0 for an image, it is not chosen.

a. Use this interpretation to verify that the above eight mappings correspond to the subsets of $S = \{a, b, c\}$ in the order given:

$$\varnothing, \{a\}, \{b\}, \{c\}, \{a, b\}, \{b, c\}, \{a, c\}, S.$$

An alternate model for x^y, which is similar in structure to the mapping model, can be constructed in the following way:

Let A be a set having x elements.

Let B be a set of ordered y-tuples. The components of these y-tuples are chosen from A, with repetition allowed. All possible such y-tuples are formed. Then $n(B) = x^y$, since there are available x choices for each of the y components. These choices could be displayed on a tree diagram of y branching stages, with each limb branching x ways at each stage.

> **Example:** Let $A = \{r, s\}$, so that $n(A) = x = 2$. Let $y = 3$. Ordered triples are to be formed from the elements of A.
>
> $$B = \{(s, s, s), (r, s, s), (s, r, s), (s, s, r), (r, r, s), (s, r, r), (r, s, r), (r, r, r)\}$$
> $$n(B) = 2^3 = 8$$

b. Devise a way of setting up a 1:1 correspondence between the members of B and the members of T^S in the previous example.

Now let the members of A in the last example be x distinguishable balls in a box. In the example the balls could be labeled r and s. A ball is now drawn at random from the box, its identity is recorded, and the ball is then returned to the box. This sampling is repeated y times, and the results recorded as a y-tuple. There will be x^y different possibilities for such ordered samples. This model, known as *sampling with replacement*, is a basic one in the theory of probability and statistics.

For still another interpretation of x^y, we consider the occupancy problem, where it is desired to count the number of ways in which y distinguishable balls can be distributed in x distinguishable boxes.

> **Example:**
>
> Let $y = 3$ 3 balls, designated 1, 2, 3.
> Let $x = 2$ 2 boxes, designated first, second.

First: | 1 2 3 | | 2 3 | | 1 3 | | 1 2 | | 3 | | 2 | | 1 | | |

Second: | | | 1 | | 2 | | 3 | | 1 2 | | 1 3 | | 2 3 | | 1 2 3 |

   c. Devise a way of setting up a 1:1 correspondence between the different distributions of this occupancy problem, and the members of B in the sampling with replacement example above.

   d. Devise a way of setting up a 1:1 correspondence between the different distributions of the occupancy problem, and the subsets of $S = \{a, b, c\}$.

Operations that "undo" raising to a power and hence would be inverse to it are deferred to a later chapter. Since raising to a power is not commutative, there will be two such operations. Thus corresponding to $2^3 = 8$, three problems arise:

$$2^3 = x \qquad x^3 = 8 \qquad 2^x = 8$$
$$\text{explicit} \qquad \text{implicit} \qquad \text{implicit}$$

The first of the implicit forms leads to the extraction of roots, and the second to logarithms.

Answers to Exercises

b. Let the order of the components (first, second, third) of the members of B correspond to a, b, and c, respectively, as the choices for the first components of the ordered pairs in the members of T^S. Let a choice of s when constructing B, correspond to a choice of zero when constructing T^S; and similarly let r correspond to 1. **c.** Let balls 1, 2, 3 correspond to the components (first, second, third) of B, respectively. Let the second box correspond to r, and the first box to s. **d.** Let balls 1, 2, and 3 correspond to a, b, and c of S, respectively. Let the first box be the "reject" box, and let the second be the "accept" box.

Problems (96)

  1.   **a.** Give T^S when $S = \{a, b\}$, and $T = \{0, 1, 2\}$.

      b. Give the set B of all ordered pairs whose components are chosen, with repetition allowed, from $A = \{r, s, t\}$.

      c. Show all the possible distributions of two balls, labeled 1 and 2, into three boxes labeled first, second, and third.

  2. By inspecting the mapping diagrams for T^S in the text example, it can be seen why this set is sometimes called a covering set whereby the elements of T cover the elements of S by means of all the mappings from S to T. The notation S/T is sometimes used for this concept. Determine S/T when $S = \{0, 1, 2, 3\}$ and $T = \{x, y\}$.

  3. Indicate how the pattern ⋰ may be used to picture the powers of 4.

  4. A box contains ten balls numbered 0, 1, 2, . . . , 9. A ball is chosen at random, its number is recorded, and then the ball is replaced in the box. If this is repeated six times, how many possibilities are there for this ordered sample?

9-5. Review

Problems (97)

1. The numbers from 1 to 10 are listed in column A. In column B the same numbers are related to the powers of 3, not using more than one of any given power, but allowing both addition and subtraction. In column C is a place value notation for each number, with underlining indicating subtraction. Continue the notation as in C for the numbers from 11 to 20.

A	B	C
1	3^0	1
2	$3^1 - 3^0$	1 1̲
3	3^1	1 0
4	$3^1 + 3^0$	1 1
5	$3^2 - 3^1 - 3^0$	1 1̲ 1̲
6	$3^2 - 3^1$	1 1̲ 0
7	$3^2 - 3^1 + 3^0$	1 1̲ 1
8	$3^2 \quad - 3^0$	1 0 1̲
9	3^2	1 0 0
10	$3^2 \quad + 3^0$	1 0 1

2. Given below are the numbers 0 to 9 as they are written in a reflected binary notation. Such reflected numeral systems change only one digit in moving to the next number. Continue for the numbers 11 to 20.

   0, 1, 11, 10, 110, 111, 101, 100, 1100, 1101.   (Answer not unique.)

3. **a.** Find five primes of the form $N^2 + 1$, where N is a natural number.
   b. Find all primes, less than 100, of the form $N^2 - 1$.
   c. As a result of **b.**, make a conjecture and try to prove it.

4. Use a tree diagram to illustrate a systematic way of determining all of the divisors of $3^3 \cdot 5$.

5. Construct divisibility rules for the following divisors:
   a. 30   **b.** 40   **c.** 45   **d.** 72

6. Given A and B, determine Q and R so that $A = QB \pm R$. Q and R are to be zero or natural numbers. R may be added or subtracted, as indicated, but R must not be greater than half of B.
   a. $A = 45, B = 7$ **c.** $A = 911, B = 32$
   b. $A = 88, B = 9$ **d.** $A = 911, B = 28$

7. Let $X = \{2, 3, 4\}$ and $Y = \{4, 5, 6\}$. The following sets of ordered pairs are such that in (x, y), $x \in X$ and $y \in Y$.

   $L = (2, 6), (3, 6), (4, 6)$ $R = (4, 5), (2, 6), (3, 4)$
   $M = (2, 6), (3, 6)$ $S = (4, 4), (2, 6), (2, 5)$
   $N = (2, 6), (3, 4), (4, 4)$ $T = (3, 6), (4, 4), (2, 5)$
   $P = (4, 4), (4, 6), (2, 5)$ $U = (2, 5), (2, 4), (3, 6)$

   a. Which of these are mappings of X into Y?
   b. Which are mappings of X onto Y?

8. Given that
   $A = \{2, 4, 5, 9, 11, 12, 13, 15\}$ $C = \{2, 3, 6, 7, 9, 11, 12, 14\}$
   $B = \{1, 2, 5, 7, 10, 12, 14, 15\}$ $D = \{2, 3, 5, 9, 10, 13, 14, 16\}$

Display the members of these sets in the accompanying diagram.

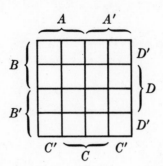

9. Given sets A, B, C, and D as in problem 8, display their members in the diagram below.

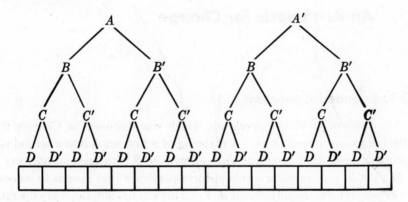

10. Compute $\displaystyle\sum_{k=2}^{k=4} t_k$ when:

    a. $t_k = (k+2)^{k-1}$ **c.** $t_1 = 2$, $t_k = kt_{k-1}$ for $k > 1$

    b. $t_k = k + (k-1)!$ **d.** $t_k = 3k - 2$ for $k = 1$, or $k = 2$,

                                   $t_k = 5$ for $k > 2$

For Further Study

Reference [C2] is a classic of mathematical exposition and is outstanding for the clarity of the explanations of fundamental concepts of mathematics and science. The author makes effective use of diagrams. For a contemporary book, written to help people "see" mathematics, read [S4].

For further reading on the fundamental operations with the natural numbers, as developed from the theory of sets, see [C4], pp. 56–117; and [O1], pp. 72–111.

10

An Arithmetic for Change

10-1. Extended Operations

The concept of binary operation, which was discussed in Chapter 9, can be extended to *n-ary* operations. A mapping of a first set S into a second set T was defined as a rule that associates each element of S with one and only one element of T. Let us now consider a rule of correspondence that assigns to *ordered subsets of n elements* of S a unique element of T. This will be called an n-ary operation from the set S into the set T. If this correspondence applies to every possible ordered subset of n elements in S, the operation is said to be *complete*, or *performable* on S. If the operation is complete and $T = S$, then the operation is closed on S. Since both the domain of definition and the range of images are now in S, we say we have an n-ary operation in S. According to whether $n = 1, 2, 3, \ldots, n$ the operation is said to be unary, binary, ternary, $\ldots$, n-ary.

Given 2^X, the set of all subsets of some set X, then a Cartesian product can be formed, corresponding to any ordered n-tuple (n greater than 1) of the members of 2^X (see p. 154). This n-ary operation is complete but not closed on 2^X, since the Cartesian product sets thus determined are not members of 2^X.

If our universe is the set of natural numbers and n is greater than 1, then to any set of n of these numbers we can always assign a unique natural number called their greatest common divisor (Section 5-3). The operation of least common multiple is, for n greater than 1, another n-ary operation that is closed over the natural numbers. Union and intersection were introduced as binary operations on sets, but as noted in Section 8-4, they can be readily extended to n-ary operations. Problems (83)3 and (84)4 were verifications that union and intersection were closed operations over a power set 2^S. For the g.c.d., the l.c.m., union, and intersection, the order of the elements in the n-tuple of elements of S is not significant, but it is significant for the Cartesian product, since this operation is not commutative.

Let S be the set consisting of zero and the natural numbers. The factorial operation assigns a unique natural number $n!$ to each member n of the set. Hence, this is a unary operation, which is closed in the set S. Squaring is another example of such closed unary operation in the set S. We have previously noted that $n \rightarrow n!$ and $n \rightarrow n^2$ are mappings of S into (but not onto) itself. A mapping of any set into the same set is the same as a closed unary operation in the set.

    a. What is the meaning of completeness for a unary operation?
    b. What is the meaning of closure for a unary operation?
    c. For a set X, let set B be a member of 2^X. Give an example of a closed unary operation on B that has been defined in the set 2^X.
    d. If the operation in **c.** is considered as a mapping, is this mapping onto?

Answers to Exercises

a. It is required that every element in S have an image.   **b.** Closure is required so that the mapping will be back into the same set.   **c.** B' is the complement. Complementation is a unary operation.   **d.** Yes, it is onto.

Problems (98)

1. Assume that $S = \{0, 1, 2, 3\}$. Since $n(S) = 4$, there are 4^2 or 16 ordered pairs of the form (x, y) with $x \in S$ and $y \in S$.
    a. For how many of these ordered pairs is $x + y$ zero or a natural number?
    b. For $x - y$?
    c. For xy?
    d. For $\dfrac{x}{y}$?
    e. For x^y?

2. Determine $A \otimes B \otimes C$ where $A = B = C = \{1, 2\}$.

3. Assume that $S = \{8, 12, 15, 16\}$. Give the g.c.d. and the l.c.m. for each triple that can be formed from the members of S. Write these in decimal numeral form.

4.   **a.** What is the g.c.d. of 20, 25, 30, 35, and 40?
    b. What is the l.c.m. of 20, 25, 30, 35, and 40?

5. Let $A = \{p, q\}$. Then if $S \in 2^A$, $S \rightarrow A - S$ is a mapping, or unary operation in 2^A. Give the family (or set) of ordered pairs of sets that are thus determined.

6. Let $A = \{p, q\}$. Then if $R \in 2^A$, $S \in 2^A$, and $T \in 2^A$, the correspondence $(R, S, T) \rightarrow R \cup S \cup T$, and $(R, S, T) \rightarrow R \cap S \cap T$ are ternary operations in 2^A.
    a. Give for each operation the ordered pair of sets thus determined when $R = \{p\}$, $S = \{q\}$, and $T = \{p, q\}$.
    b. Same as **a.** for $(R, S, T) \rightarrow (R \cup S) \cap T$, and $(R, S, T) \rightarrow R \cup (S \cap T)$.

7. Compute: **a.** 3^2 **b.** 3!   **c.** $(3!)^2$ **d.** $(3^2)!$
8. Compute: **a.** $2 \cdot 4$ **b.** 4!   **c.** 2(4!)   **d.** $(2 \cdot 4)!$

10-2. Unary Operations and Operators

In Chapter 9 all of the models discussed were based on multitude or magnitude. Both of these representations of number might be said to be static in the sense that a number is assigned to a fixed quantity or amount. Now, as suggested by the chapter title, we shall develop an arithmetical system for the study of change. Discussion will be given of ways to give a quantitative description of such dynamic concepts as increase, decrease, stretching, shrinking, and so on.

For this purpose we shall make a modification of the notation for binary operations in such a way that there is a set of unary operations corresponding to each binary operation.

The product of 3 and 5 may be written as $3 \cdot 5$. From the point of view of a binary operation we may fix our attention on:

$\boxed{3} \cdot 5$, where the first number, 3, is represented by the numeral 3, or on

$3 \cdot \boxed{5}$, where the second number, 5, is represented by the numeral 5, or on

$\boxed{3 \cdot 5}$, where the third number, 15, is represented by the composite numeral $3 \cdot 5$.

The dot symbol, which is sandwiched between the numerals 3 and 5, is an operation symbol that designates the binary operation of multiplication.

The product $3 \cdot 5$ can be analyzed in a different manner. This time we fix our attention on:

$\boxed{3 \cdot} 5$, where the composite symbol, $3 \cdot$, is called a *multiplication operator*, or on

$3 \cdot \boxed{5}$, where the first number, 5, or the *operand*, is represented by the numeral 5, or on

$\boxed{3 \cdot 5}$, where the second number, 15, or the *transform*, is represented by the composite numeral $3 \cdot 5$.

This is an instance of the unary operation of "multiplying by three" with a correspondence between a first number 5, and a second number $3 \cdot 5$, which is specified by the operator $3 \cdot$. This operator does not represent a number, but is a symbol which, if joined to a symbol or symbols representing a first number, yields a second number. It has a similar usage for variables whose domains of definition are numbers. Thus, if n is zero or a natural number, the prefixing of $3 \cdot$ to n gives $3 \cdot n$, which is the image of n under the mapping (or unary operation) $n \rightarrow 3 \cdot n$. The dot between the symbols 3 and n can be omitted by convention.

The symbol ! is called the factorial operator since it transforms the first number n into the second number $n!$.   This factorial operator is an example of a *right-operator*, or a *post-operator*, since it is placed to the right or after the operand.   The multiplication operator $3 \cdot$ is a *left-operator*, or a *pre-operator* and is written to the left of or before its operand.   We can also break $3 \cdot 5$ up into 3 and $\cdot 5$, thus considering $3 \cdot 5$ to be the transform that results from placing the operator $\cdot 5$ after the operand 3.

Further alternate notations for multiplication operators are:

1. The transform $(3)(5)$ results from joining the operator $(3)(\ )$ to the operand 5.
2. The transform $(3)(5)$ results from joining the operator $(\ )(5)$ to the operand 3.
3. The transform $3(5)$ results from joining the operator $3(\ )$ to the operand 5.
4. The transform $(3)5$ results from joining the operator $(\ )5$ to the operand 3.
5. The transform 3×5 results from joining the operator $3 \times$ to the operand 5.
6. The transform 3×5 results from joining the operator $\times 5$ to the operand 3.

If n is zero or a natural number, then $3 \cdot$ is a member of the set of multiplication operators, $\{0 \cdot, 1 \cdot, 2 \cdot, 3 \cdot, \cdots\}$ which result from substitutions for n in $n \cdot$.   Since the binary operation of multiplication is closed over zero and the natural numbers, each operator of this set can be joined to zero or any natural number as an operand. Hence, each of the following is defined if the replacements for m and n come from the set of the natural numbers and zero.

Operator	Operand	Transform	Operator	Operand	Transform
$n \cdot$	m	$n \cdot m$	$n(\ )$	m	$n(m)$
$\cdot n$	m	$m \cdot n$	$(\ )n$	m	$(m)n$
$n \times$	m	$n \times m$	$(n)(\ )$	m	$(n)(m)$
$\times n$	m	$m \times n$	$(\ )(n)$	m	$(m)(n)$

The choice of notation for multiplication operators is dependent on knowledge of the form of the operand, since parentheses may or may not be needed to extend the reach of the operator over the operand.   Such multiplication operators give a description of a change, both in kind and amount, which might be termed a stretch, a magnification, or a dilation.   However, we specifically avoid the word "increase," since we want to reserve this term for addition operators.

a. What does $6\times$ signify as a specification for binoculars?

In $15 \div 3$ and $\frac{15}{3}$, the symbols $\div$ and — may be considered as symbols for the binary operation of division, but these quotients can also be analyzed from the unary operation point of view.   The transform $15 \div 3$ results from joining the operator $\div 3$ to the operand 15.   The transform $\frac{15}{3}$ results from joining the operator $\frac{}{3}$ to the operand 15.

The notation of $\dfrac{}{n}$ for a division operator has the advantage of built-in parentheses, whereas $\div\, n$ would have to be replaced by $(\ \ )\div n$ if the operand were a sum or a difference. Clearly zero cannot be chosen for n in $\dfrac{}{n}$ or $\div\, n$, and $\dfrac{}{n}$ and $\div\, n$ can at present be joined to an operand m only when m is zero or a multiple of n, which is a severe limitation. Such an m is said to be a proper operand for $\dfrac{}{n}$.

"Contraction" and "shrinking" are words that are suggestive of the changes we associate with division operators. The word "decrease" is reserved for subtraction operators. The words "dilation" or "dilitation" may be used with both multiplication and division operators.

Answer to Exercise

a. The diameter of the image will be magnified six times.

Problems (99)

In problems 1 and 2, first obtain the transform that results from joining the multiplication operator 5( ) to the given operand. Then compute the decimal numeral.

1. a. 9 **b.** 0 **c.** $2+8$ **d.** $11-4$ **e.** $3\cdot7$ **f.** $\dfrac{12}{3}$ **g.** 5^3 **h.** $\dfrac{18}{4+5}$

2. a. 1 **b.** 3! **c.** $12\div3$ **d.** $4+3^2$ **e.** $2^2\cdot5$ **f.** $5(2+3)$ **g.** $7-7$

In problems 3 and 4, first obtain the transform that results from joining the division operator $\dfrac{}{5}$ to the given operand. If this is undefined, write "undefined." Otherwise compute the decimal numeral.

3. a. 15 **b.** 0 **c.** 8 **d.** $12+3$ **e.** $28-3$ **f.** 5^4 **g.** $7\cdot15$ **h.** $\dfrac{20}{4}$

4. a. 5 **b.** 5! **c.** 2^4 **d.** 3^2+4^2 **e.** 13^2-12^2 **f.** $\sum_{k=1}^{k=4} k$ **g.** $21-3\cdot7$

Thus far a sum, such as $3+5$, has been considered only as resulting from a binary operation. The plus sign is a symbol for this operation whereby a first number, 2, and a second number, 5, are set in correspondence with a third number, $3+5$. As a unary operation we have:

The transform or second number, $3+5$, results when the operator, $+5$, is joined to the operand or first number, 3. The transform, $3+5$, also is the result of joining the operator $3+$, to the operand, 5.

The right-operator notation of $+ n$ will be used more frequently than the left-operator notation of $m +$, although either convention is feasible. Addition operators provide a quantitative description of an increase, and like other operators, carry two kinds of information; they specify both the kind and amount of a certain change.

Only the right-operator notation of $- n$ is available for subtraction operators. Addition operators, like those for multiplication, do not lead to undefined expressions. But m is a proper operand to which the subtraction operator $- n$ can be joined to form the transform $m - n$ only if m is greater than or equal to n, as long as we are restricted to the natural numbers and zero. Because of the conventions about order of (binary) operations, addition and subtraction operators are the only types of operators that do not require the supplemental use of parentheses for some operands.

The operator $- 3$ may be read "minus 3." However, it should be emphasized that $+ n$ and $- n$ are *not* being used as symbols for signed numbers, and $- 3$ should not be read as "negative 3." For those familiar with signed numbers, striking analogies will appear as the discussion of addition and subtraction operators continues.

Some arithmetical expressions, but not all, can be thought of as the result of joining two or more operators in succession to a given operand. Thus we obtain $2\dfrac{(6 + 4)}{5}$ by starting with 6, and using in turn the operators $+ 4$, $\dfrac{}{5}$, and $2(\ )$.

Problems (100)

In problems 1 and 2, an operand is given, followed by one or more operators, which are to be joined in succession to the operand. If needed, supply parentheses with the operators. If any resulting transform is not defined, write "undefined." Otherwise compute the decimal numeral, but only after the final operator is in place.

1. a. $8; + 3$ **g.** $11; - 3$ **m.** $7; + 3, \dfrac{}{5}, - 1$ **s.** $18; - 5, \dfrac{}{3}$

   b. $0; + 3$ **h.** $2; - 3$ **n.** $6; 4 \cdot, + 3, \dfrac{}{3}$ **t.** $18; \dfrac{}{3}, - 5$

   c. $11 + 4; + 3$ **i.** $14 + 2; - 3$ **o.** $20; \dfrac{}{4}, - 2, 3(\ )$ **u.** $18; + 2, \dfrac{}{5}$

   d. $11 - 4; + 3$ **j.** $10 - 1; - 3$ **p.** $17; - 2, 4 \cdot, + 5$ **v.** $18; \dfrac{}{5}, + 2$

   e. $7 \cdot 11; + 3$ **k.** $5^0; - 3$ **q.** $5; 6 \cdot, \dfrac{}{3}, 7(\ )$ **w.** $3; + 2, - 4$

   f. $\dfrac{16}{2}; + 3$ **l.** $13 + 3; - 3$ **r.** $60; \dfrac{}{2}, \dfrac{}{3}$ **x.** $3; - 4, + 2$

2. a. $20 + 4; +4$ **g.** $8 - 4; -4$ **m.** $5; -2, 4 \cdot, \dfrac{}{6}$ **s.** $8; 3 \cdot, \dfrac{}{6}$

b. $20 - 4; +4$ **h.** $4 \cdot 4; -4$ **n.** $7; +2, \dfrac{}{3}, 5 \cdot$ **t.** $3; \dfrac{}{6}, 3 \cdot$

c. $20 \cdot 4; +4$ **i.** $\dfrac{4}{4}; -4$ **o.** $5; -2, 2 \cdot, +2$ **u.** $9; +3, 2 \cdot$

d. $\dfrac{20}{4}; +4$ **j.** $4!; -4$ **p.** $3; 2 \cdot, 5 \cdot, \dfrac{}{30}$ **v.** $9; 2 \cdot, +3$

e. $2^4; +4$ **k.** $4^2; -4$ **q.** $6; +3, +2, -10$ **w.** $15; +5, \dfrac{}{5}$

f. $4 - 4; +4$ **l.** $4 - 1; -4$ **r.** $6; +3, -10, +2$ **x.** $15; \dfrac{}{5}, +5$

For problems 3 and 4, state an operand and a sequence of operators, which, if applied in that order, will produce the given expression as a transform. Write "not possible" if this is the case for the operators we have introduced.

3. a. $\dfrac{19 - 4}{3} + 3$ **c.** $\dfrac{5 \cdot 8 + 2}{6}$ **e.** $8 \left(\dfrac{\frac{30}{2}}{5} \right)$ **f.** $\dfrac{22}{7 + 4}$

   b. $\dfrac{4 + 12 - 4}{6}$ **d.** $(5 + 2)(3 + 4)$

4. a. $2 \left(\dfrac{15}{3} - 2 \right)$ **c.** $\dfrac{5(15 - 3)}{4}$ **e.** $\dfrac{\frac{19 + 5}{2}}{3}$ **f.** $3 \cdot 4 + 2 \cdot 5$

   b. $10 - (4 + 2)$ **d.** $\dfrac{19 + 4 - 3}{5}$

10-3. Identity and Inverse Operators

We have observed in earlier chapters that for any number A,

$$A + 0 = A = 0 + A \qquad 1 \cdot A = A = A \cdot 1 \qquad A - 0 = A \qquad \text{and} \; \frac{A}{1} = A$$

The operators $+0$, $0+$, $1 \cdot$, $\cdot 1$, -0, and $\dfrac{}{1}$ produce no change so that the transform remains the same as the operand. These operators are called *identity* operators. Since change can be comprehended only by comparison with no change, such operators are of central importance. The unary operations of adding zero, subtracting zero, multiplying by 1, and dividing by 1 are all equivalent to the identity mapping. This is indicated simply as $n \rightarrow n$, rather than by $n \rightarrow n + 0$, $n \rightarrow 1 \cdot n$, and so on.

In Section 3-7, addition and subtraction were designated as inverse (binary) operations and $7 + 4 - 4 = 7$ was used as an explanatory example. This was done to conform to almost universal usage, but it is inaccurate and we can now give a more precise statement. Unary operations, rather than binary operations, are strictly inverse to each other.

From the binary operation aspect, 7 and 4 have symmetrical roles in the sum $7 + 4$. But in $7 + 4 - 4$, the 7 is involved only incidentally, with the "opposite-ness" being exhibited entirely by $+ 4$ and $- 4$. These two operators are inverses, being such that each will undo or counteract the change produced by the other, if they are applied in immediate succession to a proper operand. The stipulation about a proper operand should be noted. Thus $3 + 4 - 4 = 3$, and $\dfrac{4 \cdot 3}{4} = 3$, but $3 - 4 + 4$ and $4\left(\dfrac{3}{4}\right)$ are, at present, undefined.

> **Definition:** *Two operators are said to be inverse to each other if, when joined to a proper operand in succession, in either order, the result is to leave the operand unchanged. It also might be stated that two operators are inverse if applying them in succession is equivalent to the use of an identity operator.*

Examples:

$$\frac{3 \cdot 12}{3} = 12 \qquad\qquad 3\left(\frac{12}{3}\right) = 12 \qquad\qquad 1 \cdot 12 = 12$$

$$12 + 3 - 3 = 12 \qquad 12 - 3 + 3 = 12 \qquad 12 + 0 = 12$$

A set of unary operations can be derived from the binary operation of raising to a power by introducing a set of exponential operators, $\{(\ )^0, (\ )^1, \ldots\}$. Thus 2^3 may be considered as the transform that results from joining the operator $(\ )^3$ to the operand 2, and then omitting the parentheses, which are not needed in this instance. The identity for exponential operators is $(\ )^1$, and $(\ )^0$ has the striking property that all operands (except zero) are reduced to 1. However, the use of exponential operators is still limited in scope by the absence, thus far, of pairs of such operators that are inverse to each other. These will be introduced in a later chapter. For the present we can consider $(\ )^3$ as a command to cube the operand, or as a description of such a change, but we now have no command available to undo or offset this change.

Problems (101)

1. Give two single operators, each of which will produce the same change on a proper operand, as would result from the given pair of operators applied in succession.

   a. $7(\ ), \dfrac{\ }{7}$ **b.** $- 11, + 11$ **c.** $\dfrac{\ }{13}, 13(\ )$ **d.** $+ 6, - 6$

2. Follow the directions for 1.

   a. $+ 8, - 8$ **b.** $15(\ ), \dfrac{\ }{15}$ **c.** $- 9, + 9$ **d.** $\dfrac{\ }{10}, 10(\ )$

For problems 3 and 4, state an operand and a sequence of operators, which if applied in that order, will produce the given expression as a transform. Write "not possible" if this is the case for the operators we have introduced.

3. a. $\dfrac{7^2 - 4}{9}$ b. $\dfrac{(4+2)^3}{12}$ c. $\left(\dfrac{10}{2} - 2\right)^2$ d. $\dfrac{10}{2} - 2^2$ e. $\left(\dfrac{6^2}{9}\right)^3$

4. a. $\dfrac{(12-4)^2}{16}$ b. $2(5^2 + 9)$ c. $2 \cdot 5^2 + 9$ d. $2 \cdot 5 + 9^2$ e. $\dfrac{9 \cdot 10^2}{6}$

10-4. Composition of Mappings, Unary Operations, and Operators

At times it is convenient to have a brief, temporary name for mappings. By the notation $f: n \to n + 2$ we shall understand that for a given discussion the mapping rule $n \to n + 2$ has been given the name f. Similarly in $g: n \to n^3$ the name g has been assigned to $n \to n^3$. Now assume that f has the domain $\{0, 1, 2\}$ and g has the domain $\{2, 3, 4\}$. Next let h be the mapping given by $h: n \to (n + 2)^3$, with domain $\{0, 1, 2\}$.

f		g		h		f	g	$h = f \circ g$
n	$n+2$	n	n^3	n	$(n+2)^3$	$n \to n+2 \longrightarrow (n+2)^3$		$n \to (n+2)^3$
0	2	2	8	0	8	$0 \longrightarrow 2 \longrightarrow 8$		$0 \longrightarrow 8$
1	3	3	27	1	27	$1 \longrightarrow 3 \longrightarrow 27$		$1 \longrightarrow 27$
2	4	4	64	2	64	$2 \longrightarrow 4 \longrightarrow 64$		$2 \longrightarrow 64$

The mapping f maps 0 to 2, and g maps 2 to 8. The mapping h maps 0 to 8, directly. That is, h sets up a correspondence between 0 and 8, which was established in two stages by f followed by g.

Again, under f, 1 has the image 3; and in turn 3 has the image 27 under g. Under h, 1 has the image 27. Finally, under f, 2 maps to 4; and under g, 4 maps to 64. Under h, 2 maps to 64. Hence, we have verified that with the domains as given, the mapping h produces the same correspondences as given by mapping f followed by mapping g. To express this we write $f \circ g = h$ and say that the mapping h is the composite of f and g (in this order). The symbol for composition of mappings will be a small raised circle written between the names for the first and the second mappings.

Let us now look at $g \circ f$, which represents the composite of g and f. It will be necessary to modify the domains so that the range of images of the first mapping is the domain of definition of the second mapping.

g		f		k		g	f	$k = g \circ f$
n	n^3	n	$n+2$	n	n^3+2	$n \to n^3 \longrightarrow n^3+2$		$n \to n^3+2$
0	0	0	2	0	2	$0 \to 0 \longrightarrow 2$		$0 \longrightarrow 2$
1	1	1	3	1	3	$1 \to 1 \longrightarrow 3$		$1 \longrightarrow 3$
2	8	8	10	2	10	$2 \to 8 \longrightarrow 10$		$2 \longrightarrow 10$

The examples above show that the composition of two mappings may not be commutative, since $f \circ g$ makes 0, 1, 2 correspond to 8, 27, 64, respectively, while $g \circ f$ maps 0, 1, 2 to 2, 3, 10, respectively.   As a third example we shall choose two mappings for the composition that are more alike in kind.

$$\text{Assume } f\colon n \to 2n, \text{ with domain } \{0, 1, 2\}$$
$$g\colon n \to 3n, \text{ with domain } \{0, 2, 4\}$$
$$h\colon n \to 6n, \text{ with domain } \{0, 1, 2\}$$

f		g		h		$f \qquad g$	$h = f \circ g$
n	$2n$	n	$3n$	n	$6n$	$n \to 2n \to 6n$	$n \to 6n$
0	0	0	0	0	0	$0 \to 0 \to 0$	$0 \to 0$
1	2	2	6	1	6	$1 \to 2 \to 6$	$1 \to 6$
2	4	4	12	2	12	$2 \to 4 \to 12$	$2 \to 12$

The above results can be considered as offering some verification that the changes resulting from multiplying by 2, followed by multiplying by 3, produce the same resultant overall change as multiplying by 6.   The fact that an identity operator may substitute for the successive use of two inverse operators has already suggested some possibilities for combining two operators to produce a third.   This would be a binary operation on operators (or on the unary operations they designate).   It is desired that the third operator always be equivalent to (produce the same change as) the first two used in succession, on all proper operands.

We first observe that some pairs of operators are not adaptable to such combination.   In $3(5) - 6 = 9$, the operators $3(\;)$ and $- 6$ have been joined in succession to the operand, to produce 9.

The single operator $+ 4$ would also have transformed 5 into 9.   But multiplication by 3, followed by subtraction of 6, does not produce an increase of 4 for all operands.   For example, $3(4) - 6 = 6$, but $4 + 4 \neq 6$.   One could design an operator $3(\;) - 6$ to call for successive use of $3(\;)$ and $- 6$, but there is no single addition, subtraction, multiplication, or division operator that will produce the same change as this operator, for all operands.

The multiplication operator $3(\;)$ and the subtraction operator $- 6$ are not compatible in another respect also, since two different transforms are obtained when they are used in succession but in different order.

$$\text{For } 12; \; 3(\;), \; - 6, \qquad 3(12) - 6 = 30$$
$$\text{For } 12; \; - 6, \; 3(\;), \qquad 3(12 - 6) = 18$$

Multiplication by 3, followed by subtraction of 6, does not, in general, produce the same change as subtraction of 6, followed by multiplication by 3.

We shall limit our study to the composition of operators $0_1 \circ 0_2$ to the cases where both 0_1 and 0_2 are addition or subtraction operators, or both are multiplication or division operators, or both are exponential operators.   Within these three categories it is possible to introduce a binary operation called *composition of opera-*

tors, whereby given two operators of the same category we can determine a third operator that produces the same effect as the first two used in succession. The circle notation will be used, just as for the composition of mappings.

Examples:

$$10 + 3 + 5 = 18$$
$$10 + 5 + 3 = 18$$
$$10 + 8 = 18$$

Adding 3 and then adding 5 produces the same result as adding 5 and then adding 3. In both instances this is equivalent to adding 8. An increase of 8 is equivalent to successive increases of 3 and 5, in either order. The operators $+3$ and $+5$ can be *commuted*.

$$(+3) \circ (+5) = (+5) \circ (+3) = +8$$

$$10 + 2 + 3 + 4 = 19$$
$$10 + 2 + 7 = 19$$
$$10 + 9 = 19$$
$$10 + 5 + 4 = 19$$
$$10 + 9 = 19$$

The composition of the operators $+3$ and $+4$ gives $+7$, and the composition of $+2$ and $+7$ gives $+9$. One also obtains $+9$ by first combining $+2$ and $+3$ to get $+5$, and then combining with $+4$. The composition of the operators $+2$, $+3$, and $+4$ is associative.

$$(+2) \circ [(+3) \circ (+4)]$$
$$= [(+2) \circ (+3)] \circ (+4) = +9$$

$$\frac{8(10)}{2} = 40$$
$$8\left(\frac{10}{2}\right) = 40$$
$$4(10) = 40$$

Multiplication by 8, followed by division by 2, gives the same transformation as division by 2, followed by multiplication by 8. In both cases this is equivalent to multiplication by 4. A magnification of 8 times can be commuted with a contraction by 2, or to 1/2 of, and the resultant change is a magnification of 4 times.

$$[8(\ )] \circ \left(\frac{\ }{2}\right) = \left(\frac{\ }{2}\right) \circ [8(\ )] = 4(\ )$$

$$[(2)^3]^4 = 4{,}096$$
$$[(2)^4]^3 = 4{,}096$$
$$2^{12} = 4{,}096$$

Raising to the third power followed by raising to the fourth power is equivalent to raising to the twelfth power. The composition of the exponential operators $(\ )^3$ and $(\ )^4$ gives $(\ )^{12}$ and this composition is commutative.

$$[(\ )^3] \circ [(\ )^4] = [(\ )^4] \circ [(\ )^3] = (\ )^{12}$$

At this time the following restrictions are observed for the composition of operators:

A. For the composite $0_1 \circ 0_2$, both 0_1 and 0_2 must be selected from one of these categories:

1. Addition and subtraction operators.
2. Multiplication and division operators.
3. Exponential operators.

B. The variables used will represent only zero and the natural numbers.   There must be further restriction to avoid zero divisors, and also upon the operands to avoid differences $a - b$ where b is greater than a, and quotients $\dfrac{a}{b}$ where a is not zero or a multiple of b.

C. The exercises in the various problem sets will verify the following composition rules.

1. $(+ a) \circ (+ b) = + (a + b)$
2. $(- a) \circ (- b) = - (a + b)$
3. $(+ a) \circ (- b) = + 0$, if $a = b$
4. $(+ a) \circ (- b) = + (a - b)$, if $a > b$.
5. $(+ a) \circ (- b) = - (b - a)$, if $a < b$.
6. $[a(\;)] \circ [b(\;)] = ab(\;)$
7. $\left(\dfrac{}{a}\right) \circ \left(\dfrac{}{b}\right) = \dfrac{}{ab}$, for $a \neq 0, b \neq 0$
8. $[a(\;)] \circ \left(\dfrac{}{b}\right) = \dfrac{a}{b}(\;)$, for $b \neq 0$, and $a = 0$ or a a multiple of b.
9. $[(\;)^a] \circ [(\;)^b] = (\;)^{ab}$

It is possible to show the logical connections between these assumptions and the corresponding ones for the binary operations.   This can be done much more effectively after the number system has been extended to remove such restrictions as those above on differences and quotients.   Our immediate goal is to get as much intuitive support as possible for the reasonableness of these assumptions.   The following exercise will help in this regard.

a. Translate composition rules **1.** to **9.** into words.   Use "increase" for addition operators, "decrease" for subtraction operators.   Use such words as "magnification" and "contraction," or "stretching" and "shrinking" for multiplication and division operators.   Translate the composition symbol as "followed by," and equality by "produces the same change as."   Think of the numerical values to be substituted for a and b as magnitudes.

Commutativity and associativity are very desirable in mathematical systems. Within the categories given above, the composition $0_1 \circ 0_2$ is always commutative. For operators of every type (and all mappings), composition is associative, $0_1 \circ (0_2 \circ 0_3) = (0_1 \circ 0_2) \circ 0_3$.   Hence, we find that unary operations have greater freedom in certain of these respects than do binary operations, and this is a principal reason for their use.

The expression $3 + 5$ can be considered from either the unary or the binary operation point of view; all depends on the way we analyze it. In the diagram below lines are drawn to break $3 + 5$ into three parts; the two addends, 3 and 5, and the sign of a binary operation, $+$, between them.

$$3 \mid + \mid 5 \qquad 5 \mid + \mid 3$$

Since this binary operation is commutative, it is possible to interchange the position of the addends as in the second diagram, while leaving the plus sign where it was.

In the next diagram, lines are drawn to break $3 + 5$ into two parts; the operand 3, and the operator $+ 5$.

$$3 \mid + 5 \qquad + 5 \mid 3$$

These two parts cannot be interchanged in position, as the second diagram shows. This example further emphasizes that the operand and operator are not joined by a sign of operation, but rather by being next to each other; and that the order of this placement cannot be changed without destroying the meaning.

However, as has been verified in previous examples, two operators may commute with each other.

$$+ 3 \mid + 5 \qquad + 5 \mid + 3 \qquad n + 3 + 5 = n + 5 + 3, \text{ for all } n$$

Now consider the difference $5 - 3$. The binary operation of subtraction is not commutative; $5 - 3$ does not equal $3 - 5$. But it is important to observe that for proper operands, the operators $+ 5$ and $- 3$ can be commuted.

$$+ 5 \mid - 3 \qquad - 3 \mid + 5 \qquad n + 5 - 3 = n - 3 + 5,$$
$$\text{for all } n \text{ greater than or equal to 3}$$

The freedom in the use of the associative principle is also an asset for the composition of operators. The binary operation of subtraction is not associative since, for example, this would require that $10 - (7 - 2) = (10 - 7) - 2$. But this is false since $5 \neq 1$. Nevertheless the three operators in $+ 10 - 7 - 2$ do obey the associative principle.

$$+ 10 - 7 - 2, + 3 - 1, \text{ and } + 10 - 9, \text{ are all equivalent for proper operands}$$

We have defined $0_1 \circ 0_2$ to mean 0_1 followed by 0_2 because our operators are mainly of the right-operator type. In other branches of mathematics $0_1 \circ 0_2$ may be defined to mean 0_2 followed by 0_1, particularly where left-operators are predominant. We shall actually use the composition symbol very little. In practice one simply recognizes when the composition is possible, and the two operators are replaced by the composite (in simpler form) when this is desirable. Our purpose has been to focus attention on certain manipulations of symbols that have gone on for centuries but without comment in the literature of arithmetic.

Answers to Exercises

a. 1. An increase of a, followed by an increase of b, gives the same change as an increase whose magnitude is the sum of a and b.   **2.** A decrease of a, followed by a decrease of b, gives the same change as a decrease whose magnitude is the sum of a and b.   **3.** An increase of a, followed by a decrease of the same magnitude, produces no change.   **4.** and **5.** An increase of a, followed by a decrease of b, produces an increase if a is greater than b, and a decrease if a is less than b.   In both cases the magnitude of the change is given by the difference in the magnitudes of the increase and the decrease.   **6.** A magnification by a, followed by a magnification of b, gives the same change as the magnification ab.   **7.** A contraction by a, followed by a contraction by b, gives the same change as the contraction by ab.   **8.** A magnification by a, followed by a contraction by b gives the same change as a magnification by $\frac{a}{b}$, when $\frac{a}{b}$ is zero or a natural number.   **9.** Raising to the power a, followed by raising to the power of b, gives the same change as raising to the power ab.

Problems (102)

In problems 1 to 12, determine a single operator that is equivalent to the two or more given, assuming that they are joined in succession to a proper operand.

1. $+\,12,\,-\,7$

4. $6(\ ),\ \dfrac{\ }{2}$

7. $\dfrac{\ }{3},\ \dfrac{\ }{11}$

10. $\dfrac{\ }{2},\ 24(\ ),\ \dfrac{\ }{3}$

2. $-\,9,\,+\,3$

5. $\dfrac{\ }{3},\ 15(\ )$

8. $+\,6,\,+\,14,\,-\,10$

11. $(\ )^2,\ (\ )^5$

3. $5(\ ),\ 7(\ )$

6. $-\,4,\,-\,10$

9. $4(\ ),\ \dfrac{\ }{8},\ 2(\ )$

12. $1(\ ),\ \dfrac{\ }{1}$

In problems 13 to 18, give the composite operator in simple form.

13. $(10\,\cdot)\circ\left(\dfrac{\ }{5}\right)$

15. $(-\,2)\circ(-\,3)\circ(-\,4)$

17. $[(\ )^3]\circ[(\ )^3]$

14. $(7\,+)\circ(3\,+)$

16. $[2(\ )]\circ[3(\ )]\circ[5(\ )]$

18. $[(\ )^0]\circ[(\ )^2]$

In problems 19 to 32, replace with a single equivalent operator.

19. $-\,4+9-3$

23. $\dfrac{5(\ )}{15}$

27. $[3(\ )](2)$

20. $4[5(\ )]$

24. $10\left(\dfrac{\ }{5}\right)$

28. $\dfrac{(\ )12}{2}$

31. $\dfrac{\frac{(\ )}{2}}{4}$

21. $\dfrac{12(\ )}{3}$

25. $7\cdot7\cdot7\cdot$

29. $[(\ )^2]^3$

22. $[(\ )^3]^2$

26. $-\,7+2-3$

30. $\cdot\,5\cdot5$

32. $\dfrac{\frac{(\ )}{3}}{6}$

$N-3+8=N+5$, for N greater than 3.   This is an assertion that for any proper operand, the resultant of a decrease by 3 followed by an increase of 8, will always be an increase of 5. Obtain simpler expressions for problems 33 to 40, assuming that N is a proper operand in each case.

33. $8(6N)$ **35.** $(N^4)^2$ **37.** $N + 7 - 7$ **39.** $\dfrac{\dfrac{N}{3}}{5}$

34. $N - 5 + 10$ **36.** $20\left(\dfrac{N}{4}\right)$ **38.** $\dfrac{3N}{3}$ **40.** $\dfrac{N}{7}(21)$

In problems 41 to 52, supply the missing operator that will give a true statement.

41. $(+9) \circ (\ ) = +13$ **45.** $(\ ) \circ \dfrac{(\ )}{5} = 20(\ )$ **49.** $(-7) \circ (\ ) = +0$

42. $(+9) \circ (\ ) = +0$ **46.** $(\ )^3 \circ (\ ) = (\ )^{12}$ **50.** $(\ ) \circ (-7) = +7$

43. $(\ ) \circ (+9) = -9$ **47.** $(\ ) \circ [2(\ )] = 14(\ )$ **51.** $[7(\ )] \circ (\ ) = 1(\ )$

44. $\dfrac{(\ )}{5} \circ (\ ) = \dfrac{}{20}$ **48.** $[2(\ )] \circ (\ ) = \dfrac{}{4}$ **52.** $[2(\ )] \circ (\ ) = \dfrac{}{2}$

53. What change must be combined with an increase of 3 to give a decrease of 5?
54. What change must be combined with a decrease of 6 to give a decrease of 2?
55. What change must be combined with a decrease of 4 to give an increase of 5?
56. What change must be combined with an increase of 7 to give an increase of 10?

57. Given that $f: n \to n + 2$, $g: n \to \dfrac{n}{2}$, and $h: n \to n^2$, give the mapping rule for the following composite mappings:

    a. $f \circ g$ **b.** $f \circ h$ **c.** $g \circ h$ **d.** $h \circ g$ **e.** $h \circ f$ **f.** $g \circ f$

58. Given that $f: n \to n - 2$, $g: n \to 2n$, and $h: n \to n^2$, give the mapping rule for the following composite mappings:

    a. $f \circ g$ **b.** $f \circ h$ **c.** $g \circ h$ **d.** $h \circ g$ **e.** $h \circ f$ **f.** $g \circ f$

For problems 59 to 68, give the mapping rule for the specified composite mappings, where $a: n \to n + 5$, $b: n \to n - 3$, $c: n \to 6n$, $d: n \to \dfrac{n}{2}$, $e: n \to n^3$, $f: n \to n^4$.

59. $a \circ b$ **61.** $d \circ c$ **63.** $e \circ f$ **65.** $a \circ c$ **67.** $(a \circ c) \circ e$
60. $b \circ a$ **62.** $c \circ d$ **64.** $f \circ e$ **66.** $b \circ d$ **68.** $(b \circ d) \circ f$

10-5. Graphic Models for Unary Operations

The problem of providing models and diagrams for the illustration of unary operations is related to the similar task for binary operations discussed in Chapter 9, but the scope is different. For each of the binary operations there was an unlimited choice for each of the two numbers in the ordered pair selected. Each diagram referred to a particular case arising from such a choice.

Now for each binary operation there corresponds an unlimited number of operators (which identify unary operations) of that type, and for each operator there is an unlimited number of operands. When constructing models for operators, we desire to grasp as adequately as we can the nature of the change produced by a given operator upon *any* proper operand. In other words, what we want is a picture of the change itself, which is independent so far as is possible, of what is being changed.

The following line segment, together with its accompanying scale, is, when considered in its entirety, one of our basic models for the number 5. If an arrowhead is placed at the right, we have a model for an increase of 5, or the addition operator $+5$. If the arrowhead is placed at the left, then we have a model for a decrease of 5, or the subtraction operator -5.

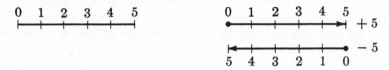

These *vectors* possess both *magnitude*, and *sense* or *orientation*. Hence, they are adapted to displaying two bits of information, which in this case are the kind and the amount of the change. The numerals for the scale could be omitted whenever the assumption is that each equal subdivision has a length of 1.

The two vectors above describe an increase of 5 and a decrease of 5, respectively, without reference to any particular operand that is to be transformed. They are not, however, completely independent of the operand. The vector for $+5$ represents an increase of 5 only because of the scale used; it could represent $+500$ equally well if the scale were properly assigned. Hence, the same scale must be used for the operand, the operator, and the transform in such a representation.

The extreme point at which the arrowhead is placed is called the *terminal* point of the vector, and the other extremity is the *initial* point. By changing the arrowhead to the opposite end we thereby interchange the initial and terminal points, and thus change the sense of the vector. This enables us to distinguish between addition and subtraction operators. *Note:* The vectors above are *not* to be thought of as representing signed numbers.

Thus far the natural numbers have been pictured either by the members of a set, or by an array of counters, or by a sequence, or by a magnitude carrying a scale. The vector concept goes beyond these. Besides the length, or magnitude of the vector as given by the scale, we have also a sense of direction. In order to show the result of joining an addition or subtraction operator to a numeral designating a number, we require a vector representation of those natural numbers that serve as operand and transform. This can be done in the following way.

A scale of adequate length is drawn extending from zero to the right. The left-to-right convention can be varied as required to down-to-up, up-to-down, or even right-to-left, but will be left-to-right unless otherwise stated. The vector diagram for any natural number is to be a *fixed* or *bound* vector with its initial point always at the point of origin, which is designated by zero on the scale. The number zero (and the vector representation of this number) is associated only with the origin. The terminal point will never be at the left of the initial point, for vectors associated with zero and the natural numbers. For zero, both points are at the origin. For the natural numbers the initial point is at zero, and the terminal point is at the right.

By contrast the vectors for addition and subtraction operators are *free* vectors that can be shifted or *translated* to the right or left while still retaining the same magnitude and sense. In example **A.** the vector for $+5$ has been translated so that its initial point coincides with the terminal point of the vector for the number 3. The vector for the transform, the number $3 + 5$ or 8, has its initial point at the origin, which is the initial point of the operand. The terminal point of the transform is at the terminal point of the operator. (All vectors are to be thought of as lying along the line segment carrying the scale but are off-set on the diagram for greater clarity.)

Examples:

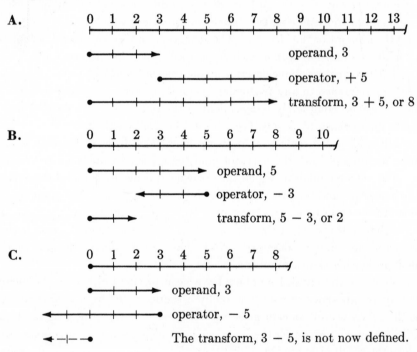

In example **C.** the vector for the transform is not defined, as 3 is not a proper operand for the subtraction operator -5. No such restriction arises when we consider the composition of addition and subtraction operators. No numbers (for which the initial point of the vector is bound to the origin) are then involved, and all vectors are free to be translated.

The association of two vectors to produce a third vector, in the manner of the examples, could be referred to as the composition of vectors, since that is the language being used for the operators corresponding to some of them.   But the universal practice is to say that the resultant vector has been obtained by *addition* of two or more vectors.   We shall follow this practice and look upon it as the first of several extensions to be given to the meaning of the word addition.

If two vectors are given by directed (sensed, oriented) line segments, the resultant vector or *vector sum* can be obtained as follows:

1. Translate the second vector so that its initial point coincides with the terminal point of the first vector.
2. The vector sum is then the vector whose initial point is that of the first vector, and whose terminal point is that of the second vector.

This addition of vectors is a binary operation on vectors that can be verified as being commutative and associative.   It can be readily extended to an n-ary operation.   To obtain the sum of n vectors, the vectors are translated in turn so that each vector after the first has its initial point at the terminal point of the preceding vector.   The vector sum then has its initial point at the initial point of the first vector, and its terminal point at the terminal point of the nth vector.

Examples: No background scale is given since all vectors are free.

A'. $+3$

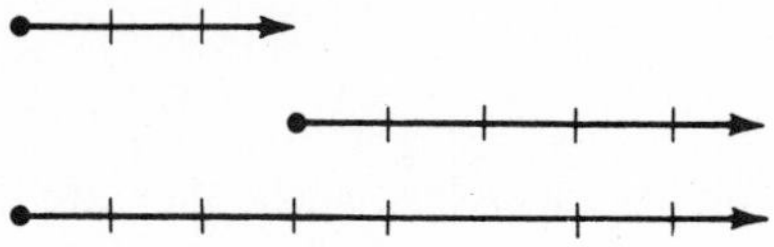

$+5$

$(+3) \circ (+5) = +8$

B'. $+5$

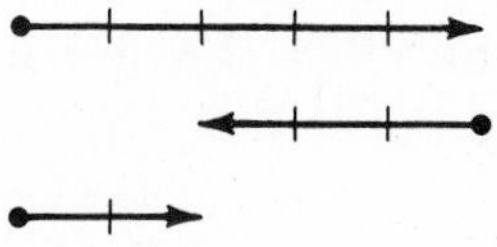

-3

$(+5) \circ (-3) = +2$

C'. $+3$

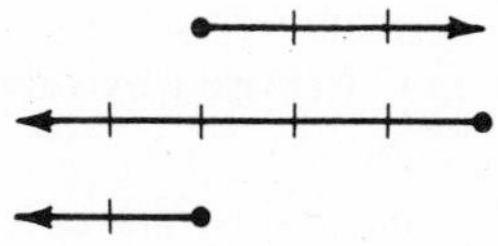

-5

$(+3) \circ (-5) = -2$

D. -3

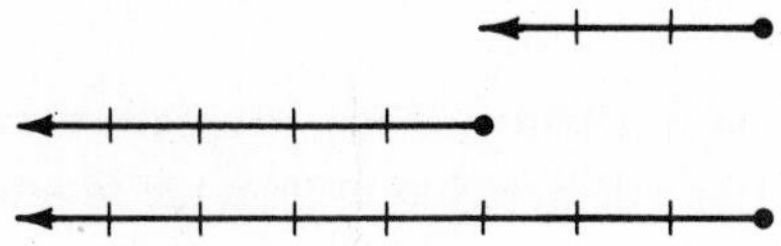

-5

$(-3) \circ (-5) = -8$

A' should be compared with A in the previous examples, B' with B, and C' with C.

a. Distinguish between natural numbers, and addition and subtraction operators as to **1.** their vector representation, **2.** their representation by numerical symbols.

b. Distinguish between the vector representation of 0, and $+ 0$, or $- 0$.

The increases and decreases specified by addition and subtraction operators can relate to a great variety of physical situations. Vectors can be used to picture changes of position, or *displacements*, giving both the magnitude or amount of the displacement, and also a choice between two opposite directions for the displacements. They can also describe gains or losses of weight or of money, the rise and fall of the ocean tides, and many other contrasting changes. We note that the magnitude itself may not have a sense of orientation attached to it, but that we often can assign such a sense to changes of the magnitude.

ANSWERS TO EXERCISES

a. The vectors associated with the natural numbers are bound vectors with their initial points always at the zero point of a fixed scale. The vectors associated with addition and subtraction operators can be translated freely, so that their initial points need not be tied to the origin of a scale. Natural numbers are represented by decimal numerals. Addition and subtraction operators are represented by $+ n$ or $- n$ where n is a numeral. **b.** The number 0 is associated only with origin of a scale. The operators $+ 0$ and $- 0$ may be associated with any point of the scale.

Problems (103)

Construct vector diagrams for the following, when they are defined.

1. **a.** $(+ 6) \circ (+ 3)$ **e.** $(+ 3) \circ (- 6)$ **h.** $(- 3) \circ (+ 6)$
   b. $6 + 3$ **f.** $3 - 6$ **i.** $(+ 2) \circ (- 3) \circ (+ 4)$
   c. $(+ 6) \circ (- 3)$ **g.** $(- 3) \circ (- 6)$ **j.** $2 - 3 + 4$
   d. $6 - 3$

2. **a.** $(+ 5) \circ (+ 4)$ **e.** $(+ 4) \circ (- 5)$ **h.** $(- 4) \circ (+ 5)$
   b. $5 + 4$ **f.** $4 - 5$ **i.** $(+ 3) \circ (- 4) \circ (+ 2)$
   c. $(+ 5) \circ (- 4)$ **g.** $(- 4) \circ (- 5)$ **j.** $3 - 4 + 2$
   d. $5 - 4$

3. **a.** A displacement of 2 units to the right, followed by one of 5 units to the left.
   b. A displacement of 2 units to the left, followed by one of 5 units to the right.

4. **a.** A gain of 3 units, followed by a gain of 4 units.
   b. A loss of 3 units, followed by a loss of 4 units.

To portray the magnifications and contractions we associate with multiplication and division operators, we will use a device that is common in advertising. This is to give a "before" and "after" picture in order to show the change. Just as for addition and subtraction operators, these models will be based on magnitude rather than multitude.   These can then be modified easily as we introduce numbers other than the natural numbers and zero.

Any natural number can be associated with the length of a line segment. Furthermore, this length can be any that is desired (except zero), by changing the scale that establishes the correspondence between the number and the line segment. Hence, in the diagram below the segment labeled "before" can represent any natural number.   This allows us also to label this segment with the variable n, with the range of this variable extending over all the natural numbers.

For all $n \neq 0$ and $m = 2$

After ├─────────────┤ $2n$ $m \cdot n$

Before ├───────┤ n $1 \cdot n$

The "after" line is twice as long as the other, and is labeled $2n$.   Taken together, as representations of a magnitude before and after a change, we have a picture of the unary operation of multiplying by 2, or doubling, and hence of the multiplication operator 2( ).

No scale is necessary, since the ratio we are illustrating does not depend on the scale used.   However, if the before segment is used as a unit (assigned a length of 1), this unit can be used to measure the after segment.   The number 2, which thus results, identifies the multiplication operator we are illustrating.

If the before and after designations are interchanged, we get a representation of the change induced by $\dfrac{}{2}$, the operator that is inverse to 2( ).

For all $n \neq 0$ and $m = 2$

After ├───────┤ $\dfrac{n}{2}$ $\dfrac{n}{m}$

Before ├─────────────┤ n $\dfrac{n}{1}$

If $m \neq 0$, then the change that will result from any multiplication operator $m(\ )$ or any division operator $\dfrac{}{m}$ can be shown with such before and after diagrams.

Several characteristics distinguish the models from those used for addition and subtraction changes.   The first, as given for $n \rightarrow 2n$, cannot be used to specify an increase.   It would first be necessary to specify a scale for measuring the before and after lengths, and the change shown (as an increase) would be different for each different choice of a scale.   Also, it would not now be possible to use variables since all that is shown is one particular change as made on one particular number.

	0	1	2	0	1	2	3	4
	├──┼──┼──┤／			├──┼──┼──┼──┤／				

After ├──────────┤   ├──────────┤$1 + 1$ ├──────────────┤$2 + 2$

Before ├──────┤   ├──────┤ 1 ├──────┤ 2

Problems (104)

Construct and label before and after diagrams for the following, based on two line segments of the proper length.

1. Tripling

2. A magnification of 6 times

3. The change produced by the operator $\dfrac{-}{3}$

4. Dividing by 5

We turn now to the development of a graphic model for changes or transformations that can be adapted to all kinds of unary operations, as symbolized by any type of operator we shall use. It will be an extension of one of the fundamental models developed in Chapter 9.

In Section 9-2, page 175, the following matching of two sequences was presented as a means of computing $7 - 3$.

$$
\begin{array}{ccccccccc}
0 & 1 & 2 & 3 & 4 & & . \, . \, . & & \text{2nd sequence} \\
| & | & | & | & | & & & & \\
0 & 1 & 2 & 3 & 4 & 5 & 6 & 7 & . \, . \, . \quad \text{1st sequence}
\end{array}
$$

At that time attention was also directed to the ordered pairs that are exhibited. These may be taken as a small but representative sample of the following infinite set of ordered pairs:

$$(3, 0), (4, 1), (5, 2), (6, 3), (7, 4), (8, 5), \ldots$$

But these ordered pairs are precisely those that are given by the mapping $n \to n - 3$. Hence, as far as zero and the natural numbers are concerned, this set of ordered pairs reveals about all that can be said about the unary operation of subtracting 3. In fact they characterize it so completely that the language convention, as used on page 148 for mappings, can be applied here. This infinite set of ordered pairs *is* the unary operation that is specified by the subtraction operator $- 3$, over the domain of the natural numbers that are greater than or equal to 3.

This set of ordered pairs, which we have already designated as a mapping, and now as a unary operation, can also be termed a *function*. Indeed, the function terminology is the older, and when the ordered pairs are pairs of numbers, is the more widely used.

The notation $f: n \to n - 3$ gives a rule for associating a number n of a given domain with its image $n - 3$. Furthermore, the temporary name f has been assigned to this mapping. Exactly the same result can be achieved with the functional notation $f(n) = n - 3$. As before, n will be the first component and $n - 3$ will be the second component of the ordered pair $(n, n - 3)$. All the ordered pairs of the infinite set above result from substitutions for n in $(n, n - 3)$. The symbol f, standing by itself, is the temporary name for this function (mapping, unary operation). $f(n)$, read "f of n," can be thought of as the transform $f(n)$ that results when the functional operator $f(\ )$ is joined to the operand n. Thus $(n, n - 3)$ is an example of $(n, f(n))$ where $f(n) = n - 3$.

a. Under what conditions does a set of ordered pairs of numbers constitute a function?   (See p. 148.)

The method of matching the two sequences can be varied as below, which emphasizes the backward shift suggested by subtracting 3.

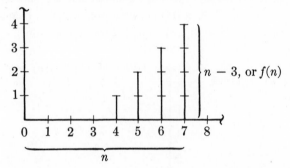

The next graphic model of functions anticipates the extensions that we shall be making in the number system to include numbers other than zero and the natural numbers.   Each member of a given ordered pair is represented by a line segment of appropriate length.   The first segment extends horizontally from zero to the designated scale division point.   From this point the line segment for the second component of the ordered pair extends vertically.   A vertical scale is added to measure the length of the second segment.

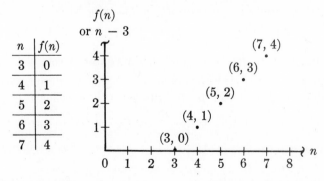

The ordered pairs shown are:
(3, 0), (4, 1), (5, 2), (6, 3),
and (7, 4)

As a final modification we retain only the upper end point of the second segment, and associate with this point the ordered pair of numbers used to locate it.   The horizontal scale is along a line called the n *axis*, and the vertical scale is along a line called the $f(n)$ *axis* in general, and the $n - 3$ axis for this particular function.   The ordered pair of numbers is said to be the *coordinates* of the point they designate. We now have a procedure for establishing a 1:1 correspondence between the ordered pairs of numbers that constitute a function and certain points of a plane.

n	$f(n)$
3	0
4	1
5	2
6	3
7	4

Table and graph for $f(n) = n - 3$, with domain $\{3, 4, 5, 6, 7\}$.

The ordered pairs $(n, f(n))$ will, at present, have components selected only from the set of the natural numbers and zero, and the corresponding points will lie in that portion of the plane which lies above and to the right of the assumed axes. The set of all points thus determined is called the *graph* of the function. When the number of ordered pairs is infinite, the graph can never be shown in its entirety. Nevertheless, a selection of the points can greatly assist the mind in forming a better concept of the function.

The next problem set uses the notation for functions and the graphic model of points in a plane to continue our study of operators and the unary operations they specify. In any comparative analysis of these the identity function (mapping, unary operation) is of fundamental importance as a basis for reference. The sets of ordered pairs $(n, n + 0)$, $(n, n - 0)$, $(n, 1 \cdot n)$, $(n, \frac{n}{1})$, (n, n^1), and (n, n) are clearly all the same, and hence these functions are identical. In recent years the notation $f(n) = I(n)$ has been increasingly used for the identity function, but the shorter form of $f(n) = n$ is still the most common. A portion of its graph is shown below together with some points of $f(n) = n + 2$, and $f(n) = n - 2$ for comparison.

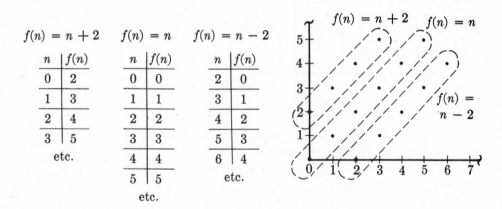

$f(n) = n + 2$		$f(n) = n$		$f(n) = n - 2$	
n	$f(n)$	n	$f(n)$	n	$f(n)$
0	2	0	0	2	0
1	3	1	1	3	1
2	4	2	2	4	2
3	5	3	3	5	3
etc.		4	4	6	4
		5	5	etc.	
		etc.			

ANSWER TO EXERCISE

a. Each different ordered pair must have different first components.

Problems (105)

For each function, construct the portion of its graph as specified. It is instructive to sketch in lightly in each change a portion of $f(n) = n$ for comparison. In this way each change pictured can be compared with no change.

1. $f(n) = n - 1$, for $n = 1, 2, 3, 4, 5$ **4.** $f(n) = 3n$, for $n = 0, 1, 2, 3$

2. $f(n) = n + 1$, for $n = 0, 1, 2, 3, 4$ **5.** $f(n) = \frac{n}{3}$, for $n = 0, 3, 6, 9$

3. $f(n) = 2n$, for $n = 0, 1, 2, 3, 4$ **6.** $f(n) = \frac{n}{2}$, for $n = 0, 2, 4, 6, 8$

7. $f(n) = n^2$, for $n = 0, 1, 2, 3$ 13. $f(n) = 9 - n^2$, for $n = 0, 1, 2, 3$

8. $f(n) = n^3$, for $n = 0, 1, 2$ 14. $f(n) = 2n - 1$, for $n = 1, 2, 3, 4$

9. $f(n) = n!$, for $n = 0, 1, 2, 3$ 15. $f(n) = 3n - 2$, for $n = 1, 2, 3$

10. $f(n) = n! - 1$, for $n = 0, 1, 2, 3$ 16. $f(n) = \dfrac{n^2}{2}$, for $n = 0, 2, 4$

11. $f(n) = 5 - n$, for $n = 0, 1, 2, 3, 4, 5$ 17. $f(n) = n(4 - n)$, for $n = 0, 1, 2, 3, 4$

12. $f(n) = 7 - 2n$, for $n = 0, 1, 2, 3$ 18. $f(n) = \displaystyle\sum_{k=0}^{k=n} k$, for $n = 0, 1, 2, 3$

The mapping given by $n \to 0 \cdot n + 2$, or by $f(n) = 0 \cdot n + 2$ is the set of ordered pairs, $\{(0, 2), (1, 2), (2, 2), (3, 2), \ldots\}$. Each can be obtained by substituting for n in $(n, 2)$. This is an example of a *constant* mapping or function. The above notations can be shortened to $n \to 2$, or $f(n) = 2$. Continue as for problems 1 to 18 for the following:

19. $f(n) = 0 \cdot n + 3$, for $n = 0, 1, 2, 3, 4, 5$
20. $f(n) = 0 \cdot n + 4$, for $n = 0, 1, 2, 3, 4, 5$
21. $f(n) = 4$, for $n = 0, 1, 2, 3, 4, 5$
22. $f(n) = 3$, for $n = 0, 1, 2, 3, 4, 5$
23. $f(n) = 0 \cdot n$, for $n = 0, 1, 2, 3, 4, 5$
24. $f(n) = 0$, for $n = 0, 1, 2, 3, 4, 5$

10-6. Removal and Cancellation of Operators

Further development of unary operations is deferred until some of the present restrictions on operands are removed, by extension of the number system to numbers other than zero and the natural numbers. However, an additional observation about inverse operators will be made, which will make possible an improved treatment of some problems that have been discussed in previous chapters.

Cancellation was mentioned in Section 3-7 in the context of binary operations. It is now possible, and more precise, to refer to cancellation as the removal from an expression of two inverse operators. Problem set (27) can be discussed in such terms. The cancellation laws for addition and multiplication (see p. 16), which are repeated below, are seen to involve the removal of the same operator from both members of an equality.

A. If $A + C = B + C$, then $A = B$
M. If $AC = BC$, and $C \neq 0$, then $A = B$

These two examples above should be distinguished from those to follow where two inverse operators are removed from a single expression, which might be one member of an equation. For emphasis, we repeat the warnings about improper cancellation, since serious mistakes can be made by removing two operators from an expression that are not actually in inverse roles. For not only must the two operators be inverse in kind, they must also be in the proper place if they are to "undo" each other.   The two **operators** that cancel must be inverse to each other, and they must occur in immediate succession, or it must be possible to rearrange them in this order by using the commutative and associative properties.   To state that two operators cancel is to claim that if both are ignored or actually removed from an expression, the resulting expression is still equivalent to the original.

> **Examples:** Since $+ 5 + 7 - 5$ is equivalent to $+ 7 + 5 - 5$, by the commutative property of these operators, it may be simplified to $+ 7$ by removing (cancelling) the inverse operators $+ 5$ and $- 5$.
>
> $$+ 5 + 7 - 5 = + 7$$
>
> Again since $5 + 7 - 5$ is equivalent in turn to $(5 + 7) - 5$, then to $(7 + 5) - 5$, and then to $7 + 5 - 5$, we can then cancel the inverse operators $+ 5$ and $- 5$ to obtain 7.   Note that we get the number 7 in this manner, and not the distinctively different result of the operator $+ 7$ as obtained above.   The above equivalences should be checked in turn and note made of when we are appealing to properties of binary operations and when to unary.
>
> $$5 + 7 - 5 = 7$$
>
> $\dfrac{3 \cdot 5 \cdot 7}{5}$ is equivalent to $\dfrac{5 \cdot 3 \cdot 7}{5}$ and then to $\dfrac{5 \, (3 \cdot 7)}{5}$.   Then it may be simplified to $3 \cdot 7$ by removing $5(\ )$ and $\dfrac{}{5}$, which are inverses.
>
> $\dfrac{30 - 5}{5} + 5$ does not equal $\dfrac{30}{5}$ or $30 + 5$.   We cannot cancel $- 5$ and $\dfrac{}{5}$ because they are not inverse operators.   The $- 5$ and $+ 5$ are a pair of inverse operators, but they are not used in immediate succession; the $\dfrac{}{5}$ is in between them, and it does not commute with either $+ 5$ or $- 5$.

a. What is objectionable about saying that addition and subtraction cancel each other?

b. What is objectionable about saying that two numbers can be cancelled from an expression, such as the two 7's in $5 + 7 - 7$?

The number 16 is represented by $9 + 7$.   If the operator $- 7$ is joined to $9 + 7$ the resulting expression of $9 + 7 - 7$ then represents 9, as is evident when the inverse operators $+ 7$ and $- 7$ are removed or cancelled.

But the change from $9 + 7$ to 9 could also have been accomplished more directly by simply removing the operator $+ 7$ from $9 + 7$.   Here then are two ways of producing a decrease of 7.   One way is to join the operator $- 7$ to the operand; another way is to remove the operator $+ 7$ (when present and accessible).

Many opportunities arise whereby instead of introducing an operator to produce a desired change, it is possible to accomplish the same change by removing an operator that is already present. The operator to be removed must be the inverse of the one that was to be joined, and it must be accessible. It is accessible if it was the last operator to be joined to the expression, or if it can be brought to this position by using the commutative and associative principles.

Example: To multiply $\dfrac{5(7 + 2)}{3}$ by 3. The 15, represented by this expression, can be multiplied by 3 to get 45 in the form of $5(7 + 2)$, by using the operator $3(\ )$ and then cancelling. Thus

$$3\left[\frac{5(7 + 2)}{3}\right] = 5(7 + 2)$$

But one can also multiply by 3 to get $5(7 + 2)$ by removing the operator $\dfrac{}{3}$, which is inverse to $3(\ )$.

This brings up the question of whether it is possible to remove an operator that isn't there! The chart below shows a possible strategy. Clearly these maneuvers can be made only when N is such an operand that all expressions used are defined. The key idea is the introduction of an appropriate identity operator as represented by two successive inverse operators, the second of which is the one to be removed.

Operand	Identity operator (In the form of two successive inverse operators)	Identity operator in place (No change in the operand)	Operator to be removed	Transform (After removal of the operator)
N	$+ a - a$	$N + a - a$	$- a$	$N + a$
N	$- a + a$	$N - a + a$	$+ a$	$N - a$
N	$\dfrac{a(\ )}{a}$	$\dfrac{a(N)}{a}$	$\dfrac{}{a}$	$a(N)$
N	$a\,\dfrac{}{a}$	$a\,\dfrac{N}{a}$	$a(\ )$	$\dfrac{N}{a}$

Summary: Assume that n is a natural number or zero in $+ n$ and $- n$, and a natural number in $n(\ )$ and $\dfrac{}{n}$. For proper operands:

An increase of n is produced by joining the operator $+ n$, or removing the operator $- n$.

A decrease of n is produced by joining the operator $- n$, or removing the operator $+ n$.

A multiplication by n is produced by joining the operator $n(\ )$, or removing the operator $\dfrac{}{n}$.

A division by n is produced by joining the operator $\dfrac{}{n}$, or removing the operator $n(\ )$.

A similar statement for exponential operators cannot be made now, because of the lack of inverse operators.

In problem sets (65) and (66) in Section 6-4 we were concerned with equivalent forms of a given statement (different form but same content). Thus $9 + 7 = 16$ is equivalent to $9 = 16 - 7$, by commutativity, subtraction, and symmetry. Let us consider this change from the operator point of view.

The statement $9 + 7 = 16$ is true because $9 + 7$ and 16 are different numerals for the same number. This number (in the form of $9 + 7$) can be decreased by 7 by removing the operator $+ 7$. This same number (in the form of 16) can be decreased by 7 by joining the operator $- 7$. As far as observable physical acts are concerned, we do not claim to have done the same thing to both members of the equation. These two acts are quite different; one is a removal and one is a joining of an operator. What we do claim is that these two different acts produce exactly the same change in the number represented by both members of the equation.

This clears up the mystery often associated with a superficial observation of what is called "transposition." There is also no need to cloud the issue by introducing signed numbers, since they are not involved.

Example: $a \cdot b = c - d$ is equivalent to $b = \dfrac{c - d}{a}$.

The operator $a \cdot$ is removed from $a \cdot b$.

The operator $\dfrac{}{a}$ is joined to $c - d$.

Recall that equivalent implies that if there are substitutes for the variables a, b, c, and d which make the first equation true (or false), the same substitutions in the second equation also make it true (or false). In other words, our manipulation of the operators has not changed a true statement to a false one, or a false statement to a true one. (Such claims are subject to the ever present restrictions of avoiding zero divisors, and undefined differences and quotients.)

Answers to Exercises

a. Addition and subtraction are binary operations and as such are not inverse to each other.
b. Natural numbers are never in inverse pairs. It is "adding 7" and "subtracting 7" that are inverse unary operations.

Problems (106)

In problems 1 to 4, it is suggested that you review the problem sets suggested, but this time thinking of the use of operators.

1. Problem set (19), page 32, odd-numbered problems.
2. Problem set (19), even-numbered problems.
3. Problem set (27), page 40, odd-numbered problems.
4. Problem set (27), even-numbered problems.

In problems 5 to 28, a change is identified by giving a number before and after a change. Describe the change, meeting the following specifications:

A. Give the basic numeral for the number, both before and after the change.
B. Give the kind and amount of the change; using the words "increase," "decrease," "multiplied by," and "divided by," as appropriate.
C. Give the use of operators, by which the change was accomplished.

Example: (Before) $9 + 7$, (After) 9.   *Answer:* 16 was decreased by 7, producing 9, by removing the operator $+ 7$.

Before	*After*		*Before*	*After*
5. $12 + 5$	12	**19.** $\dfrac{27}{3}$	27
6. $18 + 2$	2		
7. 10	$10 - 3$	**20.** $12 \div 2$	12
8. 30	$30 - 5$	**21.** $3 \cdot 5^2$	$3 \cdot 5^2 - 5$
9. $7 \cdot 8$	8	**22.** $2^2 \cdot 7 + 7$	$2^2 \cdot 7$
10. $4 \cdot 9$	4	**23.** $3 \cdot 5^2$	5^2
11. 24	$\dfrac{24}{6}$	**24.** $2^2 \cdot 7$	$\dfrac{2^2 \cdot 7}{4}$
12. 15	$15 \div 3$		
13. 21	$21 + 4$	**25.** $(7)(11) - 7$	$(7)(11)$
14. 17	$5 + 17$	**26.** $2^2 \cdot 7$	$(2^2 \cdot 7)^2$
15. $17 - 7$	17	**27.** $\dfrac{2(12 + 3)}{5}$	$2(12 + 3)$
16. $100 - 4$	100		
17. 15	$4 \cdot 15$	**28.** $2\left(\dfrac{12 + 3}{5}\right)$	$\dfrac{12 + 3}{5}$
18. 10	$3(10)$		

For problems 29 to 32, give the reason that justifies the change in form from the previous step. That is: from **a.** to **b.**, **b.** to **c.** Use the language of operators where it applies.

29. a. $r = \dfrac{s}{t}$ **b.** $r \cdot t = s$ **c.** $s = r \cdot t$

30. a. $r = s - t$ **b.** $r + t = s$ **c.** $s = r + t$

31. a. $rs = t + u$ **b.** $rs - u = t$ **c.** $t = rs - u$

32. a. $s = r \cdot t$ **b.** $\dfrac{s}{t} = r$ **c.** $r = \dfrac{s}{t}$

For Further Study

The suggestion that unary operations be used for the description of change was made many years ago in [C2], pp. 32–42; and [W6], pp. 55–57.

An excellent account of the role of operators for the specification of change can be found in Chapter 2 of [A3].

For supplementary reading and problems on n-ary operations see [E2], pp. 128–129, 153–154.

The concept of a function is of the highest importance in mathematics. It can be approached through many avenues and it is recommended that a variety of introductory treatments be read. Here is a beginning selection: [S2], pp. 92–106; [D4], pp. 89–113; [N5], pp. 164–186; [D6], pp. 136–154.

11

Fractions and Rational Numbers

11-1. Linear Scales

The scales that were used in preceding chapters were all *linear* scales. Each was constructed from a line segment on which equal lengths had been marked off. Numbers were then assigned to the various magnitudes thus determined. The manner in which the numbers are assigned determines whether the scale is linear or nonlinear.

Linear scale	Nonlinear scale
0 1 2 3 4 5 6	0 1 4 9 16 25 36
0 A B C D E F	0 A B C D E F

On each of the above scales the number 1 can be considered as assigned not only to the length of the segment extending from point 0 to point A, but also just to point A. Similarly a number was assigned to point B as well as to the length of the segment from 0 to B, to point C as well as to the length of the segment from 0 to C, and so on. Such a correspondence between a set of numbers and a set of points on a line was not developed in the analysis given in Chapter 9, but will be our next step in extending the geometrical models we have for numbers.

Now consider any two of the points designated as 0, A, B, C, D, E, or F on the scale at the left. Numbers were assigned to these points in such a way that the differences between the numbers assigned to two of the points gave a measure of the distance between the two points. This condition is not met on the scale at the right. In the first column in the following table are several distances, or lengths of line segments, which are all equal on both scales. The number differences were computed by subtracting the number assigned to the left end point from that assigned to the right end point. These differences were all the same on the left scale, which was required if they were to measure equal lengths.   But this was not the case for the other scale.

Equal lengths or distances	Number differences on the linear scale	Number differences on the nonlinear scale
From 0 to C	$3 - 0 = 3$	$9 - 0 = 9$
From A to D	$4 - 1 = 3$	$16 - 1 = 15$
From B to E	$5 - 2 = 3$	$25 - 4 = 21$
From C to F	$6 - 3 = 3$	$36 - 9 = 27$

Principle of Linear Measure: The points on a line can be numbered so that number differences measure distances.

This assumption has been applied so far only to selected points on a line segment; those at equally spaced intervals.   A major task, which will extend over the remaining chapters of this text, is to consider how this assumption can be extended to all the points of a line.

On page 219 several models were given to display the number pairs that make up a function.   An alternate model can be constructed with two scales, one above the other.   The lower scale is a linear scale based on the values of n; the corresponding points on the upper scale are then numbered as specified by $f(n)$.   The division points of the lower and upper scale thereby coincide, each point being assigned a pair of numbers $(n, f(n))$, provided $f(n)$ is defined.

Examples:

Problems (107)

In problems 1 and 2, construct a linear scale as suggested, using only zero and the natural numbers.

Two scales are to be constructed as suggested above to illustrate the functions, which are those whose graphs were to be determined in problem set (105).   Note that the upper scale is linear for precisely those functions whose graph has the property that all points of the graph lie along a line. Such functions are said to be linear.

3. #1	7. #5	11. #9	15. #13	19. #17	23. #21
4. #2	8. #6	12. #10	16. #14	20. #18	24. #22
5. #3	9. #7	13. #11	17. #15	21. #19	25. #23
6. #4	10. #8	14. #12	18. #16	22. #20	26. #24

It is desired that the diagram below be completed by assigning numbers to division points A, B, and C in such a way as to give a linear scale. This is not possible if only zero and the natural numbers are available. Thus the line segment that extends from the zero point to the point B is longer than the segments that measure 1, but shorter than those that measure 2. But there is no natural number greater than 1, but less than 2.

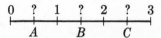

Such measurement problems, where the assumed unit does not "come out even" when applied to the magnitude being measured, extend over man's recorded history. They make it very clear that the natural numbers, which were formulated as an answer to "How many?" are not always adequate when the question is "How much?" Other kinds of numbers are required.

However, with thousands of years of experience to draw on, we can observe that there are tasks for which the natural numbers are inadequate when used one at a time but which can be handled with an ordered pair of such numbers. This is the strategy we shall use on the above measurement problem. We shall try assigning an ordered pair of numbers to each point of subdivision. It is emphasized that an ordered pair will be used; the first component can be zero or a natural number but the second can only be a natural number and zero is ruled out. Each number will be determined by counting.

First, we count the number of segments, of equal length and placed end to end, whose total length is to be 1 on the scale. This number, which is 2 in the example, is the second component of each and every ordered pair. The first component varies from point to point; it is determined as though we were constructing a linear scale with the number 1 assigned to the length of a single one of the segments previously counted.

$$\frac{0}{2} \qquad \frac{1}{2} \qquad \frac{2}{2} \qquad \frac{3}{2} \qquad \frac{4}{2} \qquad \frac{5}{2} \qquad \frac{6}{2}$$

$$0 \qquad\qquad\qquad 1 \qquad\qquad\qquad 2 \qquad\qquad\qquad 3$$

(0, 2)   (1, 2)   (2, 2)   (3, 2)   (4, 2)   (5, 2)   (6, 2)

One could continue the development using the usual notation for ordered pairs, as shown below the division points on the scale. Instead, we shall use another notation for an ordered pair; one that will signify "fraction" to the reader but which so far in this text has meant only a quotient or a ratio. When the quotient of the dividend a by the divisor b has been written as $\dfrac{a}{b}$, it has been required that b be a natural number, and that a be zero or a natural number that is a multiple of b. Similar restrictions on a and b have been assumed to hold when the ratio of a first number a to a second number b has been written as $\dfrac{a}{b}$. The suggestion that $\dfrac{a}{b}$ also be a notation for the ordered pairs given by the above counting procedure means that these restrictions must be modified. This raises several serious questions, among which are the following:

A. Is the ordered pair concept as introduced for the scale compatible with the ideas of quotient and ratio so that it is practical to use the same notation for all three?

B. Can we think of these ordered pairs as numerals for a new kind of number, and if so, what are the properties of these new numbers and how are they related to the natural numbers?

C. How well do these new numbers meet the problems of measurement, such as constructing the linear scale of our example?

These basic questions will be the principal motivation for the next several chapters.

We turn again to the scale example and note that we have two designations at the same point in several instances. Thus, we have the ordered pair $\dfrac{0}{2}$ and the number 0 at the same point; also $\dfrac{2}{2}$ and 1, $\dfrac{4}{2}$ and 2, and $\dfrac{6}{2}$ and 3. However, these work out nicely, since we have already accepted the quotient $\dfrac{0}{2}$ as another name for zero. From the definition of division, $\dfrac{0}{2} = 0$. Similarly $\dfrac{2}{2} = 1$, $\dfrac{4}{2} = 2$, and $\dfrac{6}{2} = 3$ as is required for consistency of the ordered pair and the quotient interpretations.

The real difficulty is that up to now we have designated $\dfrac{1}{2}$, $\dfrac{3}{2}$, and $\dfrac{5}{2}$ as being undefined as quotients, since they do not represent natural numbers. But it is possible to meet this difficulty in a direct manner and provide a satisfactory solution.

Symbols of the form $\dfrac{a}{b}$ where b is a numeral for a natural number, and where a is a numeral for a natural number or zero, *but is not necessarily a multiple of b*, will be called *fractions*. The numbers, to be defined later, represented by these fractions will be called *rational* numbers. It turns out that we shall be able to define these new numbers in such a way that our "impossible" problems above then become possible.   This definition will be given after looking at $\frac{1}{2}, \frac{3}{2}$, and $\frac{5}{2}$ to see what is required.

According to the definition of division the reason 1 cannot be divided by 2 in the realm of natural numbers is that there is no natural number x such that $(2)(x) = 1$. If we create a new number x (a rational number) so that $(2)(x) = 1$ can be a true statement, our first check might well be that of noting how this works out on the scale.   This looks favorable since $\frac{1}{2}$ has been assigned to one of the two equal lengths that result when the segment of length 1 is divided into two equal parts.   In other words, two of the segments of length $\frac{1}{2}$ make a segment of length 1 when placed end to end, which is just what is needed for $(2)\left(\frac{1}{2}\right) = 1$.   Hence, $x = \frac{1}{2}$ appears to be a satisfactory solution.

If we accept $\frac{1}{2}$ as a rational number such that $(2)\left(\frac{1}{2}\right) = 1$, and extend the definition of division to admit this number, then we can write $1 \div 2 = \frac{1}{2}$, or $\frac{1}{2} = \frac{1}{2}$, and think of the latter as $\boxed{\frac{1}{2}} = \boxed{\frac{1}{2}}$.   The left member is thus interpreted as a quotient of two natural numbers, and the right member as a fraction representing a rational number.   This can be read as, "When the natural number 1 is divided by the natural number 2, the quotient is the rational number $\frac{1}{2}$."   With this dual use of the notation not only is the impossible problem now assumed possible, but the problem becomes its own answer!   At least the statement of the problem has the same form as the result.

a. Use the definition of division given on page 185 and note the modifications necessary to obtain the above result.

It can also be verified on the diagram that $\frac{3}{2}$ has been assigned to the length of a segment, two of which laid end to end give a segment of length 3.   This is the measurement model needed for $2\left(\frac{3}{2}\right) = 3$, or $3 \div 2 = \frac{3}{2}$.   By extending the scale to five and locating the midpoint, we find that $\frac{5}{2}$ is one of the two equal parts of 5.   Hence $(2)\left(\frac{5}{2}\right) = 5$.

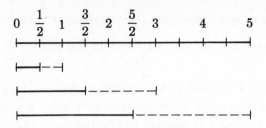

This motivates the following definition of rational numbers:

> ***Definition:** *Those numbers x that are solutions of $(b)(x) = a$, and of $(x)(b) = a$, where a is zero or a natural number and b is a natural number but may not be zero, are called rational numbers. The number x can be represented by a numeral, the fraction $\dfrac{a}{b}$, and hence $(b)\left(\dfrac{a}{b}\right) = \left(\dfrac{a}{b}\right)(b) = a$.*

This definition provides a link between the rational numbers and the natural numbers by defining the product of any rational number $\dfrac{a}{b}$ times the natural number b. The definition already demands that $\dfrac{a}{b}$ commute with a in the product $(b)\left(\dfrac{a}{b}\right)$. We further desire that the rational numbers have as many properties of the natural numbers as is possible. Hence, when operations on these numbers are defined, such properties as commutativity and associativity must be checked. It is also most important to see if the rational numbers thus defined continue to provide a useful quantitative description of the desired physical models, particularly those for measurement.

We want, of course, the solution x of $(b)(x) = a$ to be unique for a given a and b. Suppose $x = \dfrac{a}{b}$, and also $x = \dfrac{c}{d}$. Then $(b)\left(\dfrac{a}{b}\right) = a$ and $(b)\left(\dfrac{c}{d}\right) = a$, so that $(b)\left(\dfrac{a}{b}\right) = (b)\left(\dfrac{c}{d}\right)$. The requirement that $bx = a$ have a unique solution can now be seen to be equivalent to extending the cancellation law for multiplication to such products, since if this holds, then $\dfrac{a}{b} = \dfrac{c}{d}$.

The introduction of the rational numbers means that division is now almost always possible in the set of zero and the natural numbers, the sole exception being the use of zero divisors. The operation of division is now complete for the set of natural numbers. Division is not closed in the set of natural numbers, and can never be, since we must go outside this set for many of the quotients. The question of closure for division in the set of nonzero rational numbers must wait until this binary operation on the rational numbers has been defined.

---

* Later we shall extend the number system again to include still other rational numbers. At that time the numbers defined here will be termed nonnegative rational numbers. With zero excepted they will be known as the positive rational numbers.

If we set $b = 1$ in the above definition, we obtain $(1)\left(\dfrac{a}{1}\right) = a$. Now $(1)(a) = a$, and hence $(1)\left(\dfrac{a}{1}\right) = (1)(a)$. By again appealing to the cancellation property we have $\dfrac{a}{1} = a$. This is a highly significant result. The rational number $\dfrac{a}{1}$ and the natural number a are quite distinct as concepts, since a is a single natural number and the rational number $\dfrac{a}{1}$ is constructed from an ordered pair of natural numbers. The decimal numeral for a and the fraction $\dfrac{a}{1}$ are also clearly distinguishable. Nevertheless, because $\dfrac{a}{1} = a$, then in any statement about these two *numbers* (not numerals) either $\dfrac{a}{1}$ or a can be substituted for the other. This will be done constantly, and the necessity for being able to do this will be a critical guide in deciding how operations on rational numbers shall be defined.

Another important special case of $b\left(\dfrac{a}{b}\right) = a$ results from setting $a = 1$, to give $b\left(\dfrac{1}{b}\right) = 1$. Two numbers whose product is 1 are said to be *reciprocals* of each other. Thus b or $\dfrac{b}{1}$ and $\dfrac{1}{b}$ are reciprocals of each other. Reciprocals are seen to be two numbers whose product is the multiplicative identity. The following discussion anticipates the definition of the multiplication of rational numbers, which has not yet been given. It indicates that if this definition is properly made, then the term *multiplicative inverse* can be a synonym for reciprocal.

1. $b\left(\dfrac{a}{b}\right) = a$, for $b \neq 0$
        By definition.

2. $\dfrac{b}{1}\left(\dfrac{a}{b}\right) = a$
        From 1., since $b = \dfrac{b}{1}$.

3. $\dfrac{1}{b}\left[\dfrac{b}{1}\left(\dfrac{a}{b}\right)\right] = \dfrac{1}{b}(a)$
        From 2., on the assumption that multiplication by the rational number $\dfrac{1}{b}$ can be well defined.

4. $\left[\left(\dfrac{1}{b}\right)\left(\dfrac{b}{1}\right)\right]\left(\dfrac{a}{b}\right) = \dfrac{1}{b}(a)$
        From 3., assuming that multiplication of rational numbers is associative.

5. $1\left(\dfrac{a}{b}\right) = \dfrac{1}{b}(a)$
        From 4., since $\dfrac{1}{b}$ and $\dfrac{b}{1}$ are reciprocals.

6. $\dfrac{a}{b} = \dfrac{1}{b}(a)$
        From 5., assuming that $1 \cdot x = x$, also when x is a rational number.

Since $\frac{a}{b}$ is the quotient of a divided by b, the result in **6.** would permit us to conclude that if a is zero or a natural number, then to divide a by any natural number b should give the same result as the multiplication of a by $\frac{1}{b}$, where $\frac{1}{b}$ is the reciprocal or multiplicative inverse of b.

In other words, our definition of multiplication and division should be such that, in the language of unary operations, the division operator $\frac{}{b}$, should be equivalent to the multiplication operator $\frac{1}{b}(\ )$, if $b \neq 0$. Further evidence that multiplication should be defined so that **1.** to **6.** hold comes from looking at the two ways we would then have of relating the rational number $\frac{a}{b}$ to the natural number 1.   If 1 is the operand, we wish to verify that the same transform $\frac{a}{b}$ can be obtained by applying the multiplication operator $a(\ )$ or $a \cdot$ and the division operator $\frac{}{b}$ in succession, in either order.   As usual, we try this out with the rational numbers represented by magnitudes.

Example:

$$a = 2$$
$$b = 3$$

$$a\left(\frac{1}{b}\right) = \frac{a}{b} \qquad\qquad \frac{a \cdot 1}{b} = \frac{a}{b}$$

In this example the same length was designated as 1 in both cases, and the same length was finally designated as $\frac{2}{3}$.   In the first instance $\frac{2}{3}$ was obtained from 1 by first dividing by 3 and then multiplying by 2.   This interpretation of $\frac{a}{b}$ is undoubtedly the one by which the reader was introduced to fractions in elementary school.   It has been customary there to develop $\frac{2}{3}$ by first dividing some unit into three parts and then designating one of these parts as $\frac{1}{3}$.   The fraction $\frac{2}{3}$ is then presented as representing two of these parts.

In the second instance 1 was first multiplied by 2 and then divided by 3.   The definition given here of $\frac{a}{b}$ follows this interpretation.   The definition of $\frac{a}{b}$ by $a\left(\frac{1}{b}\right)$ would also be possible since the steps in the argument **1.** to **6.** are reversible by appealing to the cancellation property of multiplication rather than to its being well defined.

Summary: The fraction symbol $\frac{a}{b}$ is to represent,

1. a of the b equal parts of 1, and
2. 1 of the b equal parts of a.

Since the same notation has been used for ratio, the ratio of the rational number $\frac{a}{b}$ to 1, must be the same as the ratio of the natural number a to the natural number b.

$$\frac{a}{b} = \frac{\frac{a}{b}}{1}$$

$$\frac{\frac{2}{3}}{1} = \frac{2}{3}$$

Answer to Exercise

a. If A is zero or a natural number, and if B is a natural number, then we can divide A by B and write $\frac{A}{B}$, if and only if, there exists a number C, which is zero or a natural number such that $BC = A$. Let $A = 1, B = 2$, and let C be a rational number. $1 \div 2 = \frac{1}{2}$, since $2\left(\frac{1}{2}\right) = 1$.

Problems (108)

For problems 1 and 2, complete the scales giving both decimal numerals for the natural numbers and fractions for the rational numbers where possible.

1. (number line from 0 to 1)   2. (number line from 0 to 1)

For problems 3 to 6, assume a unit length, and based on this illustrate $\frac{a}{b}$ in the following ways: **i.** $\frac{a}{b} = a\left(\frac{1}{b}\right)$;   **ii.** $\frac{a}{b} = \frac{a \cdot 1}{b}$;   **iii.** $\frac{a}{b} = \frac{\frac{a}{b}}{1}$

3. $\frac{3}{4}$ **4.** $\frac{2}{5}$ **5.** $\frac{3}{2}$ **6.** $\frac{4}{3}$

11-2. Rational Numbers, Fractions, Quotients, and Ratios

When precision seems to justify it, we shall continue to reserve the word "fraction" for the symbol used to represent a rational number, and to use "rational number" for the number itself. The rational numbers, like the natural numbers, are actually mental constructs that never appear on paper. However, the practice of using the word "fraction" when either the symbol or the number is meant, has been established by centuries of usage, and is convenient when the context makes the intended meaning clear. The term "fraction" comes from the use of this form to represent broken or fractured parts of a unit, as we have seen on a scale.

When the symbol $\frac{N}{D}$ has been used to indicate division, N has referred to the dividend, D to the divisor, and as a whole $\frac{N}{D}$ was said to be in the form of a quotient. When the fraction meaning is intended, other names are used.

The number D is then called the *denominator* of $\frac{N}{D}$. If the unit or 1 is divided into D equal parts, then the size of each part is denoted by $\frac{1}{D}$. "Denominator" comes from the same Latin root as "nominate" which means "to name." Here it characterizes the scale by specifying how the unit is subdivided.

The number N is called the *numerator* of $\frac{N}{D}$. "Numerator" comes from the same Latin root as "numeral" which means "counter." Here it records a count of the number of parts of size $\frac{1}{D}$. As an example of the distinction between fractions and rational numbers, it may be noted that fractions have numerators and denominators, but that rational numbers do not.

The fraction symbol $\frac{N}{D}$ is also used in another context, where the ratio of a first number (or antecedent) N to a second number (or consequent) D is denoted.   All of these notions, quotient, fraction, and ratio, emphasize that we are working with an ordered pair, even to the point of using different names for N and D.   But we also want to accept $\frac{N}{D}$ as representing a *single* number, a rational number.   One of the difficulties here shows up in the names for N and D.   "Numerator" is a quantitative word telling "how many," but "denominator" is qualitative and refers to "what kind."   It was difficult to accept an ordered pair of numbers as being just one number, so only one of the two numbers got a quantitative name.   Nevertheless we must be conscious that we are working with two numbers and that they are usually treated in quite different ways.

After a time we shall want to allow N and D to be written in a variety of forms, including fractions.   For the present N and D will be limited to basic numerals for the natural numbers, or to zero in the case of N, and such fractions will be called *simple* fractions.   When N is less than D, the fraction is said to be a *proper* fraction. When N is equal to or greater than D, the fraction is said to be *improper*.   Thus $\frac{4}{5}$ is a proper fraction, but $\frac{5}{5}$ and $\frac{6}{5}$ are improper.   These names reveal a prejudice that once prevailed against accepting fractions unless the number represented was less than 1.   The word "fraction" itself has a bias in meaning, as though it should refer only to part of something.   We wish to avoid these prejudices but the names would be difficult to change after such long usage.

It was the former practice to use a greater variety of notations for the several interpretations now denoted by the fraction symbol, such as $N \div D$ for division, and $N:D$ for ratio.   There are both advantages and disadvantages in trying to develop so many ideas with the same notation.   We do get greater flexibility and many analogies become more evident.   However, one must learn to supply the proper meaning from the surrounding context.   And our development must proceed slowly, since each new maneuver must be checked against the various interpretations.

Problems (109)

For problems 1 to 6: **a.** Determine the natural number represented by each quotient.   **b.** Write the equation for which the given rational number is a solution, as given directly by the definition of a rational number.   **c.** Write the simplest equation you can that has the same solution as **b.**

1. $\frac{24}{6}$ 2. $\frac{24}{4}$ 3. $\frac{108}{18}$ 4. $\frac{108}{12}$ 5. $\frac{720}{24}$ 6. $\frac{720}{45}$

7. Express the number 5 in the form of a quotient using the following divisors:
   a. 2   **b.** 7   **c.** 19   **d.** 101   **e.** 1

8. Replace 5 by an equivalent rational number, as represented by a fraction with the following denominators:

    a. 3   **b.** 11   **c.** 32   **d.** 5   **e.** 100

9. Replace 5 by an equivalent rational number, as represented by a fraction with the following numerators:

    a. 30   **b.** 85   **c.** 1000   **d.** 555

10. Express the number 5 in the form of a quotient using the following dividends:

    a. 20   **b.** 65   **c.** 300   **d.** 5

11-3. Mixed Numbers

Instead of thinking of $\frac{3}{2}$ as representing three line segments of length $\frac{1}{2}$, we may consider it as associated with one line segment of unit length together with another of length $\frac{1}{2}$. This sum could be written as $1 + \frac{1}{2}$, but by agreement the plus sign is usually left out, so we write $1\frac{1}{2}$. Similarly, $\frac{5}{2} = 2 + \frac{1}{2}$ or $2\frac{1}{2}$.

The following diagram completes the one used on page 229. It includes equivalent ways of numbering the division points, including a scale where some points are ignored.

$$\frac{0}{1} \qquad\qquad \frac{1}{1} \qquad\qquad \frac{2}{1} \qquad\qquad \frac{3}{1}$$

$$\frac{0}{2} \qquad\qquad \frac{2}{2} \quad 1\frac{1}{2} \quad \frac{4}{2} \quad 2\frac{1}{2} \quad \frac{6}{2}$$

$$0 \quad \frac{1}{2} \quad 1 \quad \frac{3}{2} \quad 2 \quad \frac{5}{2} \quad 3$$

The sums $1 + \frac{1}{2}$ and $2 + \frac{1}{2}$ are formed by a decimal numeral representing a natural number and a fraction representing a rational number. It is the distinction between these two kinds of numbers that makes possible the simpler notation where the plus sign is omitted. Thus, $1\frac{1}{2}$ and $2\frac{1}{2}$ are known as mixed numbers, although mixed numerals would be better when the notation itself is being discussed. The fraction part of this mixture will usually be, but need not always be, a proper fraction. The change from an improper fraction form such as $\frac{3}{2}$ to the equivalent mixed numeral form of $1\frac{1}{2}$ is a quotient to sum transformation and hence may be analyzed as an extension of the distributive property to rational numbers. However, we have not as yet formally defined any of the binary operations on the rational numbers. The reader may question why this has not been done, since logically the most efficient procedure would have been to begin this chapter with a statement of all the assumptions we plan to use. Our purpose in delaying this and approaching our task in a tentative manner is to get as much insight as possible into the reasons the operations on fractions are defined as they are. Such decisions have not been made in an arbitrary fashion. Two principles serve as guideposts in the extension of number systems to include other numbers besides zero and the natural numbers.

A. *The new numbers should be useful.* One can count with the natural numbers, but measurement brings a need for the rationals. The definitions of sums, products, and so on of rational numbers should enable one to work with lengths, areas, volumes, and other measurements in a meaningful way.

B. *If at all possible, the new numbers should obey the same laws as the old.* Thus it is desired that the commutative, associative, and distributive principles still be valid, as well as properties of zero and one, and other general statements that have been written as identities. Without this, the extended system would tend to break down under the weight of its own complications.

The identity $\frac{A+B}{C} = \frac{A}{C} + \frac{B}{C}$, states that division is right-distributive with respect to addition, or alternatively, that the division operator $\frac{}{C}$ distributes over the sum $A + B$. Section 3-4 stated the assumption that both A and B were either zero or multiples of C. This restriction will now be removed.

Let $\frac{A}{C}$ be the rational number X, so that $A = CX$ by definition.

Let $\frac{B}{C}$ be the rational number Y, so that $B = CY$ by definition.

Then $A + B = CX + CY$, since addition is well defined.
$$= C(X + Y),$$
if the distributive principle is assumed to apply to rational numbers also.

Hence $\frac{A+B}{C} = X + Y$, by the definition of rational numbers.

And $\frac{A+B}{C} = \frac{A}{C} + \frac{B}{C}$ by substitution.

The introduction of the variables X and Y in the above argument was for convenience only, so that the notation would be simplified. The reader is asked to verify this in problem 21 of the next set. The extended principle is useful in changing improper fractions to the mixed numeral form.

Examples:

A.	B.	C.	D.	E.
$\dfrac{3}{2}$	$\dfrac{2+1}{2}$	$\dfrac{2}{2}+\dfrac{1}{2}$	$1+\dfrac{1}{2}$	$1\dfrac{1}{2}$
$\dfrac{5}{2}$	$\dfrac{4+1}{2}$	$\dfrac{4}{2}+\dfrac{1}{2}$	$2+\dfrac{1}{2}$	$2\dfrac{1}{2}$
$\dfrac{23}{5}$	$\dfrac{20+3}{5}$	$\dfrac{20}{5}+\dfrac{3}{5}$	$4+\dfrac{3}{5}$	$4\dfrac{3}{5}$

A. An improper fraction.

B. The numerator is expressed as a sum: One of the two addends is the largest multiple of the denominator that is not greater than the numerator.

C. The division is distributed.

D. One of the quotients can be replaced by a basic numeral for a natural number, the other represents a rational number.

E. The plus sign may be omitted if we agree it is there when needed.

Problems (110)

For problems 1 to 8, show steps **A.**, **B.**, **C.**, **D.**, and **E.**, as in the examples above.

1. $\dfrac{11}{2}$ **2.** $\dfrac{8}{3}$ **3.** $\dfrac{23}{4}$ **4.** $\dfrac{32}{7}$ **5.** $\dfrac{67}{9}$ **6.** $\dfrac{69}{8}$ **7.** $\dfrac{200}{13}$ **8.** $\dfrac{100}{17}$

For problems 9 to 14, give the same steps as in 1 to 8, but in reverse order.

9. $3\dfrac{2}{5}$ **10.** $1\dfrac{1}{9}$ **11.** $1\dfrac{5}{7}$ **12.** $8\dfrac{8}{9}$ **13.** $10\dfrac{1}{3}$ **14.** $25\dfrac{3}{4}$

For problems 15 to 20, the transformation is to be made mentally, writing down only the final result. Change each improper fraction to an equivalent mixed number, and each mixed number to an equivalent improper fraction.

15. $\dfrac{31}{2}$ **16.** $33\dfrac{1}{3}$ **17.** $8\dfrac{1}{3}$ **18.** $\dfrac{50}{3}$ **19.** $37\dfrac{1}{2}$ **20.** $87\dfrac{1}{2}$

21. Give the steps of the argument in the text that $\dfrac{A+B}{C}=\dfrac{A}{C}+\dfrac{B}{C}$, but without introducing X and Y.

22. See if you can reverse the argument in the text and hence show that $\dfrac{A}{C}+\dfrac{B}{C}=\dfrac{A+B}{C}$, if $C\neq 0$.

11-4. Equivalent Fractions

The following scale diagram includes instances of equivalent fractions that have not yet been discussed. Thus $\dfrac{4}{8},\dfrac{2}{4}$, and $\dfrac{1}{2}$ are found to measure the same segment.

Hence we set $\dfrac{4}{8} = \dfrac{2}{4} = \dfrac{1}{2}$ and consider these different fractions as being equivalent in the sense of being different names for the same rational number.

$$\dfrac{0}{1} \qquad\qquad\qquad\qquad\qquad\qquad\qquad\qquad\qquad\qquad\qquad\qquad \dfrac{1}{1}$$

$$\dfrac{0}{2} \qquad\qquad\qquad\qquad\qquad \dfrac{1}{2} \qquad\qquad\qquad\qquad\qquad \dfrac{2}{2}$$

$$\dfrac{0}{4} \qquad\qquad \dfrac{1}{4} \qquad\qquad \dfrac{2}{4} \qquad\qquad \dfrac{3}{4} \qquad\qquad \dfrac{4}{4}$$

$$\dfrac{0}{8} \quad \dfrac{1}{8} \quad \dfrac{2}{8} \quad \dfrac{3}{8} \quad \dfrac{4}{8} \quad \dfrac{5}{8} \quad \dfrac{6}{8} \quad \dfrac{7}{8} \quad \dfrac{8}{8}$$

0   1

Suppose that a rational number x is represented by the fraction $\dfrac{a}{b}$ and also by the fraction $\dfrac{c}{d}$. Then $a = bx$ and $c = dx$ by definition.

But if $a = bx$, then $ad = bxd$ if multiplication is well defined, and $ad = bdx$, if the commutative and associative properties hold.
Again if $c = dx$, then $bc = bdx$, if multiplication is well defined.
Hence $ad = bc$, by the properties of equality.

Conversely, let x be the rational number represented by the fraction $\dfrac{a}{b}$ and let y be the rational number represented by the fraction $\dfrac{c}{d}$. Then if $ad = bc$, x and y are the same rational number as the following argument shows:

If $\dfrac{a}{b} = x$, then $a = bx$ and $ad = bdx$.

If $\dfrac{c}{d} = y$, then $c = dy$ and $bc = bdy$.

Hence if $ad = bc$, then $bdx = bdy$ or $(bd)x = (bd)y$.
Therefore, $x = y$, since $bd \neq 0$.

Summary: Two fractions $\dfrac{a}{b}$ and $\dfrac{c}{d}$ are equivalent, and represent the same rational number, if and only if $ad = bc$ and $bd \neq 0$. This is commonly known as the cross-product test for equivalence of fractions.

On the following diagram the same length has been assigned to 1 on both scales. The upper scale has 21 equal subdivisions for this unit while the lower scale shows only 7; $\dfrac{6}{21}$ and $\dfrac{2}{7}$ are both assigned to the same point.

The two fractions $\dfrac{6}{21}$ and $\dfrac{2}{7}$ meet the cross-product test for equivalence since $6 \cdot 7 = 42 = 21 \cdot 2$. Both 6 and 21 are divisible by 3, and we note that the lower scale could be related to the upper by retaining only every third division point on the upper scale.

The numbers 2 and 7 are relatively prime and a study of the scale reveals that no smaller numbers than these can be used for a fraction that measures the same length that $\dfrac{6}{21}$ and $\dfrac{2}{7}$ do. A fraction whose numerator and denominator are relatively prime is said to be in lowest terms.

The relation between $\dfrac{6}{21}$ and $\dfrac{2}{7}$ is more evident if both the numerator and denominator of $\dfrac{6}{21}$ are written in prime factored form as $\dfrac{2 \cdot 3}{3 \cdot 7}$. When the cross-product test is applied to $\dfrac{2 \cdot 3}{3 \cdot 7}$ and $\dfrac{2}{7}$, we have $2 \cdot 3 \cdot 7 = 3 \cdot 7 \cdot 2$. This suggests the following generalization.

If A is zero, or a natural number, and B and N are natural numbers, it follows from $(AN)B = (BN)A$ that

$$\frac{AN}{BN} = \frac{A}{B}$$

If both the numerator and the denominator of a fraction are multiplied or divided by the same natural number, the result is an equivalent fraction that represents the same rational number as before.

For a given multiplier N, this transformation can be interpreted graphically by multiplying or dividing the number of scale divisions by N. Thus, for the previous example, $\dfrac{2}{7}$ became $\dfrac{6}{21}$ when the number of equal subdivisions of the unit was tripled. And the change from $\dfrac{6}{21}$ back to $\dfrac{2}{7}$ was accomplished by recognizing only every third division point.

If the numerator and denominator of a fraction are in prime factored form, then the reduction of the fraction to lowest terms is done simply by observing those common factors that might be omitted from both the numerator and denominator.

This follows from the fact that removing a factor is the same as removing a multiplication operator, which is equivalent to dividing by the factor removed.

Example:

$$\frac{6}{21} = \frac{2 \cdot 3}{3 \cdot 7} = \frac{3 \cdot 2}{3 \cdot 7} = \frac{2}{7}$$

Removing the multiplication operator $3 \cdot$ from $3 \cdot 2$ divides the numerator by 3.

Removing the multiplication operator $3 \cdot$ from $3 \cdot 7$ divides the denominator by 3.

Since both the numerator and denominator of $\frac{6}{21}$ have thus been divided by 3, the resulting fraction of $\frac{2}{7}$ must be equivalent to $\frac{6}{21}$.

The transformation from $\frac{A}{B}$ to $\frac{AN}{BN}$ or from $\frac{AN}{BN}$ to $\frac{A}{B}$ is of central importance in the study of rational numbers and is used repeatedly in the computations with the fractions which represent these numbers. Hence, we give several more models as evidence of its validity. Each will be a verification of $\frac{2}{3} = \frac{4}{6}$.

Examples:

1. $\frac{2}{3}$ and $\frac{4}{6}$ are measures of the same magnitude.

2.

$$2 \div 3 = \frac{2}{3} \qquad 4 \div 6 = \frac{4}{6}$$

In general if $A \div B = X$, then $A = BX$ by definition.

But if $A = BX$, then $AN = BXN = (BN)X$.

But if $AN = (BN)X$, then $AN \div BN = X$ by definition, if $N \neq 0$.

Hence, $A \div B = AN \div BN$, or $\frac{A}{B} = \frac{AN}{BN}$.

3.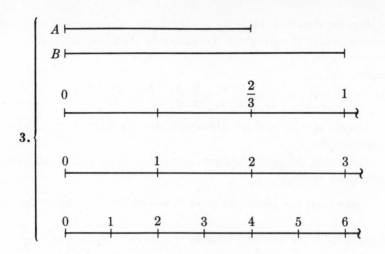

Ratio comparisons are not affected by a change of scale.   Hence, the ratio of length A to length B is:

$$\frac{2}{3} \text{ to } 1 \qquad \text{or } \frac{2}{3}$$

$$2 \text{ to } 3 \qquad \text{or } 2{:}3$$

$$4 \text{ to } 6 \qquad \text{or } 4{:}6$$

One should think of a rational number, such as the one represented by the fraction $\frac{2}{3}$, as associated with a collection or family of fractions.   For $\frac{2}{3}$ the members of this family are members of the set $\frac{2}{3}, \frac{2 \cdot 2}{2 \cdot 3}, \frac{3 \cdot 2}{3 \cdot 3}, \frac{4 \cdot 2}{4 \cdot 3}, \cdots, \frac{N \cdot 2}{N \cdot 3}, \cdots$. There is one member of this family that is unique by reason of its numerator and denominator being relatively prime.   This fraction, $\frac{2}{3}$, is then selected as the basic numeral for identifying this particular rational number.   However, for computations with this number, some member of the family other than $\frac{2}{3}$ may well be the preferred form.

For any two rational numbers x and y we can determine representations for each in the form of fractions having the same denominator.   This denominator which is common to both fractions will be a multiple of each of the two given denominators.

If $x = \frac{a}{b}$, and $y = \frac{c}{d}$,

then $x = \frac{ad}{bd}$, and $y = \frac{bc}{bd}$, since $b \neq 0$, and $d \neq 0$.

Graphically this means that for any two fractions a linear scale can always be constructed with both of these fractions assigned to scale points.

Example: To construct a scale by which both $\frac{2}{3}$ and $\frac{4}{5}$ of a unit can be measured.

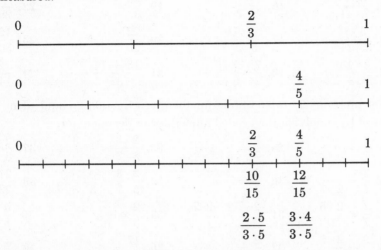

Such constructions will be used many times and are greatly facilitated if a square-ruled blackboard is available for class demonstration, and if the student works on square-ruled (coordinate) paper.

The majority of computations with fractions are simplified if both the numerator and denominator are in prime factored form. Then one cannot only divide both the numerator and denominator by removing a common factor from each, but also the numerator and denominator can both be multiplied by any desired natural number by joining the same multiplication operator to each of them.

Problems (111)

For problems 1 to 4, illustrate with two scales, one over the other and having the same unit length, but with different subdivisions.

1. $\frac{2}{5} = \frac{4}{10}$ 2. $\frac{3}{4} = \frac{6}{8}$ 3. $\frac{3}{2} = \frac{9}{6}$ 4. $\frac{4}{3} = \frac{8}{6}$

Give a graphical model that verifies that the quotients in problems 5 to 8 are equal.

5. $\frac{2}{5} = \frac{4}{10}$ 6. $\frac{3}{4} = \frac{6}{8}$ 7. $\frac{3}{2} = \frac{9}{6}$ 8. $\frac{4}{3} = \frac{8}{6}$

Show that the ratios in problems 9 to 12 are equal by measuring two lengths, and repeating the measurement with a scale having a different unit length.

9. $\frac{2}{5} = \frac{4}{10}$ 10. $\frac{3}{4} = \frac{6}{8}$ 11. $\frac{3}{2} = \frac{9}{6}$ 12. $\frac{4}{3} = \frac{8}{6}$

For problems 13 to 24 reduce each fraction to an equivalent fraction to lowest terms. Do not change any improper fractions to mixed numbers.

13. $\dfrac{3 \cdot 7}{3 \cdot 11}$ 16. $\dfrac{5}{5 \cdot 7}$ 19. $\dfrac{25}{35}$ 22. $\dfrac{11}{29 + 15}$

14. $\dfrac{5 \cdot 7}{7 \cdot 11}$ 17. $\dfrac{5^2 \cdot 7^3}{5^3 \cdot 7}$ 20. $\dfrac{72}{90}$ 23. $\dfrac{12 + 3}{30 + 3}$

15. $\dfrac{3 \cdot 13}{13}$ 18. $\dfrac{2 \cdot 3^2 \cdot 5}{2^2 \cdot 5 \cdot 7}$ 21. $\dfrac{13 + 15}{32}$ 24. $\dfrac{2 \cdot 7}{14 + 7}$

For problems 25 to 40 obtain for the given fraction an equivalent fraction as specified by supplying the needed numerator or denominator.

25. $\dfrac{2}{7} = \dfrac{}{3 \cdot 7}$ 29. $\dfrac{2}{7} = \dfrac{}{3 \cdot 7 \cdot 11}$ 33. $\dfrac{2 \cdot 3}{5 \cdot 7} = \dfrac{2 \cdot 3^2}{}$ 37. $\dfrac{2}{3} = \dfrac{104}{}$

26. $\dfrac{2}{7} = \dfrac{}{2 \cdot 7}$ 30. $\dfrac{2}{7} = \dfrac{2 \cdot 3^2}{}$ 34. $\dfrac{2 \cdot 3}{5 \cdot 7} = \dfrac{}{3 \cdot 5 \cdot 7}$ 38. $\dfrac{21}{22} = \dfrac{273}{}$

27. $\dfrac{2}{7} = \dfrac{2 \cdot 5}{}$ 31. $\dfrac{2}{7} = \dfrac{2 \cdot 3 \cdot 7}{}$ 35. $\dfrac{2}{3} = \dfrac{}{105}$ 39. $\dfrac{a}{b} = \dfrac{a^3 c}{}$

28. $\dfrac{2}{7} = \dfrac{2 \cdot 7}{}$ 32. $\dfrac{2}{7} = \dfrac{}{2 \cdot 3 \cdot 7}$ 36. $\dfrac{17}{24} = \dfrac{}{288}$ 40. $\dfrac{a}{b} = \dfrac{}{abc}$

For problems 41 to 46 construct a scale on which each of the several fractions of the group will appear at some division point.

41. $\dfrac{1}{3}, \dfrac{3}{5}$ 42. $\dfrac{3}{4}, \dfrac{3}{5}$ 43. $\dfrac{1}{2}, \dfrac{2}{3}, \dfrac{3}{4}$ 44. $\dfrac{1}{3}, \dfrac{2}{9}$ 45. $\dfrac{3}{4}, \dfrac{5}{6}$ 46. $\dfrac{2}{3}, \dfrac{5}{6}, \dfrac{11}{18}$

Problems 47 to 54 involve a pair of fractions. Supply the missing numerators and/or denominators to meet all of the following conditions:

A. Each fraction is to be replaced by an equivalent fraction.

B. Both denominators of the resulting fractions are to be the same.

C. This common denominator is to be the l.c.m. of the denominators of the given fractions.

47. $\begin{cases} \dfrac{2}{3} = \dfrac{}{3 \cdot 5} \\[2mm] \dfrac{2^2}{5} = \dfrac{}{3 \cdot 5} \end{cases}$ 49. $\begin{cases} \dfrac{2}{3^2} = \underline{} \\[2mm] \dfrac{5}{3^3} = \underline{} \end{cases}$ 51. $\begin{cases} \dfrac{5}{2^4 \cdot 3} = \underline{} \\[2mm] \dfrac{19}{2^2 \cdot 3 \cdot 5} = \underline{} \end{cases}$ 53. $\begin{cases} \dfrac{13}{36} \\[2mm] \dfrac{19}{60} \end{cases}$

48. $\begin{cases} \dfrac{3}{2 \cdot 5} = \dfrac{}{2 \cdot 3 \cdot 5 \cdot 7} \\[2mm] \dfrac{5}{3 \cdot 7} = \dfrac{}{2 \cdot 3 \cdot 5 \cdot 7} \end{cases}$ 50. $\begin{cases} \dfrac{3}{2} = \underline{} \\[2mm] \dfrac{5}{2 \cdot 3} = \underline{} \end{cases}$ 52. $\begin{cases} \dfrac{11}{2 \cdot 7} \\[2mm] \dfrac{2}{7^2 \cdot 11} \end{cases}$ 54. $\begin{cases} \dfrac{8}{25} \\[2mm] \dfrac{15}{22} \end{cases}$

For Further Study

Functional scales are sometimes called graphic scales in engineering practice, where these scales are often used.   Refer to [L4], pp. 372–378; [R4], pp. 80–87; and [S10], pp. 259–266, 275–277.

In this text the positive rational numbers are discussed before the integers, which is the historical order and the order of presentation in the elementary schools. For an introduction to fractions that also follows this order see [H2], pp. 139–143; and [W3], pp. 125–130.

Reference [H5], pp. 68–78, has an interesting collection of historical uses of fractions. For a fuller account of their history, see [S12], Vol. II, pp. 208–235.

12

Addition and Subtraction of Rational Numbers

12-1. Sums and Differences of Quotients

A study of the history of mathematics reveals that the concept of a rational number developed very slowly over a period of thousands of years. The algorithms for the operations on these numbers were worked out by trial and error, with the principal motivation coming from the practical problems of measurement, where numbers had to be assigned to parts of some assumed unit. It has been only in the past century and a half that the logical structure of these numbers and the natural numbers has become clear, even to scholars in the field. Even today the best plan for the beginning student is probably to seek first for an intuitive grasp of facts that seem useful and reasonable and let the logical arguments come later. Since the readers of this text are presumed to be returning to fractions for a second look, the historical order can be reversed. The logical structure can be developed first. We can then verify that the mathematical system thus created is a useful tool, with which practical problems can be solved.

To put this plan into action one needs to make essentially only one assumption, that of logical simplicity. By this we mean that the laws that hold for the natural numbers will be assumed to also hold for the rational numbers. Exceptions will be made only if a contradiction develops, or if physical models suggest a modification should be made.

In the quotient $\frac{a}{b}$ let b be a natural number, and for the present let a be either zero or a multiple of b. In this case $\frac{a}{b}$ represents either zero or a natural number x and we can write $\frac{a}{b} = x$.

Again, in the quotient $\frac{c}{d}$ let d be a natural number, and let c be zero or a mul-

tiple of d. We can then write $\frac{c}{d} = y$, where y is zero or a natural number.

Then $a = bx$ and $c = dy$.	From $\frac{a}{b} = x$, and $\frac{c}{d} = y$, using the definition of division.
Then $ad = bdx$ and $bc = bdy$	Since the multiplication of natural numbers is well defined, commutative and associative.
Hence, $ad + bc = bdx + bdy$	Addition is well defined.
$\qquad\qquad = bd(x + y)$	Distributive property.

Observe that $ad + bc$ is zero or a natural number, and that bd is a natural number because of closure for addition and multiplication.

Therefore $x + y = \dfrac{ad + bc}{bd}$ \qquad From the definition of division.

and $\dfrac{a}{b} + \dfrac{c}{d} = \dfrac{ad + bc}{bd}$ \qquad Substituting $\frac{a}{b}$ for x, and $\frac{c}{d}$ for y.

Under the conditions stated the sum of the two quotients $\frac{a}{b}$ and $\frac{c}{d}$ will always represent the same number as the single quotient $\dfrac{ad + bc}{bd}$.

We now remove the restriction that a be a multiple of b and that c be a multiple of d, so that x and y can represent rational numbers.   However, if the same principles hold as for natural numbers then the reasoning is unchanged and we have a formula for the sum of two rational numbers.   Or, in terms of the symbols used, we can now add any two simple fractions.

The sum of the rational number represented by $\frac{a}{b}$ *and the rational number repre-*

sented by $\frac{c}{d}$ *is the rational number represented by* $\dfrac{ad + bc}{bd}$.   The replacement of

$\frac{a}{b} + \frac{c}{d}$ by $\dfrac{ad + bc}{bd}$ is called *addition of fractions*.   It might also be termed a sum to

quotient transformation.   The student will find that the phrase "addition of fractions" is used in the literature to mean both a binary operation on rational numbers and a manipulation of fraction symbols.   This need not lead to error if one can infer from the context which meaning is intended.

In the next problem set the reader will be asked to use reasoning similar to the

above to show that if $\frac{a}{b}$ and $\frac{c}{d}$ are rational numbers with ad greater than or equal

to bc, then $\dfrac{a}{b} - \dfrac{c}{d} = \dfrac{ad - bc}{bd}$.

Both of these results can also be derived in another way.   Assume that both a

and b are either zero or multiples of c.   Then $\frac{a}{c} = x$ and $\frac{b}{c} = y$ are either zero or

natural numbers.   Hence $a = cx$ and $b = cy$ and $a + b = cx + cy$, from the definition of division and because addition is well defined.   The distributive principle

allows us to conclude that $a + b = c(x + y)$. Hence, $x + y = \dfrac{a+b}{c}$, and then
$\dfrac{a}{c} + \dfrac{b}{c} = \dfrac{a+b}{c}$. The chain of reasoning here is exactly that used in the previous case, but is here restricted to those quotients having the same divisors. By again removing the restriction that a and b be multiples of c, we get a rule for adding two fractions with like denominators. To make use of this in getting the sum of $\dfrac{a}{b}$ and $\dfrac{c}{d}$, we first replace $\dfrac{a}{b}$ and $\dfrac{c}{d}$ by appropriate equivalent fractions.

$$\frac{a}{b} + \frac{c}{d} = \frac{ad}{bd} + \frac{bc}{bd} = \frac{ad+bc}{bd}, \text{ as before}$$

And $\dfrac{a}{b} - \dfrac{c}{d} = \dfrac{ad}{bd} - \dfrac{bc}{bd} = \dfrac{ad-bc}{bd}$, if bc is not greater than ad. Since $\dfrac{a}{b} + \dfrac{c}{d} = \dfrac{ad+bc}{bd}$ applies to the sum of any two rational numbers, the binary operation of addition is closed in the set of natural numbers. We next want to show that this operation is well defined; that is, that the sum of two rational numbers does not depend on the choice of fraction names used for these numbers in the computation.

Let $\dfrac{a}{b} = \dfrac{e}{f}$ so that $af = be$.

Then $\dfrac{a}{b} + \dfrac{c}{d} = \dfrac{e}{f} + \dfrac{c}{d}$ By substitution.

$\qquad = \dfrac{ed+fc}{fd}$ Sum of two fractions.

$\qquad = \dfrac{b(ed+fc)}{bfd}$ Multiply both numerator and denominator by b.

$\qquad = \dfrac{bed+bfc}{bfd}$

$\qquad = \dfrac{(be)d+f(bc)}{f(bd)}$ The distributive, commutative, and associative principles have all been used.

$\qquad = \dfrac{(af)d+f(bc)}{f(bd)}$ Substituting af for be.

$\qquad = \dfrac{f(ad+bc)}{f(bd)}$ Again using the distributive, commutative, and associative principles.

$\qquad = \dfrac{ad+bc}{bd}$ Dividing both numerator and denominator by f (which is not zero).

Hence, we get the same result when the addend $\dfrac{a}{b}$ is replaced by the equivalent fraction $\dfrac{e}{f}$. In the same way $\dfrac{c}{d}$ can be replaced by an equivalent fraction without changing the sum.

Problems (112)

1. Give the steps of the argument that $\frac{a}{b} + \frac{c}{d} = \frac{ad + bc}{bd}$ with $a = 10$, $b = 2$, $c = 12$, $d = 3$, $x = 5$, and $y = 4$. Avoid any computation since this covers up the pattern being illustrated.

2. Give the steps of the argument that $\frac{a}{b} + \frac{c}{d} = \frac{ad + bc}{bd}$ without introducing x and y as done in the text.

3. Show that if ad is greater than or equal to bc, then $\frac{a}{b} - \frac{c}{d} = \frac{ad - bc}{bd}$.

4. Follow the directions for problem 3, using $a = 10$, $b = 2$, $c = 12$, $d = 3$, $x = 5$, $y = 4$. Do no computation.

5. Show that the rational number represented by $\frac{0}{a}$, where a is any natural number, is an additive identity for addition of rational numbers.

6. Show that the addition of rational numbers is commutative.

7. Show that the cancellation principle for addition holds for rational numbers. This means that if $\frac{a}{b} + \frac{e}{f} = \frac{c}{d} + \frac{e}{f}$, then $\frac{a}{b} = \frac{c}{d}$.

8. Show that if $\frac{c}{d} = \frac{e}{f}$, then $\frac{a}{b} + \frac{c}{d} = \frac{a}{b} + \frac{e}{f}$.

12-2. Sums and Differences of Magnitudes

We now wish to verify that the computation rules developed in Section 12-1 for the sum and difference of two fractions can be applied to problems arising in the measurement of magnitudes. The illustrative models will be based on the lengths of line segments. If $\frac{a}{b}$ represents the length of one line segment and $\frac{c}{d}$ the length of another, then we wish $\frac{a}{b} + \frac{c}{d}$ to represent the combined length of the two segments and $\frac{a}{b} - \frac{c}{d}$ or $\frac{c}{d} - \frac{a}{b}$ to represent the difference of their lengths.

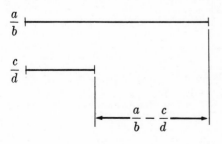
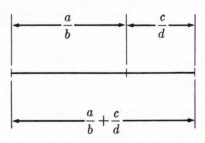

One of the graphic models for addition given in Section 9-2 can readily be extended to the addition of rational numbers.

Example: $\frac{2}{3} + \frac{1}{2} = ?$

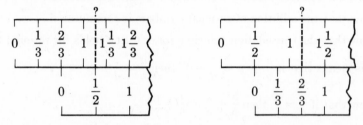

There are two ways to set the zero of one scale in correspondence with one of the addends on the other scale, but in neither case can one state what number should be assigned to the desired sum. The sum of $\frac{2}{3}$ and $\frac{1}{2}$ is greater than 1, but it is less than $1\frac{1}{3}$ or $1\frac{1}{2}$, and it cannot be measured exactly on either scale.

It was shown in Section 11-4 that a linear scale can always be constructed so that fractions representing any two rational numbers will be assigned to scale points. For $\frac{2}{3}$ and $\frac{1}{2}$ such a scale requires that the number of equal subdivisions of the unit be a multiple of both 2 and 3.

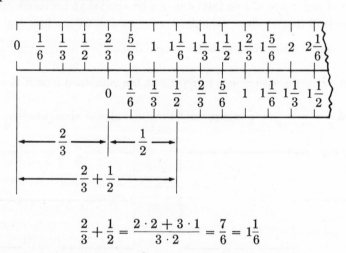

$$\frac{2}{3} + \frac{1}{2} = \frac{2 \cdot 2 + 3 \cdot 1}{3 \cdot 2} = \frac{7}{6} = 1\frac{1}{6}$$

The scales are identical. They are shifted so that the zero point of the lower scale coincides with $\frac{2}{3}$ on the upper scale. The sum, $1\frac{1}{6}$, is then found on the upper scale, corresponding to $\frac{1}{2}$ on the lower scale.

The pairs of numbers at corresponding scale points are now such that the upper number represents an increase of $\frac{2}{3}$ of the lower. We can observe that $0 + \frac{2}{3} = \frac{2}{3}$, $\frac{1}{6} + \frac{2}{3} = \frac{5}{6}, \frac{1}{3} + \frac{2}{3} = 1, \frac{1}{2} + \frac{2}{3} = 1\frac{1}{6}, \frac{2}{3} + \frac{2}{3} = 1\frac{1}{3}$, and so on. If we choose the lower number as the first component of an ordered pair, and the upper number as the second component, these ordered pairs are from the mapping $x \to x + \frac{2}{3}$, or the function $f(x) = x + \frac{2}{3}$.

$x + \frac{2}{3}$	$\frac{2}{3}$	$\frac{5}{6}$	1	$1\frac{1}{6}$	$1\frac{1}{3}$	$1\frac{1}{2}$
x	0	$\frac{1}{6}$	$\frac{1}{3}$	$\frac{1}{2}$	$\frac{2}{3}$	$\frac{5}{6}$

The vector models for addition and subtraction operators extend directly to rational numbers. From now on we will assume, unless otherwise restricted, that rational numbers can be substitutes for x in the addition operator $+ x$, and the subtraction operator $- x$.

One reason for using the fraction notation for the ratio of a to b is that the identity $\frac{a}{b} = \frac{na}{nb}$ holds for a ratio interpretation. But there can be difficulties with binary operations on rational numbers if the fraction symbols are thought of as representing ratios.

Example: A certain basketball team won 3 out of 5 of its games during the first part of the season. During the final part they won 6 out of 11. What was the ratio of games won to games played for the entire season?

	First part of season	Final part of season
Games won	* * *	* * * * * *
Games played	* * * * *	* * * * * * * * * *

The ratio of games won to games played was $\frac{3}{5}$ for the first part of the season, it was $\frac{6}{11}$ for the final part of the season, and it was $\frac{9}{16}$ for the entire season. Let us consider a possible binary operation of combining the first two ratios to produce the third. We would have

$$\frac{3}{5} \boxplus \frac{6}{11} = \frac{3+6}{5+11} \qquad \text{or in general} \qquad \frac{a}{b} \boxplus \frac{c}{d} = \frac{a+c}{b+d}$$

What we have designated as $\boxplus$ cannot properly be called addition, as previously defined for the sum of quotients and the sum of magnitudes, since we have decided that

$$\frac{3}{5} + \frac{6}{11} = \frac{3 \cdot 11 + 5 \cdot 6}{5 \cdot 11} = \frac{63}{55} = 1\frac{8}{55}$$

Sometimes when students have forgotten how correctly to obtain the sum of two rational numbers, they "invent" the operation we have designated $\boxplus$ and state that they have the sum of two fractions. But this is in error since $\frac{a}{b} + \frac{c}{d} = \frac{ad + bc}{bd}$ comes from interpreting the fractions as rational numbers, *but not as ratios*.

Problems (113)

For problems 1 to 10, the sum should be computed mentally, writing down only the final result. Do not change improper fractions to mixed numbers.

1. $\frac{1}{2} + \frac{2}{5}$ 3. $\frac{1}{3} + \frac{4}{5}$ 5. $\frac{1}{4} + \frac{2}{9}$ 7. $\frac{7}{8} - \frac{2}{3}$ 9. $\frac{5}{4} - \frac{2}{3}$

2. $\frac{3}{5} + \frac{1}{4}$ 4. $\frac{2}{3} + \frac{3}{8}$ 6. $\frac{2}{3} + \frac{2}{7}$ 8. $\frac{4}{5} - \frac{3}{7}$ 10. $\frac{7}{6} - \frac{4}{5}$

For problems 11 to 20, construct a model based on two scales.

11. $\frac{1}{3} + \frac{1}{4}$ 13. $\frac{3}{2} + \frac{5}{3}$ 15. $\frac{4}{5} + \frac{3}{2}$ 17. $\frac{1}{2} - \frac{2}{7}$ 19. $\frac{5}{4} - \frac{4}{5}$

12. $\frac{2}{5} + \frac{1}{2}$ 14. $\frac{4}{3} + \frac{3}{4}$ 16. $\frac{3}{5} + \frac{2}{3}$ 18. $\frac{3}{4} - \frac{1}{3}$ 20. $\frac{7}{3} - \frac{3}{2}$

For problems 21 to 24, illustrate as the sum of vectors.

21. $\frac{2}{3} + \frac{2}{5}$ 22. $\frac{1}{2} + \frac{5}{7}$ 23. $\frac{5}{3} - \frac{5}{4}$ 24. $\frac{7}{2} - \frac{5}{3}$

25. Construct an alternate proof for $\dfrac{a}{b} + \dfrac{c}{d} = \dfrac{ad+bc}{bd}$, assuming $\dfrac{a}{b} = a\left(\dfrac{1}{b}\right)$ and that multiplication is distributive over addition for rationals.

26. Construct two examples of $\dfrac{a}{b} + \dfrac{c}{d} = \dfrac{ad+bc}{bd}$, where a is a multiple of b, c is a multiple of d, and b and d are relatively prime.

27. Graph the function $f(x) = x + \dfrac{2}{3}$ for $x = 0, \dfrac{1}{6}, \dfrac{1}{3}, \dfrac{1}{2}, \dfrac{2}{3}, \dfrac{5}{6}, 1$.

28. Graph the function $f(x) = x - \dfrac{3}{4}$ for $x = \dfrac{3}{4}, 1, 1\dfrac{1}{4}, 1\dfrac{1}{2}, 1\dfrac{3}{4}, 2$.

If $\dfrac{a}{b} + \dfrac{c}{d} = \dfrac{ad+bc}{bd}$ is applied to the sum $\dfrac{5}{6} + \dfrac{8}{15}$ the result is

$$\frac{5}{6} + \frac{8}{15} = \frac{5 \cdot 15 + 6 \cdot 8}{6 \cdot 15} = \frac{75 + 48}{90} = \frac{123}{90}$$

But $\dfrac{123}{90}$ is not in lowest terms, since

$$\frac{123}{90} = \frac{3 \cdot 41}{3 \cdot 30} = \frac{41}{30} = 1\frac{11}{30} \quad \text{or} \quad \frac{123}{90} = 1\frac{33}{90} = 1\frac{3 \cdot 11}{3 \cdot 30} = 1\frac{11}{30}$$

This final reduction to lower terms could have been anticipated by an observation of the given denominators, 6 and 15. The computation above could be illustrated graphically by using two linear scales having 90 equal subdivisions of the unit length. But $\dfrac{5}{6}$ and $\dfrac{8}{15}$ are also scale points on a scale with only 30 subdivisions of the unit length. All that is required is that the number of such divisions be a multiple of both 6 and 15. The product of 6 and 15 is 90 and this is surely such a multiple. But 90 is not the least common multiple of 6 and 15, which 30 is. The product of two natural numbers gives their l.c.m. only when the numbers are relatively prime, which is not the case with 6 and 15. We now return to our example to show how the l.c.m. of the denominator can be used in computing the sum.

The first step is to rewrite the fractions with their denominators in prime factored form.

$$\frac{5}{6} + \frac{8}{15} = \frac{5}{2 \cdot 3} + \frac{8}{3 \cdot 5}$$

It is now easy to determine that the l.c.m. of $2 \cdot 3$ and $3 \cdot 5$ is $2 \cdot 3 \cdot 5$. With this in mind, the two given fractions can be replaced by two equivalent fractions, both of which have $2 \cdot 3 \cdot 5$ for denominators. As soon as we have two fractions with the same denominator, the identity $\dfrac{a}{c} + \dfrac{b}{c} = \dfrac{a+b}{c}$ applies.

$$\frac{5}{6} + \frac{8}{15} = \frac{5}{2 \cdot 3} + \frac{8}{3 \cdot 5}$$

$$= \frac{5 \cdot 5}{2 \cdot 3 \cdot 5} + \frac{2 \cdot 8}{2 \cdot 3 \cdot 5}$$

$$= \frac{5 \cdot 5 + 2 \cdot 8}{2 \cdot 3 \cdot 5} = \frac{41}{30} = 1\frac{11}{30}$$

When the above computation is compared with that first given for computing this sum, we note the final reduction to lowest terms is avoided and we do work with smaller numbers since the l.c.m. of the two denominators is less than their product. But the overall gain in effectiveness is not too impressive. The usual recommendation in elementary arithmetics has been to always use the l.c.m. of the denominators in computing the sum of two fractions. But this advice is often questionable. Much of the time it is not worth the trouble to get this l.c.m. Rather one should use the product of the denominators for the common denominator. The definition of the sum as $\frac{a}{b} + \frac{c}{d} = \frac{ad + bc}{bd}$ gives us a direct computation consisting of three multiplications followed by an addition of two of these products. One may still have to reduce this to lower terms, and this will always be true when the denominators are not relatively prime. But this is a simple task if the final numerator and denominator are not too large.

The clear cut advantage in using the l.c.m. is more likely to arise when one is computing the sum of more than two fractions, since

$$\frac{A_1}{B} + \frac{A_2}{B} + \cdots + \frac{A_n}{B} = \frac{A_1 + A_2 + \cdots + A_n}{B}$$

Also, computations involving both addition and subtraction can be readily handled by using a common denominator since, for example,

$$\frac{A}{D} - \frac{B}{D} + \frac{C}{D} = \frac{A - B + C}{D}, \text{ if } B \text{ is not greater than } A$$

If there is a decision to replace the several given fractions with equivalent fractions all with the same denominator, the essential step is the rewriting of the denominators in prime factored form. The l.c.m. is then readily determined and the transformation $\frac{A}{B} = \frac{NA}{NB}$ can be made easily.

Problems (114)

For problems 1 to 16, show all the steps by which the following are transformed to a single fraction or mixed numeral, making use of the l.c.m. of the denominators.

1. $\dfrac{1}{3} + \dfrac{1}{6}$ 5. $\dfrac{3}{10} + \dfrac{4}{15}$ 9. $\dfrac{13}{15} - \dfrac{11}{24}$ 13. $\dfrac{7}{15} + \dfrac{5}{12} + \dfrac{11}{18}$

2. $\dfrac{1}{5} + \dfrac{1}{15}$ 6. $\dfrac{4}{15} + \dfrac{5}{21}$ 10. $\dfrac{4}{15} + \dfrac{7}{20}$ 14. $\dfrac{5}{3} + \dfrac{2}{9} + \dfrac{5}{12}$

3. $\dfrac{3}{2} + \dfrac{5}{6}$ 7. $\dfrac{5}{12} + \dfrac{7}{18}$ 11. $\dfrac{4}{3} - \dfrac{7}{9}$ 15. $\dfrac{3}{2} + \dfrac{5}{8} - \dfrac{7}{16}$

4. $\dfrac{4}{3} + \dfrac{1}{6}$ 8. $\dfrac{7}{12} + \dfrac{3}{16}$ 12. $\dfrac{3}{4} - \dfrac{7}{16}$ 16. $\dfrac{3}{4} - \dfrac{3}{8} + \dfrac{5}{12}$

17. Obtain a formula for computing the sum of three fractions by determining an equivalent single fraction for

$$\frac{A}{B} + \frac{C}{D} + \frac{E}{F}$$

18. Use the definition of rational numbers to show that

$$\frac{A}{D} - \frac{B}{D} + \frac{C}{D} = \frac{A - B + C}{D}, \text{ if } B \text{ is not greater than } A$$

For problems 19 to 34, assume that all divisors are different from zero, and represent each of the following as a quotient.

19. $1 + \dfrac{1}{x}$ 23. $1 - \dfrac{1}{x}$ 27. $z + \dfrac{x}{y}$ 31. $\dfrac{1}{x} + \dfrac{1}{x^2}$

20. $\dfrac{1}{y} + 1$ 24. $1 - \dfrac{x}{y}$ 28. $\dfrac{u}{v} + \dfrac{x}{y}$ 32. $\dfrac{1}{x} - \dfrac{1}{x^2}$

21. $1 + \dfrac{x}{y}$ 25. $z + \dfrac{1}{x}$ 29. $\dfrac{u}{v} - \dfrac{x}{y}$ 33. $\dfrac{1}{x} + \dfrac{y}{z}$

22. $\dfrac{x}{y} + 1$ 26. $z - \dfrac{1}{x}$ 30. $\dfrac{1}{x} + \dfrac{1}{y}$ 34. $\dfrac{a}{nb} + \dfrac{c}{mb}$

12-3. Mixed Numerals and Commutative and Associative Principles

With natural numbers the instruction to "compute" was specific, since the decimal numerals are considered to be the basic numerals for any natural number. The choice of basic numerals for the rational numbers is not this definite. As noted in Section 11-4, when the question is "What number is this?" we would prefer that a proper fraction $\dfrac{a}{b}$ be in lowest terms. However, the improper fraction $\dfrac{7}{6}$ might in some circumstances be considered as simpler than the mixed numerals $1\dfrac{1}{6}$. Hence, neither of these forms is given preference over the other as a basic numeral. The computation of $\frac{1}{2} + \frac{2}{3}$ will be considered correct with either result, unless a certain form is specified.   In practice one often chooses the preferred form on the basis of $\frac{7}{6}$ being a quotient as against $1\frac{1}{6}$ being a sum. $\left(\text{Remember that } 1\frac{1}{6} \text{ is an abbrevia-}\right.$ tion for $1 + \frac{1}{6}.\Big)$

The algorithms already given may be used to compute $4\frac{2}{3} + 5\frac{1}{2}$ by replacing each mixed numeral by an equivalent improper fraction.

$$4\frac{2}{3} + 5\frac{1}{2} = \frac{14}{3} + \frac{11}{2} = \frac{2 \cdot 14 + 3 \cdot 11}{3 \cdot 2} = \frac{61}{6} = 10\frac{1}{6}$$

An alternate procedure is often more efficient than this.   The commutative and associative principles are used to obtain a rearrangement so that the natural numbers (given by the decimal numerals) and the rational numbers (given by the fractions) can be combined separately.   The method is analogous to that used in certain computations with decimal numerals.

$56 + 27$		$4\frac{2}{3} + 5\frac{1}{2}$
$(50 + 6) + (20 + 7)$	Each addend represents the sum of two numbers.	$\left(4 + \frac{2}{3}\right) + \left(5 + \frac{1}{2}\right)$
$(50 + 20) + (6 + 7)$	The commutative and associative principles	$(4 + 5) + \left(\frac{2}{3} + \frac{1}{2}\right)$
$(50 + 20) + (10 + 3)$	justify the rearrangement of the terms.	$(4 + 5) + \left(1 + \frac{1}{6}\right)$
$80 + 3$		$10 + \frac{1}{6}$
83		$10\frac{1}{6}$

It is customary to use a vertical arrangement for such computations so that the numbers to be combined fall in the same columns.   The following underlined words are remembered by convention and are not written down.

Add:

tens	units	tens	units
5	6	1	
2	7	5	
		2	3

The combination of 6 units and 7 units is replaced by 1 ten and 3 units.

Add:

decimal numerals	fractions	decimal numerals	fractions
4	$\dfrac{2}{3}$	1	
		4	
5	$\dfrac{1}{2}$	5	$\dfrac{1}{6}$

The combination of $\dfrac{2}{3}$ and $\dfrac{1}{2}$ is replaced by the decimal numeral 1 and the fraction $\dfrac{1}{6}$.

Differences such as $5\dfrac{1}{2} - 2\dfrac{2}{3}$ may also be computed either by first transforming to the improper fraction form, or by computing with the decimal numerals and the fractions separately.   The latter method may require some preliminary changes as in this example where $\dfrac{2}{3}$ is greater than $\dfrac{1}{2}$.

One possible technique is similar to "borrowing" when subtracting with decimal numerals.

Subtract:

tens	units	tens	units	
5	6	4	10 + 6	56
2	7	2	7	27
				29

Subtract:

decimal numerals	fractions	decimal numerals	fractions	
5	$\dfrac{1}{2}$	4	$\dfrac{1}{1} + \dfrac{1}{2}$	$5\dfrac{1}{2}$
2	$\dfrac{2}{3}$	2	$\dfrac{2}{3}$	$2\dfrac{2}{3}$
				$2\dfrac{5}{6}$

In one case subtraction becomes possible after one 10 is transformed from the tens to the units; in the other it becomes possible after one unit is transferred from the decimal numerals to the fractions.   Other possibilities for subtraction algorithms are indicated below.   Study these and then try to develop similar procedures for computing $5\dfrac{1}{2} - 2\dfrac{2}{3}$.

a.

tens	units	tens	units	tens	units
5	6	5	6 + 2	5	8
2	8	2	8 + 2	3	0

b.

tens	units	tens	units	tens	units	tens	units
5	6	5	$6-6$	5	0	4	10
2	8	2	$8-6$	2	2	2	2

ANSWERS TO EXERCISES

a. $5\dfrac{1}{2}$ $5\dfrac{1}{2}+\dfrac{1}{3}$ $5\dfrac{5}{6}$ **b.** $5\dfrac{1}{2}-\dfrac{1}{2}$ $5\;\;0$ $4\;\;1$

$2\dfrac{2}{3}$ $2\dfrac{2}{3}+\dfrac{1}{3}$ $3\;\;0$ $2\dfrac{2}{3}-\dfrac{1}{2}$ $2\dfrac{1}{6}$ $2\dfrac{1}{6}$

           $2\dfrac{5}{6}$ $2\dfrac{5}{6}$

Problems (115)

For problems 1 to 10, compute in two ways: **A.** By combining the decimal numerals and fractions separately. **B.** By first changing each mixed numeral to an improper fraction.

1. $3\dfrac{1}{3}+1\dfrac{5}{6}$ **4.** $4\dfrac{1}{2}-2\dfrac{3}{5}$ **7.** $4\dfrac{1}{2}-\dfrac{11}{16}$ **9.** $2\dfrac{3}{4}+1\dfrac{1}{3}-2\dfrac{5}{6}$

2. $2\dfrac{1}{4}+4\dfrac{7}{8}$ **5.** $10\dfrac{3}{10}+4\dfrac{2}{5}$ **8.** $6\dfrac{2}{5}-\dfrac{7}{10}$ **10.** $4\dfrac{1}{4}-3\dfrac{2}{3}+5\dfrac{1}{5}$

3. $3\dfrac{1}{4}-1\dfrac{2}{3}$ **6.** $12\dfrac{1}{3}+6\dfrac{4}{9}$

11. Compute $\displaystyle\sum_{k=1}^{k=n}\dfrac{1}{2^k}$ for

     a. $n=1$ **b.** $n=2$ **c.** $n=3$ **d.** $n=4$ **e.** $n=5$

12. Compute $\displaystyle\sum_{k=1}^{k=n}\dfrac{1}{k(k+1)}$ for

     a. $n=1$ **b.** $n=2$ **c.** $n=3$ **d.** $n=4$ **e.** $n=5$

13. Compute $\displaystyle\sum_{k=1}^{k=n}\left(\dfrac{1}{k}-\dfrac{1}{k+1}\right)$ for

     a. $n=1$ **b.** $n=2$ **c.** $n=3$ **d.** $n=4$ **e.** $n=5$

14. Compute $\displaystyle\sum_{k=1}^{k=n}\dfrac{1}{(2k+1)(2k-1)}$ for

     a. $n=1$ **b.** $n=2$ **c.** $n=3$ **d.** $n=4$ **e.** $n=5$

Problems (116)

For problems 1 to 24, determine the decimal numeral, proper fraction, or mixed numeral that will give a true statement as a replacement for x. If there is no such number that we have defined, write "not defined."

1. $\dfrac{1}{2} + \dfrac{5}{6} = x$

2. $x = \dfrac{7}{2} + \dfrac{7}{4}$

3. $x = \dfrac{3}{5} - \dfrac{1}{2}$

4. $x - \dfrac{1}{5} = \dfrac{1}{6}$

5. $x + \dfrac{1}{3} = \dfrac{5}{8}$

6. $\dfrac{2}{3} + x = \dfrac{5}{8}$

7. $x + \dfrac{5}{8} = \dfrac{1}{3}$

8. $\dfrac{5}{8} + x = \dfrac{2}{3}$

9. $\dfrac{3}{2} = x - \dfrac{5}{6}$

10. $2\dfrac{1}{2} = x - 3\dfrac{2}{3}$

11. $\dfrac{1}{2} = \dfrac{5}{6} - x$

12. $2\dfrac{1}{2} = 3\dfrac{2}{3} - x$

13. $\dfrac{2}{3} + x = \dfrac{4}{5}$

14. $2\dfrac{1}{5} - \dfrac{3}{4} = x$

15. $2\dfrac{1}{2} + x = \dfrac{7}{8}$

16. $\dfrac{1}{6} + x = \dfrac{1}{9}$

17. $\dfrac{1}{9} + x = \dfrac{1}{6}$

18. $\dfrac{7}{12} + \dfrac{11}{16} = x$

19. $\dfrac{4}{5} - \dfrac{4}{6} = x$

20. $x + \dfrac{2}{5} = \dfrac{2}{3}$

21. $2\dfrac{7}{8} = x - 3\dfrac{3}{10}$

22. $5 = x + 3\dfrac{5}{6}$

23. $4 = x + 5\dfrac{1}{4}$

24. $1\dfrac{3}{16} = x - \dfrac{7}{8}$

For problems 25 to 42 construct a mathematical model in the form of a single conditional equation. Do not compute.

25. What is the sum of $\dfrac{3}{5}$ and $\dfrac{7}{8}$?

26. What is the difference between $2\dfrac{1}{3}$ and $1\dfrac{1}{2}$?

27. The sum of $\dfrac{4}{5}$ and $\dfrac{5}{12}$ is how much greater than their difference?

28. If the sum of two addends is $1\dfrac{3}{8}$ and one addend is $\dfrac{5}{9}$, what is the other?

29. What is the sum of $\dfrac{7}{16}$ and the difference between 1 and $\dfrac{7}{16}$?

30. If the difference between two numbers is $2\dfrac{3}{4}$ and the smaller is $1\dfrac{7}{8}$, what is the larger number?

31. If the difference between two numbers is 3 and the larger is $5\dfrac{2}{3}$, what is the smaller number?

32. If one number is $1\dfrac{1}{5}$ more than another, and the larger number is $2\dfrac{1}{3}$, what is the smaller number?

33. If one number is $1\dfrac{1}{5}$ more than another, and the smaller number is $2\dfrac{1}{3}$, what is the larger number?

34. What number is as much more than $\dfrac{2}{3}$, as $\dfrac{3}{4}$ is more than $\dfrac{1}{3}$?

35. What number is as much more than $1\dfrac{1}{2}$, as $1\dfrac{2}{5}$ is more than $\dfrac{3}{4}$?

36. What is the sum of $\frac{7}{2}$ and $\frac{2}{7}$?

37. By how much does $\frac{3}{5}$ exceed $\frac{3}{7}$?

38. The sum of $3\frac{1}{5}$ and $2\frac{1}{2}$ is how much greater than their difference?

39. If one number is $3\frac{3}{4}$ less than the other, and the smaller number is $1\frac{3}{5}$, what is the larger number?

40. If one number is $1\frac{3}{5}$ less than the other, and the larger number is $3\frac{3}{4}$, what is the smaller number?

41. If one number is $2\frac{1}{3}$ less than another and the smaller number is $3\frac{1}{2}$, what is the sum of the two numbers?

42. What is the difference between $5\frac{1}{4}$ and the difference between $5\frac{1}{4}$ and $3\frac{1}{2}$?

For Further Study

Supplementary discussion on the development of an arithmetic of fractions out of an arithmetic of quotients may be found in [G2], pp. 32–33, 100–103.

Proofs of some of the theorems in Section 12-1 appear in [H2], pp. 150–157.

Chapter 13 of [S4] has an intuitive development of fractions that emphasizes how effective diagrams can be for clarification of ideas.

13

Inequalities

13-1. Order Relations for the Natural Numbers and Zero

A natural number given as the answer to "How many?" is said to be used in its *cardinal* sense. Thus in Section 8-8 the number of elements in a set was designated as the cardinal number of the set. This number may also be referred to as the *cardinality* of the set.

There was also in Section 8-8 a discussion of the established order of succession, which is a fundamental property of the natural numbers. An application that depends on this fixed order uses the natural numbers in their *ordinal* sense. Thus the words "first," "second," "third," and so on use natural numbers as ordinals to answer the question "Which one?" by specifying a certain position in a standard arrangement. These adjectives, "first," "second," "third," "fourth," and so on are the numeral names for the ordinal numbers, but decimal numerals can also be used to represent ordinal numbers. Thus the number for this page is an ordinal, which identifies this page in its proper order, and it may also be a cardinal, which tells how many pages have been numbered up to this point.

In Section 9-2 two sets having cardinality of 3 and 7 were used to illustrate that $3 < 7$. When numbers are used as ordinals, it is usually better to think of them as associated with points on a scale (Where?), rather than as measures of magnitudes (How much?), or as counts of multitudes (How many?). Some effective use of geometrical ideas is then possible. Thus 3 (the point so named) lies between 0 and 7.

On a scale whose division points have been assigned the numbers $0, 1, 2, \ldots, n$ in their natural order, the point a will lie between the point 0 and the point b if and only if $a < b$. If this scale is in such position that the point 0 is to the left of point 1, then the point a will be to the left of point b if and only if $a < b$. The point a will be to the right of b if and only if $a > b$.

The decimal numerals serve well as basic numerals for the natural numbers, since this notation not only provides a unique name for any given number but also provides for the immediate recognition of the larger or smaller of two different natural numbers. If the numbers are not given by decimal numerals, then a computation may be necessary before they can be arranged in order of size.

Problems (117)

Select one of these three symbols, $<$, $=$, or $>$, to place between the following pairs of numerals to give a true statement.

1. $37, 73$ 5. $9 \cdot 10, 7 \cdot 13$ 9. $5^5, 25^2$ 13. $62 - 49, 91 - 78$

2. $110, 101$ 6. $3^5, 9 \cdot 27$ 10. $7 \cdot 14, 100 - 1$ 14. $\dfrac{144}{88}, \dfrac{144}{16}$

3. $8 \cdot 9, 2 \cdot 36$ 7. $3^4, 4^3$ 11. $\dfrac{45}{9}, \dfrac{65}{13}$ 15. $\dfrac{117}{13}, \dfrac{143}{13}$

4. $7 \cdot 10, 3 \cdot 23$ 8. $2^4, 4^2$ 12. $3 \cdot 5^2, 3^2 \cdot 5$ 16. $100 - 17, 100 - 19$

The problems in the above set are illustrative of the following fundamental property of the natural numbers, known as the principle of trichotomy.

If a and b are any two numbers selected from the set of zero and the natural numbers, then one and only one of these three possibilities holds:
1. $a = b$ a and b are the same number.
2. $a < b$ This is the case if and only if there exists a natural number x such that $a + x = b$, and hence such that $x = b - a$.
3. $a > b$ This is the case if and only if there exists a natural number y such that $a = b + y$, and hence such that $y = a - b$.

The relations of less than and more than are not reflexive. In fact $a < a$ and $a > a$ are false for all a. For example, if $a < a$ were true, then there would exist a natural number x such that $a + x = a$, and hence such that $a + x = a + 0$. By the cancellation property for addition, this would require that $x = 0$, which is a contradiction of the assumption that x is a natural number.

Less than and greater than are not symmetric relations, since if $a < b$, it is false that $a > b$. If it were true that both $a < b$ and $a > b$, then there would exist natural numbers x and y such that

$$a + x = b \qquad \text{and} \qquad a = b + y$$

From this it would follow that $b + y + x = b$, or that $b + x + y = b + 0$. This would be true only if $y + x = 0$, which cannot be true if both x and y are natural numbers.

However, both relations are transitive.   If $a < b$ and $b < c$, then $a < c$.   If $a > b$ and $b > c$, then $a > c$.   Both of these conclusions and the lack of reflexivity and symmetry are quite evident if a, b, and c are pictured as points on a scale. Nevertheless, any picture that one might draw in support of the above statements can be, at best, only typical.   It can never display all the choices of a, b, and c from the set of zero and the natural numbers.   Hence, in the next problem set the reader is invited to show that with the assumption of the trichotomy principle and the definitions of less than and greater than, we then have transitivity and other results following as logical conclusions.

Two of these are the following, which show how order is preserved under addition and multiplication by natural numbers.

The Monotonic Law for Addition

   If $a > b$, then $a + c > b + c$. a, b, and c are to be chosen from the set of
                                         zero and the natural numbers.

   If $a < b$, then $a + c < b + c$.

The Monotonic Law for Multiplication

   If $a > b$, and $c \neq 0$, then $ac > bc$.   Again a, b, and c are chosen from zero
                                                   and the natural numbers.

   If $a < b$, and $c \neq 0$, then $ac < bc$.

Strong support for the validity of these laws can be given by diagrams such as the following.

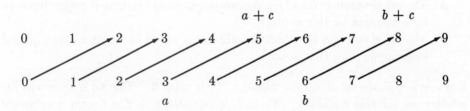

The arrows indicate the correspondence that gives the ordered pairs for the mapping $n \rightarrow n + 2$.   These are typical results of "adding c," or joining the operator $+ c$, using $c = 2$ as an example.   If $a = 3$ and $b = 6$ are selected as examples of $a < b$ or $b > a$, the preservation of this order under addition of c is evident.

Problems (118)

Construct proofs of the following.   All variables range over zero and the natural numbers unless otherwise restricted.

   1. Transitive Property
        a. If $a > b$ and $b > c$, then $a > c$.
        b. If $a < b$ and $b < c$, then $a < c$.

2. Monotonic Law for Addition
   a. If $a > b$, then $a + c > b + c$.
   b. If $a < b$, then $a + c < b + c$.
3. Monotonic Law for Multiplication
   a. If $a > b$, and $c \neq 0$, then $ac > bc$.
   b. If $a < b$, and $c \neq 0$, then $ac < bc$.
4. Cancellation Law (Addition) for Inequalities
   a. If $a + c > b + c$, then $a > b$.
   b. If $a + c < b + c$, then $a < b$.
5. Cancellation Law (Multiplication) for Inequalities
   a. If $ac > bc$, and $c \neq 0$, then $a > b$.
   b. If $ac < bc$, and $c \neq 0$, then $a < b$.
6. a. If $a > b$, and $c > d$, then $a + c > b + d$.
   b. If $a < b$, and $c < d$, then $a + c < b + d$.

13-2. Solution Sets for Equations and Inequalities

Fundamental to the study of an equation such as $x + 2 = 5$, is the agreement as to the range of the variable. This set of permissible replacements for x will often be the universal set that has been assumed for the discussion in which the given equation arises. Let us assume here that this set is that of zero and the natural numbers. The equation can now serve as a device whereby the members of this set can be partitioned into the following dichotomy:

A. The set of numbers for which the statement would be false if x were replaced by a numeral for this number.
B. The set of numbers for which the statement would be true if x were replaced by a numeral for this number.

For $x + 2 = 5$, the set B has one member, the number 3. This set is known as the *solution* set for this equation. We have designated $x + 2 = 5$ as a conditional equation. In such equations the solution set is a proper subset of the range of the variable.

By contrast, in the equation $x + 2 = 2 + x$, which is an identity, the solution set is the same set as the range of the variable. This is the meaning intended when we state that this equation is always true, or is true for all x. In the equation $x + 2 = x$ there are no replacements for x that give a true statement. In this case, the solution set is the empty set.

Corresponding to conditional equations one may also construct conditional inequalities, such as $x + 2 < 5$. If the universe consists of zero and the natural numbers, then just those numbers that are members of $\{0, 1, 2\}$ will give true statements as replacements for x. This is the solution set for $x + 2 < 5$ with the universal set as given.

Problems (119)

Determine the solution set for each of the following, assuming that the variables range over zero and the natural numbers. It is important to observe that only those numbers can be chosen which meet all of the conditions.

1. What is m, if $m < n$, $n = 10$, and $m > 7$?
2. What is m, if $m < n$, $n = 50$, m is a square, and $m > 20$?
3. What is m, if $m < n$, $n = 32$, and m is a multiple of 10?
4. What is n, if $m > n$, $m = 12$, and n is a prime?
5. Determine the set for which $x < 15$ and $10 < x$.
6. Determine the set for which $x > 4$ and $x < 10$.
7. $\{x \mid x < 19$, and $x > 14\}$.
8. $\{x \mid x < 12$, $5 < x$, and x is odd$\}$.
9. $\{x \mid x > 40$, $x < 50$, and x is prime$\}$.
10. $\{x \mid 40 < x$, $50 > x$, and $x + 1$ is a multiple of 4$\}$.
11. $\{x \mid x < 50$, and x is the square of an odd number$\}$.
12. $\{x \mid x > 40$, $x < 50$, and x is divisible by both 2 and 3$\}$.
13. $\{x \mid x < 10$, and x has an even number of divisors$\}$.
14. $\{x \mid x < 100$, and x is the square of a prime$\}$.

The solution set (in natural numbers) for $x < 4$ is $\{1, 2, 3\}$. The solution set for $x = 4$ is $\{4\}$. Suppose we want to select the natural numbers that meet either of these conditions. A notation for such a requirement can be formed by using both symbols, $<$ and $=$. The solution set for $x \leqq 4$ is $\{1, 2, 3, 4\}$. Hence, $x \leqq 4$ selects a set that is the union of the solution sets of $x < 4$ and $x = 4$.

The symbol $\leqq$ is often shortened to $\leq$. Either is read as "less than or equal to." Because of the principle of trichotomy, both have exactly the same meaning as $\not>$, which is read as "not greater than." In the same way $\not<$, which means "is not less than" is equivalent to $\geqq$ or $\geq$ which means "greater than or equal to."

It is possible to combine inequalities in such a way that will determine the intersection of certain sets. The solution sets for $x < 10$ and $5 < x$ are written below. The intersection of these two sets, which is the set $\{6, 7, 8, 9\}$, may be specified by $5 < x < 10$.

$$
\begin{array}{ll}
x < 10 & \{1, 2, 3, 4, 5, 6, 7, 8, 9\} \\
5 < x & \{6, 7, 8, 9, 10, 11, 12, \ldots\} \\
5 < x < 10 & \{6, 7, 8, 9\}
\end{array}
$$

This is read "x is greater than 5 and less than 10."
The set $\{6, 7, 8, 9\}$ could also be referred to as the natural numbers between 5 and 10 and could be specified by the alternate notations:

$$
6 \leq x < 10,
$$
$$
5 < x \leq 9,
$$
$$
6 \leq x \leq 9
$$

Problems (120)

List the following sets in roster notation.   The variables range over the natural numbers.

1. $\{x \mid 20 < x < 25\}$ 5. $\{x \mid 20 < x \leq 25\}$ 9. $\{x \mid x \leq 3\}$
2. $\{y \mid 25 \leq y \leq 30\}$ 6. $\{z \mid 25 \leq z < 30\}$ 10. $\{x \mid 25 < x < 26\}$
3. $\{x \mid 20 \leq x < 25\}$ 7. $\{x \mid 20 \leq x \leq 25\}$ 11. $\{x \mid 7 < x < 5\}$
4. $\{y \mid 25 < y \leq 30\}$ 8. $\{x \mid 25 \leq x \leq 25\}$ 12. $\{x \mid x - 2 < 2\}$

13. $\{x \mid 10 < x < 16$, and $\dfrac{x}{45}$ is in lowest terms$\}$

14. $\{x \mid 30 < x < 40$, and x and 48 are relatively prime$\}$
15. $\{x \mid 20 < x < 80$, x is a multiple of both 3 and 5$\}$

16. $\{x \mid 5 < x < 10$, $\dfrac{x}{8}$ is a proper fraction$\}$

17. $\{x \mid x < 20$, x is a multiple of 2 or 8$\}$

18. $\{x \mid x < 10$, $\dfrac{x}{y} = \dfrac{2}{3}$, y is a natural number$\}$

19. $\{x \mid x < 20$, x is a multiple of 2 and 8$\}$
20. $\{x \mid 40 < x < 50$, $x + 2$ is a multiple of 5$\}$
21. $\{x \mid 5 < 2^x < 100\}$
22. $\{x \mid 10 < 3^x < 100\}$
23. $\{x \mid 5 < x - 1 \leq 8\}$
24. $\{x \mid 3 \leq x + 2 < 7\}$

25. $\{x \mid \dfrac{x}{3}$ is a natural number, $4 < \dfrac{x}{3} < 7\}$

26. $\{x \mid x < 10$, $x = n(A \otimes B)$, $n(A) > 1$, $n(B) > 1\}$
27. $\{x \mid x < 10$, $x = n(A \cup B)$, $n(A) = 4$, $n(B) = 3\}$
28. $\{x \mid x < 10$, $x = n(A - B)$, $n(A) = 4$, $n(B) = 3\}$

13-3. Order Relations for the Rational Numbers

Every rational number has a family of equivalent fractions, which are infinite in number, by which it can be represented.   Of these, that fraction $\dfrac{a}{b}$ where a and b are relatively prime, provides a unique "family name" for this set of fractions and hence for the rational number.   However, this form, which is called the *common fraction form* to distinguish it from other notations to be given later, does have one rather serious defect.   It does not provide for immediate recognition of which of two rational numbers is the larger.   Thus $\dfrac{25}{77} < \dfrac{13}{40}$, but the reader may not find this to be obvious.   Some of the problems in the next set reveal that a set of rational numbers is not easy to arrange in order of size, when they are represented by common fractions.

The trichotomy principle extends directly to include the rational numbers. Hence, as soon as multiplication has been defined, it will be possible to show that the properties of inequalities which were developed in problem set (118) for the natural numbers, also hold for the rationals.

If $\dfrac{a}{b}$ and $\dfrac{c}{d}$ are any two numbers selected from the set of zero and the positive* rational numbers, then one and only one of these three possibilities holds:

1. $\dfrac{a}{b} = \dfrac{c}{d}$ They represent the same rational number.

2. $\dfrac{a}{b} < \dfrac{c}{d}$ This is the case if and only if there exists a positive rational number $\dfrac{x}{y}$ such that $\dfrac{a}{b} + \dfrac{x}{y} = \dfrac{c}{d}$, and hence such that
$$\frac{x}{y} = \frac{c}{d} - \frac{a}{b}.$$

3. $\dfrac{a}{b} > \dfrac{c}{d}$ This is the case if and only if there exists a positive rational number $\dfrac{u}{v}$ such that $\dfrac{a}{b} = \dfrac{c}{d} + \dfrac{u}{v}$, and hence such that
$$\frac{u}{v} = \frac{a}{b} - \frac{c}{d}.$$

It was shown in Section 11-4 that $\dfrac{a}{b} = \dfrac{c}{d}$ if and only if $ad = bc$. We now want

to show that $\dfrac{a}{b}$ is less than or greater than $\dfrac{c}{d}$ corresponding to ad being less than or

greater than bc.

If b and d are natural numbers, and $ad > bc$, then $ad - bc$ is a natural number

and $\dfrac{ad - bc}{bd}$ is a rational number.

We then have $\dfrac{c}{d} + \dfrac{ad - bc}{bd} = \dfrac{bc + (ad - bc)}{bd} = \dfrac{ad}{bd} = \dfrac{a}{b}.$

Therefore $\dfrac{a}{b} > \dfrac{c}{d}$, by the trichotomy principle.

Next, assume that $\dfrac{a}{b} > \dfrac{c}{d}$. Then, from the trichotomy principle there exists a

rational number $\dfrac{u}{v}$ such that $\dfrac{u}{v} = \dfrac{a}{b} - \dfrac{c}{d} = \dfrac{ad - bc}{bd}$. Hence, $ad - bc$ is a natural

number and $ad > bc$. By a similar argument we find that $\dfrac{a}{b} < \dfrac{c}{d}$, if and only if

$ad < bc$.

     Summary: The rational number $\dfrac{a}{b}$ is less than, equal to, or greater than

the rational number $\dfrac{c}{d}$ according as ad is less than, equal to, or greater

---

* All rational numbers thus far considered have been zero or positive. See page 232.

than bc. In particular, $\dfrac{a}{b} < \dfrac{c}{b}$, if $a < c$, and $\dfrac{a}{b} > \dfrac{c}{b}$ if $a > c$. Also $\dfrac{a}{b} < \dfrac{a}{c}$ if $b > c$, and $\dfrac{a}{b} > \dfrac{a}{c}$, if $b < c$.

Problems (121)

1. Prove that if $\dfrac{a}{b} < \dfrac{a}{c}$, then $b > c$.

2. Prove that if $\dfrac{a}{b} > \dfrac{a}{c}$, then $b < c$.

For problems 3 to 24, insert the symbols $<$, $=$, or $>$ as required to obtain a true statement.

3. $\dfrac{7}{8}, \dfrac{15}{16}$

4. $\dfrac{5}{12}, \dfrac{4}{9}$

5. $\dfrac{7}{8}, \dfrac{13}{16}$

6. $\dfrac{5}{12}, \dfrac{55}{132}$

7. $\dfrac{7}{8}, \dfrac{91}{104}$

8. $\dfrac{5}{12}, \dfrac{7}{18}$

9. $\dfrac{3}{4}, \dfrac{7}{9}$

10. $\dfrac{4}{3}, \dfrac{3}{4}$

11. $\dfrac{8}{5}, \dfrac{8}{7}$

12. $\dfrac{19}{10}, \dfrac{19}{11}$

13. $\dfrac{4}{13}, \dfrac{9}{29}$

14. $\dfrac{6}{11}, \dfrac{11}{20}$

15. $\dfrac{2}{3}, \dfrac{2+1}{3+1}$

16. $\dfrac{7}{9}, \dfrac{1+7}{1+9}$

17. $\dfrac{3}{2}, \dfrac{1+3}{1+2}$

18. $\dfrac{7}{9}, \dfrac{7-1}{9-1}$

19. $\dfrac{5}{6}, \dfrac{5\cdot7}{6\cdot7}$

20. $\dfrac{3}{14}, \dfrac{5\cdot3}{5\cdot14}$

21. $\dfrac{11}{5}, \dfrac{11-3}{5-3}$

22. $\dfrac{3}{4}, \dfrac{3+3}{2\cdot4}$

Given $0 < y < z$, and $x > 0$.

23.

  a. $\dfrac{y}{z}, \dfrac{y+x}{z+x}$

  b. $\dfrac{z}{y}, \dfrac{z+x}{y+x}$

24.

  a. $\dfrac{y}{z}, \dfrac{y-x}{z-x}$

  b. $\dfrac{z}{y}, \dfrac{z-x}{y-x}$

25. Arrange these fractions in order of increasing size, left to right.

  a. $\dfrac{6}{11}, \dfrac{2}{11}, \dfrac{9}{11}, \dfrac{8}{11}$

  b. $\dfrac{7}{8}, \dfrac{7}{5}, \dfrac{7}{3}, \dfrac{7}{6}, \dfrac{7}{9}$

  c. $\dfrac{9}{6}, \dfrac{11}{4}, \dfrac{9}{7}, \dfrac{10}{4}, \dfrac{9}{8}, \dfrac{9}{4}$

  d. $\dfrac{9}{5}, \dfrac{8}{7}, \dfrac{11}{4}, \dfrac{8}{6}, \dfrac{11}{2}, \dfrac{10}{5}, \dfrac{11}{3}, \dfrac{8}{5}, \dfrac{11}{5}$

  e. $\dfrac{2}{1}, \dfrac{3}{2}, \dfrac{4}{3}, \dfrac{5}{4}$

  f. $\dfrac{1}{4}, \dfrac{3}{8}, \dfrac{7}{16}, \dfrac{15}{32}$

26. Arrange these fractions in order of increasing size, left to right.

  a. $\dfrac{1}{2}, \dfrac{1}{3}, \dfrac{2}{3}, \dfrac{1}{4}, \dfrac{3}{4}, \dfrac{1}{5}, \dfrac{2}{5}, \dfrac{3}{5}, \dfrac{4}{5}$

  b. $\dfrac{1}{2}, \dfrac{1}{3}, \dfrac{2}{3}, \dfrac{1}{4}, \dfrac{3}{4}, \dfrac{1}{5}, \dfrac{2}{5}, \dfrac{3}{5}, \dfrac{4}{5}, \dfrac{1}{6}, \dfrac{5}{6}$

  c. $\dfrac{1}{2}, \dfrac{1}{3}, \dfrac{2}{3}, \dfrac{1}{4}, \dfrac{3}{4}, \dfrac{1}{5}, \dfrac{2}{5}, \dfrac{3}{5}, \dfrac{4}{5}, \dfrac{1}{6}, \dfrac{5}{6}, \dfrac{1}{7}, \dfrac{2}{7}, \dfrac{3}{7}, \dfrac{4}{7}, \dfrac{5}{7}, \dfrac{6}{7}.$

Suppose one were trying to measure $\frac{3}{10}$ of an inch on a ruler graduated in halves, quarters, eighths, and sixteenths. What would be the scale point nearest to $\frac{3}{10}$ on such a ruler? This would be given by $\frac{n}{16}$ where n is the natural number which produces the smallest error in $\frac{n}{16} \doteq \frac{3}{10}$. This in turn is equivalent to asking for that multiple of 10 which is nearest $3 \cdot 16$ or 48. Answer: $n = 5$. We have here used the symbol $\doteq$ to mean "approximately equal to." No attempt is made here to give this a sharp definition. It means, roughly, "the best possible, under the given conditions."

Problems (122)

Choose a natural number for n so that the difference between the resulting rational number and the given one will be as small as possible.

1. $\frac{n}{16} \doteq \frac{4}{5}$ 4. $\frac{n}{32} \doteq \frac{7}{9}$ 7. $\frac{n}{10} \doteq \frac{5}{8}$ 10. $\frac{n}{8} \doteq \frac{6}{7}$

2. $\frac{n}{16} \doteq \frac{5}{12}$ 5. $\frac{n}{32} \doteq \frac{3}{5}$ 8. $\frac{n}{10} \doteq \frac{9}{16}$ 11. $\frac{n}{100} \doteq \frac{5}{9}$

3. $\frac{n}{16} \doteq \frac{2}{3}$ 6. $\frac{n}{32} \doteq \frac{5}{6}$ 9. $\frac{n}{10} \doteq \frac{7}{12}$ 12. $\frac{n}{10} \doteq \frac{11}{3}$

In the set of natural numbers every number has a successor, and the concept of "the next one" is basic in ordering these numbers. One of the startling properties of the set of all rational numbers is that for any given rational number there is no next rational number that can be identified.

Suppose, for example, that $\frac{5}{6}$ has been suggested as a candidate for the next rational number after $\frac{4}{5}$, in order of increasing size. Now $\frac{5}{6} - \frac{4}{5} = \frac{1}{30}$, so that $\frac{5}{6}$ is indeed the next scale point on a scale whose unit has been divided into 30 equal parts. But by multiplying the number of scale divisions, we find that $\frac{1}{30} = \frac{2}{60} = \frac{3}{90} = \frac{4}{120}$ and so on. This provides a method for producing any number of fractions that represent distinct rational numbers each of which is greater than $\frac{4}{5}$ and less than $\frac{5}{6}$.

$$\frac{4}{5} < \frac{5}{6} \qquad \frac{4}{5} < \frac{49}{60} < \frac{5}{6} \qquad \frac{4}{5} < \frac{73}{90} < \frac{37}{45} < \frac{5}{6}$$

$$\frac{24}{30}, \frac{25}{30} \qquad \frac{48}{60}, \frac{49}{60}, \frac{50}{60} \qquad \frac{72}{90}, \frac{73}{90}, \frac{74}{90}, \frac{75}{90} \qquad \text{etc.}$$

The next problem set suggests still other procedures by which, given $\frac{a}{b}$ and $\frac{c}{d}$

with $\frac{a}{b} < \frac{c}{d}$, then $\frac{e}{f}$ can be determined such that $\frac{a}{b} < \frac{e}{f} < \frac{c}{d}$. If one rational number can thus be found that is larger than the smaller of the two distinct rational numbers but that is smaller than the larger of the two, then by repeating the process we can determine as many intermediate numbers as desired.

Given two different rational numbers, there is no limit to the number of different rational numbers that can be determined that are greater than the smaller of the two numbers, but are less than the larger.

Problems (123)

1. **a.** Choose $a = 4$, $b = 5$, $c = 5$, and $d = 6$ to verify that

    if $\frac{a}{b} < \frac{c}{d}$, then $\frac{a}{b} < \frac{ad + bc}{2bd} < \frac{c}{d}$.

   b. Prove that if a, b, c, and d are any natural numbers such that

    $\frac{a}{b} < \frac{c}{d}$, then $\frac{a}{b} < \frac{ad + bc}{2bd} < \frac{c}{d}$.

   c. Verify in **a.**, that $\frac{ad + bc}{2bd}$ is as much greater than $\frac{a}{b}$ as it is less than $\frac{c}{d}$.

2. **a.** Choose $a = 4$, $b = 5$, $c = 5$, and $d = 6$ to verify that

    if $\frac{a}{b} < \frac{c}{d}$, then $\frac{a}{b} < \frac{a + c}{b + d} < \frac{c}{d}$.

   b. Prove that if a, b, c, and d are any natural numbers such that

    $\frac{a}{b} < \frac{c}{d}$, then $\frac{a}{b} < \frac{a + c}{b + d} < \frac{c}{d}$.

   c. Verify in **a.** that $\frac{a + c}{b + d} - \frac{a}{b} \neq \frac{c}{d} - \frac{a + c}{b + d}$.

3. **a.** Choose $a = 4$, $b = 5$, $c = 5$, $d = 6$, $m = 2$, and $n = 3$ to verify that

    if $\frac{a}{b} < \frac{c}{d}$, then $\frac{a}{b} < \frac{ma + nc}{mb + nd} < \frac{c}{d}$.

   b. Prove that if a, b, c, and d are natural numbers such that $\frac{a}{b} < \frac{c}{d}$, then for any natural numbers m and n, it is true that $\frac{a}{b} < \frac{ma + nc}{mb + nd} < \frac{c}{d}$.

4. **a.** Prove that if a, b, c, and d are natural numbers such that $\frac{a}{b} < \frac{c}{d}$, then

    $\frac{a}{b} < \frac{2ad + bc}{3bc} < \frac{ad + 2bc}{3bd} < \frac{c}{d}$.

   b. Verify for $a = 4$, $b = 5$, $c = 5$, and $d = 6$, that the differences between consecutive fractions in **a.** are constant.

In problems 5 and 6 insert fractions in lowest terms in the spaces left blank so that the resulting fractions increase in size, left to right.

5. $\dfrac{2}{3} <$ ——— $< \dfrac{3}{4}, \dfrac{2}{3} <$ ——— $<$ ——— $< \dfrac{3}{4}, \dfrac{2}{3} <$ ——— $<$ ——— $<$ ——— $< \dfrac{3}{4}.$

6. $\dfrac{3}{4} <$ ——— $< \dfrac{4}{5}, \dfrac{3}{4} <$ ——— $<$ ——— $<$ ——— $< \dfrac{4}{5}.$

7. Determine natural numbers a, b, c, and d, as small as possible, such that $\dfrac{a}{b} = \dfrac{1}{2}, \dfrac{a}{d} = \dfrac{2}{3}$, and $\dfrac{a}{b} < \dfrac{a}{c} < \dfrac{a}{d}$.

8. Determine natural numbers a, b, c, and d, as small as possible, such that $\dfrac{a}{b} = \dfrac{2}{3}, \dfrac{a}{d} = \dfrac{3}{4}$, and $\dfrac{a}{b} < \dfrac{a}{c} < \dfrac{a}{d}$.

Let S be a set in which the order relation $<$ has been defined and for which the trichotomy principle holds. Then an element b of set S is said to be *between* elements a and c of S if and only if $a < b < c$ or $c < b < a$. If S has at least two distinct elements and there is an element of S between any two distinct elements of S, then S is said to be *dense*, or to be *densely ordered with respect to the relation* $<$. A set is *discrete* if it has no dense subset.

We have shown above that the rational numbers form a dense set. The natural numbers are an example of a discrete set. This is a most important difference between the natural and the rational numbers. If x is a natural number, then $\{x \mid 2 < x < 7\} = \{3, 4, 5, 6\}$. Since we have seen there are a countless number of rational numbers between any two such, it is quite impossible to think of listing in roster notation all the members of $\{x \mid 2 < x < 7\}$, if x is a rational number. Nevertheless, we often have to work with such sets and a way of thinking about them, or picturing them, is very desirable.

For this purpose it is better that each rational number be associated with a point on a scale rather than with a magnitude. On such a scale zero is assigned to the origin and the number 1 at a selected point.

$$0 \quad 1 \quad 2 \quad 3 \quad 4 \quad 5 \quad 6 \quad 7$$
$$2 < x < 7$$

It is now assumed that with the scale extended as necessary, for every positive rational number there is a unique point on the scale with which this number can be associated. The rational numbers in $\{x \mid 2 < x < 7, x \text{ is rational}\}$ are thus assumed to be in correspondence with certain points on the scale that lie between $x = 2$ and $x = 7$. The notation of ( ) in the diagram is used to signify that $x = 2$ and $x = 7$ (the points or the numbers associated with them) are not themselves in the set, but only the points or numbers between them.

In order to make this correspondence, we must assume the possibility of dividing the segment of unit length into a greater and greater number of equal parts, each of smaller and smaller length. This gives us an idea of the *infinite in the small*.

Recall that to claim that addition and multiplication can always be performed, it was necessary to imagine the scale as extending indefinitely to the right, without end. Here we have the *infinite in the large*.

Note that while we have assumed that there is a point on the scale assigned to each rational number, we do not claim that there is a rational number for every point. It will be shown later that such a correspondence is not possible. Even though the set of rational numbers is everywhere dense, we still will assume points on the scale to which no rational number corresponds.

Let U be a set of numbers, and let A be a subset of U. If there is a number c of U such that no member of A is greater than c, we say that c is an *upper bound* for A, or that A is *bounded above* by c. This means that for x such that $x \in A$ we have $x \leq c$.

In the same way, if there is a number b of U such that no member of A is less than b, we say that b is a *lower bound* for the set A, or that A is *bounded below* by b. Here for x such that $x \in A$ we have $x \geq b$. If the set A has both an upper and lower bound, we say that A is *bounded*.

Example 1: Let U be the set of zero and the natural numbers, and let $A_1 = \{x \mid 2 < x < 7\}$.
$$U = \{0, 1, 2, 3, 4, 5, 6, 7, 8, 9, \ldots\}$$
$$A_1 = \qquad \{3, 4, 5, 6\}$$

Then 6, 7, 8, and all greater natural numbers are all upper bounds for A_1. Zero, 1, 2, and 3 are all lower bounds for A_1.

Example 2: Let U be the set of rational numbers, and let $A_2 = \{x \mid 2 < x < 7\}$.

Then 7 and any rational number greater than 7 are upper bounds for A_2. Also 2 and any rational number less than 2 are lower bounds for A_2.

The smallest of the upper bounds of a set A is called the *least upper bound* (l.u.b.) of the set. Thus, if c is an upper bound for the set A, and if, when d is any other upper bound for A, we have $c \leq d$, then c is the least upper bound for A. In Example 1, 6 is the l.u.b. for A_1.

The largest of the lower bounds of a set A is called the *greatest lower bound* (g.l.b.) of the set A. Thus, if b is a lower bound for the set A, and if, when e is any other lower bound for A, we have $b \geq e$, then b is the greatest lower bound for A. In Example 1, 3 is the g.l.b. for A_1.

We observe that for set A_1 in Example 1 both the greatest lower bound 3, and the least upper bound 6, were members of the set A_1. The situation for set A_2 in Example 2 is not the same.

Seven is an upper bound for A_2 since for any $x < 7$ we have $x \leq 7$. (Remember

that $x \leq c$ when *either* $x < c$ or $x = c$.)   But if $y < 7$, then y is not an upper bound
for A_2.   The reason for this is that the rational numbers are dense.   Hence, if $y < 7$
there will always exist an x such that $y < x < 7$.   Since this x is a member of A_2,
and $x > y$, then y is not an upper bound for A_2.   Therefore, 7 is the l.u.b. for A_2,
even though 7 is not a member of A_2.

Also, we find that 2, which is not a member of A_2, is the greatest lower bound for
A_2.   For 2 is a lower bound for A_2, since if $x \in A_2$, we have $x > 2$ and therefore
$x \geq 2$.   But if we choose any rational z such that $z > 2$, then there exists in A_2 an
x such that $2 < x < z$, because of the denseness property of the rational numbers.
Therefore, 2 is the g.l.b. for A_2.

We conclude that in the set of rational numbers specified by $2 < x < 7$, it is not
possible to identify one of these as being the greatest, or to identify one as being the
smallest.   If we think of the points on a scale that correspond to this set of rationals
this result implies the following: No matter what point in this set is selected, there
is always a point in the set to the right of the selected point and also always one at
its left.

A significant change results if we add just two numbers, 2 and 7, to the above
set.   The resulting set, $\{x \mid 2 \leq x \leq 7\}$, still has a least upper bound of 7 and a
greatest lower bound of 2, but these bounds are now members of the set.   The
notation [ ] will be used with scale diagrams to show that these points are included.

$$2 \leq x \leq 7$$

Let U be a set of numbers over which the relations $x < y$ and $x \leq y$ are defined.
If a and b are elements of U with $a < b$, the solution set of the inequality $a < x < b$
is called the *open interval* from a to b, and may be denoted by (a, b).   If $a \leq b$, then
the solution set of $a \leq x \leq b$ is called the *closed interval* from a to b, and may be
denoted by $[a, b]$.   The half-open open intervals $(a, b]$ and $[a, b)$ are the solution
sets of $a < x \leq b$ and $a \leq x < b$, respectively.   In each case the interval is said to
be a *finite interval* and the points a and b are called *endpoints*.   Hence, a closed
interval includes its endpoints but an open interval does not.   Any point of an interval that is not an endpoint is called an *interior* point.

Examples: U is the set of natural numbers.

$(2, 7) = \{3, 4, 5, 6\}$, $[2, 7) = \{2, 3, 4, 5, 6\}$,
$(2, 7] = \{3, 4, 5, 6, 7\}$, $[2, 7] = \{2, 3, 4, 5, 6, 7\}$.

Problems (124)

1. U is the set of zero and the natural numbers.
   $A = \{n \mid 0 \leq n \leq 2\}$, $B = \{n \mid 0 < n < 5\}$.
   Identify the following sets in three ways: **i.** conditional inequality, **ii.** interval
   notation, **iii.** roster of the set.

   a. $A \cup B$ **b.** $A \cap B$ **c.** $A - B$ **d.** $B - A$

2. Follow the directions for problem 1, with $A = \{n \mid 1 < n \le 5\}$, and $B = \{n \mid 0 \le n < 5\}$.

3. U is the set of rational numbers greater than zero and less than 8.
$A = \{x \mid 0 < x < 2\}$, $B = \{x \mid 1 < x \le 5\}$, $C = \{x \mid 3 \le x \le 6\}$
Identify the following sets in three ways: **i.** conditional inequality, **ii.** interval notation, **iii.** scale diagram.

a. $A \cup B$	**f.** $B \cap C$	**k.** $B - C$	**p.** $A' \cap B'$
b. $A \cup C$	**g.** $A - B$	**l.** $C - B$	**q.** $A' \cup B'$
c. $B \cup C$	**h.** $B - A$	**m.** A'	**r.** $A \cup B \cup C$
d. $A \cap B$	**i.** $A - C$	**n.** B'	**s.** $B \cap (A \cup C)$
e. $A \cap C$	**j.** $C - A$	**o.** C'	**t.** $(B \cup C)'$

4. Follow the directions for problem 3, with $A = \{x \mid 1 \le x < 5\}$, $B = \{x \mid 2 < x \le 3\}$, $C = \{x \mid 3 \le x < 6\}$.

The first four terms of the sequence $a_n = \dfrac{n}{2n+1}$ are $a_1 = \dfrac{1}{3}$, $a_2 = \dfrac{2}{5}$, $a_3 = \dfrac{3}{7}$, and $a_4 = \dfrac{4}{9}$.

One can verify that $\dfrac{1}{3} < \dfrac{2}{5} < \dfrac{3}{7} < \dfrac{4}{9}$. Will each next term always be larger than the one it follows? One can prove that the terms of this sequence do constantly increase by choosing $a_j = \dfrac{j}{2j+1}$ and $a_{j+1} = \dfrac{j+1}{2(j+1)+1} = \dfrac{j+1}{2j+3}$, as two representative consecutive terms of a_n, and then showing that $a_j < a_{j+1}$ when j is any natural number.

Now $a_j < a_{j+1}$ requires that $\dfrac{j}{2j+1} < \dfrac{j+1}{2j+3}$.

This is true if and only if $j(2j+3) < (2j+1)(j+1)$ or $2j^2 + 3j < 2j^2 + 3j + 1$.

But this is true if and only if $0 < 1$, which is always true. Therefore, we have $a_j < a_{j+1}$ for all j. The sequence $a_n = \dfrac{n}{2n+1}$ is said to be a *monotonic increasing* sequence.

Even though $\dfrac{1}{3}, \dfrac{2}{5}, \dfrac{3}{7}$, and $\dfrac{4}{9}$ form an increasing sequence, it is still true that each of them is less than $\dfrac{1}{2}$. It can be shown that every term of this sequence will be less than $\dfrac{1}{2}$, even though these terms continually increase as we choose larger n. To show that $\dfrac{n}{2n+1} < \dfrac{1}{2}$ for all n, it is sufficient that $2n < 2n+1$. But this is certainly true when n is any natural number. Hence, $\dfrac{1}{2}$ is an upper bound for the sequence $a_n = \dfrac{n}{2n+1}$.

A stronger statement than this can be made, since it can be shown that $\frac{1}{2}$ is the least upper bound for this sequence.   If any number less than $\frac{1}{2}$ is claimed as an upper bound for this sequence, then this claim is false if a term of the sequence can be found that is larger than this supposed upper bound.   That is, if any rational number $\frac{x}{y}$ is chosen so that $\frac{x}{y} < \frac{1}{2}$, then we wish to prove that there exists a value of n, say $n = N$, such that $a_n > \frac{x}{y}$ whenever $n \geq N$.

Now if $\frac{x}{y} < \frac{1}{2}$, then $2x < y$, or $y - 2x > 0$.

We want to show how N can be chosen so that $a_N > \frac{x}{y}$.

This requires that $\frac{N}{2N + 1} > \frac{x}{y}$, or that $Ny > x(2N + 1)$.

This inequality will hold if and only if $Ny > 2Nx + x$.

This is true if and only if $Ny - 2Nx > x$, or if $N(y - 2x) > x$.

Since $y - 2x > 0$ from above, this will be true if

$$N > \frac{x}{y - 2x}$$

Now $\frac{x}{y - 2x}$ may not be a natural number, but if N is chosen as the smallest natural number that is greater than $\frac{x}{y - 2x}$, then we have $a_n > \frac{x}{y}$ when $n \geq N$. Since the sequence is monotonic increasing, not only is the Nth term greater than $\frac{x}{y}$, but so also are all later terms.   Hence, no rational number smaller than $\frac{1}{2}$ can be an upper bound.

The next example shows the method of computing N for any $\frac{x}{y} < \frac{1}{2}$.

Example: Let $\frac{x}{y}$ be $\frac{9}{20}$.   How large should N be chosen so that a_n equals $\frac{n}{2n + 1}$ is greater than $\frac{9}{20}$ whenever $n \geq N$?

Here $x = 9$ and $y = 20$, so that $\frac{x}{y - 2x} = \frac{9}{20 - 2 \cdot 9} = 4\frac{1}{2}$.

Let $N = 5$, which is the smallest natural number that is greater than $4\frac{1}{2}$.

$$a_N = \frac{5}{11} \quad \text{and} \quad \frac{5}{11} > \frac{9}{20} \quad \text{since } 5 \cdot 20 > 9 \cdot 11$$

Since the sequence is monotonic increasing, all terms of a_n for $n > 5$ will also exceed $\frac{9}{20}$.

We have shown that as n increases, the terms of the sequence $a_n = \frac{n}{2n + 1}$

constantly increase, but always remain less than an upper bound of $\frac{1}{2}$.   Further-

more $\frac{1}{2}$ is the least of all upper bounds, since no number less than $\frac{1}{2}$ is an upper

bound.   To prove this it was shown that if a rational number $\frac{x}{y}$ is chosen less than

$\frac{1}{2}$, then it is possible to select a natural number N, so that a_N, and all succeeding

terms of a_n are larger than $\frac{x}{y}$ although all are less than $\frac{1}{2}$.   The sequence $a_n =$

$\frac{n}{2n+1}$ is said to *approach the limit* of $\frac{1}{2}$, as n is assigned larger and larger values.

If $\frac{x}{y}$ is less than $\frac{1}{2}$, then no matter how close it is to $\frac{1}{2}$, as long as it does not equal $\frac{1}{2}$,

then it is possible to determine a number N so that the Nth term and all later terms

of a_n are all closer to $\frac{1}{2}$ than $\frac{x}{y}$ is.   The concept of limit is one of the most far-

reaching in all mathematics.   In a certain sense it marks the boundary between
elementary and intermediate levels of mathematics.

Problems (125)

    1. Which step in the above discussion on determining N lacks logical support
until we have defined multiplication for rational numbers?

    2. In the above example determine N when $\frac{x}{y}$ is $\frac{49}{100}$.

    3. a. Write the first 5 terms of $a_n = \dfrac{n}{n+1}$.

      b. Verify that these terms increase steadily.

      c. Prove that this sequence is monotonic increasing.

      d. Prove that 1 is an upper bound for this sequence.

      e. Prove that 1 is the least upper bound for this sequence.

      (In this proof and others of this problem set you may assume that the
properties of inequalities as given in problem set (118) for natural numbers
extend also to positive rationals.   This will be justified in later chapters).

    4. a. Write the first 5 terms of $a_n = \dfrac{2n}{3n-1}$.

      b. Verify that these terms decrease steadily.

      c. Prove that this sequence is monotonic decreasing.

      d. Prove that $\frac{2}{3}$ is a lower bound for this sequence.

    e. Prove that $\dfrac{2}{3}$ is the greatest lower bound of this sequence.

5. a. Beginning with $n = 2$, write 5 consecutive terms of $a_n = \dfrac{2n - 3}{4n - 5}$.

    b. Verify that these terms increase steadily.

    c. Prove that this sequence is monotonic increasing.

    d. Prove that $\dfrac{1}{2}$ is an upper bound for this sequence.

    e. Prove that $\dfrac{1}{2}$ is the least upper bound for this sequence.

6. a. Write the first 5 terms of $a_n = \dfrac{5n - 4}{4n}$.

    b. Verify that these terms increase steadily.

    c. Prove that this sequence is monotonic increasing.

    d. Prove that $1\dfrac{1}{4}$ is an upper bound for this sequence.

    e. Prove that $1\dfrac{1}{4}$ is the least upper bound for this sequence.

For the following sequences the reader is invited to make conjectures about the nature of the sequence and possible upper or lower bounds. Try to prove as many of these conjectures as you can.

7. $a_n = \dfrac{3n - 1}{4n + 1}$ **8.** $a_n = \dfrac{1}{n}$ **9.** $a_n = \dfrac{2n + 2}{n + 1}$ **10.** $a_n = \dfrac{n}{2n - 1}$

For Further Study

The following references contain discussions of the order properties of the natural numbers: [A1], pp. 86–89; [P1], pp. 107–111; [O1], pp. 103–111; and [W3], pp. 84–85.

Most discussions of the limit concept soon advance beyond the level of difficulty of this text. The following are suggested for further reading: [J1], pp. 171–173; [N5], pp. 121–125, 322–325; and [M8], pp. 28–39.

14

Multiplication of Rational Numbers

14-1. Products of Quotients

By appealing directly to the definition of rational numbers in terms of the natural numbers and zero, and continuing our basic assumption that the same formal laws hold as for the natural numbers, one can readily establish the form that the product of rational numbers must necessarily assume. The result is quite simple and the associated computation is straightforward. The difficulties in the multiplication of rationals, as represented by common fraction symbols, do not lie here, but rather are conceptual difficulties. For once the rule for multiplication of fractions is established, it must then be checked, not only against the various interpretations of the fraction symbol, but also for the wide variety of meanings that was built up for the operation of multiplication as applied to the natural numbers and zero. A major concern in this chapter is the presentation of as much evidence as possible why the multiplication of rational numbers really deserves the name "multiplication."

Let the quotients $\frac{a}{b}$ and $\frac{c}{d}$ be zero or natural numbers. This requires that b and d be natural numbers, while a and c may be zero or multiples of b and d, respectively.

Now assign a simple name to each of these, that is, set $\frac{a}{b} = x$, and $\frac{c}{d} = y$. By definition, we then have $a = bx$ and $c = dy$. Since multiplication (of the natural numbers and zero) is well defined, we have $ac = (bx)(dy)$.

By using the commutative and associative properties (again of the natural numbers and zero), one obtains $ac = (bd)(xy)$. The closure properties assure us that bd is a natural number, and that ac and xy are natural numbers or zero.

Hence, by definition, $xy = \frac{ac}{bd}$, or by substitution, $\left(\frac{a}{b}\right)\left(\frac{c}{d}\right) = \frac{ac}{bd}$. We now, as in Section 12-1, remove the restriction that a be a multiple of b and that c be a multiple of d, so that x and y can represent rational numbers.   By assuming that the principles used above for natural numbers hold also for rational numbers, we have a formula for the product of two rational numbers.

The product of the rational number represented by $\dfrac{a}{b}$ *and the rational number repre-*

sented by $\dfrac{c}{d}$ *is the rational number represented by* $\dfrac{ac}{bd}$.   The replacement of $\left(\dfrac{a}{b}\right)\left(\dfrac{c}{d}\right)$

by $\dfrac{ac}{bd}$ is called *multiplication of fractions*.   This is also seen to be a transformation

of a product of quotients into a quotient of products.

This definition of multiplication shows that the product of two rational numbers is again a rational number, or that the rational numbers are closed under the binary operation of multiplication.   In the next problem set, the reader is asked to verify that this definition provides for a number of other properties that are desirable for a product.   In particular, those properties of multiplication that have been anticipated in previous discussions will be found to hold.

Problems (126)

1. Give the steps of the argument that $\left(\dfrac{a}{b}\right)\left(\dfrac{c}{d}\right) = \dfrac{ac}{bd}$ with $a = 10$, $b = 2$, $c = 21$, and $d = 7$.   Avoid any computation.

2. Give the steps of the argument that $\left(\dfrac{a}{b}\right)\left(\dfrac{c}{d}\right) = \dfrac{ac}{bd}$ without introducing x and y as done in the text.

3. Prove that multiplication of rationals is well defined.   *Hint:* See the proof in Section 12-1 that addition is well defined.

4. Derive $\left(\dfrac{a}{b}\right)\left(\dfrac{c}{d}\right) = \dfrac{ac}{bd}$ by using $\dfrac{a}{b} = a\left(\dfrac{1}{b}\right)$ and $\dfrac{a}{b} = \dfrac{na}{nb}$.

5. Prove the cancellation law for multiplication of rational numbers.

6. Show that $\dfrac{1}{1}$ is an identity for multiplication of rational numbers, and that the property $\dfrac{a}{b} = \dfrac{na}{nb}$ is consistent with multiplication by 1.

7. Show that $x \cdot 0 = 0$, when x is any rational number.

8. Show that if $\dfrac{a}{b}$ is a nonzero rational then $\dfrac{a}{b}$ and $\dfrac{b}{a}$ are reciprocals.

9. Prove that the multiplication of rational numbers is commutative.

10. Prove that the multiplication of rational numbers is associative.

11. Prove that multiplication is distributive over addition, for rationals.

12. Assume $\dfrac{c}{d} \geq \dfrac{e}{f}$, and prove that $\dfrac{a}{b}\left(\dfrac{c}{d} - \dfrac{e}{f}\right) = \left(\dfrac{a}{b}\right)\left(\dfrac{c}{d}\right) - \left(\dfrac{a}{b}\right)\left(\dfrac{e}{f}\right)$.

14-2. Rational Numbers as Multipliers

A number of conceptual and graphical models were given in Section 9-3 for products of natural numbers. Some of these become meaningless when applied to rational numbers, while others extend quite readily. In general the following criterion applies: Those concepts based on counting to find "How many?" are usually awkward or meaningless for rational numbers, while those based on measuring to find "How much?" require little or no modification.

One can illustrate $3 \cdot 5$ with three mutually disjoint sets each having five elements, but it is meaningless to try such a model for $\left(\frac{2}{3}\right)\left(\frac{5}{7}\right)$. Sets and their elements are essentially integral; an object is either an element or it isn't and the criterion for membership cannot be met part way. Set theoretical ideas, being so closely tied to counting, have little to contribute to our analysis. For example, the product $3 \cdot 5$ can be determined by counting the number of elements in the Cartesian product of two sets, but there is no suggestion here on how to think about $\left(\frac{2}{3}\right)\left(\frac{5}{7}\right)$.

Again one can compute $3 \cdot 5$ as $5 + 5 + 5$, that is, by writing 5 down three times and adding. But no one would try to compute $\left(\frac{2}{3}\right)\left(\frac{5}{7}\right)$ by writing down $\frac{5}{7}$ two thirds of a time and then adding! It is clear that the multiplication of rationals cannot be directly related to repeated addition whenever the multiplier is not a natural number. However, if the multiplier is a natural number, there is no difficulty. For example, $(2)\left(\frac{5}{7}\right) = \frac{10}{7}$ and also $(2)\left(\frac{5}{7}\right) = \frac{5}{7} + \frac{5}{7} = \frac{10}{7}$. This suggests that the conceptual difficulties of the multiplication of fractions are largely concerned with fractional multipliers.

A valuable insight into such multipliers can be gained by shifting our point of view from binary operations to unary operations. Suppose we think of the product $\left(\frac{a}{b}\right)\left(\frac{c}{d}\right)$ as being the transform that results when the operator $\left(\frac{a}{b}\right)(\ )$ is joined to the operand $\frac{c}{d}$. This operator represents "multiplying by $\frac{a}{b}$."

The composition of a multiplication operator $a(\ )$ and a division operation $\overline{}_b$ to give the operator $\frac{a}{b}(\ )$ was introduced in Section 10-4, but with the restriction that a be zero or a multiple of b. We now drop this constraint and allow $\frac{a}{b}$ to be any rational number, in the composition $a(\ ) \circ \overline{}_b = \frac{a}{b}(\ )$.

Examples:

$$12(\ ) \circ \frac{}{3} = \frac{12}{3}(\ ) = 4(\ )$$

Multiplication by 12, followed by division by 3, yields the same transform as multiplication by 4.

$$2(\quad) \circ \frac{}{3} = \frac{2}{3}(\quad)$$

Multiplication by 2, followed by division by 3, is to be equivalent to multiplication by $\frac{2}{3}$.

$$8(\quad) \circ \frac{}{12} = \frac{8}{12}(\quad) = \frac{2}{3}(\quad)$$

Multiplication by 8, followed by division by 12, is to be equivalent to multiplication by $\frac{8}{12}$, and this in turn to multiplication by $\frac{2}{3}$.

The next step is the recognition that the division operator $\frac{}{b}$ is equivalent to the multiplication operator $\frac{1}{b}(\quad)$. When the operand a is a natural number or zero, we have from the previous chapter that $\frac{a}{b} = \frac{1}{b}(a)$, so that a divided by b is the same as a multiplied by $\frac{1}{b}$. If the operand is a rational number $\frac{c}{d}$, then $\frac{1}{b}\left(\frac{c}{d}\right) = \frac{c}{bd}$. With the definition of division to be given in Chapter 15, we shall find that $\frac{c}{d}$ divided by b also gives $\frac{c}{bd}$ as required. This means that for all operands we have freedom to think of the rational multiplier $\frac{a}{b}(\quad)$ as the composite of $a(\quad)$ and $\frac{1}{b}(\quad)$. Furthermore, these multiplication operators commute:

$$\left(\frac{a}{b}\right)\left(\frac{c}{d}\right) = \left[(a)\left(\frac{1}{b}\right)\right]\left(\frac{c}{d}\right) = a\left[\left(\frac{1}{b}\right)\left(\frac{c}{d}\right)\right] = a\left[\frac{c}{bd}\right] = \left(\frac{a}{1}\right)\left(\frac{c}{bd}\right) = \frac{ac}{bd}$$

$$\left(\frac{a}{b}\right)\left(\frac{c}{d}\right) = \left[\left(\frac{1}{b}\right)(a)\right]\left(\frac{c}{d}\right) = \frac{1}{b}\left[(a)\left(\frac{c}{d}\right)\right] = \frac{1}{b}\left[\left(\frac{a}{1}\right)\left(\frac{c}{d}\right)\right] = \left(\frac{1}{b}\right)\left(\frac{ac}{d}\right) = \frac{ac}{bd}$$

We now have a satisfactory solution to what has traditionally been a serious semantic difficulty to the student when the multiplication of fractions was introduced. Natural number multipliers leave the student with the generalization that multiplication always transforms the multiplicand into a larger number, since multipliers of zero and 1 are considered to be exceptional.

Again division is thought in general to produce a change to a smaller number, even though division by zero is not possible and division by 1 produces no change. With this background in mind the change produced by fraction multipliers seems most erratic, since now there is sometimes a magnification and sometimes a shrinking of the multiplicand. But this is just what is to be expected when we accept that what is called "multiplication" by a fraction as being a composite of both multiplication and division. The following examples show the effect of a variety of rational multipliers on the same operand.

Examples:

$$\left(\frac{2}{1}\right)\left(\frac{6}{1}\right) = \frac{12}{1} = 12 \qquad \text{Multiplication only.}$$

The definition of the product of rational numbers agrees with the definition for natural numbers.

$$\left(\frac{1}{3}\right)\left(\frac{6}{1}\right) = \frac{6}{3} = 2 \qquad \text{Division only.}$$

$$\left(\frac{2}{3}\right)\left(\frac{6}{1}\right) = (2)\left(\frac{1}{3}\right)\left(\frac{6}{1}\right) = (2)\left(\frac{6}{3}\right) = (2)(2) = 4$$

$$\left(\frac{2}{3}\right)\left(\frac{6}{1}\right) = \left(\frac{1}{3}\right)(2)\left(\frac{6}{1}\right) = \left(\frac{1}{3}\right)\left(\frac{12}{1}\right) = \frac{12}{3} = 4$$

Both multiplication and division are involved, and they may be used in either order. The multiplier 2 is less than the divisor 3; hence the product 4 is less than the multiplicand 6.

$$\left(\frac{3}{2}\right)\left(\frac{6}{1}\right) = (3)\left(\frac{1}{2}\right)\left(\frac{6}{1}\right) = (3)\left(\frac{6}{2}\right) = (3)(3) = 9$$

$$\left(\frac{3}{2}\right)\left(\frac{6}{1}\right) = \left(\frac{1}{2}\right)(3)\left(\frac{6}{1}\right) = \left(\frac{1}{2}\right)(18) = \frac{18}{2} = 9$$

The multiplier 3 is now greater than the divisor 2; hence the product 9 is greater than the multiplicand 6.

The identity $\left(\frac{a}{b}\right)\left(\frac{c}{d}\right) = \frac{ac}{bd}$ often does not indicate the shortest computation for obtaining the product in lowest terms.

Example:

$$\left(\frac{4}{5}\right)\left(\frac{3}{14}\right) = \frac{12}{70} = \frac{6}{35} \qquad \left(\frac{2 \cdot 2}{5}\right)\left(\frac{3}{2 \cdot 7}\right) = \frac{2 \cdot 2 \cdot 3}{5 \cdot 2 \cdot 7} = \frac{2 \cdot 3}{5 \cdot 7} = \frac{6}{35}$$

If all numerators and denominators are in prime factored form, then the final step of reduction to lowest terms can be anticipated before the numerators and denominators have been multiplied. Here both 4 and 14 can be divided by their g.c.d. of 2.

$$\left(\frac{\overset{2}{\cancel{4}}}{5}\right)\left(\frac{3}{\cancel{14}}\right) = \frac{6}{35} \qquad \left(\frac{\cancel{2} \cdot 2}{5}\right)\left(\frac{3}{\cancel{2} \cdot 7}\right) = \frac{6}{35}$$

Problems (127)

In problems 1 and 2 give all the steps (no cancellation short-cuts) of these computations in two ways, by replacing each multiplier $\frac{a}{b}$ by the product $(a)\left(\frac{1}{b}\right)$ and then using the commutative and associative principles as in the above examples.

1. a. $\left(\frac{5}{6}\right)(18)$ **b.** $\left(\frac{5}{6}\right)(17)$

2. a. $\left(\frac{7}{8}\right)\left(\frac{1}{21}\right)$ **b.** $\left(\frac{7}{8}\right)\left(\frac{1}{20}\right)$

3. Compute these products.

a. $28 \cdot \frac{1}{7}$ **i.** $\frac{3}{5} \cdot 45$ **q.** $\left(\frac{7}{7}\right)\left(\frac{3}{8}\right)$

b. $29 \cdot \frac{1}{7}$ **j.** $\frac{3}{5} \cdot 18$ **r.** $\left(\frac{5}{13}\right)\left(\frac{13}{5}\right)$

c. $\frac{1}{5} \cdot 65$ **k.** $\frac{7}{10} \cdot 6$ **s.** $\left(\frac{5}{2 \cdot 7}\right)\left(\frac{2 \cdot 3}{11}\right)$

d. $\frac{1}{5} \cdot 64$ **l.** $6 \cdot \frac{9}{4}$ **t.** $\left(\frac{2 \cdot 5}{3 \cdot 7}\right)\left(\frac{3 \cdot 3}{2 \cdot 11}\right)$

e. $8 \cdot \frac{1}{12}$ **m.** $\left(\frac{2}{5}\right)\left(\frac{4}{11}\right)$ **u.** $\left(\frac{2^2 \cdot 13}{5 \cdot 11}\right)\left(\frac{5 \cdot 7}{2^4 \cdot 3}\right)$

f. $\frac{1}{10} \cdot 35$ **n.** $\left(\frac{13}{3}\right)\left(\frac{5}{2}\right)$ **v.** $\left(\frac{35}{6}\right)\left(\frac{14}{55}\right)$

g. $21 \cdot \frac{5}{7}$ **o.** $\left(\frac{3}{4}\right)\left(\frac{12}{25}\right)$ **w.** $\left(\frac{4}{15}\right)\left(\frac{5}{16}\right)$

h. $20 \cdot \frac{5}{7}$ **p.** $(0)\left(\frac{8}{9}\right)$ **x.** $\left(\frac{15}{2}\right)\left(\frac{6}{5}\right)$

4. Compute these products.

a. $\left(\frac{1}{3}\right)(3 \cdot 5)$ **i.** $\left(\frac{5}{7}\right)(2 \cdot 7)$ **q.** $\left(\frac{11}{4}\right)\left(\frac{3}{3}\right)$

b. $\left(\frac{1}{3}\right)(2 \cdot 5)$ **j.** $\left(\frac{3}{11}\right)(2 \cdot 5)$ **r.** $\left(\frac{9}{9}\right)\left(\frac{2}{9}\right)$

c. $(7^3)\left(\frac{1}{7}\right)$ **k.** $\left(\frac{2}{3 \cdot 5}\right)(3 \cdot 7)$ **s.** $\left(\frac{5}{119}\right)\left(\frac{51}{11}\right)$

d. $(3^2)\left(\frac{1}{7}\right)$ **l.** $\left(\frac{5^2}{2 \cdot 7}\right)(3 \cdot 7)$ **t.** $\left(\frac{65}{133}\right)\left(\frac{57}{143}\right)$

e. $(5^3)\left(\frac{1}{7 \cdot 5^2}\right)$ **m.** $\left(\frac{6}{5}\right)\left(\frac{7}{11}\right)$ **u.** $\left(\frac{21}{39}\right)\left(\frac{143}{77}\right)$

f. $\left(\frac{1}{2 \cdot 3}\right)(3 \cdot 7)$ **n.** $\left(\frac{15}{4}\right)\left(\frac{7}{13}\right)$ **v.** $\left(\frac{6}{385}\right)\left(\frac{77}{30}\right)$

g. $(2 \cdot 11)\left(\frac{3}{11}\right)$ **o.** $\left(\frac{5}{8}\right)\left(\frac{9}{10}\right)$ **w.** $\left(\frac{110}{39}\right)\left(\frac{78}{55}\right)$

h. $(3 \cdot 7)\left(\frac{2}{5}\right)$ **p.** $\left(\frac{7}{16}\right)\left(\frac{0}{3}\right)$ **x.** $\left(\frac{26}{57}\right)\left(\frac{65}{77}\right)$

14-3. Graphic Models for Products

The product $\left(\frac{2}{3}\right)(1)$ is usually read $\frac{2}{3}$ of 1 rather than $\frac{2}{3}$ times 1. Two thirds of a unit is obtained by two transformations of the unit: multiplying by 2, and dividing by 3, in either order. The following examples show both orders of applying the components of the composite operator "two thirds of," or $\frac{2}{3}(\ )$.

Examples:

```
* * * * * *          A group (of six)
* *                  One third of the group
* * * *              Two of the thirds of the group
* * * * * * * * * * * *   Two of the groups
* * * *              One third of two of the groups
```

6

$\left(\frac{1}{3}\right)(6) = 2$

$(2)\left[\left(\frac{1}{3}\right)(6)\right] = 4$

$(2)(6) = 12$

$\left(\frac{1}{3}\right)\left[(2)(6)\right] = 4$

Of all the various interpretations of multiplication, that based on the concept of ratio is particularly adapted to the products of rational numbers. All of the models based on lengths of line segments used in Section 9-3 for products of natural numbers, can be used without change for products of rational numbers. It was shown there that when x and y are natural numbers, then the product xy has the same ratio to the factor x that the factor y has to the unit 1. And because multiplication is commutative, the product xy has the same ratio to the factor y that the factor x has to 1.

$$\frac{xy}{x} = \frac{y}{1} \quad \text{and} \quad \frac{xy}{y} = \frac{x}{1}$$

A justification of the extension of these equalities to the case where x and y are themselves rational numbers will be given in the next chapter. Meanwhile we give some examples as a graphic illustration of these extensions.

Example: 4 has the same ratio to 6 that $\frac{2}{3}$ has to 1, and 4 has the same

ratio to $\frac{2}{3}$ as 6 has to 1.

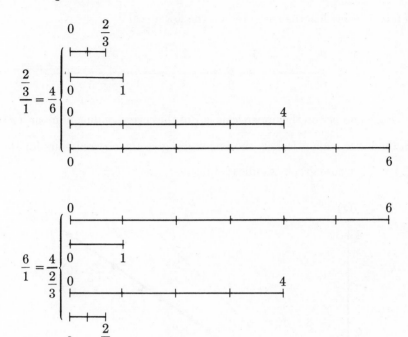

Note: As a quotient, the fraction with numerator 4 and denominator $\frac{2}{3}$ is not defined until we have defined division for rational numbers (see Chapter 15).

In each case the diagram becomes more compact and the equality of the two ratios is even more apparent when we use two scales, one over the other. This provides a direct generalization of the scales (and sequences) given in Section 9-3.

The ratio of 4 to 6 is the same as that of $\frac{2}{3}$ to 1 (same lengths measured, first on the upper scale, and then on the lower scale).

Another way to interpret this diagram is to think of 1 as being associated with all of the line segment whose length is 6, and then $\frac{2}{3}$ of this is 4. If the factors $\frac{2}{3}$ and

6 are interchanged, then the ratio of 4 to $\frac{2}{3}$ (on the upper scale) is the same as that

of 6 to 1 (same lengths measured on the lower scale).

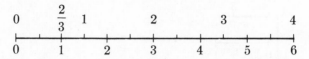

Each number on the upper scale is $\frac{2}{3}$ of the corresponding number for that point

on the lower scale. Hence, the two scales give the ordered pairs for the function

$f(x) = \frac{2}{3}x$, whose graph is indicated below.

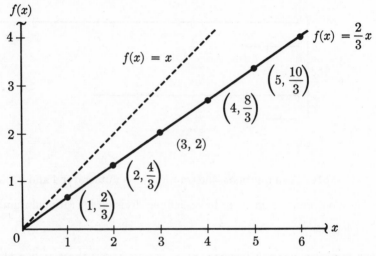

This is a linear function; if x is a rational number, the points $\left(x, \frac{2}{3}x\right)$ will lie along

the line shown. The graph of the identity function $f(x) = x$ has been included for

comparison.

The multiplication models that use similar triangles (see Section 9-3) are also
well adapted to rational numbers.

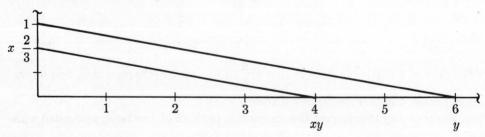

The next problem set provides practice in constructing the model above, which was based on two adjacent linear scales, one over the other. These two scales have a common origin or zero point, but the number 1 is assigned to a different length on each scale (except when the multiplier is 1). Their construction can be as follows:

$$\left(\frac{a}{b}\right)\left(\frac{c}{d}\right) = \frac{ac}{bd} \qquad \text{(multiplier)(multiplicand)} = \text{(product)}$$

The numeral 1 is assigned to the upper scale. The multiplicand $\frac{c}{d}$ is located on the upper scale, as determined by the 1. Then 1 is located on the lower scale, at the same point as $\frac{c}{d}$ on the upper scale. The multiplier $\frac{a}{b}$ is located on the lower scale, as determined by 1 on that scale. The product $\frac{ac}{bd}$ is on the upper scale, at the same point as $\frac{a}{b}$ on the lower scale.

It will now be visually evident that the product has the same ratio to the multiplicand, as the multiplier has to 1, as required for the ratio interpretation of multiplication. Observe in the example that $\frac{c}{d}$ was first divided into b equal parts, and then this result was multiplied by a. Thus $\frac{a}{b}$ is $\frac{a}{b}$ of 1, and $\frac{ac}{bd}$ is $\frac{a}{b}$ of $\frac{c}{d}$.

Example: $\left(\frac{2}{3}\right)\left(\frac{5}{7}\right) = \frac{10}{21}$ $\frac{10}{21}$ is $\frac{2}{3}$ of $\frac{5}{7}$

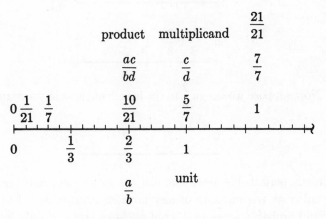

Note: These diagrams should be constructed on square-ruled paper. To do this effectively requires a proper choice of the number of spaces to assign to 1 on the upper scale since all later decisions depend on this. Experience with the problems will confirm that this number can be a multiple of bd (the product of the denominators); or of d, if c is a multiple of b.

Problems (128)

Each product is to be illustrated with a diagram as in the above example.

1. $\left(\dfrac{5}{7}\right)\left(\dfrac{2}{3}\right)$ 3. $\left(\dfrac{7}{5}\right)\left(\dfrac{2}{3}\right)$ 5. $\left(\dfrac{3}{4}\right)\left(\dfrac{8}{5}\right)$ 7. $\left(\dfrac{6}{5}\right)\left(\dfrac{3}{4}\right)$ 9. $\left(\dfrac{9}{2}\right)\left(\dfrac{4}{3}\right)$

2. $\left(\dfrac{3}{4}\right)\left(\dfrac{7}{5}\right)$ 4. $\left(\dfrac{5}{4}\right)\left(\dfrac{5}{3}\right)$ 6. $\left(\dfrac{3}{4}\right)\left(\dfrac{5}{6}\right)$ 8. $\left(\dfrac{5}{3}\right)\left(\dfrac{4}{5}\right)$ 10. $\left(\dfrac{5}{4}\right)\left(\dfrac{5}{4}\right)$

Assume that points have been chosen along a line segment to divide it into segments of equal length and that zero has been assigned to an end point. Then if any nonzero positive rational number is assigned to any other division point, a linear scale can always be completed by determining the rational numbers that correspond to the remaining division points.

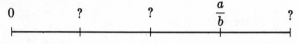

Example: Let $\dfrac{a}{b} = \dfrac{2}{3}$. If $\dfrac{2}{3}$ is assigned as the length of one segment, then the remaining scale numbers can be determined by multiplication alone. However, it would help the scale to "look right" if the numbers $\dfrac{1}{3}$ and 1 were also located.

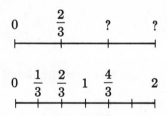

Now suppose we assign $\dfrac{2}{3}$ to the length of three of the segments.

This is permissible since one can assign any nonzero positive rational number as the measure of any nonzero magnitude. But most people would probably agree that what we have now certainly looks awkward. After all, one tends to think first of $\dfrac{2}{3}$ of being two amounts of a certain size, but the diagram is suggestive of three amounts rather than two. The use of the lower scale makes it clear that one should compute $\dfrac{1}{3}$ of $\dfrac{2}{3}$ and $\dfrac{2}{3}$ of $\dfrac{2}{3}$.

$$0 \qquad \frac{2}{9} \qquad \frac{4}{9} \qquad \frac{6}{9} \text{ or } \frac{2}{3}$$

$$0 \qquad \frac{1}{3} \qquad \frac{2}{3} \qquad 1$$

The intuitive appeal can be still further increased by locating $\frac{1}{9}$, $\frac{1}{3}$, and 1. This involves doubling the number of divisions and extending the scale.

$$0 \quad \frac{1}{9} \quad \frac{2}{9} \quad \frac{1}{3} \quad \frac{4}{9} \quad \frac{5}{9} \quad \frac{2}{3} \quad \frac{7}{9} \quad \frac{8}{9} \quad 1$$

$$0 \qquad \frac{1}{3} \qquad \frac{2}{3} \qquad 1$$

Problems (129)

For problems 1 to 16, determine the missing numbers required for a linear scale. In each case where possible, construct a diagram on squared paper that also locates 1 and $\frac{1}{a}$ where a is each denominator used.

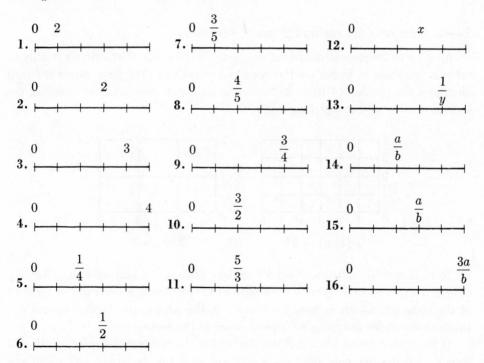

For problems 17 to 34, determine the number for the specified division point on a linear scale.

17.   0   ?   12 |—+—+—|

18.   0   ?   11 |—+—+—|

19.   0   ?   7 |—+—+—|

20.   0   ? $\frac{6}{11}$ |—+—+—|

21.   0   ? $\frac{5}{11}$ |—+—+—|

22.   0   ? $\frac{7}{8}$ |—+—+—|

23.   0   5   ? |—+—+—+—|

24.   0   5   ? |—+—+—+—|

25.   0 $\frac{1}{4}$? |—+—+—+—|

26.   0 $\frac{1}{4}$? |—+—+—+—|

27.   0 $\frac{3}{4}$? |—+—+—+—|

28.   0   7   ? |—+—+—+—|

29.   0 $\frac{3}{5}$? |—+—+—+—|

30.   0 $\frac{3}{5}$? |—+—+—+—|

31.   0   ? $\frac{3}{5}$ |—+—+—+—|

32.   0   ? x |—+—+—+—|

33.   0   ? $\frac{x}{y}$ |—+—+—+—|

34.   0 $\frac{x}{y}$? |—+—+—+—|

14-4. Area and the Multiplication of Fractions

Another measurement model for products (Section 9-3) that extends readily to rational numbers is based on the area of rectangles. The first diagram below illustrates the product (4)(6). By retaining the same rectangle, but changing the scale as shown, we get a picture of (2)(3).

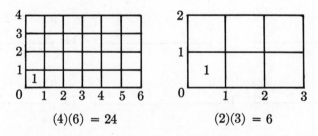

$$(4)(6) = 24 \qquad\qquad (2)(3) = 6$$

Note that three units are involved in these results. A horizontal line segment of length 1 is used to determine the length of the rectangle; a vertical line segment of the same magnitude is used for measuring the width; and finally, a square is taken as a unit for assigning an area measure to the rectangle.

It is only for convenience and simplicity that the rectangle is covered with unit squares. If desired, one could use a different scale for the length and width and assign the area number by the use of unit rectangles.

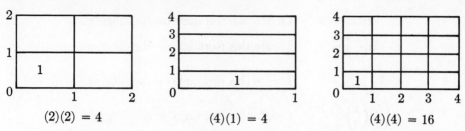

$$(2)(2) = 4 \qquad\qquad (4)(1) = 4 \qquad\qquad (4)(4) = 16$$

Still other choices of scales will involve rational numbers.   Here we can verify that the formula $\left(\dfrac{a}{b}\right)\left(\dfrac{c}{d}\right) = \dfrac{ac}{bd}$ continues to yield consistent results.   Remember that the number for the product refers to the unit area.

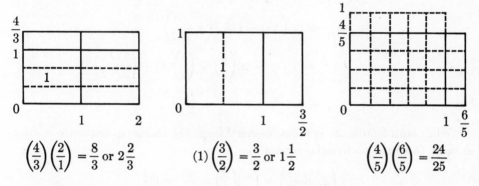

$$\left(\frac{4}{3}\right)\left(\frac{2}{1}\right) = \frac{8}{3} \text{ or } 2\frac{2}{3} \qquad (1)\left(\frac{3}{2}\right) = \frac{3}{2} \text{ or } 1\frac{1}{2} \qquad \left(\frac{4}{5}\right)\left(\frac{6}{5}\right) = \frac{24}{25}$$

The products that arise in the computation of $\left(\dfrac{a}{b}\right)\left(\dfrac{c}{d}\right)$ show up clearly in the third diagram.   There are $5 \cdot 5$ or 25 of the smaller squares that make up the unit square, and the area of the rectangle is given by a count of $4 \cdot 6$ (4 rows of 6) of these squares.

A similar diagram also provides an analysis of the product of two factors in mixed numeral form.

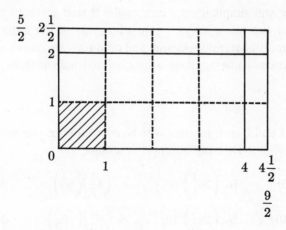

$$(2)(4) = 8 \qquad \text{Locate this rectangle on the diagram.}$$

$$(2)\left(\frac{1}{2}\right) = 1 \qquad \text{Locate this rectangle on the diagram.}$$

$$\left(\frac{1}{2}\right)(4) = 2 \qquad \text{Locate this rectangle on the diagram.}$$

$$\left(\frac{1}{2}\right)\left(\frac{1}{2}\right) = \frac{1}{4} \qquad \text{Locate this rectangle on the diagram.}$$

The area of the entire rectangle is then the sum of these four, or $11\frac{1}{4}$. The four products are those given by two applications of the distributive principle.

$$\left(2\frac{1}{2}\right)\left(4\frac{1}{2}\right) = \left(2 + \frac{1}{2}\right)\left(4 + \frac{1}{2}\right)$$

$$= (2)\left(4 + \frac{1}{2}\right) + \frac{1}{2}\left(4 + \frac{1}{2}\right)$$

$$= (2)(4) + (2)\left(\frac{1}{2}\right) + \left(\frac{1}{2}\right)(4) + \left(\frac{1}{2}\right)\left(\frac{1}{2}\right)$$

$$= 8 + 1 + 2 + \frac{1}{4} = 11\frac{1}{4}$$

When both factors are in mixed numeral form, the change to improper fractions is likely to be the preferred computation.

$$\left(2\frac{1}{2}\right)\left(4\frac{1}{2}\right) = \left(\frac{5}{2}\right)\left(\frac{9}{2}\right) = \frac{45}{4} = 11\frac{1}{4}$$

But when only one factor is a mixed numeral, the use of the distributive principle may be effective.

$$\left(3\frac{1}{2}\right)(50) = \left(3 + \frac{1}{2}\right)(50) = (3)(50) + \left(\frac{1}{2}\right)(50) = 150 + 25 = 175$$

The area of a rectangle model for the product of two rational numbers has been shown to give good analogies for the computations of these products. But for overall flexibility and simplicity the best model is that given in the previous sections, which used two linear scales. One advantage of the latter is that all four numbers—unit, multiplier, multiplicand, and product—are measures of line lengths. In the area diagrams some numbers are associated with lengths and others with areas.

Problems (130)

In problems 1 and 2 each product is to be computed in two ways: **A.** using the distributive principle; **B.** using improper fractions.

1. a. $\left(5\frac{1}{3}\right)(6)$ **b.** $\left(50\frac{1}{3}\right)(6)$ **c.** $\left(4\frac{1}{3}\right)\left(6\frac{1}{2}\right)$ **d.** $\left(5\frac{1}{3}\right)\left(7\frac{1}{2}\right)$

2. a. $\left(2\frac{3}{5}\right)(10)$ **b.** $\left(26\frac{3}{5}\right)(10)$ **c.** $\left(6\frac{3}{5}\right)\left(15\frac{2}{3}\right)$ **d.** $\left(2\frac{3}{5}\right)\left(4\frac{2}{3}\right)$

3. What number is 4 times as large as $\frac{5}{24}$? 4 times as large as $\frac{5}{23}$?

4. What number is 3 times as large as $\frac{7}{24}$? 3 times as large as $\frac{7}{25}$?

5. What number is $\frac{1}{6}$ of $\frac{12}{25}$? $\frac{1}{6}$ of $\frac{13}{25}$?

6. What number is $\frac{1}{4}$ of $\frac{12}{15}$? $\frac{1}{4}$ of $\frac{11}{15}$?

7. Compute $f(x) = (x - 1)(3 - x)$ for $x = 1, 1\frac{1}{2}, 2, 2\frac{1}{2}$, and 3.

8. Compute $f(x) = (x - 2)(4 - x)$ for $x = 2, 2\frac{1}{2}, 3, 3\frac{1}{2}$, and 4.

9. Compute $f(x) = x(2 - x)$ for $x = 0, \frac{1}{3}, \frac{2}{3}, 1, \frac{4}{3}, \frac{5}{3}$, and 2.

10. Compute $f(x) = (x - 1)(3 - x)$ for $x = 1, 1\frac{1}{3}, 1\frac{2}{3}, 2, 2\frac{1}{3}, 2\frac{2}{3}$, and 3.

11. Compute $f(x) = 1 + x^2 - 2x$ for $x = 0, \frac{1}{3}, \frac{2}{3}, 1, \frac{4}{3}, \frac{5}{3}$, and 2.

12. Compute $f(x) = 4 + x^2 - 4x$ for $x = 0, \frac{1}{2}, 1, \frac{3}{2}, 2, \frac{5}{2}, 3, \frac{7}{2}$, and 4.

13. Compute $f(n) = \left(1 + \frac{1}{n}\right)^n$ for $n = 1, 2, 3, 4$.

14. Compute $f(n) = \left(1 - \frac{1}{n}\right)^n$ for $n = 1, 2, 3, 4$.

15. Compute:

   a. $\left(\frac{3}{2}\right)^2 - 2$ **b.** $2 - \left(\frac{7}{5}\right)^2$ **c.** $\left(\frac{17}{12}\right)^2 - 2$ **d.** $2 - \left(\frac{41}{29}\right)^2$ **e.** $\left(\frac{99}{70}\right)^2 - 2$

16. Compute:

   a. $3 - \left(\frac{5}{3}\right)^2$ **b.** $\left(\frac{7}{4}\right)^2 - 3$ **c.** $3 - \left(\frac{19}{11}\right)^2$ **d.** $\left(\frac{26}{15}\right)^2 - 3$ **e.** $3 - \left(\frac{71}{41}\right)^2$

The distributive principle applies to problems 17 to 28, and hence they may be computed either as sums or differences, or as products. Consider which method will be best before computing.

17. $6\left(\frac{1}{2} + \frac{1}{3}\right)$ **21.** $\left(2\frac{1}{4} - \frac{5}{6}\right)12$ **25.** $10\left(\frac{2}{3} + \frac{1}{2} - \frac{1}{6}\right)$

18. $10\left(\frac{4}{5} + \frac{1}{2}\right)$ **22.** $\left(3\frac{1}{3} - \frac{3}{4}\right)12$ **26.** $9\left(\frac{3}{4} + \frac{1}{2} - \frac{1}{4}\right)$

19. $9\left(\frac{7}{9} + \frac{2}{3}\right)$ **23.** $6\left(\frac{3}{8} + \frac{13}{8}\right)$ **27.** $10\left(\frac{1}{2} + \frac{2}{5} - \frac{3}{10}\right)$

20. $8\left(\frac{3}{4} + \frac{5}{8}\right)$ **24.** $5\left(\frac{8}{3} + \frac{1}{3}\right)$ **28.** $9\left(\frac{2}{3} + \frac{1}{9} - \frac{2}{9}\right)$

For problems 29 and 30, the length, width, and area of the given rectangle depend on the scale used to measure them.   Determine for each scale the length, width, and area of the rectangle.

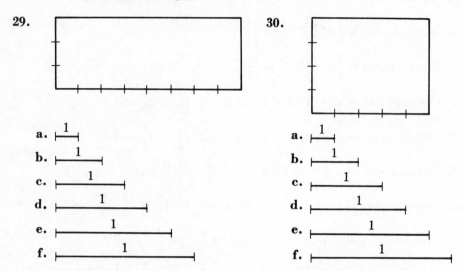

For problems 31 to 36, the shaded area has been assigned an area of 1.   In each case give the area thus determined for the rectangle.

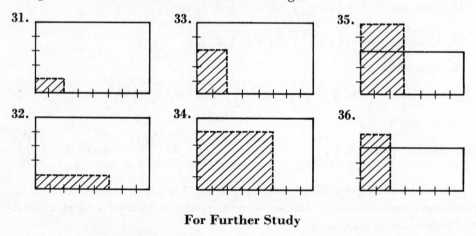

For Further Study

Nothing takes the place of a wide range of experiences with measurement for developing intuition for fractions.   There is a wealth of simple examples of the use of common fractions for measurement in Chapter III of [S3].

The best sources for discussions of graphical arithmetic (the arithmetic of line segments) are in texts on engineering graphics.   Try [L4], pp. 351–361; [R4], pp. 19–21; and [S10], pp. 6–8.

15

Division of Rational Numbers

15-1. Quotients of Quotients

With the introduction of rational numbers the quotient $\frac{a}{b}$ is always defined when a is zero or a natural number and b is a natural number. We now want to show that in the set of rational numbers division is a closed operation, except for zero divisors.

Division of rational numbers will be defined as the inverse of multiplication, just as it was for the natural numbers. It is suggested that the reader review the discussion on the relation of multiplication to division given on pages 232–235, following the definition of rational numbers. The concept of reciprocal, which was introduced there, is of particular importance. This is the relationship that each of two numbers is said to have to the other when their product is 1.

Let $\frac{a}{b}$ be any nonzero rational number. This requires that both a and b be different from zero. Then $\frac{a}{b}$ and $\frac{b}{a}$ are reciprocals since $\left(\frac{a}{b}\right)\left(\frac{b}{a}\right) = \frac{ab}{ba} = \frac{ab}{ab} = 1$. Suppose $\frac{r}{s}$ is any other reciprocal of $\frac{a}{b}$. Then $\left(\frac{a}{b}\right)\left(\frac{r}{s}\right) = 1 = \left(\frac{a}{b}\right)\left(\frac{b}{a}\right)$. From the cancellation law for multiplication, it follows that $\frac{r}{s} = \frac{b}{a}$. Hence, $\frac{b}{a}$ is *the* reciprocal of $\frac{a}{b}$.

Let $\frac{a}{b}$ be any rational number and let $\frac{c}{d}$ be any rational number different from zero. Then we can divide $\frac{a}{b}$ by $\frac{c}{d}$ to obtain a rational number z, which is a solution of $\dfrac{\frac{a}{b}}{\frac{c}{d}} = z$, or $\dfrac{a}{b} \div \dfrac{c}{d} = z$, if and only if there is a z such that $\dfrac{a}{b} = z\left(\dfrac{c}{d}\right)$. This defini-

tion should be compared with the definition of division for natural numbers as given in Section 3-1 and Section 9-3, as well as the definition of rational numbers in Section 11-1.

Next we want to show that $\dfrac{ad}{bc}$ is a solution for the above equations, and furthermore that it is the only solution so that it can be termed *the* solution. First we note that $\dfrac{ad}{bc}$ is a rational number since b, c, and d are natural numbers, and a is zero or a natural number. We next replace z by $\dfrac{ad}{bc}$, in $\dfrac{a}{b} = z\left(\dfrac{c}{d}\right)$, to verify that $\dfrac{ad}{bc}$ is a solution.

$$\frac{a}{b} = z\left(\frac{c}{d}\right) = \left(\frac{ad}{bc}\right)\left(\frac{c}{d}\right) = \frac{adc}{bcd} = \frac{(cd)a}{(cd)b} = \frac{a}{b}$$

Now assume that $\dfrac{e}{f}$ is a solution of $\dfrac{\frac{a}{b}}{\frac{c}{d}} = z$. Then $\dfrac{a}{b} = \left(\dfrac{e}{f}\right)\left(\dfrac{c}{d}\right)$. Since $\dfrac{c}{d}$ is not

zero, it has a nonzero reciprocal $\dfrac{d}{c}$. Hence

$$\left(\frac{a}{b}\right)\left(\frac{d}{c}\right) = \left[\left(\frac{e}{f}\right)\left(\frac{c}{d}\right)\right]\left(\frac{d}{c}\right) \qquad \text{Multiplication is well defined}$$

$$\frac{ad}{bc} = \left(\frac{e}{f}\right)\left[\left(\frac{c}{d}\right)\left(\frac{d}{c}\right)\right] \qquad \text{The associative principle}$$

$$= \left(\frac{e}{f}\right) \text{(1)} \qquad\qquad \text{Definition of reciprocal}$$

$$= \frac{e}{f} \qquad\qquad\qquad \text{Property of 1 as a multiplier}$$

Summary: When the rational number $\dfrac{a}{b}$ is divided by the rational number $\dfrac{c}{d}$ (where $\dfrac{c}{d}$ is not zero), the quotient is the rational number $\dfrac{ad}{bc}$.

The quotient of $\dfrac{a}{b}$ divided by $\dfrac{c}{d}$ is seen to be identical with the product of $\dfrac{a}{b}$ and the reciprocal of $\dfrac{c}{d}$, both are given by $\dfrac{ad}{bc}$. Thus, for any rational operand $\dfrac{a}{b}$, the same transform $\dfrac{ad}{bc}$ is produced by the division operator $\dfrac{\quad}{\frac{c}{d}}$ as by the multiplication operator $\dfrac{d}{c}(\ \ )$, when both c and d are not zero.

The rational numbers were introduced to make needed divisions possible.   They meet this need, since with them division (except by zero) is now always possible. Yet we shall now rarely ever divide, but rather shall multiply by the reciprocal of the proposed divisor.   A principal reason trading off division for multiplication is so attractive is that we give up an operation that is neither commutative nor associative and replace it with an operation that enjoys both of these properties.   This makes for greatly increased flexibility and simplicity in computations.

Problems (131)

1. Express the reciprocal of each as a simple fraction.

   a. 17   **c.** $\dfrac{11}{2}$ **e.** 5^2 **g.** $\dfrac{11}{5} - \dfrac{7}{6}$

   b. $\dfrac{3}{16}$ **d.** $4 \cdot 9$ **f.** $\dfrac{2}{3} + \dfrac{3}{4}$ **h.** $3\dfrac{1}{5}$

2. Express the reciprocal of each as a simple fraction.

   a. 11   **c.** $\dfrac{7}{3}$ **e.** 3^3 **g.** $\dfrac{8}{3} - \dfrac{3}{2}$

   b. $\dfrac{5}{9}$ **d.** $5 \cdot 6$ **f.** $\dfrac{3}{5} + \dfrac{1}{4}$ **h.** $4\dfrac{1}{3}$

3. Compute:

   a. $\dfrac{\frac{2}{5}}{\frac{7}{11}}$ **d.** $\dfrac{\frac{5}{7}}{\frac{2}{11}}$ **g.** $\dfrac{\frac{1}{4}}{7}$ **j.** $\dfrac{5}{2\frac{1}{3}}$

   b. $\dfrac{\frac{11}{5}}{\frac{7}{2}}$ **e.** $\dfrac{\frac{3}{5}}{8}$ **h.** $\dfrac{\frac{1}{4}}{7}$ **k.** $\dfrac{\frac{3}{4}}{\frac{4}{3}}$

   c. $\dfrac{\frac{5}{2}}{\frac{7}{11}}$ **f.** $\dfrac{3}{\frac{5}{8}}$ **i.** $\dfrac{2\frac{1}{3}}{5}$ **l.** $\dfrac{1}{\frac{1}{6}}$

4. Compute:

   a. $\dfrac{\frac{3}{2}}{\frac{11}{13}}$ **d.** $\dfrac{\frac{11}{2}}{\frac{13}{3}}$ **g.** $\dfrac{\frac{1}{5}}{3}$ **j.** $\dfrac{7}{4\frac{2}{3}}$

   b. $\dfrac{\frac{3}{11}}{\frac{2}{13}}$ **e.** $\dfrac{\frac{2}{7}}{5}$ **h.** $\dfrac{1}{\frac{5}{3}}$ **k.** $\dfrac{\frac{2}{5}}{\frac{5}{2}}$

   c. $\dfrac{\frac{3}{2}}{\frac{13}{11}}$ **f.** $\dfrac{2}{\frac{7}{5}}$ **i.** $\dfrac{4\frac{2}{3}}{7}$ **l.** $\dfrac{1}{\frac{1}{9}}$

5. Give four examples of a pair of fractions $\dfrac{a}{b}$ and $\dfrac{c}{d}$ such that a, b, c, and d are

natural numbers and $\dfrac{\dfrac{a}{b}}{\dfrac{c}{d}} = \dfrac{6}{77}$.

6. Give four examples of a pair of fractions $\dfrac{a}{b}$ and $\dfrac{c}{d}$ such that a, b, c, and d are

natural numbers and $\dfrac{a}{b} \div \dfrac{c}{d} = \dfrac{10}{91}$.

15-2. Complex Fractions

Until this chapter our use of the fraction form $\dfrac{N}{D}$ had been limited to simple frac-

tions where N was a decimal numeral for zero or a natural number, and D was a

decimal numeral for a natural number. In the previous section the form $\dfrac{N}{D}$ was

used to signify N divided by D, where N and D were rational numbers represented by fractions. The resulting fractions are called *complex* fractions. In fact,
any fraction form that departs from the simple fraction specifications may be included in this category.

The reduction of $\dfrac{\dfrac{a}{b}}{\dfrac{c}{d}}$ to the equivalent form of $\dfrac{ad}{bc}$ may be considered as a trans-

formation from a quotient of quotients to a quotient of products. It also constitutes a method for reducing a complex fraction of this type to an equivalent simple
fraction. Hence, in any computation, whether addition, subtraction, multiplication, or division, where such complex fractions might arise, the first step could be to
replace these by simple fractions before proceeding further. However, we wish to
show that it is not required that this change always be made. In other words,
complex fractions are indeed fractions and share common properties with simple
fractions in spite of their somewhat prejudiced name.

The cross-product test for the equivalence of two fractions $\dfrac{r}{s}$ and $\dfrac{t}{u}$ was devel-

oped in Section 11-4 for simple fractions. But this test also applies when r, s, t,
and u are themselves fractions.

Let $r = \dfrac{a}{b}$, $s = \dfrac{c}{d}$, $t = \dfrac{e}{f}$, and $u = \dfrac{g}{h}$ (with b, c, d, f, g, and h not equal to zero).

Then $\dfrac{r}{s} = \dfrac{\dfrac{a}{b}}{\dfrac{c}{d}} = \dfrac{ad}{bc}$, and $\dfrac{t}{u} = \dfrac{\dfrac{e}{f}}{\dfrac{g}{h}} = \dfrac{eh}{fg}$.

Hence $\dfrac{r}{s} = \dfrac{t}{u}$ if and only if $(ad)(fg) = (bc)(eh)$.

By applying the cross-product test directly to $\dfrac{\frac{a}{b}}{\frac{c}{d}}$ and $\dfrac{\frac{e}{f}}{\frac{g}{h}}$, we find these two com-

plex fractions would be equal, if and only if $\left(\dfrac{a}{b}\right)\left(\dfrac{g}{h}\right) = \left(\dfrac{c}{d}\right)\left(\dfrac{e}{f}\right)$, and hence if and

only if $\dfrac{ag}{bh} = \dfrac{ce}{df}$. But this requires that $(ag)(df) = (bh)(ce)$, which is equivalent to

the first result by applying the commutative and associative properties. We con-

clude that $\dfrac{r}{s} = \dfrac{t}{u}$ if and only if $ru = st$, where r and t are rational numbers, and s and

u are nonzero rational numbers.

This makes possible an important extension of the fundamental identity $\dfrac{AN}{BN}$

$= \dfrac{A}{B}$. This was introduced in Section 11-4 only for the case where $\dfrac{A}{B}$ is a simple

fraction and N is a natural number. We can now admit complex fractions for $\dfrac{A}{B}$,

and in particular the multiplier N can itself be a rational number, given in common

fraction form. As an application of these ideas we give two methods below by

which the complex fraction form $\dfrac{\frac{a}{b}}{\frac{c}{d}}$ can be reduced to $\dfrac{ad}{bc}$.

Examples:

A. $\dfrac{A}{B} = \dfrac{NA}{NB}$, with A and B rational numbers and N a natural number.

$$\frac{\frac{a}{b}}{\frac{c}{d}} = \frac{(bd)\left(\dfrac{a}{b}\right)}{(bd)\left(\dfrac{c}{d}\right)} = \frac{ad}{bc} \qquad (bd \text{ is nonzero, since } b \text{ and } d \text{ are nonzero})$$

B. $\dfrac{A}{B} = \dfrac{NA}{NB}$, with A, B, and N all rational numbers.

$$\frac{\frac{a}{b}}{\frac{c}{d}} = \frac{\left(\dfrac{d}{c}\right)\left(\dfrac{a}{b}\right)}{\left(\dfrac{d}{c}\right)\left(\dfrac{c}{d}\right)} = \frac{\dfrac{da}{cb}}{1} = \frac{ad}{bc} \qquad \left(\dfrac{c}{d} \text{ and its reciprocal } \dfrac{d}{c} \text{ are nonzero}\right)$$

The next diagram shows first a scale model of $\dfrac{9}{15}$. By doubling the number of

scale divisions we then have $\dfrac{18}{30}$ as the number assigned to the same length. We next divide the number of scale divisions by three, obtaining $\frac{6}{10}$. But multiplication by 2, followed by division by 3, are both specified by the rational multiplier of $\frac{2}{3}$.

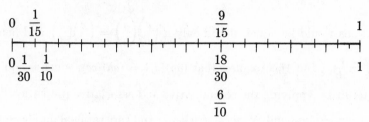

$$\frac{9}{15} = \frac{2 \cdot 9}{2 \cdot 15} = \frac{18}{30} \qquad \frac{18}{30} = \frac{\dfrac{18}{3}}{\dfrac{30}{3}} = \frac{6}{10} \qquad \frac{9}{15} = \frac{\left(\dfrac{2}{3}\right)(9)}{\left(\dfrac{2}{3}\right)(15)} = \frac{6}{10} \ .$$

It is true that complex fractions do involve conceptual difficulties when we try to think of $\frac{N}{D}$ as meaning N of the D equal parts of some unit. This may be an explanation why students who can command only this interpretation of a fraction usually feel quite insecure with complex fractions. The next series of diagrams present an example where these difficulties are analyzed. We begin with a scale diagram of $\frac{30}{42}$ and try dividing the number of scale divisions by 7.

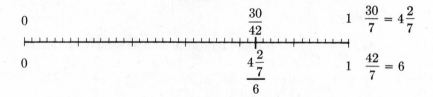

The denominator works out well enough since $\frac{42}{7} = 6$, so that the unit is now divided into six equal parts. But the numerator is determined by four of these lengths plus an odd piece which is only $\frac{2}{7}$ of this length. Hence, we have the complex fraction $\dfrac{4\frac{2}{7}}{6}$.

We return to $\frac{30}{42}$ and this time try dividing the number of scale divisions by 5. The results are possibly even less fortunate than when we divided by 7.

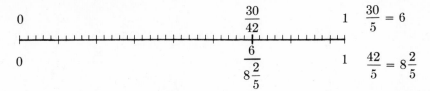

Since 30 is a multiple of 5 we get a numerator of 6, but are in trouble with the denominator.   The unit is now divided so that we have eight equal lengths and an extra segment, which is $\frac{2}{5}$ of this length.   The awkwardness of this situation will be apparent if the student tries to assign a fraction name to this complex fraction, and then tries to pronounce this name!

If simplicity is our goal we should of course take advantage of the fact that the g.c.d. of 30 and 42 is 6, since $\frac{30}{42} = \frac{2 \cdot 3 \cdot 5}{2 \cdot 3 \cdot 7} = \frac{5}{7}$.

It should be clear that the "parts of a whole" concept of a fraction is intuitively simple only when both numerator and denominator are natural numbers.   But it is important to recognize that the complex fractions obtained as above are indeed equivalent, and no computational error results from substituting one for another. The reader is asked to take time to verify that the following pairs of fractions do meet the cross-product test.

a. $\dfrac{30}{42} = \dfrac{4\frac{2}{7}}{6}$ b. $\dfrac{30}{42} = \dfrac{6}{8\frac{2}{5}}$ c. $\dfrac{30}{42} = \dfrac{5}{7}$ d. $\dfrac{4\frac{2}{7}}{6} = \dfrac{6}{8\frac{2}{5}}$

Problems (132)

In problems 1 to 18, each complex fraction has a numerator or a denominator or both, which are either mixed numerals or simple fractions.   The method used in example A. above is appropriate for reducing these to simple fraction form.   This means a natural number is introduced as a multiplier for both numerator and denominator.   The computation should be done mentally if at all possible, writing down only the final result.

1. $\dfrac{1\frac{1}{3}}{2\frac{1}{2}}$ 2. $\dfrac{1\frac{1}{2}}{2\frac{2}{3}}$ 3. $\dfrac{1\frac{3}{4}}{4\frac{1}{2}}$ 4. $\dfrac{2\frac{1}{4}}{3\frac{1}{2}}$ 5. $\dfrac{\frac{1}{2}}{\frac{5}{6}}$ 6. $\dfrac{\frac{1}{6}}{\frac{1}{2}}$

7. $\dfrac{\frac{3}{10}}{\frac{5}{2}}$ 9. $\dfrac{\frac{1}{2}}{5}$ 11. $\dfrac{7}{\frac{1}{3}}$ 13. $\dfrac{1\frac{1}{2}}{4}$ 15. $\dfrac{2}{4\frac{1}{3}}$ 17. $\dfrac{\frac{1}{5}}{\frac{1}{4}}$

8. $\dfrac{\frac{5}{8}}{1\frac{3}{4}}$ 10. $\dfrac{\frac{1}{3}}{4}$ 12. $\dfrac{3}{\frac{1}{2}}$ 14. $\dfrac{2\frac{1}{2}}{3}$ 16. $\dfrac{3}{3\frac{1}{2}}$ 18. $\dfrac{\frac{1}{4}}{\frac{1}{3}}$

Problems 19 to 30 are to be treated as were 1 to 18, but it may also be necessary to divide the new numerator and denominator by their g.c.d. so that the fraction is in lowest terms.

19. $\dfrac{1\frac{4}{5}}{18}$ 21. $\dfrac{7}{2\frac{1}{3}}$ 23. $\dfrac{2\frac{1}{5}}{1\frac{2}{3}}$ 25. $\dfrac{\frac{13}{4}}{\frac{3}{2}}$ 27. $\dfrac{1\frac{1}{6}}{3\frac{1}{2}}$ 29. $\dfrac{1}{3\frac{1}{4}}$

20. $\dfrac{1\frac{3}{5}}{16}$ 22. $\dfrac{8}{1\frac{1}{3}}$ 24. $\dfrac{2\frac{1}{6}}{3\frac{2}{5}}$ 26. $\dfrac{2\frac{1}{3}}{3\frac{1}{2}}$ 28. $\dfrac{9}{1\frac{1}{8}}$ 30. $\dfrac{1}{2\frac{3}{4}}$

The method suggested for problems 1 to 30 becomes less practical when the natural number multiplier is a large number or when the reduction to lowest terms becomes critical. The method indicated in example **B.** can then be used, where the multiplier for numerator and denominator is the reciprocal of the denominator. Since this must always produce a new denominator of 1 (which is then ignored), some steps can be left out, yielding the traditional "invert and multiply" procedure for dividing two fractions. The numerator and denominator are first transformed to simple fractions if need be; the numerator is then multiplied by the reciprocal of the denominator. This method is to be used for problems 31 to 36.

31. $\dfrac{2\frac{7}{8}}{3\frac{5}{12}}$ 33. $\dfrac{\frac{4}{15}}{\frac{18}{25}}$ 35. $\dfrac{\frac{5}{21}}{6\frac{5}{6}}$

32. $\dfrac{4\frac{2}{9}}{2\frac{4}{15}}$ 34. $\dfrac{\frac{15}{16}}{\frac{5}{24}}$ 36. $\dfrac{2\frac{2}{9}}{2\frac{1}{12}}$

37. Solve for X:

a. $5X = 9$ c. $5 \cdot 9 = X$ e. $5 = \dfrac{9}{X}$ g. $5 = \dfrac{X}{9}$

b. $5 = 9X$ d. $5 \cdot 9 = \dfrac{1}{X}$ f. $\dfrac{5}{X} = 9$ h. $\dfrac{X}{3} = \dfrac{4}{7}$

i. $\dfrac{X}{4} = \dfrac{3}{7}$ **l.** $\dfrac{3}{4} = \dfrac{7}{X}$ **o.** $\dfrac{X}{a} = \dfrac{b}{c}$ **r.** $\dfrac{X}{8} = \dfrac{\frac{2}{3}}{5}$

j. $\dfrac{3}{X} = \dfrac{4}{7}$ **m.** $\dfrac{1}{X} = \dfrac{4}{7}$ **p.** $\dfrac{a}{X} = \dfrac{b}{c}$

k. $\dfrac{3}{4} = \dfrac{X}{7}$ **n.** $\dfrac{1}{3} = \dfrac{1}{X}$ **q.** $\dfrac{X}{\frac{2}{3}} = \dfrac{5}{8}$

38. Solve for X:

a. $15X = 6$ **f.** $5X = \dfrac{3}{10}$ **k.** $\dfrac{3}{4} = \dfrac{X}{2}$ **p.** $\dfrac{4}{X} = \dfrac{2}{3}$

b. $15 = 6X$ **g.** $\dfrac{X}{5} = \dfrac{3}{10}$ **l.** $\dfrac{3}{4} = \dfrac{2}{X}$ **q.** $\dfrac{4}{5} = \dfrac{X}{\frac{1}{2}}$

c. $\dfrac{X}{6} = 15$ **h.** $\dfrac{5}{X} = \dfrac{3}{10}$ **m.** $\dfrac{3X}{4} = 5$ **r.** $\dfrac{\frac{4}{3}}{5} = \dfrac{1}{2}X$

d. $\dfrac{6}{X} = 15$ **i.** $1\frac{1}{3}X = 5$ **n.** $\dfrac{1}{X} = 2\frac{1}{2}$

e. $5X = \dfrac{10}{3}$ **j.** $\dfrac{3}{4} = 2X$ **o.** $2\frac{1}{4} = \dfrac{X}{3}$

For problems 39 to 46, use two scales, one over the other, to illustrate the given complex fraction and the equivalent simple fraction in lowest terms.

39. $\dfrac{2\frac{1}{2}}{4}$ **41.** $\dfrac{1\frac{2}{3}}{3}$ **43.** $\dfrac{2}{4\frac{1}{2}}$ **45.** $\dfrac{\frac{3}{5}}{1\frac{2}{5}}$

40. $\dfrac{2\frac{1}{3}}{4}$ **42.** $\dfrac{1\frac{3}{4}}{3}$ **44.** $\dfrac{2}{3\frac{2}{3}}$ **46.** $\dfrac{1\frac{1}{4}}{2\frac{1}{4}}$

In problems 47 to 52, the range of the variables can be either natural numbers or rational numbers, but zero denominators are to be avoided.

47. Prove that if $\dfrac{a}{b} = \dfrac{c}{d}$, then $\dfrac{a}{c} = \dfrac{b}{d}$.

48. Prove that if $\dfrac{a}{b} = \dfrac{c}{d}$, then $\dfrac{b}{a} = \dfrac{d}{c}$.

49. Prove that if $\dfrac{a}{b} = \dfrac{a+c}{b+d}$, then $\dfrac{a}{b} = \dfrac{c}{d}$.

50. Prove that if $\dfrac{a}{b} = \dfrac{c}{d}$, then $\dfrac{a}{b} = \dfrac{a+c}{b+d}$.

51. Prove that if $\dfrac{a}{b} = \dfrac{c}{d}$, then $\dfrac{a+b}{b} = \dfrac{c+d}{d}$.

52. Prove that if $\dfrac{a+b}{b} = \dfrac{c+d}{d}$, then $\dfrac{a}{b} = \dfrac{c}{d}$.

15-3. Division and Ratio Comparisons

The introduction to the division of rational numbers given in Section 15-1 was based on the definition of division as the inverse of multiplication. There are still other ways of showing that the rule which results, $\dfrac{a}{b} \div \dfrac{c}{d} = \dfrac{ad}{bc}$, is logically consistent with those previously given for other operations on both rational and natural numbers. But there is always the question as to just how convincing such arguments are to those with limited experience in formal deductive reasoning. There is evidence that they carry little conviction until one has attained to a certain mental perspective, commonly called "mathematical maturity." Such a point of view requires time to develop, and in particular, it requires skill and confidence in the use of variables, since it is by their use that we claim our statements to be always true. Increasing reliance will be placed on mathematical proof in succeeding chapters. Meanwhile it is very important for the student to develop a strong intuitive feeling for the correctness of the results of his computations. For this we turn again to the analysis of physical and graphical models.

The reader should keep in mind that the time being spent on discussions of various models for the different operations is not in hope of obtaining better or more efficient ways of computing answers to various problems. Rather we wish to make these answers look reasonable, as judged by comparison with a physical situation from which the problem could have arisen. This seems to be of particular value at a time when the ideas about division that have been developed for whole numbers are to be extended and modified as required for fractions.

The ratio interpretation of division was discussed in Section 9-3, but with the restriction that N_1 be zero or a multiple of the natural number N_2 when the ratio of N_1 to N_2 was designated as $\dfrac{N_1}{N_2}$ or as $N_1 : N_2$. We now wish to remove this restriction and allow N_1 to be any rational number and N_2 to be any nonzero rational number. The key idea in this extension is that the ratio of two magnitudes is not to depend on the scale used to measure them.

The same two line segments are measured with three different scales in the diagrams below.

A. The ratio comparison of m to n is that of 4 to 2.

The ratio comparison of n to m is that of 2 to 4.

B. The ratio comparison of m to n is that of 2 to 1.

The ratio comparison of n to m is that of 1 to 2.

C. The ratio comparison of m to n is that of $1\frac{1}{3}$ to $\frac{2}{3}$.

The ratio comparison of n to m is that of $\frac{2}{3}$ to $1\frac{1}{3}$.

$$\frac{4}{2} = \frac{2}{1} = \frac{1\frac{1}{3}}{\frac{2}{3}} \qquad \frac{2}{4} = \frac{1}{2} = \frac{\frac{2}{3}}{1\frac{1}{3}}$$

These sets of three fractions meet the cross-product test for equivalence, and hence are equivalent fractions that represent the same rational number.   They are also accepted as representing the same ratio.   The fractions $\frac{2}{1}$ and $\frac{1}{2}$, which are simple fractions in lowest terms, are considered to be the simplest expressions of these ratios.

Example: What is the simplest expression for the ratio of $1\frac{2}{3}$ to $2\frac{1}{2}$?

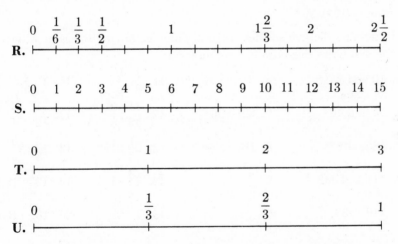

Each number on scale **S** is six times the corresponding number on scale **R**. $1\frac{2}{3}$ compares to $2\frac{1}{2}$, as 10 does to 15.

$$\frac{1\frac{2}{3}}{2\frac{1}{2}} = \frac{(6)\left(1\frac{2}{3}\right)}{(6)\left(2\frac{1}{2}\right)} = \frac{10}{15}$$

Each number on scale **T** is $\frac{1}{5}$ of the corresponding number on scale **S**.

10 compares to 15, as 2 does to 3.

$$\frac{10}{15} = \frac{\dfrac{10}{5}}{\dfrac{15}{5}} = \frac{2}{3}$$

Each number on scale **U** is $\dfrac{2}{5}$ of the corresponding number on scale **R**.

$$\frac{1\frac{2}{3}}{2\frac{1}{2}} = \frac{\left(\dfrac{2}{5}\right)\left(\dfrac{5}{3}\right)}{\left(\dfrac{2}{5}\right)\left(\dfrac{5}{2}\right)} = \frac{\dfrac{2}{3}}{1} = \frac{2}{3}$$

The ratio of 2 to 3 is considered to be simpler than that of $\dfrac{2}{3}$ to 1.

Summary: To find the ratio of A to B, set $\dfrac{A}{B}$, and transform to an equivalent simple fraction in lowest terms.

$$1\frac{2}{3} : 2\frac{1}{2} = 2 : 3$$

Problems (133)

Determine the two smallest natural numbers having the same ratio as the following, and write this ratio in fraction form.

1. 10 and 25

2. 14 and 40

3. 58 and 87

4. 111 and 148

5. 210 : 168

6. 315 : 126

7. 320 : 96

8. 567 : 324

9. $\dfrac{3}{8} : \dfrac{7}{16}$

10. $\dfrac{1}{3} : \dfrac{4}{9}$

11. $\dfrac{7}{8} : \dfrac{5}{6}$

12. $\dfrac{11}{12} : \dfrac{3}{8}$

13. $2\dfrac{1}{3} : 1$

14. $4\dfrac{3}{4} : 1$

15. $1 : 2\dfrac{5}{8}$

16. $1 : \dfrac{3}{5}$

17. $2\dfrac{1}{2} : 1\dfrac{3}{4}$

18. $1\dfrac{3}{8} : 2\dfrac{5}{6}$

19. $12\dfrac{1}{2} : 100$

20. $16\dfrac{2}{3} : 100$

15-4. Division and Repeated Subtraction

For natural numbers the interpretation of division as repeated subtraction is almost always the concept by which division is introduced, and it continues to be the rationale that underlies the majority of division computations. But the need and use of this idea is sharply reduced when rational numbers are the dividend and divisor. A principal reason for this is that we think of a subtraction as being an integral act that is either accomplished or not accomplished, and a quotient that would record a partial success is essentially without meaning. Also when $\frac{a}{b}$ or $a \div b$ is to be a formulation for, "How many times can b be subtracted from a?" or "How many b's in a?" we expect the divisor b (the amount taken away) to be smaller than the dividend a.

The next examples begin as in Section 9-3 where repeated subtraction was first related to a certain type of partitioning of a set, then to the matching of two sequences, and finally to two adjacent scales.   This latter model is the only one that extends to the use of rational numbers.

Example A: $\dfrac{8}{2} = \dfrac{4}{1} = 4$

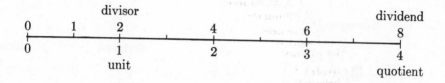

The divisor 2 can be subtracted from the dividend 8 a total of four times, or it can be "measured off" four times.   There are four 2's in 8.

For the next example, the 2 and the 8 are interchanged as dividend and divisor. The repeated subtraction interpretation now breaks down, but we shall see what happens to the graphical model if we continue to match the unit to the divisor and look for the quotient opposite the dividend.

Example B: $\dfrac{2}{8} = \dfrac{1}{4}$

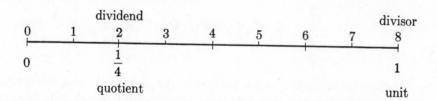

The dividend and divisor have now exchanged their order on the upper scale. But the divisor still corresponds to the unit on the lower scale, and the dividend still corresponds to the quotient.   We would not now ask, "How many 8's in 2?" or "How many times can 8 be subtracted from 2?"   The question should rather be, "What part of 8 is in 2?" or "2 is what part of 8?"   The division of the dividend 2 by the divisor 8 now gives the ratio comparison of 2 to 8, that is, 2 is found to be $\frac{1}{4}$ of 8.   Note, however, that the order in which 8 and 2 appear in the first question is the reverse of that in, "What is the ratio of 2 to 8?"

Example C:

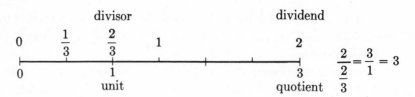

The fractional divisor of $\frac{2}{3}$ in example **C** presents no difficulties since it is smaller than the dividend 2, and can be measured off a whole number of times.   There are three lengths of $\frac{2}{3}$ in a length of 2.

Example D:

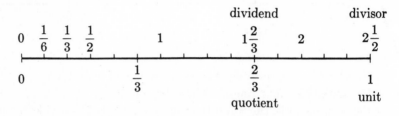

In example **D** we have the scales that were used on page 307, as **R** and **U**, to show that the ratio comparison of $1\frac{2}{3}$ to $2\frac{1}{2}$ was that of $\frac{2}{3}$ to 1.   But it also answers the questions, "$1\frac{2}{3}$ is what part of $2\frac{1}{2}$?" or "What part of $2\frac{1}{2}$ is in $1\frac{2}{3}$?"

$$\frac{1\frac{2}{3}}{2\frac{1}{2}} = \frac{2}{3} \qquad 1\frac{2}{3} = \left(\frac{2}{3}\right)\left(2\frac{1}{2}\right) \qquad 1\frac{2}{3} \text{ is } \frac{2}{3} \text{ of } 2\frac{1}{2}$$

A remainder arises in division only when the division is being interpreted as a repeated subtraction, and then only when the attempt to divide falls short of completion.   Hence, there is no question of a remainder when one is making a ratio comparison, or performing the computation $\frac{a}{b} \div \frac{c}{d} = \frac{ad}{bc}$.   Fortunately the question of a remainder seldom arises when dividend and divisor are rational numbers, since this must be thought out with care if errors are to be avoided.   The difficulties show up in the following example:

> **Example:** One and one half yards of ribbon are available for tying up Christmas packages.   If each package requires two thirds of a yard of

ribbon, how many packages can be tied and how much ribbon will be left over, if any?

(notation as used in Section 3-2)

$$1\frac{1}{2} = \left(\ \ \right)\left(\frac{2}{3}\right) + \left[\ \ \right]$$

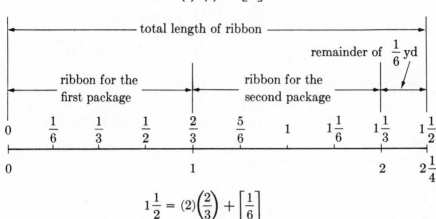

$$1\frac{1}{2} = (2)\left(\frac{2}{3}\right) + \left[\frac{1}{6}\right]$$

The most common error for this problem lies in dividing $1\frac{1}{2}$ by $\frac{2}{3}$, and then misinterpreting the quotient of $2\frac{1}{4}$. For $\frac{1}{4}$ is not a remainder, and does not give the information sought. What the $\frac{1}{4}$ does signify is that the actual remainder of $\frac{1}{6}$ is $\frac{1}{4}$ of the divisor of $\frac{2}{3}$. In other words, the $2\frac{1}{4}$ tells us there is sufficient ribbon to tie two packages, and what remains is one quarter of that required for an additional package. The division of $1\frac{1}{2}$ by $\frac{2}{3}$ does determine the natural number 2. When 2 times $\frac{2}{3}$, or $\frac{4}{3}$, is subtracted from $1\frac{1}{2}$, we get the correct remainder of $\frac{1}{6}$.

Summary: If the remainder is sought, as well as how many times A is contained in B, determine $B = (\ \ )A + [\ \ ]$, where the number for $(\ \ )$ is a natural number or zero, and is as large as possible, so that the number for $[\ \ ]$ is less than A.

Problems (134)

1. How many $1\frac{1}{3}$'s are in 12?   **3.** How many $\frac{3}{4}$'s are in $3\frac{3}{4}$?

2. How many $2\frac{1}{2}$'s are in 20?   **4.** How many $\frac{5}{8}$'s are in $4\frac{3}{8}$?

5. What part of 14 is in $1\frac{3}{4}$?   **11.** $1\frac{2}{3}$ is what part of 4?

6. What part of 15 is in $1\frac{2}{3}$?   **12.** $2\frac{4}{5}$ is what part of 21?

7. What part of 26 is in $9\frac{3}{4}$?   **13.** 1 is what part of $2\frac{1}{6}$?

8. What part of 20 is in $16\frac{2}{3}$?   **14.** 1 is what part of $5\frac{1}{2}$?

9. $\frac{2}{3}$ is what part of $1\frac{1}{2}$?   **15.** 26 is what part of 91?

10. $\frac{3}{4}$ is what part of $1\frac{7}{8}$?   **16.** 49 is what part of 56?

In problems 17 to 28, Q and R are to be determined for $N_1 = N_2 Q + R$ such that:

Q is zero or a natural number;
R must be less than N_2.

17. $16 = 1\frac{1}{3}Q + R$ **21.** $\frac{7}{8} = \frac{2}{3}Q + R$ **25.** $6\frac{1}{2} = 2\frac{1}{3}Q + R$

18. $25 = 2\frac{1}{2}Q + R$ **22.** $\frac{5}{6} = \frac{1}{4}Q + R$ **26.** $7\frac{1}{4} = 1\frac{2}{5}Q + R$

19. $4\frac{1}{4} = \frac{3}{4}Q + R$ **23.** $\frac{2}{3} = \frac{7}{8}Q + R$ **27.** $1 = \frac{2}{11}Q + R$

20. $3\frac{1}{2} = \frac{5}{8}Q + R$ **24.** $\frac{1}{4} = \frac{5}{6}Q + R$ **28.** $1 = \frac{3}{7}Q + R$

For problems 29 and 30, construct models using two scales as in examples **A, B, C,** and **D** in this section.

29. a. $12 \div 2$ **b.** $2 \div 12$ **c.** $\dfrac{6}{3\frac{3}{4}}$ **d.** $\dfrac{1\frac{3}{4}}{2\frac{5}{8}}$

30. a. $6 \div 3$ **b.** $3 \div 6$ **c.** $\dfrac{4}{2\frac{2}{5}}$ **d.** $\dfrac{1\frac{2}{3}}{4\frac{1}{6}}$

15-5. Division as Partition

Another interpretation of division, which was discussed for natural numbers in Section 9-3, is that of partition. If the dividend is to be any rational number, we then represent it by a continuous magnitude such as a line segment, rather than by a set of n elements as was the case in Chapter 9. If the divisor is then a natural number, there is no difficulty with the partition model.   Thus, if a is any rational number and b is any natural number, the fraction $\frac{a}{b}$ represents one of the b equal parts of a as required.   The case where $b > a$ offers no particular difficulty here, in contrast to the repeated subtraction model.   The trouble arises when the divisor is not a natural number.   The next series of examples present some typical cases for study.

Examples:

A. $\frac{5}{6}$ represents one of the two equal parts of $1\frac{2}{3}$.

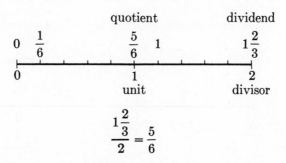

$$\frac{1\frac{2}{3}}{2} = \frac{5}{6}$$

If $1\frac{2}{3}$ is divided into two equal shares, one share will be $\frac{5}{6}$.   The relative placement of dividend, divisor, quotient, and unit should be compared with that for the repeated subtraction model in the previous section.

B. $\dfrac{1\frac{2}{3}}{2\frac{1}{2}}$ represents one of the two equal parts obtained by dividing $1\frac{2}{3}$

in such a way that there are two parts of the same size, and another one-half this size.

$$\frac{1\frac{2}{3}}{2\frac{1}{2}} = \frac{2}{3}$$

If $1\frac{2}{3}$ is to represent $2\frac{1}{2}$ shares, then one of these shares is given by $\frac{2}{3}$.
The divisor again represents the number of shares.

C. $\dfrac{1\frac{2}{3}}{\dfrac{2}{3}}$

One may well ask what, if anything, this complex fraction means from the partition point of view.

We shall try to salvage something from this by constructing a diagram as before, and phrasing the question as, "If $1\frac{2}{3}$ represents $\frac{2}{3}$ of a share, what should one share be?"   *Answer:* One share is $2\frac{1}{2}$.

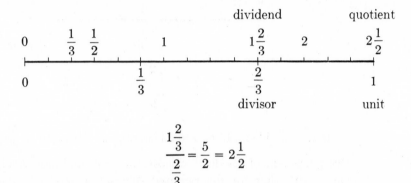

$$\frac{1\frac{2}{3}}{\frac{2}{3}} = \frac{5}{2} = 2\frac{1}{2}$$

In Section 9-3, after a variety of models for division had been considered, it was noted that some of them were of no practical value as computational tools because the answer must be known before the model can be constructed.   This same problem arises when we are using two linear scales to picture quotients of rational numbers.   There are two such models; one for repeated subtraction as in examples **A., B., C.,** and **D.** in Section 15-4; and one for partition as in examples **A., B.,** and **C.** above.   But only the first of these is a useful tool for computing quotients.

In the repeated subtraction model both dividend and divisor are on the same scale and the unit for this scale is then chosen so that both numbers can be readily located.   The unit on the second scale then matches the divisor on the first.   With the number 1 thus fixed on the second scale, the scale divisions are then assigned numbers and the quotient is found opposite the dividend.

But in the partition model one begins by locating only the dividend on one scale and matching this with the divisor on the second scale.   The next problem is to locate the number 1 on the second scale.   If this is done, then the quotient will be found back on the first scale opposite to this 1.   But if one is working on squared paper, there is no guarantee that this 1 will fall on a division point as is desired.   In fact if the unit has not been properly located when the first scale was drawn, there is trouble.   Even after the quotient is known, the student may find it a challenge to construct the partition model.

Problems (135)

1. These problems are those for which repeated subtraction models were given in examples **A., B., C.,** and **D.** in Section 15-4.   This time use two scales to construct a partition model.

   a. $\dfrac{8}{2}$ **b.** $\dfrac{2}{8}$ **c.** $\dfrac{2}{\frac{2}{3}}$ **d.** $\dfrac{1\frac{2}{3}}{2\frac{1}{2}}$

2. Use two scales to construct a partition model for these quotients.

   a. $\dfrac{6}{3}$ **b.** $\dfrac{3}{6}$ **c.** $\dfrac{3}{\frac{2}{5}}$ **d.** $\dfrac{1\frac{1}{2}}{1\frac{1}{3}}$

   For each quotient in problems 3 and 4, construct both a repeated subtraction and a partition model.

   3. a. $\dfrac{2}{5}$ **b.** $\dfrac{\frac{2}{3}}{\frac{4}{5}}$ **c.** $\dfrac{\frac{4}{5}}{\frac{2}{3}}$

   4. a. $\dfrac{1}{\frac{1}{4}}$ **b.** $\dfrac{\frac{2}{5}}{3}$ **c.** $\dfrac{3}{\frac{2}{5}}$

   In problems 5 to 20, the first of two numbers represents a quantity to be divided into shares.   The second number, if greater than 1, represents a proposed number of shares.   If less than 1, the second number represents what part of a share the first number is.   In each case determine the amount to be assigned to one share.

5. 20, 4	**9.** 12, $1\frac{1}{2}$	**13.** $4\frac{1}{2}$, 3	**17.** $\frac{3}{7}$, $\frac{3}{5}$
6. 36, 12	**10.** 8, $1\frac{1}{3}$	**14.** $3\frac{1}{3}$, 5	**18.** $\frac{4}{7}$, $\frac{4}{9}$
7. 7, 3	**11.** 16, 20	**15.** 1, $2\frac{3}{4}$	**19.** $1\frac{1}{4}$, $3\frac{3}{4}$
8. 9, 4	**12.** 15, 25	**16.** 1, $3\frac{1}{5}$	**20.** $\frac{3}{4}$, $2\frac{2}{5}$

15-6. Implicit Statements of Division

For both natural and rational numbers the definition of division was such that the search for a quotient of a dividend by a divisor was equated to determining a multiplier that would transform the divisor into the dividend. When the elementary school child is struggling with $15 \div 3 = ?$, he is advised to consider $? \times 3 = 15$, that is, "What must 3 be multiplied by to get a product of 15?" Here the idea is to link the new problem of division to a result assumed to have been memorized in the past. The following example suggests how the reciprocal can be used in determining the needed multiplier.

Example: $(\quad)(3) = 15$.

We first determine a multiplier that will transform 3 into 1.
This will be the reciprocal of 3.

$$\frac{1}{3}(3) = 1$$

Now we seek a multiplier that will transform 1 into 15.

Since $15 \cdot 1 = 15$, by substitution we have $15\left[\left(\frac{1}{3}\right)(3)\right] = 15$.

Then $\left[(15)\left(\frac{1}{3}\right)\right](3) = 15$, by the associative principle.

We still have not found out what the quotient is when 15 is divided by 3. But we can be sure that whatever this number is, it must be the same as the product of 15 and $\frac{1}{3}$. By using the commutative law, this is the same as the product of $\frac{1}{3}$ and 15. In other words, 15 divided by 3 must be equivalent to $\frac{1}{3}$ of 15. The advantage in replacing the first problem by the second may not seem too impressive in this example, and in particular it wouldn't to a child who is trying to recall a multiplication fact. But the idea may be useful in a more complex situation where appeal to a memorized product would be futile.

Example: $\frac{5}{7} \div \frac{2}{3} = (\quad)$ is equivalent to $(\quad)\left(\frac{2}{3}\right) = \frac{5}{7}$.

There are now few people who could be expected to recall the needed multiplier from memory.

$$\left(\frac{3}{2}\right)\left(\frac{2}{3}\right) = 1 \qquad \left(\frac{5}{7}\right)(1) = \frac{5}{7} \qquad \left(\frac{5}{7}\right)\left[\left(\frac{3}{2}\right)\left(\frac{2}{3}\right)\right] = \frac{5}{7}$$

$$\left[\left(\frac{5}{7}\right)\left(\frac{3}{2}\right)\right]\left(\frac{2}{3}\right) = \frac{5}{7} \qquad \frac{5}{7} \div \frac{2}{3} = \left(\frac{5}{7}\right)\left(\frac{3}{2}\right) = \frac{15}{14}$$

If we now do this in the general case, we again confirm a familiar result. Let $\frac{a}{b}$ be any rational number and let $\frac{c}{d}$ be any nonzero rational number.

$$\frac{a}{b} \div \frac{c}{d} = (\ \ ), \text{ or } \frac{\dfrac{a}{b}}{\dfrac{c}{d}} = (\ \ ) \text{ is equivalent by definition to } (\ \ )\left(\frac{c}{d}\right) = \frac{a}{b}$$

Since $\dfrac{c}{d}$ is not zero, it has a nonzero reciprocal.

$$\left(\frac{d}{c}\right)\left(\frac{c}{d}\right) = 1 \qquad \left(\frac{a}{b}\right)(1) = \frac{a}{b} \qquad \left(\frac{a}{b}\right)\left[\left(\frac{d}{c}\right)\left(\frac{c}{d}\right)\right] = \frac{a}{b}$$

$$\left[\left(\frac{a}{b}\right)\left(\frac{d}{c}\right)\right]\left(\frac{c}{d}\right) = \frac{a}{b} \qquad \text{Hence} \qquad \frac{a}{b} \div \frac{c}{d} = \left(\frac{a}{b}\right)\left(\frac{d}{c}\right) \qquad \text{and} \qquad \frac{\dfrac{a}{b}}{\dfrac{c}{d}} = \left(\frac{a}{b}\right)\left(\frac{d}{c}\right)$$

This provides another justification of the "invert and multiply" rule to add to those given in Sections 15-1 and 15-2.

The following examples illustrate some of the variety of ways by which the missing factor problem can be stated.

Examples:

$(3)(\ \ ) = 15$ If the product is 15, and one of two factors is 3, what is the other factor?

$(\ \ )(3) = 15$ If 3 measures the width of a rectangle, and 15 measures the area, what is the length of the rectangle?

$15 = (3)(\ \ )$ 15 is 3 times what number?   *Answer:* $\dfrac{15}{3} = 5,$

$$15 = 3(5)$$

$15 = \left(\dfrac{1}{3}\right)(\ \ )$ 15 is $\dfrac{1}{3}$ of what number?   *Answer:* $\dfrac{15}{\dfrac{1}{3}} = 45,$

$$15 = \left(\frac{1}{3}\right)(45)$$

$15 = (\ \ )(3)$ 15 is how many times 3?   *Answer:* $\dfrac{15}{3} = 5,$

$$15 = (5)(3)$$

$3 = (\ \ )(15)$ 3 is what part of 15?   *Answer:* $\dfrac{3}{15} = \dfrac{1}{5},$

$$3 = \left(\frac{1}{5}\right)(15)$$

Note that in the above examples we say "3 times," but "$\dfrac{1}{3}$ of." That is, "times" follows a multiplier greater than 1, and "of" follows a multiplier less than 1. This convention is common, but not universal, particularly when the multiplier is a mixed numeral. For example, "$2\dfrac{1}{2}$ times," and "$2\dfrac{1}{2}$ of" are both used.

We have shown that the quotient $\dfrac{R_1}{R_2}$ of a first rational number R_1 by a second rational number R_2 (where $R_2 \neq 0$) can always be replaced by an equivalent product, which is the first number times the reciprocal of the second.

$$\text{If } R_2 \neq 0, \quad \text{then} \quad \frac{R_1}{R_2} = R_1 \cdot \frac{1}{R_2}$$

It is also possible, although less commonly required, to replace the product of any two nonzero numbers by either of two quotients:

If R_1 and R_2 are both different from zero,

$$R_1 \cdot R_2 = \frac{R_1}{\dfrac{1}{R_2}} \quad \text{and} \quad R_1 \cdot R_2 = \frac{R_2}{\dfrac{1}{R_1}}$$

The possibility of always being able to divide by a nonzero number, and hence of determining a multiplier for the divisor that will transform it into the dividend, is related to an important property of both natural and rational numbers. By assuming that one can always come up with a new natural number $n + 1$ to combine with the first n natural numbers, we thereby create an infinite set. But if there is always 1 more, then there must always be any fixed number m of different natural numbers that can be joined to any set of n natural numbers.

Another way to say this is that the set of natural numbers has no upper bound. Moreover, if a is any natural number, then the set of multiples of a, $\{a, 2a, 3a, \ldots\}$ does not have an upper bound. If n be some small natural number and N is some very large natural number, then there is a natural number N_1 such that $(N_1)(n) \geq N$. The Greek mathematician Archimedes, after whom this property of the natural numbers is named, gave a striking example of it. For the very large number he suggested that we think of all the grains of sand on the seashore. For the relatively small number, think of the number of grains of sand that could be carried in a cup. Then there is a natural number N_1 sufficiently large that this many cupfuls is more than all the sands of the sea. Given time, this enormous excavation project might be carried out a cupful at a time.

Now consider the division problem $N = (\ )n + [\ ]$. The "Axiom of Archimedes" assures us there is a multiple of n that is at least as big as N. Two situations arise: Either N is an exact multiple of n and $N = N_1 n$, or N can be sandwiched between two consecutive multiples of n, that is, $N_1 n < N < (N_1 + 1)n$. If then n is any natural number, and N is either zero or any natural number, one can always find a number N_1, which is zero or a natural number, such that

$$N_1 \leq \frac{N}{n} < N_1 + 1$$

The number N_1 is then either zero, or the greatest natural number that is not greater than $\dfrac{N}{n}$, and we indicate this by the bracket notation: $N_1 = \left[\dfrac{N}{n}\right]$

Examples: $\left[\dfrac{2}{3}\right] = 0,$ $\left[3\dfrac{3}{4}\right] = 3,$ $\left[\dfrac{100}{9}\right] = 11.$

Since the natural numbers have the Archimedean property, it follows readily that the rational numbers also have this property. Let $\dfrac{a}{b}$ and $\dfrac{c}{d}$ be any two nonzero rational numbers. Then both ad and bc are natural numbers. The Archimedean property assures us that we can find a natural number N_1 such that $N_1(ad) \geq bc$, and a natural number N_2 such that $ad \leq N_2 bc$.

Hence

$$\frac{N_1 a}{b} \geq \frac{c}{d} \quad \text{or} \quad N_1\!\left(\frac{a}{b}\right) \geq \frac{c}{d}$$

$$\text{and} \quad \frac{a}{b} \leq \frac{N_2 c}{d} \quad \text{or} \quad \frac{a}{b} \leq N_2\!\left(\frac{c}{d}\right)$$

We have already been making use of this in the construction of linear scales. For we have assumed that in assigning a measure to the length of a line segment, one may take an arbitrarily small (but not zero) portion of the segment as having the length of 1. The Archimedean property of the rational numbers assures us that there is a natural number N such that N of these small segments laid end to end will have a total length equal to or greater than that of the segment we are measuring.

The definitions of some terms that were given prior to the introduction of rational numbers must now be reconsidered. For the division of any first natural number by a second is only rarely possible, while any rational number may be divided by any other, provided only that the second rational number is not zero. Formerly, with natural numbers, 8 was said to be divisible by 2, but not by 3. Now the rational number 8 is divisible by the rational number 3. The two cases can be distinguished by saying that 8 is exactly divisible by 2, but not exactly divisible by 3.

If any of the factors of a product are rational numbers, the concept of multiple loses its distinctiveness, and hence its usefulness. Thus, if a and b are any two nonzero rational numbers, a rational number c always exists such that $ac = b$, and a rational number d exists such that $a = bd$. The definition for multiples as given for natural numbers is not extended to cover the above cases, since this would result in every nonzero rational being a multiple of every other nonzero rational.

However, if the rational number a can be expressed as a product of a rational number b times a natural number n, then we say that a is a multiple of b, or better, an integral multiple of b.

Examples:

$$8 = (6)\!\left(\frac{4}{3}\right) \qquad 8 \text{ is an integral multiple of } \frac{4}{3}.$$

$$\frac{8}{9} = (4)\!\left(\frac{2}{9}\right) \qquad \frac{8}{9} \text{ is an integral multiple of } \frac{2}{9}.$$

There is no natural number n such that $8 = (n)\left(\dfrac{3}{4}\right)$. Hence 8 is not an integral multiple of $\dfrac{3}{4}$.

All of the natural numbers and zero are in one of three classes: (1) The special class containing zero and 1, (2) the primes, (3) the composite numbers. But the attribute of being prime or not prime has no meaning with the rational numbers, since every nonzero rational number is a factor of every other nonzero rational number. Hence such a relation as being relatively prime does not apply to two rational numbers, and neither do we speak of their g.c.d. or their l.c.m.*

Problems (136)

For problems 1 to 6, replace each quotient by an equivalent product, and then by a simple fraction in lowest terms.

1. $\dfrac{2}{5} \div \dfrac{5}{8}$ 3. $1\dfrac{1}{2} \div 2\dfrac{1}{3}$ 5. $9 \div \dfrac{2}{3}$

2. $\dfrac{3}{4} \div \dfrac{9}{10}$ 4. $2\dfrac{1}{2} \div \dfrac{3}{5}$ 6. $8 \div \dfrac{5}{4}$

For problems 7 to 22, compute the required factor or product.

7. $(\quad)\left(\dfrac{2}{3}\right) = \dfrac{5}{9}$ 13. $\dfrac{1}{4} = (\quad)\left(\dfrac{3}{5}\right)$ 19. $(\quad) = \left(\dfrac{3}{8}\right)\left(\dfrac{9}{5}\right)$

8. $(\quad)\left(\dfrac{2}{7}\right) = \dfrac{3}{5}$ 14. $\dfrac{3}{4} = (\quad)\left(\dfrac{7}{8}\right)$ 20. $(\quad) = \left(\dfrac{5}{4}\right)\left(1\dfrac{7}{8}\right)$

9. $\left(\dfrac{3}{5}\right)(\quad) = \dfrac{1}{4}$ 15. $1\dfrac{1}{3} = \left(\dfrac{6}{5}\right)(\quad)$ 21. $\dfrac{3}{8} = \left(2\dfrac{1}{4}\right)(\quad)$

10. $\left(\dfrac{3}{4}\right)(\quad) = \dfrac{7}{8}$ 16. $\dfrac{9}{5} = \left(\dfrac{3}{4}\right)(\quad)$ 22. $\dfrac{5}{4} = \left(1\dfrac{7}{8}\right)(\quad)$

11. $\left(\dfrac{3}{5}\right)\left(\dfrac{1}{4}\right) = (\quad)$ 17. $2\dfrac{1}{4} = (\quad)\left(\dfrac{3}{8}\right)$

12. $\left(\dfrac{3}{4}\right)\left(\dfrac{7}{8}\right) = (\quad)$ 18. $1\dfrac{7}{8} = (\quad)\left(\dfrac{5}{4}\right)$

23. 10 is $\dfrac{2}{5}$ of what number?   27. 10 is how many times $\dfrac{2}{5}$?

24. 12 is $\dfrac{2}{3}$ of what number?   28. 12 is how many times $\dfrac{2}{3}$?

25. 10 is $\dfrac{5}{2}$ times what number?   29. $\dfrac{2}{5}$ is what part of 10?

26. 12 is $\dfrac{3}{2}$ times what number?   30. $\dfrac{2}{3}$ is what part of 12?

* But see Problems 1 and 2 of set (137).

31. $\frac{1}{8}$ is $\frac{2}{3}$ of what number?

35. 1 is what part of $1\frac{2}{5}$?

32. $\frac{5}{8}$ is $\frac{1}{2}$ of what number?

36. What is $\frac{3}{8}$ of $\frac{2}{3}$?

33. $\frac{2}{5}$ is how many times $\frac{1}{3}$?

37. $\frac{5}{6}$ is what part of 1?

34. $\frac{3}{4}$ is $2\frac{1}{2}$ times what number?

38. 1 is how many times $\frac{5}{12}$?

In problems 39 and 40, determine for each given rational number R the number N such that $N \leq R < N + 1$, and N is zero or a natural number.

39. a. $R = \dfrac{35}{4}$ **b.** $R = \dfrac{7}{8}$ **c.** $R = \dfrac{1000}{19}$ **d.** $R = \dfrac{767}{13}$

40. a. $R = \dfrac{3}{16}$ **b.** $R = \dfrac{90}{7}$ **c.** $R = \dfrac{1139}{17}$ **d.** $R = \dfrac{501}{51}$

41. Compute:

a. $\left[\dfrac{27}{5}\right]$

d. $\left[2\dfrac{3}{10} + 3\dfrac{1}{2}\right] - \left(\left[2\dfrac{3}{10}\right] + \left[3\dfrac{1}{2}\right]\right)$

b. $\left[2\dfrac{1}{3}\right]$

e. $\left[1\dfrac{3}{4} + 2\dfrac{1}{3}\right] - \left(\left[1\dfrac{3}{4}\right] + \left[2\dfrac{1}{3}\right]\right)$

c. $\left[2 - \dfrac{1}{3}\right]$

42. Compute:

a. $\left[\dfrac{1}{9}\right]$

d. $\left(\left[4\dfrac{7}{8}\right] - \left[3\dfrac{2}{3}\right]\right) - \left[4\dfrac{7}{8} - 3\dfrac{2}{3}\right]$

b. $\left[5\dfrac{9}{10}\right]$

e. $\left(\left[3\dfrac{2}{5}\right] - \left[2\dfrac{1}{2}\right]\right) - \left[3\dfrac{2}{5} - 2\dfrac{1}{2}\right]$

c. $\left[4\dfrac{1}{4} - \dfrac{1}{3}\right]$

15-7. Miscellaneous Problems

Problems (137)

For two or more natural numbers, their g.c.d. could be equivalently defined as the greatest natural number such that each of the given numbers is a multiple of this number. By analogy, we might seek to determine for two or more nonzero rational numbers, the greatest rational number such that each of the given rational numbers is an integral multiple of this number. We have already made use of this idea in asking for the simplest scale (the one with the smallest number of equal subdivisions of the unit) on which two or more fractions are all assigned to scale division points. The number assigned to the length of one of these subdivisions of the unit might be termed the greatest common measure of the several rational numbers, a phrase once widely used as a synonym for greatest common divisor.

By analogy to the l.c.m. of several natural numbers, we might seek to determine for two or more nonzero rational numbers, the smallest rational number that is an integral multiple of each of the given rational numbers. For each set of rational numbers in problems 1 and 2 you are asked to determine: **i.** The greatest rational number such that each of the given numbers is an integral multiple of this number; **ii.** the least rational number that is an integral multiple of each of the given numbers; **iii.** the least natural number that is an integral multiple of each of the given numbers.

1. **a.** $\dfrac{2}{3}, \dfrac{1}{4}$ **b.** $\dfrac{3}{4}, \dfrac{5}{6}$ **c.** $\dfrac{2}{3}, \dfrac{7}{9}$ **d.** $\dfrac{1}{3}, \dfrac{3}{4}, \dfrac{2}{5}$ **e.** $\dfrac{3}{8}, \dfrac{5}{12}, \dfrac{7}{16}$

2. **a.** $\dfrac{3}{5}, \dfrac{1}{4}$ **b.** $\dfrac{1}{6}, \dfrac{5}{8}$ **c.** $\dfrac{2}{5}, \dfrac{3}{25}$ **d.** $\dfrac{1}{2}, \dfrac{2}{3}, \dfrac{3}{5}$ **e.** $\dfrac{5}{6}, \dfrac{5}{8}, \dfrac{5}{12}$

The number system was extended from the natural numbers to the rational numbers by using ordered pairs of natural numbers. This extension is independent of the system of numeration by which each natural number in these pairs is represented. In particular, bases other than ten could be used. In problems 3 and 4 you are asked to verify this by: **A.** carrying out the computation while retaining all numerals in the specified base; **B.** transforming all numerals in both the given problem and the result to base ten, and checking the computation.

3. **a.** base three, $\dfrac{1}{2} + \dfrac{2}{12}$ **f.** base two, $\dfrac{111}{1000} - \dfrac{11}{100}$

   b. base five, $\dfrac{1}{2} + \dfrac{2}{10}$ **g.** base four, $\left(\dfrac{2}{3}\right)\left(\dfrac{10}{11}\right)$

   c. base twelve, $\dfrac{1}{2} + \dfrac{2}{5}$ **h.** base four, $\dfrac{3}{10} \div \dfrac{11}{20}$

   d. base nine, $\dfrac{26}{8} - \dfrac{5}{4}$

   e. base six, $\dfrac{3}{4} - \dfrac{11}{24}$ **i.** base two, $\dfrac{\frac{1}{10}}{\frac{101}{110}}$

4. **a.** base four, $\dfrac{3}{2} + \dfrac{11}{12}$ **f.** base nine, $\left(\dfrac{11}{23}\right)\left(\dfrac{10}{24}\right)$

   b. base six, $\dfrac{3}{2} + \dfrac{5}{10}$ **g.** base eight, $7 \div 4\dfrac{2}{3}$

   c. base two, $\dfrac{1}{10} + \dfrac{1}{101}$ **h.** base five, $2\dfrac{1}{4} \div \dfrac{3}{10}$

   d. base three, $\dfrac{1}{12} - \dfrac{1}{22}$

   e. base twelve, $\dfrac{7}{18} - \dfrac{4}{13}$ **i.** base four, $\dfrac{\frac{11}{20}}{1\frac{1}{10}}$

In problems 5 to 10, a certain pattern may be observed in a series of computations.   Make a conjecture about this pattern and see if you can devise a proof of it.

5. For each fraction construct a new fraction in this manner: **A.** The numerator is the numerator of the given fraction plus the reciprocal of its denominator; **B.** the denominator is the denominator of the given fraction plus the reciprocal of the numerator.

   a. $\dfrac{2}{3}$ **b.** $\dfrac{5}{8}$ **c.** $\dfrac{7}{2}$ **d.** $\dfrac{1}{4}$ **e.** $\dfrac{3}{1}$

6. Two unequal nonzero numbers are given.   Divide their difference by the difference of their reciprocals (larger minus smaller in each case).

   a. 2, 5   **b.** 8, 3   **c.** 10, 1   **d.** $\dfrac{2}{3}, \dfrac{5}{4}$ **e.** $\dfrac{3}{8}, 1$

7. A rational number, greater than 1, is given.   Perform these computations, in the order given: **A.** Subtract 1, and take the reciprocal of the difference. **B.** Add 1 to the result, and take the reciprocal of the sum.   **C.** Subtract the result from 1, and take the reciprocal of the difference.

   a. 3   **b.** 7   **c.** $\dfrac{5}{4}$ **d.** $4\dfrac{1}{2}$ **e.** $1\dfrac{1}{9}$

8. Two nonzero numbers are given, whose difference is 1.   Compute the difference of their reciprocals.

   a. 2, 3   **b.** 4, 5   **c.** 9, 10   **d.** $\dfrac{4}{5}, \dfrac{9}{5}$ **e.** $3\dfrac{1}{3}, 4\dfrac{1}{3}$

9. For each pair of numbers, compute both their sum and their product.

   a. 2, 2   **b.** 3, $1\dfrac{1}{2}$ **c.** 8, $\dfrac{8}{7}$ **d.** $\dfrac{7}{5}, \dfrac{7}{2}$ **e.** $2\dfrac{1}{4}, 1\dfrac{4}{5}$

10. For each pair of numbers, compute both the difference between the first and the second, and the quotient of the first by the second.

   a. 4, 2   **b.** $4\dfrac{1}{2}, 3$ **c.** $\dfrac{15}{3}, 4$ **d.** $\dfrac{9}{2}, \dfrac{3}{2}$ **e.** $4\dfrac{1}{12}, 2\dfrac{1}{3}$

For problems 11 to 22, supply numbers of your choice (avoid zero or 1) and then construct a mathematical model in the form of a conditional equation.

11. How many (   )'s in [   ]?
12. What part of (   ) is in [   ]?
13. If (   ) represents [   ] shares, what would one share be?
14. If (   ) represents one share, what would [   ] shares be?
15. If (   ) represents [   ] of a share, what would one share be?
16. (   ) is [   ] times what number?
17. (   ) is [   ] of what number?
18. (   ) is how many times [   ]?
19. (   ) is what part of [   ]?
20. If (   ) is one factor, and [   ] is another factor, what is their product?
21. If (   ) is a product of two factors, one of which is [   ], what is the other?
22. What number has the same ratio to (   ) as [   ] has to {   }?

For problems 23 to 30, construct a mathematical model in the form of a conditional equation. Then compute.

23. A typist requires $\frac{2}{5}$ of a minute to address and stamp an envelope. If this rate can be maintained, how many can she do in 20 minutes?

24. If $1\frac{1}{2}$ cups of chopped nuts are needed in a recipe for 24 cookies, how many cups should be used in making 36 cookies?

25. If 500 pages of paper make a stack $2\frac{1}{2}$ in. high, what is the thickness of 1 page?

26. A tennis team won 8 matches and lost 6. What part of their games was won?

27. A cable is $1\frac{3}{8}$ in. in diameter. How many of these can lie side by side in an opening 12 in. wide?

28. A dress with a marked price of $28 was offered for sale at $\frac{1}{4}$ off. What was the sale price?

29. A city lot of $\frac{2}{5}$ of an acre sold for $2,000. This price was at how many dollars per acre?

30. If a race of $\frac{7}{8}$ of a mile is run on a track whose length is $1\frac{1}{4}$ miles, what part of the track is used?

For Further Study

Most authors seem to be in agreement that acquaintance with a variety of conceptual models for interpretation of fractions is of equal importance with a logical development that emphasizes assumptions, definitions, and theorems. A variety of approaches may be found in [M11], pp. 205–258; [R2], pp. 69–87; [S8], pp. 219–291; and [W2], pp. 205–230.

16

Comparison, Change, and Relations

16-1. Differences and Ratios

In many of the applications of arithmetic the central task is the assignment of a number as a measure of a certain relationship that one number has to another. This gives a comparison of one number with the other.

There are a variety of relationships that one quantity may have to another. In arithmetic we shall be particularly concerned with two of these: comparison using the difference as found by subtraction, and comparison by the ratio obtained by division. The following example is illustrated both with counters, which would be adequate for natural numbers; and with line segments, which are desirable for rational numbers.

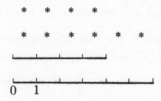

Given the numbers 4 and 6 as an example, we first use their difference to form the comparison. This difference is found by subtracting the smaller number from the larger: $6 - 4 = 2$.

We can then state that

$$4 \text{ is } 2 \text{ less than } 6$$
$$\text{or} \quad 6 \text{ is } 2 \text{ more than } 4$$

Suppose we now look at this from the point of view of the direct operation of addition.   The difference is seen to be the number which, if added to the smaller number, results in the larger.

$$4 + (\ ) = 6 \qquad 4 + (2) = 6$$

Alternatively, but possibly less readily, we may think of the difference as that number which, when subtracted from the larger number, results in the smaller.

$$6 - (\ ) = 4 \qquad 6 - (2) = 4$$

Note that at present we cannot speak of the difference between a and b unless we have information as to which is the larger.   This restricts the use of variables in discussions of difference comparisons.

> **Summary:** For all L and S, with $L > S$, $L - S$ represents how much more L is than S, and also how much less S is than L. $S + (L - S) = L$, and $L - (L - S) = S$.

It is customary when comparing two unlike objects to refer to their "differences."   This use of the word is often not in a numerical sense, but does suggest that we tend first to use subtraction when making a numerical comparison.   Just as the concept of division seems more subtle than that of subtraction, we find that a ratio involves a higher order of abstraction than does a difference.

The ratio of a first number to a second is found by division, with the first number as the dividend and the second as the divisor.

For the ratio of 4 to 6 we have $\frac{4}{6}$, or $\frac{2}{3}$.   Hence, 4 is $\frac{2}{3}$ of 6.

For the ratio of 6 to 4 we have $\frac{6}{4}$, or $\frac{3}{2}$, or $1\frac{1}{2}$.   6 is $1\frac{1}{2}$ times 4.

Difference comparisons relate either a large number to a small, or a small to a large.   Ratio comparisons always relate a *first* number to a *second*.   This allows the ratio of a to b to be fixed as $\frac{a}{b}$, without regard to which is the larger.   The only constraint is that b is not zero.   The two difference comparisons above both use the same number 2, with either "less than" or "more than."   The two ratio comparisons are made with $\frac{2}{3}$ and its reciprocal $\frac{3}{2}$, with the language varied only slightly as from "of" to "times."   As noted in Section 15-6 this language convention for "of" and "times" is not critical to the meaning and is not always followed.

The ratio of a first number to a second is also determined by the multiplier needed for the second number to get the first as a result.   This follows from the definition of division in terms of multiplication.

$$4 = (\ )(6) \qquad 4 = \frac{2}{3}(6) \qquad 6 = (\ )(4) \qquad 6 = 1\frac{1}{2}(4)$$

The ratio might also be determined from the divisor needed to use with the first number as a dividend to get the second number as a quotient.   This can be verified by the cross-product test.

$$\frac{4}{(\ )} = 6 \qquad \frac{4}{\frac{2}{3}} = 6 \qquad \frac{6}{(\ )} = 4 \qquad \frac{6}{\frac{3}{2}} = 4$$

Summary: For all F and S, with $S \neq 0$, the ratio $\frac{F}{S}$ represents what part F is of S if $F < S$, and how many times F is of S if $F \geq S$.

$$\left(\frac{F}{S}\right)(S) = F \qquad \text{and} \qquad \frac{F}{\frac{F}{S}} = S$$

Problems (138)

Four comparison statements were given above for 4 and 6.   Write four such comparison statements for the following pairs.

1. 5, 15	**4.** 9, 15	**7.** $\frac{3}{5}, 1\frac{4}{5}$	**10.** $\frac{8}{5}, 1$
2. 3, 18	**5.** 1, 7	**8.** $\frac{2}{3}, 2\frac{2}{3}$	**11.** $\frac{7}{8}, 5\frac{1}{4}$
3. 12, 16	**6.** 10, 1	**9.** $\frac{3}{4}, 1$	**12.** $\frac{4}{5}, 2\frac{2}{15}$

16-2. The Basis for Comparison

In order to form a comparison, there should be a basis or standard of comparison. The number 0, representing none, is this standard reference number for difference comparisons.   Zero is the best number to use because it is the identity for addition, and no change results if 0 is added to or subtracted from any number.

The subtraction statement $6 - 4 = 2$, which can be read as "6 is 2 more than 4," may also be written $6 - 4 = 2 - 0$, and then read as "6 is as much more than 4 as 2 is more than 0."   If a difference comparison is understood, this could be shortened to, "6 compares to 4 as 2 compares to 0."

With ratio comparisons, it can be seen that not 0, but 1, should be the standard or base number for reference.   Again, this choice of 1 is due to the fact that 1 is the identity for multiplication, and thus no change results when 1 is used as a multiplier or divisor.

The division statement $\frac{8}{2} = 4$, which can be read as "8 is 4 times 2," could be written as $\dfrac{8}{2} = \dfrac{4}{1}$, and then read as "8 is as many times 2 as 4 is times 1." With a

ratio comparison understood, this could be shortened to "8 compares to 2 as 4 compares to 1." The diagram below illustrates this and also shows that "2 is the same part of 8 that 1 is of 4" or that "2 compares to 8 as 1 compares to 4."

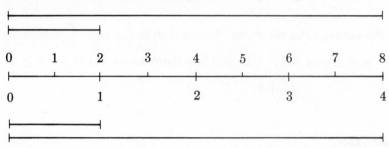

For the ratio comparison of 4 to 6, we have $\dfrac{4}{6} = \dfrac{\frac{2}{3}}{1}$, and $\dfrac{4}{6} = \dfrac{2}{3}$, which may be

read as, "4 has the same ratio to 6 that $\dfrac{2}{3}$ has to 1," and as "4 has the same ratio to

6 that 2 has to 3," respectively. This shows that we do not always insist that 1 be the reference number, but may decide that the simplest expression of a ratio is in

terms of the two smallest possible natural numbers. $4 = \left(\dfrac{2}{3}\right)(6)$ is equivalent

to, "4 compares to 6 as 2 does to 3."

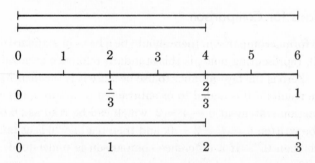

It should be clear why 0 can be omitted from the equation form of a difference comparison, and why 1 can similarly be omitted from ratio comparisons. But because of these omissions the important role that these "silent" numbers play in comparisons may not be appreciated.

    a. The equality of two ratios is defined in terms of the direct operation of multi-

plication. Thus $\dfrac{a}{b} = \dfrac{c}{d}$ if and only if $ad = bc$.

By analogy, what should be the test for equality of the differences $a - b$ and $c - d$?

b. Why is there, at present, less restriction when working with $\dfrac{a}{b} = \dfrac{c}{d}$, than with $a - b = c - d$?

ANSWERS TO EXERCISES

a. $a - b = c - d$ if and only if $a + d = b + c$.   **b.** $\dfrac{a}{b}$ and $\dfrac{c}{d}$ are always defined as rational numbers, provided only that both b and d are not zero. $a - b$ and $c - d$ are not now defined unless $a \geq b$ and $c \geq d$.

Problems (139)

State the following comparisons in sentence form:

1. $13 - 4 = 9 - 0$

2. $64 - 19 = 45 - 0$

3. $2\frac{1}{3} - 1\frac{3}{4} = \frac{7}{12} - 0$

4. $\frac{3}{7} - \frac{3}{8} = \frac{3}{56} - 0$

5. $97 - 25 = 100 - 28$

6. $82 - 38 = 84 - 40$

7. $3 - 1\frac{1}{4} = 3\frac{3}{4} - 2$

8. $2\frac{1}{2} - 1\frac{2}{3} = 2\frac{5}{6} - 2$

9. $\dfrac{35}{28} = \dfrac{1\frac{1}{4}}{1}$

10. $\dfrac{28}{35} = \dfrac{\frac{4}{5}}{1}$

11. $\dfrac{2}{\frac{3}{4}} = \dfrac{8}{3}$

12. $\dfrac{2}{\frac{5}{8}} = \dfrac{16}{5}$

16-3. Reciprocals and Ratio Comparisons

Let a and b be any two nonzero numbers.   Then $\dfrac{a}{b}$ is the ratio of a to b, and $\dfrac{b}{a}$ is the ratio of b to a.   Since $\left(\dfrac{a}{b}\right)\left(\dfrac{b}{a}\right) = 1$, we see that the ratio of a first number to a second and the ratio of the second number to the first are reciprocals.   This reciprocal relationship appears in part-whole ratio comparisons.   If the part has a certain ratio to the whole, then the reciprocal of this ratio is the ratio of the whole to the part.

The length of AD is 4 times that of AB.

The length of AB is $\dfrac{1}{4}$ that of AD.

The length of AD is $\dfrac{4}{3}$ times that of AC.

The length of AC is $\dfrac{3}{4}$ that of AD.

If a similar analysis were to be made for difference comparisons, then for $a \neq b$ it would be necessary to consider both $a - b$ and $b - a$. Such a discussion must wait until the number system has again been extended, this time to make subtraction always possible so that both $a - b$ and $b - a$ are then defined.*

a. By the introduction of rational numbers we are assured that for any two non-zero numbers a and b that $\dfrac{a}{b}$ and $\dfrac{b}{a}$ are always defined and that their *product* is equal to the *identity* for *multiplication*. Assume that the number system has been extended so that subtraction is now always possible. By analogy with the above, what should be true about $a - b$ and $b - a$ when $a \neq b$?

Answer to Exercise

a. $a - b$ and $b - a$ would both be defined, and their *sum* should equal zero, the *identity* for *addition*.

Problems (140)

Complete the following statements of ratio comparisons.

1. 80 is $\dfrac{4}{5}$ of 100 and 100 is _____ times 80.

2. 30 is $\dfrac{3}{10}$ of 100 and 100 is _____ times 30.

3. 175 is $\dfrac{7}{4}$ times 100 and 100 is _____ of 175.

4. 250 is $2\dfrac{1}{2}$ times 100 and 100 is _____ of 250.

5. $37\dfrac{1}{2}$ is _____ of 100, and 100 is $2\dfrac{2}{3}$ times $37\dfrac{1}{2}$.

6. $83\dfrac{1}{3}$ is _____ of 100, and 100 is $1\dfrac{1}{5}$ times $83\dfrac{1}{3}$.

7. $11\dfrac{1}{4}$ is _____ of 15, and 15 is _____ times $11\dfrac{1}{4}$.

8. $7\dfrac{1}{3}$ is _____ of 11, and 11 is _____ times $7\dfrac{1}{3}$.

9. $\dfrac{5}{6}$ is _____ times $\dfrac{5}{16}$, and $\dfrac{5}{16}$ is _____ of $\dfrac{5}{6}$.

10. $\dfrac{2}{9}$ is _____ times $\dfrac{2}{15}$, and $\dfrac{2}{15}$ is _____ of $\dfrac{2}{9}$.

11. $\dfrac{5}{11}$ is _____ of $\dfrac{15}{44}$, and $\dfrac{15}{44}$ is _____ times $\dfrac{5}{11}$.

12. $\dfrac{2}{3}$ is _____ of $\dfrac{10}{21}$, and $\dfrac{10}{21}$ is _____ times $\dfrac{2}{3}$.

* See Chapter 17.

13. $\frac{a}{b}$ is _____ of $\frac{c}{d}$, and $\frac{c}{d}$ is _____ times $\frac{a}{b}$. $\frac{a}{b} \neq 0, \frac{c}{d} \neq 0, \frac{a}{b} < \frac{c}{d}$.

14. $\frac{a}{b}$ is _____ of 1, and 1 is _____ times $\frac{a}{b}$. $\frac{a}{b} \neq 0$, and $\frac{a}{b} < 1$.

16-4. Absolute and Relative Comparisons

If we compare a quantity before and after a change, we get a measure of the change. The following examples show the contrast in point of view between a difference and a ratio comparison.

> **Example 1:** Suppose the price of ground round steak is now 80 cents a pound. Some years ago the price was as low as 20 cents a pound. How has the price changed over the years?
>
> D_1. Use a difference comparison. Subtract 20 from 80 to get 60. The price has increased 60 cents a pound.
>
> R_1. Use a ratio comparison. Divide 80 by 20 to get a ratio of 4 to 1. The price is 4 times what it was.

> **Example 2:** Assume that a certain model of automobile was selling for $800 some years ago, and that it now sells for $3,200. How has the price changed over the years?
>
> D_2. Use a difference comparison. Subtract 800 from 3,200 to get 2,400. The price has increased $2,400.
>
> R_2. Use a ratio comparison. Divide 3,200 by 800 to get a ratio of 4 to 1. The price is now 4 times what it was.

Note that in the difference comparisons the words "cents a pound" or "dollars" could not be omitted from the statements without destroying the meaning. When applications are made to physical quantities, difference comparisons are made only when the units for the dimensions associated with each number are the same, and these units must be stated in the comparison. For this reason, such comparisons are sometimes said to be *absolute* comparisons.

When ratio comparisons are made of two quantities of like units, this comparison will not mention the units. In both examples it could be said that the price was 4 times what it formerly was, with no mention of either cents a pound or dollars. Even though the difference (absolute) comparison was an increase of 60 cents in one example and $2,400 in the other, we speak of the price of meat and the price of automobiles as having undergone the same relative change, because the comparison "4 times" applies to both. For such reasons, ratio comparisons may be said to be *relative* comparisons.

Suppose the quantities being compared have been represented by the lengths of two line segments as in the diagram below. An essential contrast between absolute and relative comparisons is then as follows:

Both quantities are measured with the same scale.

The ratio of the two lengths is the same no matter what scale is used.

The differences of the two lengths depend on the scale used.

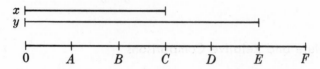

Example: How does the length of x compare with that of y?

  A. Let a measure of 1 unit be assigned to line segment $\overline{OA}$ in the diagram.

       Then x is 2 less than y, since $5 - 3 = 2$. Furthermore, if x is 3 days and y is 5 days, then the difference is not 2, but 2 days. Since the ratio of 3 to 5 is $\frac{3}{5}$, then x is $\frac{3}{5}$ of y, with no mention of units.

  B. Let a measure of 1 unit be assigned to line segment $\overline{OB}$.

       Then x is 1 (unit) less than y, since $2\frac{1}{2} - 1\frac{1}{2} = 1$.

       But x is still $\frac{3}{5}$ of y, since $\dfrac{1\frac{1}{2}}{2\frac{1}{2}} = \dfrac{3}{5}$

Problems (141)

Continue, as above, to give x, y, and then both their difference and their ratio comparisons. The line segment is given, followed by the measure to be assigned to it.

1. $\overline{OC}$; 1 unit	**3.** $\overline{OE}$; 1 unit	**5.** $\overline{OB}$; 3 pounds	**7.** $\overline{OD}$; \$1,000
2. $\overline{OD}$; 1 unit	**4.** $\overline{OF}$; 1 unit	**6.** $\overline{OC}$; 10 degrees	**8.** $\overline{OE}$; 60 seconds

16-5. Comparisons and Unary Operations

A useful way of analyzing comparisons is to think of what would be necessary to change one number to another. In other words, comparison may be thought of as a measure of the kind and amount of "doing," in terms of a certain operation, that it takes to start with one number and obtain the other number as a result. But this is exactly the task for which unary operations, as represented by operators, are suited.

The extension to be made in the use of unary operations is analogous to a way of looking at binary operations. Binary operations are rules of correspondence by which a uniquely determined third number is assigned to an ordered pair of numbers. Thus to a pair of addends, (a_1, a_2), addition assigns their sum $a_1 + a_2$. We can also consider the ordered pair $(a_1, a_1 + a_2)$, which is an addend and a sum of this addend and another, and then ask for the addend, which together with the first addend would have the given sum. The definition of subtraction that we have used is constructed from this "missing addend" problem.

A unary operation (see Section 10-1) is a rule of correspondence that assigns a second number, called the transform, to an ordered pair consisting of a first number, called the operand, and an operator. Thus the number $3 + 2$ corresponds to the ordered pair $(3, +2)$. No notation was used for the act of joining the operator to the operand; this was accomplished by placing the operator in correct position relative to the operand.

Examples A:

operand	operator		transform
(6,	$-2)$	$\longrightarrow$	$6 - 2$, or 4
(4,	$+2)$	$\longrightarrow$	$4 + 2$, or 6
(6,	$\frac{2}{3}(\ ))$	$\longrightarrow$	$\frac{2}{3}(6)$, or 4
(4,	$\frac{3}{2}(\ ))$	$\longrightarrow$	$\frac{3}{2}(4)$, or 6

Now consider an ordered pair consisting of a transform and an operand and ask for the operator, which if joined to the given transform, will produce the given operand. Since there may very well be a variety of such operators, we narrow the problem to a search for operators of a certain type.

Examples B: Given the transform 4, and the operand 6. What is the operator (addition or subtraction) that will change 4 back to 6?

Answer: $+2$

Given the transform 6, and the operand 4. What is the operator (addition or subtraction) that will change 6 back to 4?   *Answer:* -2

Given the transform 4, and the operand 6. What is the multiplication operator that will change 4 back to 6?   *Answer:* $\frac{3}{2}(\ )$

Given the transform 6, and the operand 4. What is the multiplication operator that will change 6 back to 4?   *Answer:* $\frac{2}{3}(\ )$

a. Check these four examples against the four above, and verify their inverse character.

In the comparison of a first number to a second, the second number is taken as the reference number, so we ask how the second number may be transformed into the first. This information is given by specifying the operator that will effect such a change. It carries two bits of information: (1) qualitative, the kind of change; and (2) quantitative, the amount of change.

The examples in **C** parallel those in **B** and display the analogy between comparisons and unary operations.

Examples C: What is the difference comparison of 6 and 4?

Answer: 6 is 2 more than 4.

What is the difference comparison of 4 and 6?

Answer: 4 is 2 less than 6.

What is the ratio comparison of 6 to 4?   *Answer:* 6 is $\frac{3}{2}$ times 4.

What is the ratio comparison of 4 to 6?   *Answer:* 4 is $\frac{2}{3}$ of 6.

Problems (142)

For each pair of numbers state: **i.** the difference comparison of the first to the second, using more than or less than as required; **ii.** the addition or subtraction operator that will transform the second into the first; **iii.** the ratio comparison of the first to the second; **iv.** the multiplication operator that will transform the second into the first.

1. (15, 25)   **3.** $\left(1, \frac{3}{8}\right)$ **5.** $\left(\frac{3}{4}, \frac{3}{5}\right)$

2. (14, 35)   **4.** $\left(1, \frac{7}{4}\right)$ **6.** $\left(4, \frac{1}{4}\right)$

16-6. Related Changes

If A and B are rational numbers, then a rectangle of width A, length B, and area C, is a useful model of the product $A \cdot B = C$. If in a given product $A \cdot B$, changes are made in one or both of the factors, one may then ask what change will result in their product, and further inquire if the change in the product is simply related to the changes in the factors. Sometimes a sketch of the rectangle before and after the change can provide some geometrical evidence for answers to such questions. Such diagrams also provide a check on algebraic arguments using variables.

Example: If the width of a rectangle is divided by 2, and the length is multiplied by 3, how is the area C changed?

$$A_1 \cdot B_1 = C_1 \qquad A_2 = \frac{A_1}{2} \qquad B_2 = 3B_1$$

$$C_2 = A_2 \cdot B_2$$

$$= \left(\frac{A_1}{2}\right)(3B_1)$$

$$= \frac{3}{2}(A_1 B_1)$$

$$C_2 = \frac{3}{2} C_1 \qquad \text{The area was multiplied by } \frac{3}{2}$$

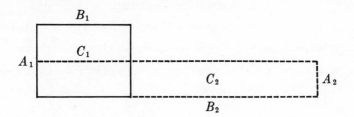

In this case the change in the product is simply related to the changes in the factors. Let the operators $\dfrac{}{2}$, $3(\ )$, and $\dfrac{3}{2}(\ )$ represent the changes in width, length, and area respectively. Then $\left(\dfrac{}{2}\right) \circ 3(\ ) = \dfrac{3}{2}(\ )$.

> **Example:** If the width of a rectangle is not changed, and the length is increased by 2 units, how is the area changed?
>
> $$A_1 \cdot B_1 = C_1 \qquad A_2 = A_1 \qquad B_2 = B_1 + 2$$
>
> $$\begin{aligned} C_2 &= A_2 \cdot B_2 \\ &= A_1(B_1 + 2) \\ &= A_1 \cdot B_1 + 2A_1 \\ C_2 &= C_1 + 2A_1 \end{aligned}$$

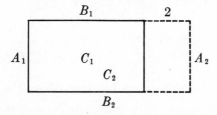

The number of area units was increased by twice the number of width units.

It was assumed that the increase of 2 was in the same units as had been used to measure the length and width. The change in the area is not simply related to the change in the length; in fact, this change cannot be determined until the width is known. The diagram cannot be considered as typical of the change in the area, as was true in the first example.

These examples point to basic differences between sums and products, and to the conflict between additive and multiplicative changes or comparisons.

a. Translate the results in the above examples into the language of factors and product.

ANSWER TO EXERCISE

a. If, in a product of two factors, one factor is divided by 2, and one is multiplied by 3, then the product will be multiplied by $\frac{3}{2}$. If, in a product of two factors, one factor is not changed and the other is increased by 2, the product will be increased by twice the unchanged factor.

Problems (143)

It is suggested that these problems be solved by algebraic arguments using variables, and then verified with geometric diagrams and specific numerical examples. In describing additive changes, use "increased by" or "decreased by." When describing multiplicative changes, use "multiplied by" or "divided by."

In problems 1 to 10, A, B, and C are the width, length, and area of a rectangle, and the change in the area is to be determined.

1. A is multiplied by 2, and B is not changed.
2. A is not changed, and B is divided by 3.
3. A is multiplied by 3, and B is multiplied by 2.
4. A is decreased by 3, and B is not changed.
5. A is divided by 6, and B is multiplied by 4.
6. A is divided by 3, and B is divided by 5.
7. A is multiplied by $\frac{2}{3}$, and B is multiplied by 3.
8. A is multiplied by 2, and B is divided by 2.
9. A is not changed, and B is decreased by 1.
10. A is divided by 2, and B is multiplied by 6.
11. If the product of two factors is zero, then _____.
12. If the product of two nonzero factors is equal to one of the factors, then the other factor is _____.
13. If the product of two factors is less than one of the factors, then the other factor is _____.
14. If the product of two factors is less than either of the factors, then both factors are _____.
15. If the product of two factors is greater than either factor, then both factors are _____.
16. If the product of two factors is greater than one factor but less than the other, then one factor is _____ and the other factor is _____.

In problems 17 to 26, A and B are the addends, and C is the sum in $A + B = C$. The change in C is to be determined from the changes in A and B.

17. A is not changed, and B is increased by 5.
18. A is decreased by 3, and B is not changed.
19. A is decreased by 3, and B is decreased by 4.
20. A is increased by 2, and B is increased by 6.
21. A is decreased by 5, and B is increased by 2.

22. A is increased by 5, and B is decreased by 2.
23. A is not changed, and B is multiplied by 4.
24. A is divided by 3, and B is not changed.
25. A and B are both multiplied by 5.
26. A and B are both divided by 6.

16-7. Ratios and Rates

Numbers followed by units, such as 7 feet, are often referred to as *denominate numbers*. With this usage, numbers that are not associated with a dimensional unit are then called *pure numbers*. This is a bit confusing, since the words "denominate" and "pure" are not to be interpreted as designating different kinds of numbers. Rather, a denominate number is an ordered pair; it consists of a number as given by a numeral, followed by a dimensional unit, which may be given by a word or an abbreviation for it, or possibly by a special symbol. Thus we have the equivalent forms of 7 feet, 7 ft and 7'. Computations with denominate numbers involve no new mathematical principles, but do require knowledge of relative size of the units to be used. Tables listing such information are commonly available and are not given here.

A formula for difference comparisons might be given as $N_1 - N_2 = D$, and read as "the first number minus the second number gives the difference." In applying this formula, one must recognize that all three numbers must be associated with the same unit. One way of handling this is by using both numerals and words (or abbreviations) side by side in the equation form.

$$5 \text{ hours} - 3 \text{ hours} = 2 \text{ hours} \qquad \text{or} \qquad 5 \text{ hr} - 3 \text{ hr} = 2 \text{ hr}$$

The suggestion that units as well as numbers be substituted for variables is often made in science instruction. This practice helps to prevent such absurdities as 5 hours − 3 men = ? and such gross errors as 5 hours − 3 minutes = ? We shall follow an alternate convention of using parallel equations as a dimensional check. Thus, for the last example, one would have $5 - 3 = 2$ for the numerical relationship, and hours − hours = hours for the check on the dimensions. The latter can often be handled mentally, but to omit it entirely is to fail to take advantage of a very powerful tool in problem analysis.

If dimensions as well as numbers are substituted in the formula for the area of a rectangle, there might result, as an example,

$$\begin{cases} A = LW \\ L = 5 \text{ ft} \\ W = 3 \text{ ft} \end{cases} \quad \begin{aligned} A &= (5 \text{ ft})(3 \text{ ft}) \\ &= 15 \text{ ft}^2 \end{aligned} \quad \begin{aligned} &\textit{Dimension check:} \\ &\text{ft}^2 = (\text{ft})(\text{ft}) \end{aligned}$$

It is not suggested that the implied "multiplication" of feet times feet to obtain square feet is to be interpreted as is multiplication when defined for numbers. There is only an analogy, but one that proves to be very useful in practice. It is true that only certain dimension words are likely to be used in this way. Thus one does not expect to see (quarts)(quarts) = quarts^2, or (marbles)(marbles) = marbles^2. It is not that such concepts could not be formulated and used consistently. Rather it is just that no one (to the author's knowledge) has found such combinations to be useful.

The ratio comparison of 5 hours to 3 hours is considered to be a dimensionless number (see Section 16-4). This suggests a "cancellation" of dimensions from quotients that is analogous to removal of a common factor from both dividend and divisor, or numerator and denominator.

$$\frac{5 \text{ hours}}{3 \text{ hours}} = \frac{5}{3}$$

Thus far, ratio comparisons have been made only for pairs of numbers of like dimensions. But quotients arise constantly where dividend and divisors are of unlike dimensions. If one travels at a constant speed and covers 100 miles in 2 hours, this is said to be at the *rate* of 50 miles per hour.

$$\frac{100 \text{ mi}}{2 \text{ hr}} = 50 \frac{\text{mi}}{\text{hr}}$$

There is almost an unlimited variety of such rates that arise in arithmetical problems. Thus if 20 apples are divided equally among 4 persons, the quotient gives the rate as 5 apples per person. The order of words in the phrase "_____ per _____" is significant, the first word being the unit or units associated with the numerator, and the second the units for the denominator. Some authors suggest that the word "rate" should be used when a comparison by division involves unlike units, and that "ratio" should be restricted to the dimensionless or "pure" number that results when both numbers have the same units. Such a convention may have some merit for elementary instruction but has so far not been widely adopted.

Since $\frac{100}{2} = \frac{300}{6}$, a trip of 300 miles in 6 hours would be at the same average rate as one of 100 miles in 2 hours.

$$\frac{100 \text{ mi}}{2 \text{ hr}} = \frac{300 \text{ mi}}{6 \text{ hr}}$$

Since $\frac{a}{b} = \frac{c}{d}$, if and only if $\frac{a}{c} = \frac{b}{d}$, the above equation can be rewritten as

$$\frac{100 \text{ mi}}{300 \text{ mi}} = \frac{2 \text{ hr}}{6 \text{ hr}}$$

In either case, $\frac{100}{2} = \frac{300}{6}$, or $\frac{100}{300} = \frac{2}{6}$, the statement of equality of the two quotients *is said to be a proportion.* An older notation for proportions was $a : b = c : d$, or $a : b :: c : d$. In this proportion a and d were called the *extremes* and b and c were called the *means*.   The correctness of a statement of proportion was tested by the requirement that the product of the extremes should equal the product of the means.

a. Since $a:b = c:d$ and $\dfrac{a}{b} = \dfrac{c}{d}$ are equivalent notations for the same proportion, what does the above test for a proportion become when the fraction form is used?

Dimension checks for rate problems often involve complex fraction forms. Thus, if 20 apples are to be divided at the rate of 5 apples per person, the quotient of $\dfrac{20}{5}$ gives us the number of persons that could receive equal portions.   The dimension check involves the simplification of $\dfrac{\text{apples}}{\dfrac{\text{apples}}{\text{person}}}$.   The procedure used parallels that of simplifying the complex fraction $\dfrac{a}{\dfrac{a}{p}}$ where a and p are nonzero rational numbers.

$$\frac{a}{\dfrac{a}{p}} = a \cdot \frac{p}{a} = p \qquad \frac{\text{apples}}{\dfrac{\text{apples}}{\text{person}}} = (\text{apples})\left(\frac{\text{persons}}{\text{apple}}\right) = \text{persons}$$

The choice of singular or plural is not critical for dimension words, but when the denominator is 1, the corresponding dimension should be singular, and for simplicity the singular is generally used with all abbreviations.   Thus hr would be used rather than hrs.

We now have the tools for constructing dimension checks for a variety of problems.   The example below is based on problem 9 in set (18).

> **Example:** A school band raised $1,805 in a campaign to buy new uniforms. How much was left over after buying 39 uniforms at $44 each?
> *Data, with dimensions:* 1,805 dollars, 39 uniforms, 44 dollars per uniform.
> *Conditional equation model:* $1805 - (39)(44) = N$
> *Dimension check:* $\text{dollars} - (\text{uniforms})\left(\dfrac{\text{dollars}}{\text{uniform}}\right) = \text{dollars}$
> $\qquad\qquad\qquad \text{dollars} - \text{dollars} \qquad\quad = \text{dollars}$

The dimensional check often suggests alternate ways of constructing the equation model.   The next example is of problem 7 of set (28).

> **Example:** A ticket sale was organized by distributing 1,500 tickets equally to 6 chairmen, each of whom divided these equally among 10 ticket sellers.   How many tickets would each seller receive?
> *Data, with dimensions:* 1,500 tickets, 6 chairmen, 10 ticket sellers per chairman
> *Conditional equation model* (1): $\dfrac{\dfrac{1500}{6}}{10} = N$

$$\textit{Dimension check (1):} \quad \frac{\dfrac{\text{tickets}}{\text{chairmen}}}{\dfrac{\text{ticket sellers}}{\text{chairmen}}} = \frac{\text{tickets}}{\text{ticket sellers}}$$

$$\textit{Conditional equation model (2):} \quad \frac{1500}{6 \cdot 10} = N$$

$$\textit{Dimension check (2):} \quad \frac{\text{tickets}}{(\text{chairman}) \left(\dfrac{\text{ticket sellers}}{\text{chairman}} \right)} = \frac{\text{tickets}}{\text{ticket sellers}}$$

ANSWER TO EXERCISE

a.. The product of extremes and means test is equivalent to the cross-product test for the equivalence of two fractions.

Problems (144)

For problems 1 to 20, determine the missing term in the proportion.

1. $\dfrac{N}{25} = \dfrac{96}{150}$ 6. $\dfrac{4}{11} = \dfrac{32}{N}$ 11. $\dfrac{4}{x} = \dfrac{10}{11}$ 16. $1\dfrac{1}{2} : 4 = x : 5$

2. $\dfrac{N}{77} = \dfrac{113}{7}$ 7. $\dfrac{108}{27} = \dfrac{52}{N}$ 12. $\dfrac{3}{x} = \dfrac{7}{6}$ 17. $x : \dfrac{3}{4} = \dfrac{2}{5} : \dfrac{3}{5}$

3. $\dfrac{96}{16} = \dfrac{N}{2}$ 8. $\dfrac{17}{40} = \dfrac{N}{1,000}$ 13. $x : \dfrac{3}{4} = 4 : 5$ 18. $x : \dfrac{3}{7} = \dfrac{4}{9} : 1\dfrac{5}{9}$

4. $\dfrac{343}{511} = \dfrac{N}{73}$ 9. $\dfrac{3}{4} = \dfrac{5}{x}$ 14. $x : \dfrac{2}{5} = 7 : 3$ 19. $7 : 5 = 5 : x$

5. $\dfrac{3}{N} = \dfrac{12}{28}$ 10. $\dfrac{4}{5} = \dfrac{6}{x}$ 15. $\dfrac{1}{2} : 1\dfrac{1}{3} = x : 4$ 20. $9 : 1 = 1 : x$

For problems 21 to 26, construct an equation model in the form of a proportion, and then solve.

21. If an automatic machine is to produce 9,000 bolts in a $7\dfrac{1}{2}$ hr day, what must be its average rate per hr?

22. If a page of 32 lines contains 288 words, there are an average of how many words per line?

23. If 36 grams of water yield 32 grams of oxygen, how many grams of water will be required to yield 10 grams of oxygen?

24. If 36 grams of water yield 4 grams of hydrogen, how much hydrogen can be obtained from 25 grams of water?

25. If a watch loses $1\dfrac{1}{2}$ minutes time in 10 hours, how much should it lose in 24 hours?

26. A jam recipe calls for 3 pounds of sugar for 5 pounds of fruit. How much sugar would be needed for 12 pounds of fruit?

In problems 27 to 34, the dimension check forms are to be simplified.

27. $\dfrac{\text{mi}}{\dfrac{\text{mi}}{\text{hr}}}$ **29.** $\dfrac{\dfrac{\text{lb}}{\text{ft}}}{\text{ft}}$ **31.** $\left(\dfrac{\text{ft}^3}{\text{min}}\right)\left(\dfrac{\text{min}}{\text{hr}}\right)$ **33.** $\left(\dfrac{\text{ft}^3}{\text{hr}}\right)\left(\dfrac{\text{hr}}{\text{min}}\right)\left(\dfrac{\text{gal}}{\text{ft}^3}\right)$

28. $\dfrac{\text{ft}}{\dfrac{\text{ft}}{\text{sec}}}$ **30.** $\dfrac{\dfrac{\text{ft}}{\text{sec}}}{\text{sec}}$ **32.** $\left(\dfrac{\text{lb}}{\text{yd}}\right)\left(\dfrac{\text{yd}}{\text{ft}}\right)$ **34.** $\left(\dfrac{\text{mi}}{\text{hr}}\right)\left(\dfrac{\text{hr}}{\text{sec}}\right)\left(\dfrac{\text{ft}}{\text{mi}}\right)$

Construct dimension equation checks for the following.   The numbers refer to previous problem sets.

35. (8) #2	**39.** (18) #2	**43.** (18) #8	**47.** (28) #10
36. (8) #5	**40.** (18) #3	**44.** (18) #14	**48.** (28) #12
37. (8) #7	**41.** (18) #7	**45.** (28) #2	**49.** (68) #3
38. (8) #20	**42.** (18) #6	**46.** (28) #3	**50.** (68) #6

16-8. Relations

We have had many occasions to refer to the relation that one number has to another.   This chapter has been mainly concerned with the relations:

> a is x less than b
> a is x more than b
> a is x times b
> a is the xth part of b

In previous chapters we have met such relations as:

> a is a multiple of b
> a is divisible by b
> a and b are relatively prime
> a is equal to b
> A is a subset of B, and so on

The idea of a relation is so basic that we shall not try to define it in terms of still simpler ideas.   Instead we shall try to clarify the meaning by giving it a mathematical characterization.   This opens the way to many new applications of mathematics, because relations arise in almost every aspect of life.   Thus in a group of people one might observe such relations as:

> a is the father of b
> a dislikes b
> a is acquainted with b
> a is the same age as b, and so on

Relations may be classified by the number of terms required to be related, in order to make sense.   "Is the mother of" requires two terms, a mother and a child.   This is a *binary* or *dyadic* relation.   Between is a *triadic* relation; 6 is between 5 and

7. Our discussion will be limited to dyadic relations, and the notation $a\ R\ b$ will be used to mean, "a stands in the R relation to b."

Relations have a sense, or order. $a\ R\ b$ is a relation *from a to b*. If a relation does not hold from a to b we write $a\ \not R\ b$.

Problems (145)

All problems below refer to the set A where $A = \{1, 2, 3, 4\}$. You are asked to construct a set T whose elements are ordered pairs. These ordered pairs have as components only members of A, and the first component must be in the given R relation to the second component. T is the set of all possible such ordered pairs. That is,

$$T = \{x \mid x = (a, b), a \in A, b \in A, \text{ and } a\ R\ b\}$$

Example: Let $a\ R\ b$ mean, "a is the square of b." Then $T = \{(1, 1), (4, 2)\}$.

1. a is a divisor of b.	**10.** $a > b$
2. a is a multiple of b.	**11.** $a \geq b$
3. a is relatively prime to b.	**12.** $a \leq b$
4. a is not equal to b.	**13.** $a - b \leq 1$
5. a is equal to b.	**14.** $a - b \geq 2$
6. a is the successor of b.	**15.** $a + b = 4$
7. a is 2 less than b.	**16.** $a = 2b$
8. a is 3 more than b.	**17.** $a = \dfrac{b}{2}$
9. $a < b$	**18.** $a \cdot b = 1$

Each of the results in the previous problem set was a subset of the Cartesian product $A \otimes A$ where $A = \{1, 2, 3, 4\}$. For this set A the ordered pairs that were selected by applying the test condition $a\ R\ b$ provide a good model of what one means by a given relation R. This suggests a set-theoretic definition of a relation.

Let A and B be sets. A relation R from A to B is any subset of $A \otimes B$. The *domain* of the relation R is a subset of A, which is the set of first components in R. This is the set $\{x \mid x \in A, (x, y) \in R \text{ for some } y \in B\}$. The *range* or counter domain of R is a subset of B, which is the set of second components in R. This is the set $\{y \mid y \in B, (x, y) \in R \text{ for some } x \in A\}$. The *field* of a binary relation is the union of its domain and range. If a does not have the relation R to b, then $(a, b) \notin R$ and $a\ \not R\ b$.

Mappings and functions are sets of ordered pairs with the added condition that no two pairs have the same first component. Hence, these are special cases of the broader concept of relation. Even for sets with a small number of elements there are a large number of possible relations that are admitted by the definition. These include the useful ones, which have earned names and sometimes special symbols, as well as many of no interest. There are two extreme cases of relations. One of these is the empty or null relation, which must be included because the empty set is a subset of *every* set, including sets that are Cartesian product sets.   Also, since every set is a subset of itself, then $R = A \otimes B$ must be a relation from A to B.

    a. Describe the empty relation between two sets, A and B.

    b. Describe the relation $R = A \otimes B$ between sets, A and B.

If A and B are the same set, then the relation R is said to be in A, and the domain, range, and field are subsets of A.

ANSWERS TO EXERCISES

a. Here the sets A and B are completely unrelated.   No element of A stands in relation to any element of B.   **b.** Here every element of A is related to every element of B.

Problems (146)

    1. In problem set (145), give the domain, range, and field for problems 1, 5, 7, 15, and 17.

    2. In problem set (145), give the domain, range, and field for problems 2, 6, 8, 16, and 18.

    3. In problem set (145), which of the relations defined in the odd-numbered problems are functions?

    4. In problem set (145), which of the relations defined in the even-numbered problems are functions?

    5. What is the total possible number of relations in the empty set?   In a singleton set?   In a set of two elements?   In a set of three elements?   In a set of four elements such as $\{1, 2, 3, 4\}$?   In a set of n elements?   *Hint:* Consider the number of possible mappings from $A \otimes A$ into the set (yes, no).   (See Section 9-4.)

    6. In problem set (145), let $a\,R\,b$ be as in problems 5, 9, and 10, respectively. Which of the problems in this set determine $a\,R\,b$?

Since relations are subsets of Cartesian products, the various ways of displaying such sets as were given in Section 8-9 are available for relations.

      Examples: Let $A = \{1, 2, 3, 4\}$ and $R = \{(1, 1),\ (1, 2),\ (2, 3),\ (3, 2),$ (4, 3)\}$.

      A. This is the coordinate model for displaying ordered pairs as is used for the graphs of functions.

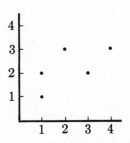

    a. Why is this relation not a function?

    b. What would the null relation look like?

B. This is a modification of example **A.**, using a grid with dots at the points where the relation holds.

C. This model is related to the hint for problem 5 in set (146) where 1 represents "yes" and 0 represents "no." Also the elements of **A.** are matched to rows and columns. Thus the inclusion of the ordered pair (1, 2) in R is indicated by a 1 in the first row and the second column.

$$\begin{array}{c} \\ R \\ o \\ w \\ s \end{array} \begin{array}{c} \text{\textit{Columns}} \\ 1\ 2\ 3\ 4 \\ \begin{array}{c} 1 \\ 2 \\ 3 \\ 4 \end{array} \left[\begin{array}{cccc} 1 & 1 & 0 & 0 \\ 0 & 0 & 1 & 0 \\ 0 & 1 & 0 & 0 \\ 0 & 0 & 1 & 0 \end{array}\right] \end{array}$$

D. The elements of the set are represented by small circles. If $a\,R\,a$ holds, then circle a is made solid. If $a\,R\,b$ holds, an arrow is drawn from a to b, and if $b\,R\,a$ also holds, then no arrowhead is used. The pattern for the circles is any convenient one that facilitates the drawing of the arrows.

The 16 possible relations in a set S of two elements are given below and illustrated with grid diagrams as in example **B.** $S = \{a, b\}$.

1. { }

9. $\{(b, a), (b, b)\}$

2. $\{(a, a)\}$

10. $\{(a, b), (b, b)\}$

3. $\{(b, b)\}$

11. $\{(a, b), (b, a)\}$

4. $\{(b, a)\}$

12. $\{(a, a), (b, a), (b, b)\}$

5. $\{(a, b)\}$

13. $\{(a, b), (b, a), (b, b)\}$

6. $\{(a, a), (b, b)\}$

14. $\{(a, a), (a, b), (b, a)\}$

7. $\{(a, a), (b, a)\}$

15. $\{(a, a), (a, b), (b, b)\}$

8. $\{(a, a), (a, b)\}$

16. $\{(a, a), (a, b), (b, a), (b, b)\}$

These are the 16 possible subsets of $\{a, b\} \otimes \{a, b\}$.

ANSWERS TO EXERCISES

a. Because (1, 1) and (1, 2) are two different ordered pairs with the same first component.

b. It would be blank.

Problems (147)

1. Construct diagrams as in example **A.** for the relations given by problems 1 and 3 in set (145).

2. Construct diagrams as in example **A.** for the relations given by problems 2 and 4 in set (145).

3. Construct diagrams as in **B.** for problems 5 and 7 in set (145).

4. Construct diagrams as in **B.** for problems 6 and 8 in set (145).

5. Construct diagrams as in **C.** for problems 9 and 11 in set (145).

6. Construct diagrams as in **C.** for problems 10 and 12 in set (145).

7. Construct diagrams as in **D.** for problems 13, 15, and 17 in set (145).

8. Construct diagrams as in **D.** for problems 14, 16, and 18 in set (145).

9. In the set above of the 16 possible relations in a set of two elements, select the odd-numbered relations and construct diagram **D.**

10. Follow the directions for problem 9, for the even-numbered relations.

16-9. Properties of Relations

The most used relation in elementary mathematics is that of equality. Three of its properties (see Section 1-9), that of being reflexive, symmetric, and transitive, are in constant use in mathematical arguments. These "R, S, and T" properties are also of value in classifying other relations. The following definitions are based on the requirement that one of these properties either always holds, or never holds, or holds part of but not all of the time. For certain sets and relations in them, the field of the relation may be a proper subset of the set which the relation is in. This means there is at least one element in the set that is not involved in the relation at all. In such cases it is important to observe if a test condition must be checked against every element of the set, or only for the members of the field of the relation.

a. In which problems of set (145) is the field of the relation a proper subset of $A = \{1, 2, 3, 4\}$?

R_1. A relation R is *reflexive* in the set S if for every x in S, $x\, R\, x$ holds. This is termed "total reflexivity" by some authors who then define:

$R_1{}'$. A relation R is *reflexive in its field* in the set S, if whenever $x\, R\, y$, then $x\, R\, x$ and $y\, R\, y$.

R_2. A relation R is *irreflexive* in the set S if, for every x in S, it is never the case that $x\, R\, x$.

R_3. Relations that are neither reflexive or irreflexive are said to be *nonreflexive*.

S_1.   A relation R is *symmetric* in the set S, if for every x and y in S, whenever $x R y$, then $y R x$.

S_2.   A relation R is *asymmetric* in the set S, if for every x and y in S, whenever $x R y$, it is not the case that $y R x$.

S_3.   A relation R is *antisymmetric* in the set S, if for every x and y in S, whenever $x R y$ and $y R x$, then $x = y$.

S_4.   A relation R that is neither symmetric, asymmetric, or antisymmetric is said to be *nonsymmetric*.

T_1.   A relation R is *transitive* in the set S, if for every x, y, and z in S, whenever $x R y$ and $y R z$, then $x R z$.

T_2.   A relation R is *intransitive* in the set S, if for every x, y, and z in S, whenever $x R y$ and $y R z$, then it is not the case that $x R z$.

T_3.   A relation R that is neither transitive nor intransitive is said to be *nontransitive*.

Relations can also be classified according to the extent that they link the elements of the set together.

C.   A relation R is *connected* in the set S, if for every x and y in S, whenever $x \neq y$, then $x R y$ or $y R x$.

SC.   A relation R is *strongly connected* in the set S if for every x and y in S, either $x R y$ or $y R x$.

Examples:

A. $S = \{1, 2, 3\}$ $R = \{(1, 3), (2, 1), (3, 2)\}$.
Check for reflexivity:
None of $(1, 1)$, $(2, 2)$, and $(3, 3)$ are in R.
R is irreflexive. (R_2).
Check for symmetry:
$(1, 3) \in R$, $(3, 1) \notin R$. $(2, 1) \in R$, $(1, 2) \notin R$.
$(3, 2) \in R$, $(2, 3) \notin R$.
R is asymmetric. (S_2).
Check for transitivity:
$(1, 3)$ and $(3, 2)$ are in R, but $(1, 2) \notin R$.
$(2, 1)$ and $(1, 3)$ are in R, but $(2, 3) \notin R$.
$(3, 2)$ and $(2, 1)$ are in R, but $(3, 1) \notin R$.
R is intransitive. (T_2).

B. $S = \{a, b, c\}$ $R = \{(a, b), (a, c), (b, a), (b, b)\}$.
Check for reflexivity:
$(b, b) \in R$, $(a, a) \notin R$.
R is nonreflexive. (R_3).
Check for symmetry:

$(a, c) \in R$, $(c, a) \notin R$. Does not meet test for symmetry.
$(a, b) \in R$, $(b, a) \in R$. Does not meet test for asymmetry.
$(a, b) \in R$, $(b, a) \in R$, $a \neq b$. R is not antisymmetric.
R is nonsymmetric. (S_4).

Check for transitivity:
$(b, a) \in R$, $(a, c) \in R$, $(b, c) \notin R$. R is not transitive.
$(b, a) \in R$, $(a, b) \in R$, $(b, b) \in R$. R is not intransitive.
R is nontransitive. (T_3).

C. $S = \{p, q, r\}$ $R = \{(p, p), (p, r), (q, q), (r, r)\}$.
Check for reflexivity:

$$\begin{array}{cc} & \begin{array}{ccc} p & q & r \end{array} \\ \begin{array}{c} p \\ q \\ r \end{array} & \begin{pmatrix} 1 & 0 & 1 \\ 0 & 1 & 0 \\ 0 & 0 & 1 \end{pmatrix} \end{array}$$

(p, p), (q, q), and (r, r) are in R.
R is reflexive. (R_1).
Check for symmetry:
$(p, r) \in R$, $(r, p) \notin R$. R is not symmetric.
$(p, p) \in R$, $(p, p) \in R$. R is not asymmetric.
R is antisymmetric. (S_3).
Check for transitivity:
$(p, p) \in R$, $(p, p) \in R$, and $(p, p) \in R$.
$(p, p) \in R$, $(p, r) \in R$, and $(p, r) \in R$.
$(p, r) \in R$, $(r, r) \in R$, and $(p, r) \in R$.
$(q, q) \in R$, $(q, q) \in R$, and $(q, q) \in R$.
$(r, r) \in R$, $(r, r) \in R$, and $(r, r) \in R$.
R is transitive. (T_1).

ANSWER TO EXERCISE

a. 8, 15, 16, 17, 18.

Problems (148)

1. Classify the relations given by the odd-numbered problems in problem set (145) as to their R, S, and T properties, and the connective property, if any.
2. Follow the directions for problem 1, for the even-numbered problems.
3. For the 16 possible relations in a set of two elements, as listed in Section 16-8, classify the odd-numbered relations as to their R, S, and T properties, and the connective property, if any.
4. Follow the directions for problem 3, for the even-numbered relations.

For problems 5 to 20, determine the R, S, and T properties for the given set and relation.

5. People, "Is a descendant of."
6. Tournament members, "Lost a game to."
7. People, "Is the mother of."
8. People, "Has confidence in."
9. People, "Is the brother of."

10. People, "Is married to."

11. People, "Has the same weight as."

12. People, "Lives within 1 mile of."

13. People, "Is not taller than."

14. People, "Votes the same as."

15. Sets, "Is a subset of."

16. Sets, "Is disjoint from."

17. Lines in a plane, "Is parallel to."

18. Lines in a plane, "Is perpendicular to."

19. People, "Is a first cousin of."

20. People, "Is an ancestor of."

16-10. Equivalence Relations and Partitions

The relation of equality is not the only relation to have all three properties of being reflexive, symmetric, and transitive [see problems 11, 14, and 17 in set (148)]. All such relations are known as equivalence relations. Both $a \sim b$ and $a \approx b$ are widely used as general notations for "a is equivalent to b." The broad meaning of equivalence is that of "just the same in a certain respect." This property or quality that two things have in common varies for different situations and must be identified in defining equivalence for a particular context. The numerals $3 + 2$ and 5 are clearly distinguishable in form and appearance. But if we are thinking of the numbers they represent, they share the property of representing the same number. The equation $3 + 2 = 5$ tells us that the numerals $3 + 2$ and 5 are equivalent, in that they represent the same number.

Consider the two rectangles R and S, whose lengths and widths are 6 and 2, and 4 and 3, respectively. These two rectangles are alike in having the same area of 12. A common convention in geometry is to then write $R = S$, and to mean by this that R and S are the names of two geometric figures that have the same area.

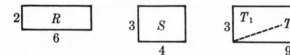

Let T be a rectangle of length 9 and width of 3. Its area is then different from that of R and S and we write $T \neq R$, and $T \neq S$. But in geometry the concept of *similarity* (roughly, "is the same shape as") is defined, so that rectangle T is similar to R but not to S. The above general notation for equivalence is here used specifically for similarity, and we write $T \sim R$ and $T \nsim S$.

We could demand that both of these properties hold for two geometric figures; that they have the same area and that they have the same shape. The two figures are then *congruent*, and $\cong$ is the usual notation for this relation. In the diagrams above the rectangle T can be divided into two congruent triangles so that $T_1 \cong T_2$.

Let $S_1 = \{a, b, c\}$ and $S_2 = \{e, f, g\}$. Then $S_1 \neq S_2$, for equality between two sets demands that they have exactly the same members. But the members of S_1 and S_2 can be placed in 1:1 correspondence, $n(S_1) = n(S_2)$, and S_1 and S_2 are said to have the same cardinal number (see Section 8-8). "Having the same cardinal number" is an equivalence relation on sets, since it is reflexive, symmetric, and transitive. Set A has the same cardinal number as Set A. If A has the same cardinal number as B, then B has the same cardinal number as A. If A has the same cardinal number as B, and B has the same cardinal number as C, then A has the same cardinal number as C. Hence even though sets S_1 and S_2 above are not equal, they may be said to be equivalent, in the sense of having the same cardinal number.

If two natural numbers are both even or both odd, they are said to have the same parity. "Having the same parity" is an equivalence relation on the set of natural numbers which partitions this set into cells; the even numbers and the odd numbers. Each even number is equivalent to itself and to every other even number, in the sense of parity; and in the same way any two odd numbers are equivalent. The cells of a partition that is determined by an equivalence relation on a set are known as *equivalence classes*. The convention of using the word "classes" helps to avoid confusion between the distinct ideas of equivalent sets and equivalence sets, so the latter term will not be used even though equivalence classes are indeed sets.

We can refer to equivalence relations as being *on* a set instead of just being *in* a set as is true of relations in general. This usage is appropriate, since the reflexive property assures us that every member of the set is in the field of the relation.

Another equivalence relation that is akin to parity is "having the same unit's digit as," as applied to decimal numerals. This equivalence relation partitions all decimal numerals into ten equivalence classes corresponding to the ten digits, $0, 1, \ldots, 9$.

Of the 16 possible relations on the set $\{a, b\}$, two are equivalence relations.

The grid diagram ⬚ corresponds to the partition $\big\{\{a\}, \{b\}\big\}$.

The grid diagram ⬚ corresponds to the partition $\big\{\{a, b\}\big\}$.

Listed below are all the possible equivalence relations on a set S where $S = \{a, b, c\}$ so that $n(S) = 3$, as well as the associated partitions of this set.

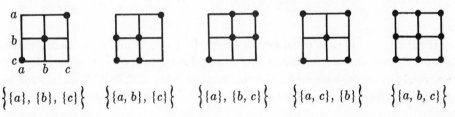

$\big\{\{a\}, \{b\}, \{c\}\big\}$ $\big\{\{a, b\}, \{c\}\big\}$ $\big\{\{a\}, \{b, c\}\big\}$ $\big\{\{a, c\}, \{b\}\big\}$ $\big\{\{a, b, c\}\big\}$

The equivalence relation with the minimum number of ordered pairs is the one that partitions the set into individuals. It is known as the *identity* relation. The equivalence relation with the maximum number of ordered pairs is the Cartesian product set $S \otimes S$. Here all members are equivalent to each other and thus form a single equivalence class.

In Section 8-6, the importance of partitions for the problem of sorting and classification was noted. We can now see that the concept of an equivalence class is a very closely related idea. For example, there may be many students in a school but they can be partitioned into a small number of cells by such equivalence relations as, "was born in the same month as," "last name has the same first letter as the last name of," "is a classmate of," and so on. Since equivalence classes are so widely used, the following notation is introduced.

Let S be a nonempty set and let $\sim$ be an equivalence relation on S. We then for $x \in S$ define an equivalence class by

$$[x] = \{y \mid y \in S, x \sim y\}$$

The set $[x]$ is called the equivalence class of the element x with respect to the equivalence relation $\sim$. One must remember that the definition of $[x]$ depends on the particular equivalence relation $\sim$, although this fact is not indicated by the notation. One also relies on the context to distinguish this use of a bracket notation from that used in Section 15-6. For the equivalence class $[x]$, x is called a representative for the class.

> **Example:** Let S be the set of all natural numbers, and let the equivalence
> relation $\sim$ be "has the same parity as." Then
> $\qquad [1] = \{1, 3, 5, 7, \ldots\}$ and $\qquad [2] = \{2, 4, 6, 8, \ldots\}$
> are the two resulting equivalence classes, and 1 and 2 can be taken as
> representatives of these classes, respectively.
> To confirm this, we note that: $[1]$, by definition, includes all numbers
> y such that $y \sim 1$. Hence $1 \in [1]$ since $1 \sim 1$, and furthermore for any
> odd number z we have $z \in [1]$ since $z \sim 1$. Similarly, $2 \in [2]$, as are all
> even numbers.
> Then 1 and 2, being the smallest members of their respective equivalence
> classes, are reasonable choices as "representatives."
> If zero were included in S, then $0 \in [2]$, and $[0]$ and $[2]$ are the same
> equivalence class, so that zero could now represent the even numbers if
> desired.

It can be shown, by a proof omitted here, that if $\sim$ is any equivalence relation on a set S, then the set of equivalence classes determined by $\sim$ is a partition of S. Conversely, it can also be shown that for any partition of S, an equivalence relation can be defined by requiring $a \sim b$ if and only if a and b are in the same cell of the partition.

The cross-product test for the equivalence of fractions, namely, that $\frac{a}{b} = \frac{c}{d}$ if and only if $ad = bc$, can be readily shown to determine an equivalence relation on the set of all fractions. Let the fractions $\frac{a}{b}$ and $\frac{c}{d}$ be defined as equivalent, that is $\frac{a}{b} \sim \frac{c}{d}$ if and only if $ad = bc$.   It is assumed that a and c are zero or natural numbers, and b and d are natural numbers.

$R.$ The relation $\sim$ is reflexive, since from $ab = ba$ we have $\frac{a}{b} \sim \frac{a}{b}$ by the definition.

$S.$ The relation $\sim$ is symmetric. Let $\frac{a}{b} \sim \frac{c}{d}$, and then by definition $ad = bc$.
Then since equality is an equivalence relation (and hence symmetric) we have $bc = ad$.   Then $cb = da$ by the commutativity of multiplication. Hence $\frac{c}{d} \sim \frac{a}{b}$ by definition, as required.

$T.$ The relation $\sim$ is transitive. Let $\frac{a}{b} \sim \frac{c}{d}$ and $\frac{c}{d} \sim \frac{e}{f}$. Then by definition $ad = bc$ and $cf = de$.   Since multiplication is well defined, we have $adf = bcf$ and $bcf = bde$.   Then since equality is an equivalence relation (and hence transitive), we have $adf = bde$.   Since $d \neq 0$, it follows from the commutativity and associativity of multiplication and the cancellation law that $af = be$.   Then by definition $\frac{a}{b} \sim \frac{e}{f}$ as required.

The relation $\sim$ is therefore an equivalence relation and hence divides the set of all fractions into equivalence classes.   Any member of these classes could be chosen as a representative, the most common choice being the fraction whose numerator and denominator are relatively prime.

$$\frac{0}{1} \text{ is a representative of } \left[\frac{0}{1}\right] \text{ or } \left\{\frac{0}{1}, \frac{0}{2}, \frac{0}{3}, \cdots\right\}$$

$$\frac{1}{1} \text{ is a representative of } \left[\frac{1}{1}\right] \text{ or } \left\{\frac{1}{1}, \frac{2}{2}, \frac{3}{3}, \cdots\right\}$$

$$\frac{1}{2} \text{ is a representative of } \left[\frac{1}{2}\right] \text{ or } \left\{\frac{1}{2}, \frac{2}{4}, \frac{3}{6}, \cdots\right\}$$

etc.

By continuing the above development an introduction to rational numbers can be made by defining a rational number to be an equivalence class of fractions, using the above equivalence relation.   Such an approach is well adapted to logical clarity and can also serve as a model for other extensions of the number system.

Problems (149)

1. Let $A = \{a, b, c, d\}$.   Illustrate, with grid diagrams, the equivalence relations on A given by these partitions:

    a. $\{\{a\}, \{b\}, \{c\}, \{d\}\}$ **d.** $\{\{b, d\}, \{a\}, \{c\}\}$ **f.** $\{\{a, d\}, \{b, c\}\}$

    b. $\{\{a, b\}, \{c\}, \{d\}\}$ **e.** $\{\{a, c\}, \{b, d\}\}$ **g.** $\{\{a, c, d\}, \{b\}\}$

    c. $\{\{a, d\}, \{b\}, \{c\}\}$

2. Let $S = \{x, y, z\}$, and consider its power set 2^S. Using "has the same cardinal number as," and the set 2^S, give the set of all equivalence classes thus determined.

3. Let D be a set of "differences" defined as follows:

$D = \{x \mid x = a - b, a \geq b, a \text{ and } b \text{ are zero or natural numbers}\}$

Let $\sim$ be defined as $a - b \sim c - d$ if and only if $a + d = b + c$. Show that $\sim$ is an equivalence relation on D.

4. Let S be the set of all rationals, greater than or equal to zero. Let $\sim$ be defined as $a \sim b$ if and only if the difference between a and b (larger minus smaller when unequal) is zero or a natural number. Partition the following set with this relation.

$$\left\{\frac{4}{3}, \frac{9}{3}, \frac{2}{3}, \frac{11}{3}, \frac{6}{3}, \frac{0}{3}, \frac{10}{3}, \frac{1}{3}, \frac{7}{3}, \frac{8}{3}, \frac{3}{3}, \frac{5}{3}\right\}$$

5. In each case combine with the set a minimum number of ordered pairs to make it an equivalence relation, and then illustrate as in example **D.**, Section 16-8.

    a. $\{(1, 1), (2, 2), (3, 2), (3, 3), (4, 4)\}$

    b. $\{(1, 1), (1, 2), (2, 2), (3, 3), (4, 1), (4, 4)\}$

    c. $\{(1, 3), (2, 4), (3, 5), (1, 1), (2, 2), (4, 2), (3, 1)\}$

6. For each of the following partitions of $A = \{1, 2, 3, 4\}$, give the equivalence relation thus determined, and then illustrate as in example **D.**, Section 16-8.

    a. $\{\{1, 3\}, \{2\}, \{4\}\}$　　 **c.** $\{\{1\}, \{2, 3, 4\}\}$

    b. $\{\{3, 4\}, \{1\}, \{2\}\}$　　 **d.** $\{\{1, 2\}, \{3, 4\}\}$

16-11. Order Relations

• Some relations are said to *order* sets in various weak and strong senses. These ordering relations exist in considerable variety with many applications in economics, sociology, psychology, and other behavioral sciences as well as in the physical sciences and mathematics itself. Partly because of the wide usage of these ideas the vocabulary is far from being standardized. Hence the names used below to identify types of order have considerable but by no means universal acceptance. When these terms are encountered in different contexts the reader must be prepared to check the definitions the author is using.

1. A relation R is a *quasi-ordering* of the set S if and only if R is reflexive and transitive.

2. A relation R is a *partial ordering* of the set S if and only if R is reflexive, antisymmetric, and transitive.

3. A relation R is a *simple* (also linear or total) *ordering* of the set S if and only if it is reflexive, antisymmetric, transitive and connected in S.

4. A relation R is a *weak ordering* of the set S if and only if R is reflexive, transitive, and strongly connected.

5. A relation R is a *strict partial ordering* of the set S if and only if R is asymmetric and transitive.

6. A relation R is a *strict simple ordering* of the set S if and only if R is asymmetric, transitive, and connected.

a. Which of these orderings are quasi-orderings?

b. Is an equivalence relation a quasi-ordering?

One reason these order relations have varied definitions as well as names is that the R, S, and T classifications given in Section 16-9 are not completely independent. The following theorems can be shown to hold for all relations.

A. If R is asymmetric, then it is also irreflexive.

B. If R is intransitive, then it is also irreflexive.

C. If R is transitive and irreflexive, then it is also asymmetric.

D. If R is symmetric and transitive, then it is also reflexive in its field, but not necessarily totally reflexive.

Verify these examples of ordering relations:

c. $<$ for numbers, and "is taller than" for people are both strict simple and strict partial orderings.

d. $\subset$ for sets is a strict partial but not a strict simple ordering.

e. $\leq$ for numbers is both a simple and a partial ordering.

f. $\subseteq$ for sets is a partial but not a simple ordering.

We shall have occasion to use the symbols $<$, $\leq$, $>$, and $\geq$ only for numbers but they are also used in the literature for their respective orderings in many kinds of sets. If $a \leq x$ for every x in S, then a is said to be a *first* element of S, with respect to $<$. A set is *well ordered*, with respect to $<$, if there is a first element of the set and a first element of every subset. The natural order of the natural numbers gives a well-ordered set with respect to $<$. By contrast, the rational numbers in the open interval $0 < x < 1$ are not well ordered with respect to $<$.

The relation "is a divisor of" is a partial ordering for the natural numbers and the diagrams for divisors of a number given in Section 5-2 suggest a way of illustrating a partial ordering. Let the elements of the set correspond to points. Then if R is a partial order relation the points are arranged so that if a and b are members of S and $a \, R \, b$ then either $a = b$ or one can go from point a to point b by moving always upward on a series of line segments (or from b to a by moving downward). The relation "is a subset of" is a partial ordering among sets and $\subseteq$ is a common notation for partial orderings in general. A set with such a relation $\subseteq$ defined is called a partially ordered system. The diagrams suggested above are often called Hasse diagrams after the mathematician H. Hasse. The following examples of partially ordered systems include the corresponding diagram as in example **C** in Section 16-8.

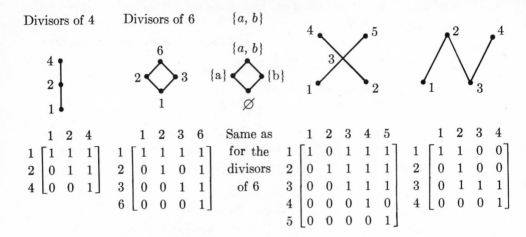

The set $\{1, 2, 4\}$ is connected and simply ordered by the relation "a divides b," and is called a *chain* as suggested by its diagram. The set $\{1, 2, 3, 6\}$ is not simply ordered, but it has two subsets, $\{1, 2, 6\}$ and $\{1, 3, 6\}$, which are connected and form chains. In selecting these chains the idea of covering is useful. If a_1 and a_2 are elements of a partially ordered set such that $a_1 > a_2$ but there is no element a such that $a_1 > a > a_2$, then a_1 is said to *cover* a_2. The line segments of a Hasse diagram connect an element only to those elements it covers or to those elements that cover it. (These are the links of the chain.)

The square arrays of zeros and ones are special cases of the rectangular arrays used in Section 8-9 to display the members of a Cartesian product. Any such rectangular array of elements, together with certain agreements about their use, is called a *matrix*. Recall that the rows go from left to right, the columns from the top down, and elements are designated by their row-column position (in that order).

Both the diagrams as in example **D**, Section 16-8, and the Hasse diagrams are called *graphs*. This is a different use of the word graph than in "graph of a function." The theory of graphs is a growing branch of mathematics with much of the same subject matter as the theory of relations. Instead of using a solid circle ● and an open circle ○ to distinguish $a \, R \, a$ from $a \, \cancel{R} \, a$ in nonreflexive systems, a dot can be used with a self loop ⟳ when $a \, R \, a$ holds. In a system known to be reflexive or irreflexive, only the dot is needed since all elements are related to themselves, or none are. When the points of a graph are connected by directed line segments, as in example **D**, we speak of *directed graphs*, or *digraphs*.

All of the order relations listed above share the transitive property. A so-called dominance relation may be defined which is nontransitive, asymmetric, irreflexive, and connected. Its graph will then have every point connected to every other, but only by a directed arrow and not a line segment. Two dominance relations in the set $\{a, b, c\}$ are shown on page 355 by graph and by matrix.

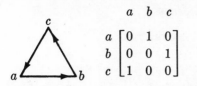

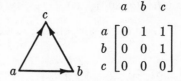

g. If the set is one of teams in a tournament and the dominance relation is "beats," what does an "upset" signify?

ANSWERS TO EXERCISES

a. 1, 2, 3, 4.   **b.** Yes.   **g.** The transitive property has failed to hold.

Problems (150)

For problems 1 and 2, let $S = \{1, 2\}$

1. Give the grid diagram and the type of order relation determined on S by
  a. <   **b.** ≥

2. Give the grid diagram and the type of order relation determined on S by
  a. >   **b.** ≤

3. What type of ordering relations are the following, as applied to people?
  a. Is a descendant of   **b.** Has the same weight as   **c.** At least as tall as

4. What type of ordering relations are the following, as applied to people?
  a. Not any heavier   **b.** Is an ancestor of   **c.** Votes the same as

5. Identify these relations as to type of ordering.

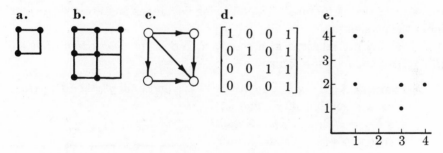

f. $\{(b, c), (a, d), (c, d), (a, c), (b, d), (a, b)\}$

6. Identify these relations as to type of ordering.

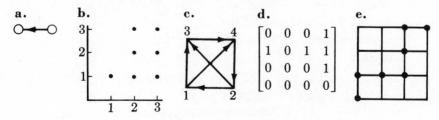

f. $\{(x, w), (y, w), (z, y), (y, x), (z, x), (z, w)\}$

7. Give the corresponding matrix, or Hasse diagram.

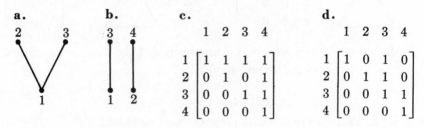

a.

b.

c.

$$\begin{array}{c|cccc} & 1 & 2 & 3 & 4 \\ \hline 1 & 1 & 1 & 1 & 1 \\ 2 & 0 & 1 & 0 & 1 \\ 3 & 0 & 0 & 1 & 1 \\ 4 & 0 & 0 & 0 & 1 \end{array}$$

d.

$$\begin{array}{c|cccc} & 1 & 2 & 3 & 4 \\ \hline 1 & 1 & 0 & 1 & 0 \\ 2 & 0 & 1 & 1 & 0 \\ 3 & 0 & 0 & 1 & 1 \\ 4 & 0 & 0 & 0 & 1 \end{array}$$

8. Give the corresponding matrix, or Hasse diagram.

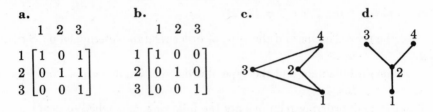

a.

$$\begin{array}{c|ccc} & 1 & 2 & 3 \\ \hline 1 & 1 & 0 & 1 \\ 2 & 0 & 1 & 1 \\ 3 & 0 & 0 & 1 \end{array}$$

b.

$$\begin{array}{c|ccc} & 1 & 2 & 3 \\ \hline 1 & 1 & 0 & 0 \\ 2 & 0 & 1 & 0 \\ 3 & 0 & 0 & 1 \end{array}$$

c.

d.

16-12. Operations on Relations

One advantage of defining relations as sets is that one then has available the resources of the theory of sets (as in Chapter 8) for forming new relations (sets) and for analyzing their structure. The following definitions and exercises give only a hint of the possibilities.

If R and S are relations in a set A, $R \cap S$ is the *intersection* of R and S. $a(R \cap S)b$ if and only if $a R b$ and $a S b$.

Example A: Let $x R_1 y$ represent "x is a divisor of y"; let $x R_2 y$ represent "x is a multiple of y"; and let $x R y = x(R_1 \cap R_2)y$. Recall that two sets are equal if and only if they have the same elements.

Then R is the identity relation.

Every natural number is a divisor of itself and a multiple of itself.

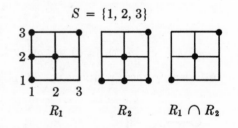

$S = \{1, 2, 3\}$

R_1 R_2 $R_1 \cap R_2$

If R and S are relations in a set A, $R \cup S$ is the *union* of R and S. $a(R \cup S)b$ if and only if $a R b$ or $a S b$.

Example B: If R is "the son of" and S is "the daughter of" then $R \cup S$ is "the child of."

Example C: Let S, R_1, and R_2 be as in Example **A.** Then $R_1 \cup R_2$ is $S \otimes S$ except for the pairs (2, 3) and (3, 2). This is the only pair from S such that neither of the relations hold. For all other pairs one or both relations hold.

If R and S are relations in a set A, $R - S$ is the *relative complement* of S with respect to R, or the *difference* of R and S. $a(R - S)b$ if and only if $a\ R\ b$ and $a\ \not S\ b$. Let $U = A \otimes A$ be the universal relation on a set A then $U - S$ may be written as S', and $R - S = R \cap S'$. S' is then known as the complement or negation of S, since it is the relation between two things that holds if and only if the relation S does not hold.

Example D: Let S, R_1, and R_2 be as in Example **A.**

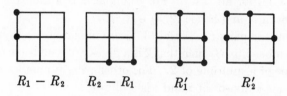

$R_1 - R_2$ $R_2 - R_1$ R_1' R_2'

Let $x\ Br\ y$ represent "x is the brother of y." Let $x\ Si\ y$ represent "x is the sister of y." Let $x\ Sb\ y$ represent "x is the sibling of y" (sibling means "brother or sister of"). Then

$$Sb = Br \cup Si \qquad Br \cap Si = \varnothing \qquad Sb - Br = Si \qquad Sb - Si = Br$$

If $R \subseteq S$, then R is said to be a subrelation of S. This means that every ordered pair in R is also in S. If $R \subseteq S$ and $S \subseteq R$, then $R = S$.

In the above examples, the identity relation $R_1 \cap R_2$ is a subrelation of both R_1 and R_2. Each of the relations Br and Si is a subrelation of Sb.

If R is a relation in a set A, then the *converse* relation $\breve{R}$ is the relation $a\ \breve{R}\ b$ that holds if and only if $b\ R\ a$. The reader should verify the following for S, R_1 and R_2 as in the previous examples.

a. $R_1 = \breve{R}_2$

b. $R_2 = \breve{R}_1$

c. $(R_1 \cap R_2) = \overbrace{(R_1 \cap R_2)}$

d. $(R_1 \cup R_2) = \overbrace{(R_1 \cup R_2)}$

e. $R_1 - R_2 = \overbrace{(R_2 - R_1)}$

f. $R_2 - R_1 = \overbrace{(R_1 - R_2)}$

g. $R_1' = \breve{R}_2'$

h. $R_2' = \breve{R}_1'$

i. What symmetry is present in the pairs of diagrams for exercises **a.** to **h.**?

j. What property of any one relation can be identified by the same symmetry in its grid diagram or matrix?

Union, intersection, difference, complement, and subset are defined for all sets and no modification is needed to apply them to those special sets which are relations. But the definition of a converse relation depends on the fact that relations have ordered pairs as elements. The symbol ˘ was used as an operator to designate the unary operation on relations of "taking the converse." If A is a set, then the set of all subsets of $A \otimes A$, or $2^{A \otimes A}$ is the set of all relations in A.   Each of these relations has a unique converse.   We now define a binary operation on relations which also depends on the elements of relations being ordered pairs.

If R and S are binary relations, then by the *relative product* of R and S, written R/S, we mean the relation that holds between x and y if and only if there exists a z in the set such that both $x \, R \, z$ and $z \, R \, y$ hold.   The operation is not commutative. Thus if F means "is a friend of" and T means "a teacher of," then $a(F/T)b$ means that a is a friend of a teacher of b.   But this is different from $a(T/F)b$, which means that a is a teacher of a friend of b.

> **Example E:** If S, R_1, and R_2 are as in Example **A.** then R_2/R_1 is the universal relation since "a is a multiple of a divisor of b" holds for all pairs (a, b) in $S \otimes S$.   This happens because 1 can be the z required by the definition, for all cases.   For example, 2 is a multiple of 1, which is a divisor of 3, and hence $(2, 3) \in R_2/R_1$.
>
> But the pairs $(2, 3)$ and $(3, 2)$ are missing from R_1/R_2, since there is no number z (in S) such that 2 is a divisor of a multiple of 3, or that 3 is a divisor of a multiple of 2.   For other pairs a number z does exist such that a is a divisor of z and z is a divisor of b.
>
> **Example F:** The diagrams below define certain relations R and S on a set of three elements.   Verify that R/S and S/R are as shown.

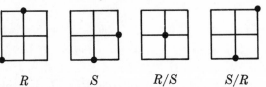

$$R \qquad\qquad S \qquad\qquad R/S \qquad\qquad S/R$$

The relative product is associative; both $aM/(T/F)b$ and $a(M/T)/Fb$ might mean, "a is the mother of a teacher of a friend of b," so that the parentheses could be omitted.   By using the same relation in such repeated relative products we are led to the idea of powers of a relation.

> **Example G:** Let R represent "a child of."   Then R^2 or R/R represents "a child of a child of" or "a grandchild of."   And R^3 or $R/R/R$ represents "a great-grandchild of."

Answers to Exercises

i. There is mirror-image symmetry with respect to the principal diagonal.   This diagonal is from lower left to upper right for grids and from upper left to lower right for matrices.
j. When relations in a set have the symmetric property, the diagrams have the same symmetry as in **i.**

Problems (151)

The relations to be used in problems 1 to 30 have been defined on the set consisting of zero, the natural numbers, and the rational numbers greater than zero, but are here illustrated for a set of three elements, such as $\{a, b, c\}$ with $a < b < c$.

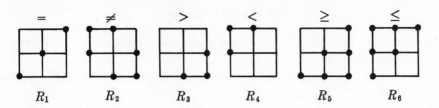

$$R_1 \qquad R_2 \qquad R_3 \qquad R_4 \qquad R_5 \qquad R_6$$

Determine the following relations:

1. $\breve{R}_1$	7. $R_1{}'$	13. $R_1 \cup R_2$	19. $R_2 \cap R_5$	25. $R_5 - R_3$
2. $\breve{R}_2$	8. $R_2{}'$	14. $R_1 \cap R_2$	20. $R_2 \cap R_6$	26. $R_6 - R_4$
3. $\breve{R}_3$	9. $R_3{}'$	15. $R_1 \cap R_3$	21. $R_1{}^2$	27. $R_6 - R_2$
4. $\breve{R}_4$	10. $R_4{}'$	16. $R_1 \cup R_3$	22. $R_3{}^2$	28. $R_5 - R_2$
5. $\breve{R}_5$	11. $R_5{}'$	17. $R_1 \cup R_4$	23. R_1/R_3	29. $R_2{}^2$
6. $\breve{R}_6$	12. $R_6{}'$	18. $R_1 \cap R_4$	24. R_1/R_4	30. R_4/R_3

If a set S is partially ordered by a relation P, it can be shown that $\breve{P}$ also partially orders S, and these two partially ordered sets are said to be duals.   The given
Hasse diagrams define partially ordered sets, in problems 31 to 34.   Construct the
diagram of the dual.

31. 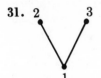   **32.**   **33.** 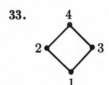   **34.**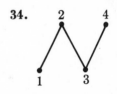

For problems 35 to 58, the relations are denoted by the specified symbols.

Parent: Pa	Son: So	Husband: Hu	Sister: Si
Father: Fa	Daughter: Da	Wife: Wi	Sibling: Sb
Mother: Mo	Child: Ch	Brother: Br	Spouse: Sp

Let J represent the relation of nonidentity or "is not equal to," and determine the
following family relations.

35. $\breve{Pa}$	41. $Br \cup Si$	47. So/Ch	53. $(So/Fa) \cap (So/Mo) \cap J$
36. $\breve{Ch}$	42. $Hu \cup Wi$	48. Da/Ch	54. $(So/Pa) \cap Br' \cap J$
37. $\breve{Wi}$	43. $Fa \cup Mo$	49. Fa/Sp	55. $(Br/Wi) \cup (Hu/Si)$
38. $\breve{Hu}$	44. $So \cup Da$	50. Mo/Sp	56. $Ch/(Br \cup Si)$
39. Pa^2	45. Fa/Mo	51. $\breve{Mo} \cup \breve{Fa}$	57. $(Br \cup Si)/Pa$
40. Ch^2	46. Mo/Fa	52. $\breve{So} \cup \breve{Da}$	58. $Ch/[(Br \cup Si)/(Mo \cup Fa)]$

For Further Study

Reference [L3], pp. 149–169, has a good analysis of comparisons by differences, and comparisons by ratios.

A collection of interesting miscellanea on comparisons appears in [M3], Chapter V; see also Chapter XII on units.

The classification of relations given in this text is patterned after that in Chapter 10 of [S16].   For additional discussion and problems on relations and ordering refer to [F1], pp. 63–73, 84–88; [E2], pp. 148–165; [S9], pp. 79–88; and [C1], pp. 42–46.

There is a detailed discussion of the connection between equivalence relations and partitions in [H3], pp. 88–93; and [W7], pp. 23–26.

17

Operators and Signed Numbers

17-1. The Opposite Operator

Five types of operators have been introduced thus far. They represent five unary operations, which correspond to the binary operations of addition, subtraction, multiplication, division, and raising to a power. Both unary and binary operations are based on a rule of correspondence between an ordered pair of objects and a third object. A unary operation associates two unlike objects, a change and a number, to produce a number. This is symbolized by joining an operator to a numeral to produce a numeral. The composition of operators is a binary operation on a set of operators, so all objects are alike. Two changes are associated to give a composite or resultant change.

	change, operator		number, numeral				number, numeral	
(	2( )	,	6	)	$\longrightarrow$	(	2(6) or 12	)

	change, operator		change, operator				change, operator	
(	2( )	,	$\overline{}$ 3	)	$\longrightarrow$	(	$\frac{2}{3}$( )	)

We now introduce a unary operation that involves a transformation of a change into a change of an opposite character. The operator for this, to be called the *opposite* operator, transforms an increase into a decrease of the same amount, and a decrease into an increase of the same amount. The opposite operator is written as $-1(\ )$, and the proper operands are, for the present, addition or subtraction operators representing increases or decreases.

change, *operator*	*change,* *operator*		*change,* *operator*
$(\quad -1(\ )$	$,\quad +3\quad)$	$\longrightarrow$	$(\quad -1(+3)\text{ or }-3\quad)$

change, *operator*	*change,* *operator*		*change,* *operator*
$(\quad -1(\ )$	$,\quad -\dfrac{3}{4}\quad)$	$\longrightarrow$	$\left(\quad -1\left(-\dfrac{3}{4}\right)\text{ or }+\dfrac{3}{4}\quad \right)$

The joining of $-1(\ )$ to an addition or subtraction operator is a unary operation. The operators $-1(\ )$ and $+3$ are most unlike in kind and $-1(\ )$ is always joined to $+3$; the association is never the other way around.

The operator $+1(\ )$ is an operator of the same type as $-1(\ )$, which serves as an identity or no-change operator. Thus $+1(+3) = +3$, and $+1\left(-\dfrac{3}{4}\right) = -\dfrac{3}{4}$. Two successive applications of $-1(\ )$ are equivalent to $+1(\ )$. $-1[-1(+3)]$ $= -1(-3) = +3$. Both $+1(\ )$ and $-1(\ )$ are commonly replaced by the abbreviated forms of $+(\ )$ and $-(\ )$. Hence $-[-(+3)] = -(-3) = +3$.

The reader might well question the use of a multiplication notation for these operators, since there would seem to be nothing about the change from an increase to a decrease that is suggestive of multiplication. Further analysis will reveal several reasons the notation is appropriate, one of which is the possibility of a composition of these operators with other multiplication operators.

Examples:
$$[-1(\ )] \circ [2(\ )] = -2(\ )\qquad -2(-3) = +6$$
$$[+1(\ )] \circ \left[\frac{1}{3}(\ )\right] = +\frac{1}{3}(\ )\qquad +\frac{1}{3}(-9) = -3$$

The composite operator $-2(\ )$ calls for two changes—a change to the opposite, and a magnification by a factor of 2.

It is also possible to use numerals for operands for the operators $+1(\ )$ and $-1(\ )$. Here they play a constructive role; by their use numerals, representing numbers, are transformed into addition and subtraction operators.

$$+1(5) = +5 \qquad +\frac{1}{2}(8) = +4 \qquad +(n) = +n \qquad +m(n) = +mn$$
$$-1\left(2\frac{1}{2}\right) = -2\frac{1}{2} \qquad -2(1) = -2 \qquad -(n) = -n \qquad -m(n) = -mn$$

When the operands for $+1(\ )$ and $-1(\ )$ or for the composite operators $+n(\ )$ and $-n(\ )$ are sums or differences, there is a striking analogy to the distributive property of multiplication with respect to addition or subtraction. For this purpose the sum $a + b$ and the difference $a - b$ are not thought of as the results of binary operations on a and b, but rather as the transforms when the operators $+ b$ and $- b$ are joined to a.

Examples:

$$+1(5 - 2) = +5 - 2 \qquad +(5 - 2) = +5 - 2$$

The operator $+1(\ \ )$, or $+(\ \ )$, transforms 5 to $+5$, and -2 to -2.

$$-1(5 - 2) = -5 + 2 \qquad -(5 - 2) = -5 + 2$$

The operator $-1(\ \ )$, or $-(\ \ )$, transforms 5 to -5, and -2 to $+2$.

$$+3(5 - 2) = +15 - 6 \qquad -3(5 - 2) = -15 + 6$$

Compare $50 + (10 + 5) = 65$ with $50 + 10 + 5 = 65.$

$$50 - (10 + 5) = 35 \qquad\qquad 50 - 10 - 5 = 35.$$
$$50 + (10 - 5) = 55 \qquad\qquad 50 + 10 - 5 = 55.$$
$$50 - (10 - 5) = 45 \qquad\qquad 50 - 10 + 5 = 45.$$
$$50 + 2(10 + 5) = 80 \qquad\quad 50 + 20 + 10 = 80.$$
$$50 + 2(10 - 5) = 60 \qquad\quad 50 + 20 - 10 = 60.$$
$$50 - 2(10 + 5) = 20 \qquad\quad 50 - 20 - 10 = 20.$$
$$50 - 2(10 - 5) = 40 \qquad\quad 50 - 20 + 10 = 40.$$

It must be emphasized that by introducing the opposite operator and taking the unary point of view in the above manipulations we have in no way extended the number system. Thus $+n(b - c)$ is equal to $+nb - nc$ only when both expressions are defined, and at present this requires that $b \geq c$. What we do have is a direct approach to some of the most used symbol manipulations in all of elementary mathematics.

The notable gain here is in the extended application of the distributive principle whereby products are replaced by sums and differences. Previously we could replace $2(10 - 5)$ by $20 - 10$ but found this same combination of symbols inaccessible in $50 - 2(10 - 5)$. We now recognize $-2(\ \ )$ as an operator of dual character and these two changes can be separated by writing (or thinking), $-1[2(\ \ )]$. This makes it possible to first use the distributive principle and then the opposite operator.

$$50 - 2(10 - 5) = 50 - 1[2(10 - 5)]$$
$$= 50 - 1(20 - 10)$$
$$= 50 - 20 + 10$$

The directions to "simplify" are very common in mathematical discussions, but the term is very loosely defined. This seems to be inevitable since the demands of simplicity vary with each context. As used in the next problem set, "simplify" means, roughly, "Write with as few parentheses as possible."

Problems (152)

Simplify:

1. $-1(+10)$ **2.** $+1(-6)$ **3.** $+1\left(-\dfrac{1}{4}\right)$ **4.** $-1(-5)$ **5.** $-(-50)$

6. $+(+12)$ **11.** $-(7-2)$ **16.** $+2(9)$ **21.** $+1(-1)$ **26.** $-4(7+3)$

7. $+\left(-\dfrac{3}{5}\right)$ **12.** $+(5+3)$ **17.** $+5(1)$ **22.** $+1(1)$ **27.** $-2(7+7)$

8. $-\left(+1\dfrac{1}{2}\right)$ **13.** $-(6+4)$ **18.** $-3(1)$ **23.** $-1(+1)$ **28.** $+6(2+3)$

9. $+(7-2)$ **14.** $+(6-4)$ **19.** $-1(1)$ **24.** $+1(+1)$ **29.** $-7(6-1)$

10. $-(5+3)$ **15.** $-3(7)$ **20.** $-1(-1)$ **25.** $+5(8-2)$ **30.** $-5(9-3)$

For problems 31 to 46, proper operands are assumed. In particular the range of the variables is to be restricted so that the subtraction of a larger number from a smaller does not arise.

Simplify:

31. $m-(n)$ **35.** $m-(n-p)$ **39.** $a+b(c-d)$ **43.** $a+b(c+d)$

32. $m+(n)$ **36.** $m+(n+p)$ **40.** $w+x(y+z)$ **44.** $w+x(y-z)$

33. $m+(n-p)$ **37.** $-(s+t)$ **41.** $a-b(c+d)$ **45.** $a-b(c-d)$

34. $m-(n+p)$ **38.** $+(s-t)$ **42.** $w-x(y-z)$ **46.** $w-x(y+z)$

It is possible to confirm the results in the above problems by using only binary operations. As examples, give reasons that support the following arguments. Note the use of parentheses to make it easier to accept a compound expression as a single entity.

47. For $n \geq p$,

$(n-p) = n - p$ (?)

$(n-p) + p = n$ (?)

$m + [(n-p) + p] = m + n$ (?)

$[m + (n-p)] + p = m + n$ (?)

$m + (n-p) = (m+n) - p$ (?)

$m + (n-p) = m + n - p$ (?)

48. For $m \geq n + p$,

Let $m - (n+p) = x$

$m = (n+p) + x$ (?)

$m = n + (p+x)$ (?)

$m - n = p + x$ (?)

$(m-n) - p = x$ (?)

$(m-n) - p = m - (n+p)$ (?)

$m - n - p = m - (n+p)$ (?)

17-2. An Arithmetic of Differences

The motivation for the introduction of the positive rational numbers came mainly from the practical needs of measurement. It is true that the creation of these numbers and the fractions for representing them makes the division of two natural numbers a and b always possible and assures a unique solution of the equation $\dfrac{a}{b} = x$. But the facts about fractions were developed by trial and error long before man conceived of the theoretical need that the binary operation of division should be possible for the set of natural numbers.

The situation is strikingly different when we consider extending the number system to make subtraction always possible. Here the practical needs are so small that man for ages was reluctant to even consider such a possibility, much less give it general acceptance. The development of negative numbers (which solve the subtraction problem) was a response to theoretical demands. The mystery that surrounded these numbers could not be explained until theories of mathematical structure had been formulated with sufficient clarity, which did not take place until the first half of the nineteenth century. As an example of theory coming before practice, the laws of signs (for manipulating negative numbers) were stated centuries before a single instance was known of a practical use for such numbers.

Even today, when negative numbers are introduced in the junior high school, the number of formulas that require substitution of negative numbers for the variables is small indeed. The effort to extend such applications has often led, and still does, to "practical" applications that are fanciful to the point of absurdity.

In our next extension of the number system our plan will be to parallel quite closely the manner by which the rational numbers were introduced, except that we will not, in the early stages, feel the same urgency for practical applications. The structural laws of the natural numbers were developed largely from analysis of sums and products since $a + b$ and ab are always defined when a and b are natural numbers. In the first chapters on fractions the goal was an arithmetic of quotients, and the principal guide to its development was the requirement of logical simplicity. We turn now to consideration of a possible arithmetic of differences, again hoping for the greatest possible consistency with the principles already accepted for the natural and rational numbers.

For the ordered pair (a, b) let both a and b be selected from the set of zero and the natural numbers. Whenever $a \geq b$, then the interpretation of (a, b) as representing the difference $a - b$ will be possible, and will be much used as a guide. Whenever $a < b$, then (a, b) cannot, at present, be given this interpretation of $a - b$. But our goal will be the development of a system where this restriction can be removed.

If N is the set of zero and the natural numbers, then $N \otimes N$ is the set of ordered pairs we are considering. Our first task is the development of an appropriate equivalence relation that will partition the members of $N \otimes N$ into equivalence classes. We shall want (a, b) and (c, d) to be equivalent if $a - b$ and $c - d$ represent the same difference.

Assume that $a \geq b$ for a pair (a, b) and $c \geq d$ for the pair (c, d). Then there exists a z, where z is zero or a natural number, such that $a - b = z$ and $c - d = z$. Then by the definition of subtraction we have $a = b + z$ and $c = d + z$. Since addition is well defined for zero and the natural numbers, we have $a + d + z = b + z + c$. Then by using the commutative and associative principles and the cancellation law for addition, we obtain $a + d = b + c$. Hence, if (a, b) and (c, d) are to be identified as "having the same difference," it is necessary that $a + d = b + c$.

But this condition that $a + d = b + c$ is also sufficient to ensure that $a - b = c - d$ provided that $a \geq b$ and $c \geq d$. For if $a \geq b$ and $c \geq d$, we can let $a - b = x$ and $c - d = y$ and then $a = b + x$ and $c = d + y$. Then $a + d + y = b + x + c$, $(a + d) + y = (b + c) + x$, and $y = x$ or $a - b = c - d$.

a. The student should supply the reasons for the above argument.

Examples: Since $15 - 8 = 11 - 4$, then $15 + 4 = 8 + 11$.
Since $18 + 7 = 15 + 10$, then $18 - 15 = 10 - 7$.

The above argument depends on the fact that $a \geq b$ and $c \geq d$ to have the sub-traction interpretation available. But in the next problem set the reader is asked to prove that the condition $a + d = b + c$ is an equivalence relation for all (a, b) and (c, d) in $N \otimes N$. It will then be possible to write $(a, b) \sim (c, d)$, if and only if $a + d = b + c$ without concern for the relative size of a and b or c and d.

There is nothing in the above discussion that would not hold equally well if a, b, c, and d had been allowed to be rational numbers. The restriction at present to zero and the natural numbers is only for simplicity and will eventually be removed. This extension to ordered pairs of rational numbers will be immediate, provided our proofs appeal only to properties shared by both natural and rational numbers. When a and b are restricted to zero and the natural numbers, then the set of equivalence classes given by $(a, b) \sim (c, d)$ if and only if $a + d = b + c$ is called the set of integers. This set is often denoted by I.

It was shown in Section 16-10 that each rational number corresponds to (or is) an equivalence class of ordered pairs. There each ordered pair (a, b) was interpreted as a quotient $\frac{a}{b}$, with a being zero or a natural number, and b being a natural number. The equivalence relation used in this instance was that $(a, b) \sim (c, d)$ if and only if $ad = bc$. Each integer corresponds to (or is) an equivalence class also. Here the equivalence relation used is that $(a, b) \sim (c, d)$ if and only if $a + d = b + c$. We shall refer to the former as equivalence classes of quotients and the latter as equivalence classes of differences. In this section we shall always mean differences unless specifically mentioned otherwise. These two equivalence classes can also be distinguished by the notations $\left[\frac{a}{b}\right]$ and $[a, b]$.

Let (a, b) be a member of some equivalence class. Recall that any ordered pair can be in only one equivalence class, since the equivalence classes form a partition. Now add any natural number x to both a and b.

Then $(a + x, b + x) \sim (a, b)$, since $(a + x) + b = (b + x) + a$.

Again let x be a natural number such that $a \geq x$ and $b \geq x$, so that x can be subtracted from both a and b.

Then $(a - x, b - x) \sim (a, b)$, since $(a - x) + b = (b - x) + a$.

To establish the latter equality, let $a - x = z$, and then $(a - x) + b = z + b = b + z$. Also, if $a - x = z$, then $a = x + z$. Hence, $(b - x) + a = b - x + x + z = b + z$. Therefore $(a - x) + b = (b - x) + a$, since both are equal to $b + z$.

Once a representative of a particular equivalence class has been chosen, the above equivalence enables us to readily determine other members of this class. Some examples of these equivalence classes are given below.

$$I = \begin{Bmatrix} \{(0, 0), (1, 1), (2, 2), (3, 3), \ldots\} \\ \{(1, 0), (2, 1), (3, 2), (4, 3), \ldots\} \\ \{(0, 1), (1, 2), (2, 3), (3, 4), \ldots\} \\ \{(2, 0), (3, 1), (4, 2), (5, 3), \ldots\} \\ \{(0, 2), (1, 3), (2, 4), (3, 5), \ldots\} \\ \quad \cdot \quad\quad \cdot \quad\quad \cdot \quad\quad \cdot \\ \quad \cdot \quad\quad \cdot \quad\quad \cdot \quad\quad \cdot \\ \quad \cdot \quad\quad \cdot \quad\quad \cdot \quad\quad \cdot \end{Bmatrix}$$

Can one add integers? If so, how? To get answers to these questions, we begin by restricting our investigation to only those pairs that have difference interpretations, such as the first, second, and fourth of the above members of I. We desire a method of expressing the sum of two differences, such as $(a - b) + (c - d)$, as a difference.

Let $a \geq b$, and $c \geq d$. Then x and y are zero or natural numbers such that $a - b = x$, and $c - d = y$.

Then $a = x + b$ and $c = y + d$, by the definition of subtraction, and the commutativity of addition.

$(a + c) = (x + b) + (y + d)$, since addition is well defined.

$(a + c) = (x + y) + (b + d)$, by using the commutative and associative laws.

$x + y = (a + c) - (b + d)$, by the definition of subtraction.

$(a - b) + (c - d) = (a + c) - (b + d)$, by substitution.

The last equation has the sum of two differences expressed as a difference, which is necessary if addition is to be a closed binary operation in a set of differences. Hence, if we want to preserve the difference interpretation for our ordered pairs, the definition of addition should be as follows:

Definition: *For $[a, b] \in I$, and $[c, d] \in I$, $[a, b] \oplus [c, d] = [a + c, b + d]$. The symbol $+$ is used for ordinary addition where zero or natural numbers are the addends, while $\oplus$ is used for the sum of two equivalence classes.*

Summary: To find the sum of two integers, first select a representative from the equivalence class of each integer. The ordered pair given by the above rule is then a representative of the equivalence class of the integer which is the sum of the given integers.

Example: Let $[2, 0] = \{(2, 0), (\underline{3}, \underline{1}), (4, 2), (5, 3), \ldots\}$
and $[3, 0] = \{(3, 0), (4, 1), (\underline{5}, \underline{2}), (6, 3), \ldots\}$
and $[5, 0] = \{(5, 0), (6, 1), (7, 2), (\underline{8}, \underline{3}), \ldots\}$

Choose $(3, 1)$ and $(5, 2)$ as representatives of the first two equivalence classes. Then $[3, 1] \oplus [5, 2] = [8, 3]$ and $(8, 3)$ is a representative of the third class above.

Now we wish to verify that no matter what representative is chosen from the first equivalence class, and no matter what representative is chosen from the second class, we always get some representative of the third class, by using the definition of sum.

b. Verify this for several cases in the above example.

If this property can be proven to hold for the sum of any two integers, then we shall say that the sum of two integers is *well defined with respect to the equivalence relation that determines them.* And in the particular example above we can write $[2, 0] + [3, 0] = [5, 0]$.

Let (a, b) and (a', b') be members of the same equivalence class. Then

$$[a, b] = [a', b']$$

Let (c, d) and (c', d') be members of the same equivalence class. Then

$$[c, d] = [c', d']$$

What we need to show is that $[a, b] \oplus [c, d] = [a', b'] \oplus [c', d']$. $[a, b] \oplus [c, d]$ $= [a + c, b + d]$ and $[a', b'] \oplus [c', d'] = [a' + c', b' + d']$ by the definition of sum. Then since $(a, b) \sim (a', b')$ and $(c, d) \sim (c', d')$ we have

$$a + b' = b + a' \qquad \text{and} \qquad c + d' = d + c'$$

Then $a + b' + c + d' = b + a' + d + c'$, since addition is well defined.
And $(a + c) + (b' + d') = (b + d) + (a' + c')$ by commutativity and associativity.
Hence $[a + c, b + d] = [a' + c', b' + d']$ by the definition of equivalence class.
And $[a, b] \oplus [c, d] = [a', b'] \oplus [c', d']$ as required.

We also want to be sure that sums of integers have still other properties that are common to sums of natural numbers and sums of rational numbers. Several of these proofs are left as exercises in the next problem set.

ANSWER TO EXERCISE

a. Definition of subtraction. Addition is well defined. Commutative and associative principles. Cancellation law, substitution, and symmetry of equality.

Problems (153)

1. Let $N = \{x \mid x \text{ is zero or a natural number}\}$
   Let $(a, b) \in N \otimes N$, and let $(c, d) \in N \otimes N$.
   Assume that $(a, b) \sim (c, d)$ if and only if $a + d = b + c$.
   Prove that $\sim$ is then an equivalence relation on $N \otimes N$.
2. Let $a = b + z$, where a, b, and z are zero or natural numbers. What representative of $[a, b]$ has the smallest pair of numbers?
3. Show that the binary operation $\oplus$ is commutative.
4. Show that the binary operation $\oplus$ is associative.

5. a. Show that $[a, a]$ is an identity element for $\oplus$ by showing that for all $[x, y]$, $[x, y] \oplus [a, a] = [x, y] = [a, a] \oplus [x, y]$.

   b. Show that $[a, a]$ is *the* identity element, that is, it is unique.

6. Give an example to prove that the operation $\square$ is *not* well defined if $[a, b] \,\square\, [c, d] = [ac, bd]$.

We now look at the product of two differences for an indication of how to multiply two integers. How shall the product of two differences, such as $(a - b)$ $(c - d)$, be expressed as a difference?

$$\text{Let } a \geq b \text{ and } c \geq d \text{ so that } a - b = x \text{ and } c - d = y \qquad (1)$$
$$\text{Then } a = b + x, \text{ and } ad = bd + dx \qquad (2)$$
$$\text{Also } c = d + y, \text{ and } bc = bd + by \qquad (3)$$
$$ac = bd + by + dx + xy \qquad (4)$$
$$ac + bd = bd + by + bd + dx + xy \qquad (5)$$
$$= (bd + by) + (bd + dx) + xy \qquad (6)$$
$$= (bc + ad) + xy \qquad (7)$$
$$xy = (ac + bd) - (bc + ad) \qquad (8)$$
$$(a - b)(c - d) = (ac + bd) - (ad + bc) \qquad (9)$$

a. Give reasons to support the above argument.

The final equation above has the product of two differences expressed as a difference, which is necessary if multiplication is to be a closed binary operation in a set of differences. Since we want to preserve the difference interpretation (when possible), the following definition of multiplication is given for integers. The symbol $\odot$ will be used for the product of the two equivalence classes.

> **Definition:** *For $[a, b] \in I$, and $[c, d] \in I$, $[a, b] \odot [c, d] = [ac + bd, ad + bc]$.*

> **Summary:** To find the product of two integers, first select a representative from the equivalence class of each integer. Then the ordered pair given by the above rule is a representative of the equivalence class of the integer that is the product of the given integers.

> **Example:** $[2, 0] \odot [3, 0] = [2 \cdot 3 + 0 \cdot 0, 2 \cdot 0 + 0 \cdot 3] = [6, 0]$.

b. What is $[3, 1] \odot [5, 2]$? Note that $[3, 1] = [2, 0]$ and $[5, 2] = [3, 0]$. Does $[3, 1] \odot [5, 2] = [6, 0]$?

Since we want to use this definition for all products of integers, including those factors where a representative pair (a, b) has $a < b$, it is necessary to verify that this definition of a product does possess the desired properties.

Answers to Exercises

a. (1) x and y are zero or natural numbers by definition of $\leq$. (2) and (3) Definition of subtraction, and multiplication is well defined. (4) Multiplication is well defined, and distributive property. (5) Addition is well defined, and commutative and associative property. (6) Associative property. (7) Substitution. (8) Definition of subtraction. (9) Substitution and commutativity. **b.** [17, 11] = [6, 0].

Problems (154)

1. Let $[a, b] = [a', b']$ and $[c, d] = [c', d']$. Show that multiplication is well defined with respect to $\sim$ by showing that $[a, b] \odot [c, d] = [a', b'] \odot [c', d']$.
2. Show that the binary operation $\odot$ is commutative.
3. Show that the binary operation $\odot$ is associative.
4. Show that the binary operation $\odot$ is left-distributive with respect to the binary operation $\oplus$. (Right distributivity follows from the commutative properties.)
5. **a.** Show that $[a + 1, a]$ is a multiplicative identity for $\odot$.
   b. Show that $[a + 1, a]$ is the unique multiplicative identity.
6. Show that $[a, b] \odot [a, a] = [a, a]$.

So far our investigation of the integers has confirmed only that they possess a number of properties in common with the natural and rational numbers. But our ultimate goal is an *extension* of the number system. In particular it is hoped that an arithmetic of differences will remove restrictions on subtraction just as the arithmetic of quotients led to removal of restrictions on division. We now wish to show that this is indeed true.

When the product of two numbers is 1, we say that they are reciprocals and that each is the multiplicative inverse of the other. After the introduction of the rational numbers, it was found that each nonzero rational had a unique reciprocal or multiplicative inverse. If two integers have a sum of the additive identity, we say that they are *opposites* and that each is an *additive inverse* of the other. For any integer $[a, b]$ we have

$$[a, b] \oplus [b, a] = [a + b, b + a] = [a, a] = [0, 0]$$

Hence $[a, b]$ and $[b, a]$ are opposites, or additive inverses, since $[0, 0]$ is the additive identity for integers [see problem 5 of set (153)].

We can now readily demonstrate the cancellation law for addition of integers.

If $[a, b] \oplus [c, d] = [a, b] \oplus [e, f]$, then

$$[b, a] \oplus ([a, b] \oplus [c, d]) = [b, a] \oplus ([a, b] \oplus [e, f]) \tag{1}$$
$$([b, a] \oplus [a, b]) \oplus [c, d] = ([b, a] \oplus [a, b]) \oplus [e, f] \tag{2}$$
$$[0, 0] \oplus [c, d] = [0, 0] \oplus [e, f] \tag{3}$$
$$\text{and} \quad [c, d] = [e, f] \tag{4}$$

a. Supply the reasons above.

If E and F are any two integers, then the equation $E \oplus X = F$ has a solution with X an integer.

Let $E = [c, d]$ and $F = [a, b]$.
Then $X = [a + d, b + c]$ is a solution of $E \oplus X = F$ since

$$[c, d] \oplus [a + d, b + c] = [a + d + c, d + b + c] = [a, b]$$

Furthermore, $X = [a + d, b + c]$ is the *only* solution, since if $[c, d] \oplus X = [a, b]$,
then $[d, c] \oplus [c, d] \oplus X = [d, c] \oplus [a, b]$.
Then $[0, 0] \oplus X = [d, c] \oplus [a, b]$
    and $X = [d + a, c + b] = [a + d, b + c]$.

If e and f are rational numbers and there exists a rational number x such that
$e + x = f$, then by the definition of subtraction, $x = f - e$.   This guides us to the
following definition of subtraction:

Definition: *The rule* $[a, b] \ominus [c, d] = [a, b] \oplus [d, c]$ *defines a binary operation
on integers called subtraction, which is symbolized by the sign* $\ominus$.

The solution to the equation $E \oplus X = F$ can then be written as

$$X = F \ominus E = [a, b] \ominus [c, d] = [a, b] \oplus [d, c] = [a + d, b + c]$$

The definition of subtraction has remained the same in one important respect,
as given for natural numbers, rational numbers, and now for integers.   The problem
of defining a difference $F \ominus E$ so that there is a number X such that $X = F \ominus E$, is
exactly the same problem as determining a number X such that $E \oplus X = F$.
With integers this problem has a solution for all E and F, and the key is the existence
of the additive inverse for any integer.   We subtract E from F by adding to F the
additive inverse of E.

There still remains this question, "Is it reasonable to refer to integers as numbers?"   So far we have identified them only as equivalence classes, but have noted
quite a few number-like properties.   Still more reasons for referring to the integers
as a new kind of number will be given in the next section.

ANSWER TO EXERCISE

a. (1) Addition of integers is well defined.   (2) Associative property of addition of integers.
(3) Definition of additive inverse for integers.   (4) The additive identity for integers.

Problems (155)

Compute.   Assume that in the resulting equivalence class $[a, b]$, a and b are a
pair of numbers that are as small as possible.

1. $[4, 0] \oplus [6, 0]$	**11.** $[6, 0] \oplus [0, 4]$	**21.** $[0, 8] \ominus [0, 3]$
2. $[2, 0] \oplus [8, 0]$	**12.** $[7, 0] \oplus [0, 3]$	**22.** $[0, 6] \ominus [0, 1]$
3. $[7, 3] \oplus [8, 2]$	**13.** $[10, 5] \oplus [5, 10]$	**23.** $[0, 3] \ominus [8, 0]$
4. $[3, 1] \oplus [12, 4]$	**14.** $[1, 2] \oplus [2, 1]$	**24.** $[0, 1] \ominus [6, 0]$
5. $[0, 2] \oplus [0, 7]$	**15.** $[8, 0] \ominus [3, 0]$	**25.** $[10, 8] \odot [10, 6]$
6. $[0, 4] \oplus [0, 5]$	**16.** $[6, 0] \ominus [1, 0]$	**26.** $[10, 7] \odot [10, 5]$
7. $[5, 7] \oplus [4, 1]$	**17.** $[3, 0] \ominus [8, 0]$	**27.** $[2, 0] \odot [4, 0]$
8. $[2, 9] \oplus [10, 2]$	**18.** $[1, 0] \ominus [6, 0]$	**28.** $[5, 0] \odot [3, 0]$
9. $[4, 0] \oplus [0, 6]$	**19.** $[0, 3] \ominus [0, 8]$	**29.** $[5, 0] \odot [1, 0]$
10. $[3, 0] \oplus [0, 7]$	**20.** $[0, 1] \ominus [0, 6]$	**30.** $[1, 0] \odot [10, 0]$

31. $[5, 0] \odot [0, 0]$
32. $[0, 1] \odot [10, 0]$
33. $[5, 0] \odot [5, 0]$
34. $[1, 1] \odot [10, 0]$
35. $[2, 2] \odot [3, 3]$
36. $[0, 3] \odot [5, 0]$
37. $[2, 0] \odot [0, 4]$
38. $[0, 3] \odot [0, 5]$

39. $[0, 2] \odot [4, 0]$
40. $[3, 3] \odot [3, 3]$
41. $[0, 2] \odot [0, 4]$
42. $[10, 9] \odot [20, 19]$
43. $[1, 0] \odot [1, 0]$
44. $[10, 9] \odot [19, 20]$
45. $[1, 0] \odot [0, 1]$
46. $[9, 10] \odot [20, 19]$

47. $[0, 1] \odot [1, 0]$
48. $[9, 10] \odot [19, 20]$
49. $[0, 1] \odot [0, 1]$
50. $[10, 0] \odot [10, 9]$
51. $[10, 9] \odot [8, 7]$
52. $[0, 2] \odot [4, 6]$
53. $[4, 5] \odot [6, 7]$
54. $[9, 6] \odot [3, 0]$

Solve for the integer X. For the representation of each equivalence class use a pair at least one of whose components is zero.

55. $[3, 0] \oplus X = [9, 0]$
56. $X \oplus [2, 0] = [7, 0]$
57. $[9, 0] \oplus X = [3, 0]$
58. $X \oplus [7, 0] = [2, 0]$
59. $[0, 3] \oplus X = [9, 0]$
60. $[7, 0] = [0, 2] \oplus X$

61. $[3, 0] \oplus X = [0, 9]$
62. $[0, 7] = [2, 0] \oplus X$
63. $[0, 3] \oplus X = [0, 9]$
64. $[0, 7] = X \oplus [0, 2]$
65. $[0, 9] \oplus X = [3, 0]$
66. $[2, 0] = X \oplus [0, 7]$

67. $[9, 0] \oplus X = [0, 3]$
68. $[10, 3] \oplus X = [8, 10]$
69. $[0, 9] \oplus X = [0, 3]$
70. $X \oplus [3, 10] = [8, 10]$
71. $[0, 3] \oplus X = [0, 3]$
72. $[10, 8] = [10, 8] \oplus X$

Compute:

73. $[3, 1] \oplus [5, 3] \oplus [8, 5]$
74. $[3, 0] \odot [4, 1] \odot [5, 2]$
75. $[12, 3] \ominus [6, 2] \ominus [3, 1]$
76. $[2, 0] \ominus [4, 0] \ominus [6, 0]$
77. $[8, 6] \odot [9, 6] \odot [11, 6]$
78. $[0, 0] \ominus [5, 0] \ominus [5, 0]$
79. $[2, 0] \oplus [3, 0] \ominus [5, 0]$
80. $[0, 0] \ominus [0, 5] \ominus [0, 5]$

81. Solve for $[x, y]$:
   a. $[a, b] \oplus [x, y] = [c, d]$ b. $[a, b] \ominus [x, y] = [c, d]$
82. Show that the binary operation $\ominus$ is well defined.

17-3. An Isomorphism

Our purpose in this section will be to show how a proper subset of the integers can be tied very closely to the set of zero and the natural numbers. This will be one more reason for identifying integers as numbers. This association will be made by a mapping and for this discussion some further notation for mappings and functions will be useful. Let $f : n \to n - 3$ be the mapping for which the functional notation is $f(n) = n - 3$. The ordered pairs that constitute this particular function are $(n, n - 3)$ and for any function f of n they would be written $(n, f(n))$. The symbol n is a variable whose range of permissible substitutions is the domain of the function or mapping f. The range of the variable $f(n)$ is the range of the function f. In using this symbol $f(n)$ as a variable, the substitutions are made only for the symbol n; the symbol f is carried along as a constant reminder of the name of the function. Hence, if n_1 is a particular member of the domain of f, then $f(n_1)$ identifies the element in the range of f, which is the image of n_1. This notation extends to the case where the domain of f consists of ordered n-tuples.

Examples:

$$f(n) = n - 3 \qquad f(3) = 3 - 3 = 0; \quad f\left(5\tfrac{1}{2}\right) = 5\tfrac{1}{2} - 3 = 2\tfrac{1}{2}.$$

$$f(n) = (n - 2)! \qquad f(5) = (5 - 2)! = 3! = 6; \quad f\left(1\tfrac{1}{2}\right) \text{ has not been}$$

defined.

$$f(x) = \left(\frac{2}{x}\right)^x \qquad f(3) = \left(\frac{2}{3}\right)^3 = \frac{8}{27}; \quad f(0) \text{ is not defined.}$$

$$g(a, b) = a + b \qquad g(2, 3) = 2 + 3 = 5; \quad g(a, b) = g(b, a) \text{ for all}$$
numbers we have defined (the commutative property).

Let I_1 and I_2 be any two particular integers and let $f(I_1, I_2) = I_1 \oplus I_2$. Then $f([2, 0], [3, 0]) = [2, 0] \oplus [3, 0] = [2 + 3, 0 + 0] = [5, 0]$.

There are times when it is convenient to think of $f(\ )$ as a *functional operator*. By its use x_1 is transformed to $f(x_1)$. To say that $f(\ )$ transforms n to $f(n)$ is an extension of the domain and range of the function to variables.

Problems (156)

1. $f(n) = n^2 + n - 1; f(3) = ?$
2. $g(n) = (3n - 1)^2; g(2) = ?$
3. $t_n = 20 - n^2; t_3 = ?$
4. $b_n = b_{n-1} - b_{n-2}; b_4 = ?$
5. $F(n) = \sum_{k=1}^{k=n} \frac{2}{k}; F(3) = ?$
6. $G(n) = \sum_{k=1}^{k=n} (k - 1)!; G(4) = ?$
7. $f(x, y, z) = x + y^z; f(1, 2, 3) = ?$

8. $h(m, n) = 2^{m+n}; h(4, 3) = ?$
9. Let $f_1(I_1, I_2) = I_1 \oplus I_2$; $f_1([0, 5], [4, 2]) = ?$
10. Let $f_2(I_1, I_2) = I_1 \ominus I_2$; $f_2([7, 0], [0, 3]) = ?$
11. Let $f_3(I_1, I_2) = I_1 \odot I_2$; $f_3([0, 4], [0, 3]) = ?$
12. Let $f_1(I_1, I_2) = I_1 \oplus I_2$; $f_1([7, 3], [2, 2]) = ?$
13. Let $f_2(I_1, I_2) = I_1 \ominus I_2$; $f_2([0, 0], [0, 9]) = ?$
14. Let $f_3(I_1, I_2) = I_1 \odot I_2$; $f_3([8, 0], [50, 49]) = ?$

We have had many instances of the importance of equivalence in the development of the number system. There is another "alike" concept that is fundamental throughout mathematics, known as *"isomorphism."* This refers particularly to mathematical models, or systems that are alike in certain ways in their form and structure, so that they exhibit similarities of behavior as they are used.

Let $S_1 = \{a_1, b_1, c_1, \ldots\}$ and let $(x, y) \rightarrow x * y$ be a binary operation in S_1.
Let $S_2 = \{a_2, b_2, c_2, \ldots\}$ and let $(x, y) \rightarrow x \circledast y$ be a binary operation in S_2.
Let $F: S_1 \rightarrow S_2$ be a mapping from S_1 onto S_2. Then if $z \in S_1$, then $F(z)$ is the image of z in S_2. Let F be such that:

1. F is a 1:1 correspondence.
2. If x and y are in S_1, then whenever one of $x * y$ and $F(x) \circledast F(y)$ is de-
    fined, so is the other.
3. Whenever $x \in S_1$ and $y \in S_1$, then $F(x * y) = F(x) \circledast F(y)$.
Then F is called an *isomorphism* of S_1 with S_2 with respect to the operations $*$
and $\circledast$. An alternate usage is to say that the mapping F from S_1 onto S_2
is "operation preserving."

> **Example:** Let $S_1 = \{0, 1, 2, 3, \ldots, n, \ldots\}$ and let addition be the binary
> operation in this set.
>
> Let $S_2 = \{1, 2, 4, 8, \ldots, 2^n, \ldots\}$ and let multiplication be the binary
> operation in this set.
>
> Then the mapping $F: x \to 2^x$ is an isomorphism of S_1 and S_2 with re-
> spect to addition in S_1 and multiplication in S_2.
>
> This means that **A.** and **B.** as below always give the same result.

A. Choose two elements in one of the sets.	Choose 2 and 3 in S_1
Perform the operation defined in that set.	$2 + 3 = 5$
Determine the image of this result in the other set.	$5 \to 2^5$, or $\underline{32}$
B. Choose the same elements as in **A.**	2 and 3
Determine the image of these elements in the other set.	$2 \to 2^2$ or 4; $3 \to 2^3$ or 8
Perform the operation on these images that is defined for them.	$2^2 \cdot 2^3 = 2^5$; $4 \cdot 8 = \underline{32}$

a. Verify the above isomorphism by choosing 16 and 64 in S_2 and $F: 2^x \to x$.

Further discussion of the integers will be simplified by first agreeing on a "best"
or standard representative for each equivalence class. A natural choice of this
kind for equivalence classes of ordered pairs of natural numbers would seem to be
that pair consisting of the smallest possible numbers. For the rational numbers
such a representative for $\left[\dfrac{a}{b}\right]$ was determined by dividing both components by their
common prime factors so that in the standard representative a and b were relatively
prime. It is true for all integers that $[a - x, b - x] = [a, b]$, if $a \geq x$ and $b \geq x$.

This means we can subtract the same natural number from each component
until we get an ordered pair, at least one of whose components is zero. This form
is the choice for the standard representative of each equivalence class. By its use
we obtain a partition of all the integers into three types. This follows from the
trichotomy principle for zero and the natural numbers, which assures us that if a
and b are from this set then exactly one of the following holds: $a > b$, $a = b$, or
$a < b$.

1. *For all integers $[a, b]$, if $a > b$, there is a unique natural number n such that*

$[a, b] = [n, 0]$. For if $a > b$ there is a unique natural number n such that $a = n + b$. Then $[a, b] = [n + b, b] = [n, 0]$. If n and n_1 are such that $[a, b] = [n, 0]$ and $[a, b] = [n_1, 0]$, then $[n, 0] = [n_1, 0]$ so that

$$n + 0 = 0 + n_1 \qquad \text{and} \qquad n = n_1$$

2. *If $a = b$, then the integer $[a, b]$ is always the unique integer $[0, 0]$.* Here $[a, b] = [a - b, b - b] = [0, 0]$. This integer has been shown to be the identity or "zero" for $\oplus$.

3. *For all integers $[a, b]$, if $a < b$, there is a unique natural number n such that $[a, b] = [0, n]$.* The proof parallels that for **1.**

Each integer $[a, b]$ can be therefore represented by exactly one of "$[n, 0]$," "$[0, 0]$," or "$[0, n]$," where n is a natural number. We now introduce a briefer notation and a name for these three types of integers.

1. An integer $[n, 0]$ will be represented by ^+n, and referred to as a *positive integer*.

2. The integer $[0, 0]$ will be represented by 0, and called the *zero* integer.

3. An integer $[0, n]$ will be represented by ^-n, and referred to as a *negative integer*.

We are now ready to exhibit an isomorphism between the set S_1 consisting of the zero integer and the positive integers, and the set S_2 consisting of zero and the natural numbers. This isomorphism will be shown with respect to $\oplus$ and $\odot$ in S_1 and $+$ and $\cdot$, respectively, in S_2. The possibility of a mapping for this correspondence can be seen in the following diagram.

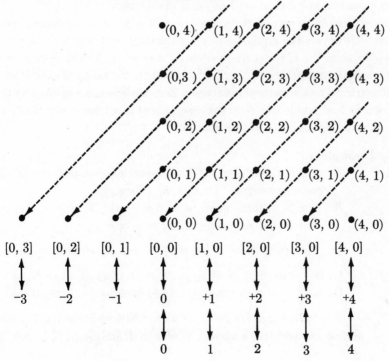

The members of each equivalence class lie along the dashed lines. The mapping for the isomorphism is $F\colon [n, 0] \to n$, for $n \geq 0$. It then is necessary to show that the image of the sum (or product) is equal to the sum (or product) of the images under the mapping.

Let m and n be zero or natural numbers.

Then $[m, 0] \oplus [n, 0] = [m + n, 0]$ and $[m + n, 0] \to m + n$

and $[m, 0] \odot [n, 0] = [mn, 0]$ and $[mn, 0] \to m \cdot n$

The flexibility given by this isomorphism will be much used. Thus, we shall feel free to think of $m + n$ as being the sum of two natural numbers, or also as the sum of two positive integers, and this will be done without bothering to change the notation to $[m, 0] \oplus [n, 0]$. Again if $m < n$, then $m - n$ is not defined if m and n are natural numbers. But $[m, 0] \ominus [n, 0]$ is defined, and we will often change interpretations without changing the notation. Henceforth, we shall use $\odot$, $\oplus$, and $\ominus$ for integers only when the equivalence class notation is being used.

There are clearly members of I that do not enter into this isomorphism. The natural numbers are said to be *embedded* within the integers, and the integers form an *extension* of the natural numbers. The forms $^+m + {}^+n$ and $(^+m)(^+n)$ do not represent an extension of the meaning of addition and multiplication because of the isomorphism above. But when a negative integer ^-m is used as an addend or as a factor, this is "addition" and "multiplication" in a new and extended sense. In the next sections we will consider some possibilities of using the integers in constructing mathematical models of physical phenomena.

The *superscript* notation of ^+n and ^-n will now be the principal one for the integers. However, the equivalence class notation will still be of great value in proofs by making use of the correspondence, $^+n \leftrightarrow [n, 0], 0 \leftrightarrow [0, 0]$, and $^-n \leftrightarrow [0, n]$, where n is a natural number. For both ^+n and ^-n the range of substitutions for n will be restricted to the natural numbers. Zero has the same symbol when used as an integer as had previously been the case. Zero is neither positive nor negative, but is its own opposite or additive inverse.

Examples:

A. $(^+m)(^+n) = {}^+(mn)$. The product of two positive integers is a positive integer. $[m, 0][n, 0] = [mn, 0]$.

B. If $m > n$, then $^+m + {}^-n = {}^+(m - n)$. If $m > n$, there exists an x such that $m = n + x$, and $m - n = x$.

$$[m, 0] \oplus [0, n] = [m, n] = [n + x, n] = [x, 0] = [m - n, 0]$$

C. $0 - n = {}^-n$. $[0, 0] \ominus [n, 0] = [0, 0] \oplus [0, n] = [0, n] = {}^-n$.

D. $m - n = m + (^-n)$. $[m, 0] \ominus [n, 0] = [m, 0] \oplus [0, n]$.

Note the instances in **C.** and **D.** where subtracting is replaced by adding the additive inverse. (Refer to definition of $\ominus$.) Observe also in **C.** and **D.** that equality is being used as an equivalence relation rather than as logical identity, as defined in Section 9-1. By writing $n = {}^+n$ we do not then assert that the natural number n and the positive integer ${}^+n$ are the same object, but only that they are equivalent up to an isomorphism. That is, each may be interchanged for the other, under specified circumstances.

Problems (157)

Give the arguments to support the following, making use of the isomorphism between the natural numbers and the positive integers, and the equivalence of the superscript and equivalence class notations for all integers.

1. $({}^-m)({}^-n) = {}^+(mn)$
2. $({}^+m)({}^-n) = {}^-(mn)$
3. $({}^-m)({}^+n) = {}^-(mn)$
4. ${}^+m + {}^+n = {}^+(m + n)$
5. ${}^-m + {}^-n = {}^-(m + n)$
6. If $m < n$, ${}^+m + {}^-n = {}^-(n - m)$
7. ${}^+m + {}^-m = 0$
8. $({}^+1)(n) = {}^+n$

9. $({}^-1)(n) = {}^-n$
10. If $m > n$, ${}^+m - {}^+n = {}^+(m - n)$
11. If $m < n$, ${}^+m - {}^+n = {}^-(n - m)$
12. ${}^+m - {}^-n = {}^+(m + n)$
13. ${}^-m - {}^+n = {}^-(m + n)$
14. If $m > n$, ${}^-m - {}^-n = {}^-(m - n)$
15. If $m < n$, ${}^-m - {}^-n = {}^+(n - m)$
16. $0 + {}^-m = {}^-m$

17. For any natural numbers m and n, $m - n = [m, n]$.
18. **a.** $0 - {}^+m = {}^-m$ **b.** $0 - {}^-m = {}^+m$ **c.** ${}^+m - {}^+m = 0$ **d.** ${}^-m - {}^-m = 0$

17-4. Order and Absolute Value

The diagram in the previous section, which illustrated the isomorphism between the natural numbers and the positive integers, presented a selection of the integers in a certain order. This order was controlled by the order for the positive integers, but the diagram was also suggestive of an ordering for the negative integers. We now turn to the ordering of positive integers for a clue to the ordering of all integers.

In Section 13-1, the relation "less than" was defined for natural numbers so that $x < y$ if and only if there exists a natural number z such that $x + z = y$, and hence such that $z = y - x$. Hence, we require that if x and y are positive integers, then $x < y$ if and only if there exists a positive integer z such that $x + z = y$, and hence such that $z = y - x$.

Let $x = [a, b]$, $y = [c, d]$, and $z = [e, f]$ be positive integers so that $a > b$, $c > d$, and $e > f$. Then if $x < y$, we have $x + z = y$, or $[a, b] \oplus [e, f] = [c, d]$. Hence, $[a + e, b + f] = [c, d]$ and $a + e + d = b + f + c$, or $(a + d) + e = (b + c) + f$. Then if $e > f$, we have $a + d < b + c$. On the other hand, let x and y be given as above and let $a + d < b + c$. There then exists a natural number g such that $(a + d) + g = b + c$, or that $a + g + d = b + 0 + c$. Hence $[a + g, b + 0] = [c, d]$, and $[a, b] \oplus [g, 0] = [c, d]$. Therefore, $x + [g, 0] = y$, and $[g, 0]$ is the natural number g. Hence $x < y$.

Observe that this argument used only the fact that z was a positive integer and was thus independent of the fact that x and y were positive integers. This suggests that we extend to *all* integers x and y the definition that $x < y$ if and only if there exists a positive integer z such that $x + z = y$, or $z = y - x$. By the argument above this is equivalent to:

$$[a, b] \oslash [c, d] \text{ if and only if } a + d < b + c$$

The notation $\oslash$ will be retained until it has been shown to have the same properties as $<$. One of these requirements is that $\oslash$ be well defined.

Let $(a', b') \sim (a, b)$, and $(c', d') \sim (c, d)$.
Then $[a', b'] = [a, b]$, and $[c', d'] = [c, d]$.
Hence $a' + b = b' + a$, and $c' + d = d' + c$. $\hspace{2cm}$ (1)
Then if $[a, b] \oslash [c, d]$, we have $a + d < b + c$, by definition.

$$(a + d) + (b' + d') < (b + c) + (b' + d') \hspace{2cm} (2)$$
$$(a + b') + (d + d') < (c + d') + (b + b') \hspace{2cm} (3)$$
$$(a' + b) + (d + d') < (c' + d) + (b + b') \hspace{2cm} (4)$$
$$(a' + d') + (b + d) < (b' + c') + (b + d) \hspace{2cm} (5)$$
$$a' + d' < b' + c' \hspace{2cm} (6)$$
$$[a', b'] \oslash [c', d'] \hspace{2cm} (7)$$

a. Supply the reasons for this argument.
b. Verify that $^-4 \oslash {}^-3 \oslash {}^-2 \oslash {}^-1 \oslash 0$.

The trichotomy principle is preserved for all integers. For two natural numbers $a + d$ and $b + c$ exactly one of the following is true: $a + d < b + c$, $a + d = b + c$, or $a + d > b + c$. Hence, if $[a, b]$ and $[c, d]$ are any two integers exactly one of the following must be true:

$$[a, b] \oslash [c, d]$$
$$[a, b] = [c, d]$$
$$\text{or } [a, b] \oslash [c, d]$$

In Section 16-11, the relation $<$ was found to be a strict simple ordering of the natural numbers, since it was asymmetric, transitive, and connected. The trichotomy principle shows that $\oslash$ is connected for the set I of all integers. Since if $a + d < b + c$, it is never the case that $a + d > b + c$, the relation $\oslash$ is asymmetric. To show that it is also transitive, assume that $[a, b] \oslash [c, d]$ and that $[c, d] \oslash [e, f]$. Then from $a + d < b + c$ and from $c + f < d + e$ we find that

$$(a + d) + (c + f) < (b + c) + (d + e)$$
$$\text{or that } (a + f) + (c + d) < (b + e) + (c + d)$$

Therefore,

$$a + f < b + e \hspace{1cm} \text{and} \hspace{1cm} [a, b] \oslash [e, f]$$

The monotonic and cancellation laws as given in Section 13-1 for natural numbers also extend to integers, with one very important exception. If, in an equality, both members are multiplied by a positive integer, the sense of the inequality remains the same, *but if both members are multiplied by the same negative integer, the sense of the inequality is reversed.*

If m is a natural number, then $m > 0$, and every positive integer is greater than zero, by the isomorphism.   Furthermore, $[0, m] \bigcirc\!\!\!< [0, 0]$, so that for every negative integer ^-m, we have $^-m < 0$.

The correspondence of the above properties of $\bigcirc\!\!\!<$ and $<$ justifies the dropping of the notation $\bigcirc\!\!\!<$ and the extension of $<$ to all integers.

By appealing to the definition of inequality and to the trichotomy principle, the following principles can be shown to hold for all integers:

1. $x + y < x + z$ if and only if $y < z$.
2. If $u > 0$, then $uy < uz$ if and only if $y < z$.
3. If $u > 0$, then $uy > uz$ if and only if $y > z$.

There are, of course, corresponding statements for the relation $>$.   These should be compared with those for natural numbers given in problem set (118).

When we assert that the natural number n and the positive number $[n, 0]$ or ^+n are isomorphic, we do *not* mean that they are indistinguishable.   All that is claimed, and no more, is that either may replace the other as an addend in a sum, or as a factor in a product, or as a component of an order relation.   These, of course, lead to still other identifications but n and ^+n remain distinct concepts.

Thus ^+n is defined as an ordered pair, but a natural number is not.   Any attempt to define a natural number as a pair of natural numbers would clearly be faulty because of the circularity.   Integers can be either positive or negative.   But natural numbers can never be negative and it is therefore misleading and inappropriate to speak of a positive natural number.   The positive integers are *signed* numbers; they have a sense or orientation, which makes them of value in representing opposites as well as magnitude.   The natural numbers are unsigned; they can represent magnitude but they carry no sense of orientation.

In the next section we consider changing the notation for positive integers from ^+n to $+n$, and for negative integers from ^-n to $-n$, since the latter notation is the standard one.   In anticipation of this the following definitions are introduced:

1. *For all integers* x, $+(x) = x$, *and* $+ 1(x) = x$.
2. *For all integers* x, $-(x) = -x = 0 - x$, *and* $-1(x) = -x$.

The first of these states that the operators $+(\ \ )$ and $+1(\ \ )$ are identity operators when the operand x is an integer, and thus no change is produced.   Both of these operators are like multiplying by positive 1 in this respect.

The second states that $-(\ \ )$ and $-1(\ \ )$ are opposite operators, which for an operand that is an integer, give its additive inverse as a transform.

Recall that if z is the additive inverse of x,

then $x + z = 0$, and $z = 0 - x$.

Hence by identifying $0 - x$ with $-x$,

we make $-(\ )$ the operator which gives the additive inverse.

Note that the operators $-(\ )$ and $-1(\ )$ produce the same effect on an integer as multiplying by negative 1.

All the integers can be arranged in pairs, by pairing each one with its (unique) additive inverse. Thus, zero is paired with itself, $^+1$ with $^-1$, $^+2$ with $^-2$, and so on. We now define a property of the integers, which is the same for both members of any of the above pairs, and which distinguishes that pair from any other pair of additive inverses. The *absolute value* of an integer x is denoted by $|x|$ and is equal to x if x is positive or zero, and is equal to $-x$ if x is negative. That is,

$$|x| = x, \quad \text{if } x \geq 0$$
$$\text{and} \quad |x| = -x, \quad \text{if } x < 0$$

By this every positive integer is defined to be the same as its absolute value. To obtain the absolute value of a negative number, we take its additive inverse, which is positive.

Examples:

$|0| = 0$

$|^+1| = ^+1$ $\qquad |^-1| = -(^-1) = ^+1$ $\qquad$ Hence $|^+1| = |^-1|$

$|^+2| = ^+2$ $\qquad |^-2| = -(^-2) = ^+2$ $\qquad$ Hence $|^+2| = |^-2|$

Since the integers provide a set in which subtraction is always defined, we are now in a position to extend the discussion of difference comparisons given in Chapter 16. If a and b are integers, then $a - b$ is a unique integer. Furthermore, $a - b$ is positive if and only if $a > b$, $a - b$ is zero if and only if $a = b$, and $a - b$ is negative if and only if $a < b$. The difference between a first number a and a second number b can now always be taken as $a - b$, without regard to the relative size of a and b.

Examples:

$^+7 - {}^+2 = {}^+5 \qquad\qquad {}^+7 > {}^+2$

$^+2 - {}^+7 = {}^-5 \qquad\qquad {}^+2 < {}^+7$

$^+7 - {}^+7 = 0 \qquad\qquad {}^+7 = {}^+7$

$^+2 - {}^-7 = {}^+9 \qquad\qquad {}^+2 > {}^-7$

$^-2 - {}^+7 = {}^-9 \qquad\qquad {}^-2 < {}^+7$

ANSWERS TO EXERCISES

a. (1) Definition of equality of integers. (2) Monotonic law for addition. (3) Commutative and associative principles. (4) Substitution from (1). (5) Commutative and associative principles. (6) Cancellation law. (7) Definition of ⬭. **b.** [0, 4] ⬭ [0, 3] since $3 < 4$. [0, 3] ⬭ [0, 2] since $2 < 3$. [0, 2] ⬭ [0, 1] since $1 < 2$. [0, 1] ⬭ [0, 0] since $0 < 1$.

Problems (158)

Compute:

1. $^+8 + ^+3$	**5.** $^+8 - ^+3$	**9.** $^+3 - ^+8$	**13.** $^+6 - ^-4$	**17.** $^+4 - ^-6$
2. $^+8 + ^-3$	**6.** $^+8 - ^-3$	**10.** $^+3 - ^-8$	**14.** $^-6 - ^+4$	**18.** $^-4 - ^+6$
3. $^-8 + ^+3$	**7.** $^-8 - ^+3$	**11.** $^-3 - ^-8$	**15.** $^-6 - ^-4$	**19.** $^-4 - ^-6$
4. $^-8 + ^-3$	**8.** $^-8 - ^-3$	**12.** $^-3 - ^+8$	**16.** $^+6 - ^+4$	**20.** $^+4 - ^+6$

Subtract the second number from the first, and thus obtain the difference comparison of the first number to the second.

21. $^+3, ^+10$	**27.** $^+10, ^-3$	**33.** $^+3, ^-10$	**39.** $2, ^-6$	**45.** $0, 2$
22. $^+4, ^+1$	**28.** $^+1, ^-4$	**34.** $^+4, ^-1$	**40.** $3, ^-3$	**46.** $3, 0$
23. $^+10, ^+3$	**29.** $^-10, ^-3$	**35.** $^-10, ^+3$	**41.** $^-6, ^-6$	**47.** $0, ^-2$
24. $^+1, ^+4$	**30.** $^-1, ^-4$	**36.** $^-1, ^+4$	**42.** $^-3, 3$	**48.** $^-3, 0$
25. $^-3, ^+10$	**31.** $^-3, ^-10$	**37.** $2, 6$	**43.** $^-2, 6$	**49.** $^-2, 0$
26. $^-4, ^+1$	**32.** $^-4, ^-1$	**38.** $3, 3$	**44.** $^-3, ^-3$	**50.** $0, ^-3$

Give the absolute value for each of the following:

51. $^+12$	**52.** $^-10$	**53.** 4	**54.** $^+100$	**55.** $^-17$	**56.** 25

17-5. Computations with Signed Numbers

We have used the notations ^+n and $+n$, and ^-n and $-n$ for very different ideas. The symbol $^+5$ represents a positive integer, while $+5$ represents an addition operator. Also, $^-5$ represents an oriented but fixed magnitude; while -5 is a symbol for a change, a decrease of 5. Because these concepts are so very different, the correspondence now to be introduced is indeed remarkable.

There is a wide category of situations where the symbols ^+n and $+n$, and ^-n and $-n$, can be interchanged at will. This correspondence will be put into effect by using ^+n and n, and ^-n and $-n$ as alternate notations for positive and negative integers, respectively, when n is a natural number. What we have to watch out for are possible conflicts between $+n$ as a positive integer and $+n$ as an operator.

We also adopt the convention for variables that only natural numbers can replace the x in ^+x or ^-x, but that there be no restriction of this kind on substitutions for x in $+x$ or $-x$.

It must be emphasized that one cannot always interchange ^+n and $+n$ or ^-n and $-n$. We have noted already that many times ^+n and n are interchangeable. Suppose further that ^+n and $+n$ were always identical in meaning. This would imply that sometimes the operator $+n$ cannot be distinguished from the number n, which is absurd. Before we take up a number of cases where ^+n and n, and ^-n and $-n$ are interchangeable, let us consider some instances where this cannot be done, because the plus and minus signs are used in an operational sense (either as part of an operator or as a symbol for a binary operation).

Examples:

$5 + 3$ $5 \; {}^+3$ is a meaningless combination of symbols.

$5 - 3$ $5 \; {}^-3$ is also without meaning.

$5 + 3(4 - 1)$ $5 \; {}^+3(4 - 1)$ is without meaning.

The next examples are arranged in pairs. They give examples of the cases that arise when integers are substituted for variables in sums, differences, and products, In the left column the notation of ${}^+n$ and ${}^-n$ is used for integers. In the right column the notation of $+n$ and $-n$ is used for integers. Notice here that there is no conflict with the conventions as defined for operators, since correct results are obtained if these rules are applied.

Examples:

A. $f_1(x, y) = x + y$

$$f_1({}^+4, {}^+7) = {}^+4 + {}^+7 \qquad f_1(+4, +7) = +4 + (+7)$$
$$= {}^+11 \qquad\qquad\qquad\qquad = +4 + 7 = +11$$
$$f_1({}^+4, {}^-7) = {}^+4 + {}^-7 \qquad f_1(+4, -7) = +4 + (-7)$$
$$= {}^-3 \qquad\qquad\qquad\qquad = +4 - 7 = -3$$
$$f_1({}^-4, {}^+7) = {}^-4 + {}^+7 \qquad f_1(-4, +7) = -4 + (+7)$$
$$= {}^+3 \qquad\qquad\qquad\qquad = -4 + 7 = +3$$
$$f_1({}^-4, {}^-7) = {}^-4 + {}^-7 \qquad f_1(-4, -7) = -4 + (-7)$$
$$= {}^-11 \qquad\qquad\qquad\qquad = -4 - 7 = -11$$

When analyzing these examples, particular note should be made as to when parentheses are inserted when making substitutions, and when they can be omitted.

B. $f_2(x, y) = x - y$

$$f_2({}^+4, {}^+7) = {}^+4 - {}^+7 \qquad f_2(+4, +7) = +4 - (+7)$$
$$= {}^+4 + {}^-7 = {}^-3 \qquad\qquad = +4 - 7 = -3$$
$$f_2({}^+4, {}^-7) = {}^+4 - {}^-7 \qquad f_2(+4, -7) = +4 - (-7)$$
$$= {}^+4 + {}^+7 = {}^+11 \qquad\qquad = +4 + 7 = +11$$
$$f_2({}^-4, {}^+7) = {}^-4 - {}^+7 \qquad f_2(-4, +7) = -4 - (+7)$$
$$= {}^-4 + {}^-7 = {}^-11 \qquad\qquad = -4 - 7 = -11$$
$$f_2({}^-4, {}^-7) = {}^-4 - {}^-7 \qquad f_2(-4, -7) = -4 - (-7)$$
$$= {}^-4 + {}^+7 = {}^+3 \qquad\qquad = -4 + 7 = +3$$

C. $f_3(x, y) = xy$

$$f_3({}^+4, {}^+7) = ({}^+4)({}^+7) \qquad f_3(+4, +7) = (+4)(+7)$$
$$= {}^+28 \qquad\qquad\qquad\qquad = +28$$

In this case $(+4)(+7)$ must be considered as a product of integers, since no operator interpretation has been defined for this combination of symbols. However, there is an analogy with $+4(+7) = +28$.

$$f_3(^+4, \, ^-7) = (^+4)(^-7) \qquad f_3(+4, \, -7) = (+4)(-7)$$
$$= \, ^-28 \qquad\qquad\qquad = -28$$
$$f_3(^-4, \, ^+7) = (^-4)(^+7) \qquad f_3(-4, \, +7) = (-4)(+7)$$
$$= \, ^-28 \qquad\qquad\qquad = -28$$
$$f_3(^-4, \, ^-7) = (^-4)(^-7) \qquad f_3(-4, \, -7) = (-4)(-7)$$
$$= \, ^+28 \qquad\qquad\qquad = +28$$

More complex sums, differences, and products can be reduced to the above types, one step at a time. The standard notation for the integers is that used in the right-hand column. However, some authorities recommend that the superscript notation be retained for a considerable time until some facility is gained in computation. There would seem to be several good reasons for immediately adopting the standard notation. This notation is much simpler because fewer kinds of symbols are used. And we should keep in mind that operators are used continually in mathematical discourse but that signed numbers appear relatively infrequently. When such a symbol as -3 is met *in context*, and not in specially devised exercises, the odds are overwhelming that it should be interpreted as a decrease of 3 (an operator) rather than as negative 3 (an integer). Hence, we shall drop the superscript notation unless some special emphasis is required.

When applying "rules of signs" to expressions containing plus and minus signs, one must keep in mind the reach or extent of influence of these symbols.

Example:

$$- \{a - b \, [c + d - (-e)]\}$$
$$- \{a - b \, [c + d + e]\}$$
$$- \{a - bc - bd - be\}$$
$$- a + bc + bd + be$$

The symbol e is within the reach of, or is influenced by, the minus sign to its left; by the minus sign to the left of the parentheses; not by the plus sign; by the minus sign just to the left of b; and by the minus sign to the left of the brace.

The opposite operator $-1(\ \ )$ or $-(\ \ )$ is the "active" one in contrast to the identity $+1(\ \ )$ or $+(\ \ )$, which produces no change of sign. Hence, one can concentrate only on the minus signs when making decisions about sign. But two consecutive applications of the operator $-1(\ \ )$ are equivalent to one of $+1(\ \ )$ so that the final criterion for sign depends on whether the symbol is reached by an even or an odd number of minus signs.

By adopting the notation $+n$ for ^+n the isomorphism between the positive integers and the natural numbers is indicated by $+n \to n$ as well as by $^+n \to n$. This suggests the omission or the insertion of plus signs at will. *But this can be done only when the plus sign is being used to identify a positive number, never when the plus sign is in the operator role.* The plus sign can never be omitted from the operator $+n$.

Example: $(a + b)$ is interchangeable with $(+a + (+b))$, but the plus sign cannot be left out in $a + b$.

a. Can the plus sign be omitted from $+10$?
b. Can the plus sign be omitted from $+(12 - 2)$?
c. Which sign can be omitted in $(+7 + 3)$?

With rational numbers a distinction between number (idea) and symbol (mark) can be made by using "rational number" for the number and "fraction" for the symbol. No such distinction has become widely adopted for integers. The following convention would be a step in this direction: Use "negative one" and "positive two" when referring to -1 and $+2$ as numbers, and use "minus one" and "plus two" when thinking of the symbols themselves. While one should be able to make such distinctions, it becomes pedantic to an extreme to always insist on them.

If $x = -1$, then

$$x^2 = (-1)^2 = (-1)(-1) = +1 \text{ or } 1$$
$$x^3 = (-1)^3 = (-1)(-1)(-1) = -1$$
$$x^4 = (-1)^4 = (-1)(-1)(-1)(-1) = +1 \text{ or } 1$$
$$x^5 = (-1)^5 = (-1)(-1)(-1)(-1)(-1) = -1$$

etc.

In general,

$$(-1)^n = +1 \text{ or } 1 \text{ if } n \text{ is even}$$
$$= -1, \text{ if } n \text{ is odd}$$

(This means we accept $(-1)^0 = 1$.)

The powers of -1 are a very useful component of many mathematical models. By their use we can give directions to add or subtract alternately, or to assign a positive or negative sense alternately.

Examples: If $a_n = (-1)^n(n + 1)$, then $a_1 = -2$, $a_2 = +3$ or 3, and $a_3 = -4$.

If $S_n = \sum_{k=1}^{k=n} [(-1)^n(n + 1)]$, then $S_1 = -2$, $S_2 = -2 + 3 = +1$, $S_3 = -2 + 3 - 4 = -3$.

ANSWERS TO EXERCISES

a. Yes, if $+10$ is a positive number; No, if it is an operator.   **b.** Same as for **a.**   **c.** Only the plus sign at the left of 7.

Problems (159)

In problems 1 to 6, do the substitutions only, with no further simplification or computation. Insert parentheses only when required.

1. $[(w + x)y + z]$ (w: 2, x: -4, y: $+3$, z: -1)   (Notation as in Section 6-1.)
2. $[(w - x)y - z]$ (w: -2, x: 4, y: -3, z: $+1$)

3. $[(w - x)y + z]$ $(w: +2, x: -4, y: 3, z: 1)$
4. $[(w + x)y - z]$ $(w: -2, x: +4, y: -3, z: -1)$
5. $[(r + s)(t + u)]$ $(r: +8, s: -5, t: -6, u: 9)$
6. $[(r - s)(t + u)]$ $(r: 8, s: -5, t: +6, u: -9)$

The convention of nesting various types of parentheses as in $[(\ )]$ or $\{[(\ )]\}$ is only for convenience in reading. The repeated use of a single type of grouping symbol is also correct as in $((\ ))$, or $(((\ )))$, or $[[\ ]]$. Use only one type of parentheses in problems 7 to 12. Otherwise the directions are as in problems 1 to 6.

7. $((r + s)(t - u))$ $(r: -8, s: 5, t: +6, u: +9)$
8. $((r - s)(t - u))$ $(r: -8, s: +5, t: -6, u: -9)$
9. $(lm + np)$ $(l: -7, m: 10, n: +5, p: -2)$
10. $(lm - np)$ $(l: 7, m: -10, n: 5, p: +2)$
11. $(ab - bc)$ $(a: +12, b: -4, c: 3)$
12. $(ab + ac)$ $(a: -12, b: 4, c: -3)$

Return to problems 1 to 12, and complete the computation.

13. #1   16. #4   19. #7   22. #10
14. #2   17. #5   20. #8   23. #11
15. #3   18. #6   21. #9   24. #12

25. If $f(x, y, z) = x + yz$, then $f(-2, 3, 5) = ?$
26. If $f(x, y, z) = x - yz$, then $f(2, -3, 5) = ?$
27. If $f(x, y, z) = xy - z$, then $f(-2, 3, -5) = ?$
28. If $f(x, y, z) = xy + z$, then $f(2, -3, -5) = ?$
29. If $f(x, y, z) = x(y + z)$, then $f(-2, -3, 5) = ?$
30. If $f(x, y, z) = x(y - z)$ then $f(-2, -3, -5) = ?$

31. If $g(r, s, t) = (r - s)t$, then $g(4, -1, 4) = ?$
32. If $g(r, s, t) = (r + s)t$, then $g(-4, 1, -4) = ?$
33. If $g(r, s, t) = r - (s + t)$ then $g(-4, -1, 4) = ?$
34. If $g(r, s, t) = r - (s - t)$ then $g(4, 1, -4) = ?$
35. If $h(t) = t^2 - t$, then $h(-1) = ?$
36. If $h(t) = t - t^2$ then $h(-1) = ?$

Compute:

37. $|-7 + 3|$ 38. $|2 - 10|$ 39. $|9 - (-2)|$ 40. $|6(-4)|$
41. If $b_n = (-1)^n(2n)$, compute b_1, b_2, b_3, b_4, and b_5.
42. If $t_n = (-1)^n(6 - n)$, compute t_1, t_2, t_3, t_4, and t_5.
43. If $S_n = \sum_{k=1}^{k=n} [(-1)^k k^2]$, compute S_1, S_2, S_3, and S_4.
44. If $S_n = \sum_{k=1}^{k=n} [(-1)^k k(k + 1)]$, compute S_1, S_2, S_3, and S_4.

Let $A = \{-3, -2, -1, 0, 1, 2, 3\}$. Let z be a member of A. For what subset of A do the following hold?

45. $\lvert z \rvert = 2$	51. $\lvert z \rvert > 3$	57. $\lvert z - 2 \rvert < 2$	63. $\lvert z \rvert = z$
46. $\lvert z \rvert = 3$	52. $\lvert z \rvert > 1$	58. $\lvert z - 1 \rvert < 1$	64. $\lvert z \rvert + z = 0$
47. $\lvert z \rvert = 0$	53. $\lvert z - 1 \rvert = 0$	59. $\lvert z - 1 \rvert > 2$	65. $\lvert z \rvert = 2z$
48. $\lvert z \rvert = -1$	54. $\lvert z - 3 \rvert = 0$	60. $\lvert z + 1 \rvert > 2$	66. $2\lvert z \rvert = z$
49. $\lvert z \rvert < 2$	55. $\lvert z + 2 \rvert = 0$	61. $\lvert z + 2 \rvert \geq 3$	67. $\lvert z \rvert = z^2$
50. $\lvert z \rvert < 1$	56. $\lvert z + 1 \rvert = 0$	62. $\lvert z - 2 \rvert \leq 1$	68. $\lvert z \rvert > z$

The set I of integers has the same limitation on division as does the set of the natural numbers and zero, to which the nonnegative integers are isomorphic. *The integer x is divisible by the integer y, and we can write $\dfrac{x}{y} = z$ if and only if there is an integer z such that $yz = x$.* This is a direct extension of the definition of division for natural numbers as stated in Section 3-1. The decisions about the proper sign for quotients can be determined from the corresponding products.

Let x, y, and z be integers such that $yz = x$ and $\dfrac{x}{y} = z$. The integer x can be positive, zero, or negative, as represented by ^{+}m, 0, or ^{-}m. The integer y can be positive or negative, as represented by ^{+}n or ^{-}n, but must not be zero. By using the results in problem set (157) we have these possible cases:

$$(^{+}m)(^{+}n) = {}^{+}(mn); \frac{^{+}(mn)}{^{+}m} = {}^{+}n \qquad (^{-}m)(^{+}n) = {}^{-}(mn); \frac{^{-}(mn)}{^{-}m} = {}^{+}n$$

$$(^{-}m)(^{-}n) = {}^{+}(mn); \frac{^{+}(mn)}{^{-}m} = {}^{-}n \qquad (^{+}m)(^{-}n) = {}^{-}(mn); \frac{^{-}(mn)}{^{+}m} = {}^{-}n$$

$$(^{+}m)(0) = 0; \frac{0}{^{+}m} = 0 \qquad\qquad (^{-}m)(0) = 0; \frac{0}{^{-}m} = 0$$

Hence the quotient (or the product) of two positive or two negative integers is a positive integer. The quotient (or the product) of one positive and one negative integer, or of one negative and one positive integer, is a negative integer. The quotient of zero and either a positive or negative integer is zero.

It can be shown (see Section 18-1) that if a and b are integers, with $b \neq 0$, there is a unique integer q such that

$$a = qb + r \qquad \text{where } 0 \leq r < \lvert b \rvert$$

The number r, which is nonnegative and less than the absolute value of b, is called the least nonnegative remainder of a by division with b.

Examples:

$$a = 17, b = 5 \qquad\qquad a = 17, b = -5$$

$$17 = q(5) + r \qquad\qquad 17 = q(-5) + r$$
$$17 = (3)(5) + 2 \qquad\qquad 17 = (-3)(-5) + 2$$

$$q = 3, r = 2 \qquad\qquad q = -3, r = 2$$

$$a = -17, b = 5 \qquad\qquad a = -17, b = -5$$

$$-17 = q(5) + r \qquad\qquad -17 = q(-5) + r$$
$$-17 = (-4)(5) + 3 \qquad\quad -17 = (4)(-5) + 3$$

$$q = -4, r = 3 \qquad\qquad\quad q = 4, r = 3$$

Problems (160)

For the given a and b, determine integers q and r such that $a = qb + r$ with $0 \leq r < |b|$.

1. $a = 37, b = 8$	9. $a = -100, b = -15$
2. $a = 39, b = 6$	10. $a = 321, b = -74$
3. $a = 37, b = -8$	11. $a = -328, b = 19$
4. $a = -39, b = -6$	12. $a = -225, b = 15$
5. $a = -37, b = 8$	13. $a = 5, b = 17$
6. $a = 39, b = -6$	14. $a = 5, b = -17$
7. $a = -37, b = -8$	15. $a = -5, b = 17$
8. $a = -39, b = 6$	16. $a = -5, b = -17$

17-6. Rational Numbers

In Chapters 1 to 10 the discussion was limited to the natural numbers and zero. If a and b are in this set, then $a + b$ and ab are always defined but $\frac{a}{b}$ is defined only if $b \neq 0$ and z is zero or a multiple of b, and $a - b$ is defined only if $a \geq b$. The numbers introduced in Chapters 11 to 16 as rational numbers will henceforth be called nonnegative rational numbers, since it will turn out that they are only a proper subset of the rational numbers as defined in the next extension of the number system.   In the set of nonnegative rationals, closure is still maintained for addition and multiplication and division is now always possible if the divisor is not zero. But if x and y are nonnegative rationals, subtraction is still possible in this set only if $x \geq y$.

In the set of integers addition, multiplication, and subtraction are now all closed binary operations, but for division there is no improvement over the set of the natural numbers and zero.

Each of these systems, the nonnegative rationals and the integers, is an extension of the system of natural numbers and zero; based on the respective isomorphisms, $\frac{n}{1} \rightarrow n$, and $^+n \rightarrow n$.   The next extension will be to the *rational numbers*, the goal being a system in which both subtraction and division (except by zero) are possible.   There are several ways to construct such a set using techniques that have already been used in constructing the nonnegative rationals and the integers.

It would have been possible to proceed directly from the nonnegative rationals to the rationals, by adjoining to the set an opposite or additive inverse for each number (zero alone already has one). The numbers $\frac{p}{q}$ with p and q natural numbers could first be identified as positive rational numbers, $^{+}\left(\frac{p}{q}\right)$. Then to each positive rational number $^{+}\left(\frac{p}{q}\right)$ there is introduced a negative rational number $^{-}\left(\frac{p}{q}\right)$ with the property that $^{+}\left(\frac{p}{q}\right) + {}^{-}\left(\frac{p}{q}\right) = 0$. The positive member of such a pair would be the absolute value of each member of the pair. The set of rational numbers would thus consist of the positive rational numbers, zero, and the negative rational numbers. Addition and multiplication can be defined by analogy with the positive rationals and then shown to have the necessary properties. The correspondence $^{+}\left(\frac{n}{1}\right) \rightarrow {}^{+}n$ then establishes an isomorphism between a subset of the rationals and the integers.

The rational numbers can also be constructed by using equivalence classes of ordered pairs. These pairs can be either ordered pairs of nonnegative rationals or ordered pairs of integers. Since no essentially new ideas arise in either development, they will only be sketched in outline in the succeeding paragraphs.

Let (x, y) be an ordered pair of integers with y not zero. That is, $x \in I$, $y \in I$, and $y \neq 0$. Let $(x_1, y_1) \sim (x_2, y_2)$ if and only if $x_1 y_2 = x_2 y_1$. This was shown in Section 16-10 to be an equivalence relation when the ordered pairs were taken from the set of zero and the natural numbers. But the same proof is valid when the components of the ordered pairs are integers. This equivalence relation partitions $I \otimes I$, with the second component not zero, into equivalence classes for which the notation $\left[\dfrac{x}{y}\right]$ may be used. Each equivalence class is called a rational number and the set of R of rational numbers is the set of all such equivalence classes. It would now be possible to define addition and multiplication in this set and investigate their properties in a manner that would closely parallel the development of the positive rationals in Chapters 11 to 15. The only new feature would be the question of positive and negative sense for each result, and this decision could be made by a generalization of the laws of signs for integers.

The construction of the rational numbers as equivalence classes of nonnegative rationals can be accomplished by steps that parallel those used in this chapter to construct the integers. As a preliminary, let us consider the possibility of allowing a and b in the equivalence class $[a, b]$ to be integers as well as natural numbers or zero as has been the previous restriction. Then $(a, b) \sim (c, d)$ if and only if

$a + d = b + c$ is still an equivalence relation for such ordered pairs, since the proof of this holds equally well when a, b, c, and d are integers.

Example: $(-5, -2) \sim (3, 6)$ since $-5 + (6) = 1 = -2 + (3)$.

This means that the diagram in Section 17-3, which illustrates several equivalence classes, could be extended as below if desired.

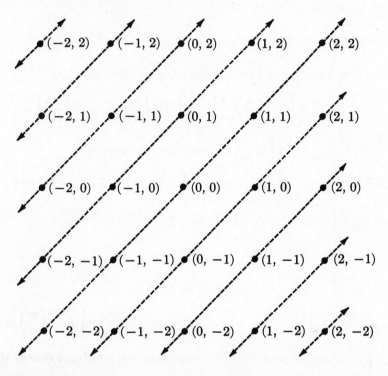

This method of extending the equivalence classes $[a, b]$ gives nothing new, since no new types of equivalence classes result from it. But we do make progress if a and b in $[a, b]$ are allowed to be nonnegative rationals. The proofs in the development from Section 17-2 on still hold as before. Thus the condition that $(a, b) \sim (c, d)$ if and only if $a + d = b + c$ is still an equivalence relation on all (a, b) and (c, d) in $R \otimes R$ where R is the set of nonnegative rationals.

Examples: $\left(2\frac{1}{2}, \frac{1}{2}\right) \sim \left(3\frac{1}{4}, 1\frac{1}{4}\right)$ since $2\frac{1}{2} + 1\frac{1}{4} = 3\frac{3}{4} = \frac{1}{2} + 3\frac{1}{4}$.

$\left(2, 3\frac{1}{3}\right) \sim \left(\frac{1}{2}, 1\frac{5}{6}\right)$ since $2 + 1\frac{5}{6} = 3\frac{5}{6} = 3\frac{1}{3} + \frac{1}{2}$.

This extension of $[a, b]$ requires no modification of the definitions for sum, products, or differences, nor for the proofs of the properties of these operations. The standard representations of these equivalence classes divide into three categories:

$\left[\dfrac{m}{n}, 0\right]$, $[0, 0]$, and $\left[0, \dfrac{m}{n}\right]$, where m is a natural number or zero, and n is a natural

number.   Because $\left[\dfrac{m}{n}, 0\right]$ and $\left[0, \dfrac{m}{n}\right]$ are additive inverses, subtraction is always

possible.   But it is also true that division is now always possible (with the ever present exception of zero divisors), because each of the equivalence classes other than $[0, 0]$ now has a multiplicative inverse.

Let m and n be natural numbers.

Then $\left[\dfrac{m}{n}, 0\right]$ and $\left[\dfrac{n}{m}, 0\right]$ are multiplicative inverses, since

$$\left[\dfrac{m}{n}, 0\right] \odot \left[\dfrac{n}{m}, 0\right] = \left[\left(\dfrac{m}{n}\right)\left(\dfrac{n}{m}\right) + (0)(0), \left(\dfrac{m}{n}\right)(0) + (0)\left(\dfrac{n}{m}\right)\right] = [1, 0]$$

Similarly, $\left[0, \dfrac{m}{n}\right]$ and $\left[0, \dfrac{n}{m}\right]$ are multiplicative inverses.

a. If $\left[\dfrac{a}{b}, 0\right] \odot X = \left[\dfrac{c}{d}, 0\right]$, then $X = ?$ (a, b, and d are not equal to zero)

b. If $\left[\dfrac{a}{b}, 0\right] \odot X = \left[0, \dfrac{c}{d}\right]$, then $X = ?$

c. If $\left[0, \dfrac{a}{b}\right] \odot X = \left[\dfrac{c}{d}, 0\right]$, then $X = ?$

d. If $\left[0, \dfrac{a}{b}\right] \odot X = \left[0, \dfrac{c}{d}\right]$, then $X = ?$

We adopt $^+\left(\dfrac{m}{n}\right)$ or $+\dfrac{m}{n}$ as a briefer notation for $\left[\dfrac{m}{n}, 0\right]$ and $^-\left(\dfrac{m}{n}\right)$ or $-\dfrac{m}{n}$ for

$\left[0, \dfrac{m}{n}\right]$.   We can now verify the following identities, which are usually discussed in algebra texts as "the three signs of a fraction."

$$\dfrac{+m}{+n} = \dfrac{-m}{-n} = +\dfrac{m}{n} \qquad \text{and} \qquad \dfrac{-m}{+n} = \dfrac{+m}{-n} = -\dfrac{m}{n}$$

For example, to show that $\dfrac{+m}{-n} = -\dfrac{m}{n}$, let $\dfrac{+m}{-n} = x$

Then $+m = (x)(-n)$ and $[m, 0] = x \odot [0, n]$.

Hence $\left[\dfrac{m}{1}, 0\right] = x \odot \left[0, \dfrac{n}{1}\right]$.

Therefore, $x = \left[0, \dfrac{m}{n}\right] = -\dfrac{m}{n}$.

By such arguments it can be shown that one obtains the same system of rational numbers whether they be constructed as quotients of integers or as differences of nonnegative rationals.   In each case we have a system in which addition, subtraction, and multiplication are closed and division is possible except for zero divisors.

ANSWERS TO EXERCISES

a. $\left[\dfrac{bc}{ad}, 0\right]$.   **b.** $\left[0, \dfrac{bc}{ad}\right]$.   **c.** $\left[0, \dfrac{bc}{ad}\right]$.   **d.** $\left[\dfrac{bc}{ad}, 0\right]$.

Problems (161)

1. Show that $\dfrac{-m}{+n} = -\dfrac{m}{n}$

2. Show that $\dfrac{-m}{-n} = +\dfrac{m}{n}$

3. If $a_n = \left(-\dfrac{1}{2}\right)^n$, compute a_1, a_2, a_3, and a_4.

4. If $b_n = 1 - \left(-\dfrac{1}{3}\right)^n$, compute b_1, b_2, b_3, and b_4.

5. If $S_n = \sum\limits_{k=1}^{k=n}\left[(-1)^{k+1}\left(\dfrac{1}{k}\right)\right]$, compute S_1, S_2, S_3, and S_4.

6. If $S_n = \sum\limits_{k=1}^{k=n}\left[(-1)^k\left(\dfrac{1}{k+1}\right)\right]$, compute S_1, S_2, S_3, and S_4.

If the variable x can assume negative as well as positive rational values, then the bracket operator [ ] is extended in definition so that $[x]$ represents *the greatest integer not greater than x*.   Thus $\left[2\dfrac{1}{2}\right] = 2$, and $\left[-2\dfrac{1}{2}\right] = -3$.

7. Compute:

   a. $\left[5\dfrac{2}{3}\right]$ **b.** $\left[-5\dfrac{2}{3}\right]$ **c.** $\left[\dfrac{101}{4}\right]$ **d.** $\left[-\dfrac{101}{4}\right]$ **e.** $\left[-\dfrac{100}{4}\right]$

8. Compute:

   a. $\left[\dfrac{7}{8}\right]$ **b.** $\left[-\dfrac{7}{8}\right]$ **c.** $\left[\dfrac{91}{13}\right]$ **d.** $\left[-\dfrac{91}{13}\right]$ **e.** $\left[-\dfrac{90}{13}\right]$

9 If $f(x) = x^2 - x + 1$, compute:

   a. $f(1)$ **b.** $f\left(\dfrac{1}{2}\right)$ **c.** $f(0)$ **d.** $f\left(-\dfrac{1}{2}\right)$ **e.** $f(-1)$

10. If $f(x) = 3x^2 - x - 2$, compute:

   a. $f(1)$ **b.** $f\left(\dfrac{1}{3}\right)$ **c.** $f(0)$ **d.** $f\left(-\dfrac{2}{3}\right)$ **e.** $f(-1)$

17-7. Models for Signed Numbers

The preceding sections of this chapter have indicated how the number system may be extended beyond the natural numbers, zero, and the positive rationals to include the negative integers and the negative rationals.   While not all details have been given, we have further found these latter systems to be logically consistent with the former.   Let us delay no longer in facing the inevitable question, "Do these new numbers have any practical value?"   In particular are there phenomena in life with characteristics for which these numbers can serve as an abstract model, but for which the unsigned numbers would be inadequate?   We will look first for geometric answers to these questions, since these not only have value in themselves but also serve as aids in the visualization of still other applications.

A variety of graphical models for the natural numbers and zero were discussed in Chapter 9. Later, when the positive rationals were introduced, a check was made to see which of these models could be extended or modified to serve for the extended number system. This will again be our procedure in looking for ways to picture signed numbers.

Set theoretical concepts offer little promise here but there are some possibilities with sequences. When the universe of discussion was zero and the natural numbers the sequence 0, 1, 2, 3, . . . was formed by beginning with zero and continuing as required by using the successor mapping $n \to n + 1$. If the domain of definition of n is extended to include the negative integers, we have

$$\cdots -3, \; -2, \; -1, \; 0, \; 1, \; 2, \; 3 \cdots$$

This ordered array now extends indefinitely in both directions and lacks both a beginning and an end. Not only does each number have a unique successor, as before, but also each number now has a unique predecessor. This set of successors, taken as a whole, is not a sequence. But if some member of this set is chosen arbitrarily as a first member, a subset is determined that is a sequence. For example, $-3, \; -2, \; -1, \; 0, \; 1, \; 2, \; 3, \; \ldots$ is such a sequence. Sequences whose first member is an arbitrary but fixed integer and such that $a_{i+1} = a_i + 1$ will be called *successor sequences*. While zero here no longer has the unique property of being the first term, it now has an important role because of following symmetry. Two integers with the same absolute value (an integer and its opposite) are in symmetric positions with respect to zero in any successor sequence that includes them. That is, if x is the ith successor (or predecessor) of zero, then zero is the ith successor (or predecessor) of $-x$.

The two sequences below are as used in Section 9-2 to illustrate $3 + 4 = 7$. For each pair of numbers that are in correspondence, the upper number is 4 more than the lower. But some numbers in the upper sequence lack a correspondent in the lower.

$$
\begin{array}{ccccccccc}
0 & 1 & 2 & 3 & 4 & 5 & 6 & 7 & \cdots \\
 & & & | & | & | & | & \\
 & & & 0 & 1 & 2 & 3 & & \cdots
\end{array}
$$

These exceptions are removed when the negative integers are adjoined.

$$
\begin{array}{ccccccccccc}
\cdots & -3 & -2 & -1 & 0 & 1 & 2 & 3 & 4 & 5 & 6 & 7 & \cdots \\
 & | & | & | & | & | & | & | & | & | & | & | \\
 & -7 & -6 & -5 & -4 & -3 & -2 & -1 & 0 & 1 & 2 & 3 & \cdots
\end{array}
$$

If two successor sequences are used to construct two identical linear scales, we have a model that extends readily to sums and differences of rationals. Thus we have below, for the range shown, a picture of both of "$1\frac{2}{3}$ more," and of "$1\frac{2}{3}$ less."

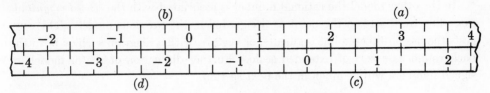

Verify these computations with the aid of the two scales.

a. $1\frac{1}{3} + 1\frac{2}{3} = 3$.   **b.** $-2 + 1\frac{2}{3} = -\frac{1}{3}$.   **c.** $2\frac{1}{3} - 1\frac{2}{3} = \frac{2}{3}$.   **d.** $-\frac{2}{3} - 1\frac{2}{3} = -2\frac{1}{3}$.

When scales were introduced for the illustration of natural and rational numbers and operations on them, emphasis was given to the fact that the length assigned to 1 (the distance from zero to 1) was arbitrary and often governed only by convenience.   In the extended scales above we have gone a step farther: the location of the zero point has now become arbitrary.   Such scales find practical applications because it is sometimes not convenient, or even possible, to begin a measurement at "none" of the quantity being measured.

The change in point of view is shown by diagrams **A.** and **B.**   Diagram **A.** shows a *half-line* or *ray*.   It has a beginning, which has been marked with zero, but there is no restriction on its extension to the right.   The number 1 can be assigned to any arbitrary point, which is distinct from the zero point, and this establishes a correspondence, which assigns a unique point to each natural and positive rational number.

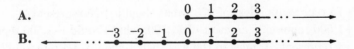

Diagram **B.** is designed to represent a line, without a beginning or an end, and now zero as well as one has been assigned to an arbitrary point.   The pairs of points that are at equal distances from the zero point are distinctive: the numbers assigned to them are additive inverses.   The diagram makes clear why such pairs are called opposites.   The members of such pairs have the same absolute value.   Hence, when the rational numbers are associated with the points of a line as in **B.**, a geometrical interpretation can be given to the absolute value of the rational number x.   Thus, $|x|$ is the measure of the distance from the point x to the zero point.   As a measure of such a distance the absolute value should be thought of as unsigned rather than as a positive number.

A diagram such as **B.** provides two models for a rational number.   In one of these the emphasis is on the association of the number with its own unique point.   This model is particularly useful when order relations are being studied.   When this is the point of view the diagram **B.** is called a *number line*.   It is often termed *the* number line, recognizing that all such diagrams are similar except for scale factor.

In the other model the rational number is associated with the *sensed magnitude* extending from zero to the point as designated in the previous model. This suggests the use of directed line segments, or vectors, with a diagram such as **B.** in the background as a sort of extended scale. Further discussion of vector models of signed numbers will be given in the next section.

Problems (162)

In problems 1 to 12, a choice is to be made between diagrams **A.** and **B.** for the most appropriate scale for measuring the given quantity.

1. Temperature	**5.** Longitude	**9.** Voltage, direct-current
2. Altitude	**6.** Intensity of light	**10.** Financial condition
3. Age of a person	**7.** Intensity of sound	**11.** Voltage, alternating-
4. Years of employment	**8.** Yearly rainfall	current
		12. Depth of a well

Problems 13 to 20 indicate some of the usefulness of signed numbers in recording not only the amount but also "oppositeness."

13. If $+15$ represents 15 degrees above zero, what should -15 represent?

14. If -68 represents 68 feet below sea level, what should $+68$ represent?

15. If $+2\frac{1}{2}$ represents $2\frac{1}{2}$ hours after noon, what should $-2\frac{1}{2}$ represent?

16. If -2 represents 2 steps to the left, what should $+2$ represent?

17. If -75 represents a loss of \$75, what should $+75$ represent?

18. If $+1,500$ represents an asset of \$1,500, what should $-1,500$ represent?

19. If -4 represents 4 miles to the west, what should $+4$ represent?

20. If $+2$ represents a rise of 2 points, what should -2 represent?

21. Construct a single diagram consisting of two adjacent scales from which all of the following can be read directly and give the result:

$$\textbf{a. } \frac{4}{5} + 1\frac{2}{5} \qquad \textbf{b. } -3\frac{1}{5} + 1\frac{2}{5} \qquad \textbf{c. } \frac{4}{5} - 1\frac{2}{5} \qquad \textbf{d. } -2\frac{2}{5} - 1\frac{2}{5}$$

22. Construct a single diagram consisting of two adjacent scales from which all of the following can be read directly and give the result:

$$\textbf{a. } -1\frac{1}{2} + \frac{5}{6} \qquad \textbf{b. } 1\frac{1}{3} + \frac{5}{6} \qquad \textbf{c. } -1\frac{2}{3} - \frac{5}{6} \qquad \textbf{d. } \frac{1}{6} - \frac{5}{6}$$

The first two sequences below show typical pairs determined by the mapping $n \to 3n$ (or $n \to \frac{n}{3}$), for zero and the natural number. The sequences are then extended to allow extension of the domain and range of the mapping.

$$
\begin{array}{cccc}
0 & 3 & 6 & 9 \quad \cdots \\
| & | & | & | \\
0 & 1 & 2 & 3 \quad \cdots
\end{array}
$$

$$
\begin{array}{ccccccccc}
\cdots & -9 & -6 & -3 & 0 & 3 & 6 & 9 & \cdots \\
 & | & | & | & | & | & | & | \\
\cdots & -3 & -2 & -1 & 0 & 1 & 2 & 3 & \cdots
\end{array}
$$

The operands and transforms given by a negative multiplication or division operator can be shown by reversing the direction of one of the scales or sequences.   The zero points still correspond, however.

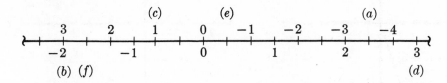

The following computations may be read directly from the two scales above:

a. $\left(2\frac{1}{3}\right)\left(-\frac{3}{2}\right) = -3\frac{1}{2}$ **c.** $\left(-\frac{2}{3}\right)\left(-\frac{3}{2}\right) = 1$ **e.** $\left(\frac{1}{3}\right)\left(-\frac{3}{2}\right) = -\frac{1}{2}$

b. $\dfrac{3}{-\frac{3}{2}} = -2$ **d.** $\dfrac{-4\frac{1}{2}}{-\frac{3}{2}} = 3$ **f.** $\dfrac{2\frac{1}{2}}{-\frac{3}{2}} = -1\frac{2}{3}$

One of the constructions given in Section 9-3 for the geometrical analysis of products was based on parallel lines and similar triangles.   It generalizes readily to signed numbers.

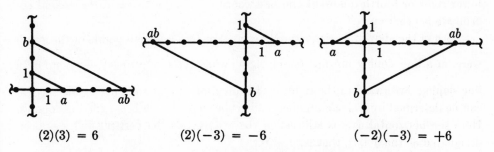

(2)(3) = 6   (2)(−3) = −6   (−2)(−3) = +6

The diagram in Section 17-6 for displaying equivalence classes indicates how pairs of signed numbers may be used to distinguish points in a plane.   This allows the graphs of functions as introduced in Section 10-4 to be extended in scope corresponding to the extended domain and range of the functions when signed numbers are admitted. The graphs below are of the functions $f(x) = 3x$, and $g(x)$ $= -\frac{3}{2}x$, which were illustrated by two sequences and two scales, respectively. Verify this for each point designated on the graphs.

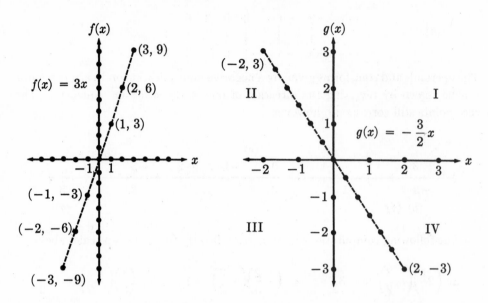

The two axes assumed for x and $f(x)$ are now lines rather than rays as had been true prior to this chapter.   These axes divide the plane in four quadrants as shown above.   In the upper right or first quadrant both coordinates of the points are positive.   The intersection of the axes is at the point $(0, 0)$ and other points on the axes have one zero coordinate.   In the upper left or second quadrant are the points whose first coordinates are negative and second coordinates are positive.   The third quadrant is at the lower left.   Here both coordinates are negative.   In the lower right or fourth quadrant the first coordinate is positive and the second co-ordinate is negative.

Both of the above functions were linear.   For $f(x) = 3x$, all points of the graph were on a line sloping upward to the right, while those of $g(x) = -\frac{3}{2}x$ were on a line sloping downward to the right.   The direction of a line M that is not vertical can be described by a single number, called the slope, which is assigned as follows. Here the horizontal axis is still called the x axis, but the vertical axis has been designated as the y axis, that is, $y = f(x)$.

Let P_1 and P_2 be any two arbitrary but distinct points on line M, with co-ordinates of (x_1, y_1) and (x_2, y_2) respectively.   If point P_3 is introduced to complete the right triangle as shown, its coordinates are (x_2, y_1).   By the *rise* from P_1 to P_2 we mean the number $y_2 - y_1$, which may be positive, negative, or zero.   By the *run* from P_1 to P_2 we mean the number $x_2 - x_1$, which may be positive or negative, but not zero, since M is not to be vertical.   The ratio

$$\frac{\text{rise from } P_1 \text{ to } P_2}{\text{run from } P_1 \text{ to } P_2}$$

is called the *slope* from P_1 to P_2.

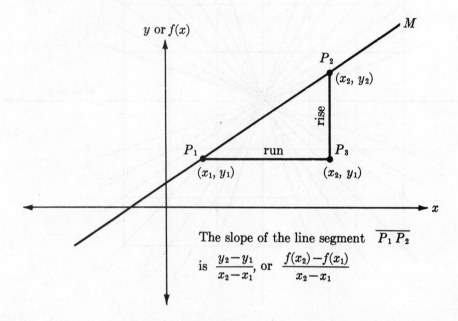

The slope of the line segment $\overline{P_1 P_2}$

is $\dfrac{y_2 - y_1}{x_2 - x_1}$, or $\dfrac{f(x_2) - f(x_1)}{x_2 - x_1}$

The pairs of points in the following exercises are taken from the graphs of $f(x) = 3x$ and $g(x) = -\dfrac{3}{2}x$. The slope will be found to be independent of the choice of two points whose coordinates are used in the slope formula.   It is characteristic of a straight line that its slope is everywhere constant.   Compute the slope of the line segment joining the following pairs of points:

g. $(1, 3)$ and $(3, 9)$.   **h.** $(-1, -3)$ and $(1, 3)$.   **i.** $(0, 0)$ and $(2, 6)$.   **j.** $(-3, -9)$ and $(0, 0)$.   **k.** $\left(\dfrac{2}{3}, -1\right)$ and $(2, -3)$.   **l.** $\left(\dfrac{1}{3}, -\dfrac{1}{2}\right)$ and $\left(1\dfrac{2}{3}, -2\dfrac{1}{2}\right)$.   **m.** $\left(-\dfrac{2}{3}, 1\right)$ and $(-2, 3)$.

In the following diagram, a grid has been formed of vertical and horizontal lines. The x and y axes have been determined so that the coordinates of the points of intersection are integers.   The slopes of a number of lines through the origin are displayed.

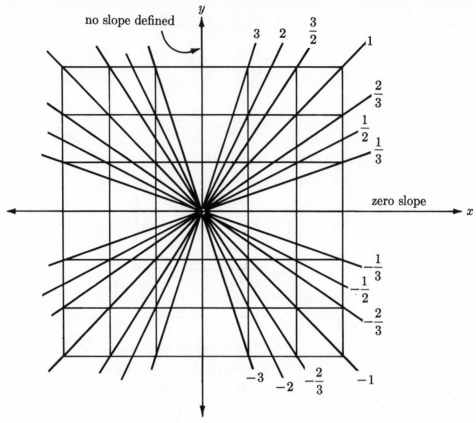

n. For the above diagram list, in pairs, the slopes that are reciprocals. These are the pairs $\left(\dfrac{a}{b}, \dfrac{b}{a}\right)$. Do the members of each pair have a common geometric property?

o. For the above diagram list, in pairs, the slopes that are negative reciprocals. These are the pairs $\left(\dfrac{a}{b}, -\dfrac{b}{a}\right)$. Do the members of each pair have a common geometric property?

ANSWERS TO EXERCISES

g. $\dfrac{6}{2} = 3.$ **h.** $\dfrac{6}{2} = 3.$ **i.** $\dfrac{6}{2} = 3.$ **j.** $\dfrac{9}{3} = 3.$ **k.** $\dfrac{-2}{\frac{4}{3}} = -\dfrac{3}{2}.$ **l.** $\dfrac{-2}{\frac{4}{3}} = -\dfrac{3}{2}.$ **m.** $\dfrac{2}{-\frac{4}{3}} =$

$-\dfrac{3}{2}.$ **n.** $3, \dfrac{1}{3}; 2, \dfrac{1}{2}; \dfrac{3}{2}, \dfrac{2}{3}; 1, 1.$ The lines with these slopes make equal angles with the line of

slope 1. $-3, -\dfrac{1}{3}; -2, -\dfrac{1}{2}; -\dfrac{2}{3}, -\dfrac{3}{2}; -1, -1.$ The lines with these slopes make equal

angles with the line of slope $-1.$ **o.** $3, -\dfrac{1}{3}; 2, -\dfrac{1}{2}; \dfrac{3}{2}, -\dfrac{2}{3}; 1, -1; \dfrac{2}{3}, -\dfrac{3}{2}; \dfrac{1}{2}, -2; \dfrac{1}{3},$

$-3.$ The lines with these slopes are perpendicular to each other.

Problems (163)

1. Construct two adjacent scales from which all of the following can be read directly, and give each result.

   a. $\dfrac{3}{5}\left(2\dfrac{1}{2}\right)$ **b.** $-\dfrac{6}{5}\left(2\dfrac{1}{2}\right)$ **c.** $\dfrac{3}{2\frac{1}{2}}$ **d.** $\dfrac{-1\frac{1}{2}}{2\frac{1}{2}}$

2. Construct two adjacent scales from which all of the following can be read directly, and give each result.

   a. $\left(3\dfrac{1}{2}\right)\left(-\dfrac{2}{3}\right)$ **b.** $(-3)\left(-\dfrac{2}{3}\right)$ **c.** $\dfrac{\frac{1}{3}}{-\frac{2}{3}}$ **d.** $\dfrac{-\frac{2}{3}}{-\frac{2}{3}}$

For problems 3 to 26, both the domain and range of the functions are to be sub-sets of $S = \{-4, -3, -2, -1, 0, 1, 2, 3, 4\}$. Construct the graph of each function, showing all ordered pairs $(n, f(n))$ that meet the above condition.

3. $f(n) = n - 1$ **9.** $f(n) = \dfrac{n}{3}$ **15.** $f(n) = n^2$ **21.** $f(n) = |\,n\,|$

4. $f(n) = n + 2$ **10.** $f(n) = \dfrac{n}{2}$ **16.** $f(n) = -n^2$ **22.** $f(n) = -\,|\,n\,|$

5. $f(n) = 2n$ **11.** $f(n) = -\dfrac{n}{3}$ **17.** $f(n) = 4 - n^2$ **23.** $f(n) = n(n - 1)$

6. $f(n) = 3n$ **12.** $f(n) = -\dfrac{n}{2}$ **18.** $f(n) = n^2 + 1$ **24.** $f(n) = \dfrac{n^2}{2}$

7. $f(n) = -2n$ **13.** $f(n) = 3 - n$ **19.** $f(n) = 2n - 1$ **25.** $f(n) = -1$
8. $f(n) = -3n$ **14.** $f(n) = 1 - n$ **20.** $f(n) = 3n - 2$ **26.** $f(n) = n(1 - n)$

For problems 27 to 38, both the domain and range of the relation are to be sub-sets of $S = \{-2, -1, 0, 1, 2\}$. Construct the graph of each relation showing all ordered pairs (x, y) that meet the above condition. The x axis is to be horizontal, and the y axis is vertical.

27. $y = x$ **30.** $y < x$ **33.** y is a divisor of x **36.** $y \geq x$
28. $y \neq x$ **31.** $y < 2 - x^2$ **34.** y is a multiple of x **37.** $y \leq x$

29. $y > x$ **32.** $y > x^2 - 2$ **35.** y is the opposite of x **38.** $y = \dfrac{1}{x}$

17-8. Vectors and Signed Numbers

In Section 10-5, when the operator $-\,5$ was joined to the operand 3 the resulting transform of $3 - 5$ was not defined at that time so that the vector model could not be completed. This restriction no longer holds, since vectors with their origin at zero and their terminal point to the left of zero can now be associated with negative integers and rational numbers.

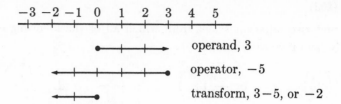

operand, 3

operator, −5

transform, 3−5, or −2

Since $m - n$ is now defined for all rational numbers m and n whether they are positive, negative, or zero, there is now no restriction on the operand m to which the subtraction operator $- n$ is to be joined. The expression $- m + n$ may be regarded either as the composite of the operator $- m$ and the operator $+ n$, or as the transform that results when the operator $+ n$ is joined to the operand (the signed number $- m$). The vector diagram will be the same in both cases except that vectors representing numbers are bound (initial point at zero) while the vectors representing addition and subtraction operators are free to translate as desired.

Example: Both diagrams show $-5 + 3 = -2$.

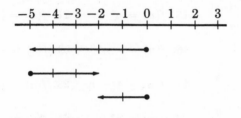

The vectors for the *numbers* −5 and −2 are bound to the origin.

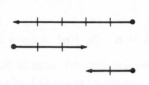

The vector diagram for the composition of the *operators* does not have a fixed position relative to the background scale.

Both interpretations are also possible for $+ m + n$, $+ m - n$, and $- m - n$. At times still a third interpretation is desired (still with the same vector diagram). Each of the expressions can also represent a binary operation on two signed numbers since

$$+ m + n = {}^{+}m + ({}^{+}n)$$
$$+ m - n = {}^{+}m + ({}^{-}n)$$
$$- m + n = {}^{-}m + ({}^{+}n)$$
$$\text{and} \quad - m - n = {}^{-}m + ({}^{-}n)$$

Recall that $+ m$ or ${}^{+}m$ was defined as the equivalence class $[m, 0]$, and that $- n$ or ${}^{-}n$ is the equivalence class $[0, n]$. Each member of an equivalence class $[a, b]$ can be associated with a vector whose initial point is at b and terminal point at a. For a given equivalence class $[a, b]$, the vectors for each ordered pair (a, b) will have the same length and the same direction.

Examples:

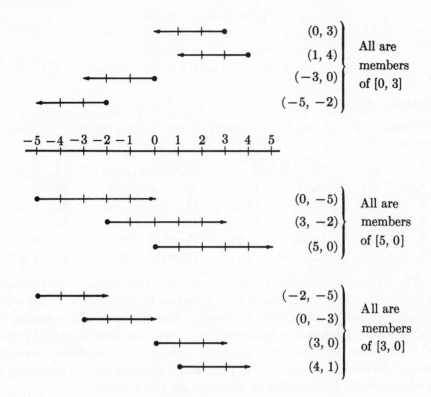

$$\left.\begin{array}{l} (0,\,3) \\ (1,\,4) \\ (-3,\,0) \\ (-5,\,-2) \end{array}\right\} \begin{array}{l} \text{All are} \\ \text{members} \\ \text{of } [0,\,3] \end{array}$$

$$\left.\begin{array}{l} (0,\,-5) \\ (3,\,-2) \\ (5,\,0) \end{array}\right\} \begin{array}{l} \text{All are} \\ \text{members} \\ \text{of } [5,\,0] \end{array}$$

$$\left.\begin{array}{l} (-2,\,-5) \\ (0,\,-3) \\ (3,\,0) \\ (4,\,1) \end{array}\right\} \begin{array}{l} \text{All are} \\ \text{members} \\ \text{of } [3,\,0] \end{array}$$

The forms $[x,\,0]$, $[0,\,0]$, and $[0,\,x]$ where x is positive have been chosen as the standard representatives for the equivalence classes, which define the rational numbers. This convention amounts to choosing only vectors, which are never to the left of zero and which have either their initial or their terminal point at zero. (Both the initial and the terminal point are at zero for the null or zero vector.) When vectors are used as a model for the binary operation of addition of rational numbers, the vectors used are selected as desired, corresponding to each equivalence class, as required by the following:

a. The vector for the first addend is selected with its initial point at zero.

b. The vector for the second addend is selected with its initial point at the terminal point at the first vector.

c. The vector sum is the vector whose initial point is that of the first vector and whose terminal point is that of the second vector.

The effect of the opposite operator $-1(\ )$ or $-(\ )$ on a vector, is that of reversal of direction (with no change in length). The difference $a - b$ of two rational numbers a and b has been defined as $a + (-b)$, or the sum of the a and the additive inverse of b. Hence to subtract the vector b from the vector a, change the direction of b before joining this vector to the vector for a.

$$^+m + (^+n) = + m + n = {^+m} - (^-n)$$
$$^+m + (^-n) = + m - n = {^+m} - (^+n)$$
$$^-m + (^+n) = - m + n = {^-m} - (^-n)$$
$$^-m + (^-n) = - m - n = {^-m} - (^+n)$$

Problems (164)

Construct vector diagrams for the following. Include the extended scale background.

1. $+6+2$	7. $-6-2$	13. $-6-(+2)$	19. $^+6+(^-2)$
2. $+1+4$	8. $-4-1$	14. $+1-(-4)$	20. $^-4+(^+1)$
3. $+6-2$	9. $+6-(+2)$	15. $-6-(-2)$	21. $^-6-(^-2)$
4. $-4+1$	10. $-4-(-1)$	16. $-1-(-4)$	22. $^-1+(^+4)$
5. $-6+2$	11. $+6-(-2)$	17. $^+6+(^+2)$	23. $^-6-(^+2)$
6. $-1+4$	12. $-4-(+1)$	18. $^+1+(^+4)$	24. $^-4+(^-1)$

The composite operator $-m(\ \ )$ authorizes two changes: magnification if $m > 1$, no change of magnitude if $m = 1$, and contraction if $m < 1$; and a change of sense (reversal of direction for a vector). With this in mind it is possible to extend to signed numbers the multiplication models that were developed in Section 9-3 for the ratio interpretation of products. The ratio of the product to one factor remains the same as the ratio of the other factor to 1, but now we must keep track of relative sense of orientation as well as relative magnitude.

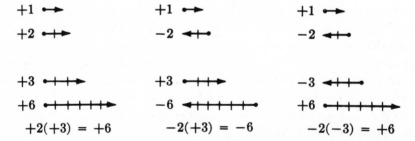

A study of the preceding diagrams indicates that the operators $+ m$ and $- m$ produce the same changes on an operand n as are required to transform $+ 1$ to $+ m$ or to $- m$, respectively. These changes are either changes of magnitude or sense, or both. Products of signed numbers can always be analyzed in this manner. Only occasionally do products of two or more signed numbers arise in applied problems in elementary mathematics. A more common situation is that of a single signed number within the reach of the operator $+ m(\ \ )$ or $- m(\ \ )$. The greatest use of the product rules for signs does not involve signed numbers at all, but arises in the extension of the distributive principle as developed in Section 17-1.

Problems (165)

Construct vector diagrams for the following:

1. $+1, +3, +5, +3(+5)$

2. $+1, +\frac{2}{3}, +6, +\frac{2}{3}(+6)$

3. $+1, +3, -5, +3(-5)$

4. $+1, +\frac{2}{3}, -6, +\frac{2}{3}(-6)$

5. $+1, -3, +5, -3(+5)$

6. $+1, -\frac{2}{3}, +6, -\frac{2}{3}(+6)$

7. $+1, -3, -5, -3(-5)$

8. $+1, -\frac{2}{3}, -6, -\frac{2}{3}(-6)$

For Further Study

In reference [G2], pp. 95–96, there is a suggestion for an analogy from which one can "infer" the laws of signs for manipulations of signed numbers. Although the author does not mention the concept of unary operations or operators in this connection, there are some interesting parallels to this point of view that can be noted.

There are a number of texts now available in which the integers are introduced through equivalence classes of ordered pairs: [A2], pp. 44–54; [B2], pp. 136–148; [D5], pp. 50–66; [D7], pp. 17–36; [F3], pp. 90–103; [H3], pp. 95–113; [K1], pp. 184–191; [W1], pp. 25–48; and [W7], pp. 63–71.

A discussion of various alternatives for the construction of the integers and the rational numbers appears in [C4], pp. 359–364.

Conceptual models for integers are not as readily available as for rational numbers. There are some novel suggestions in [S4], pp. 291–311.

18

Some Mathematical Systems

18-1. Some Structure for Mathematical Systems

By a mathematical system we shall mean a set of elements, together with one or more operations or relations defined on the set. Sometimes certain members of the set are identified as having unique properties. The construction of the mathematical system then proceeds by the introduction of definitions of concepts that prove useful, and by deducing theorems that follow from the assumed properties of the operations and relations. The system of natural numbers and zero and the system of nonnegative rational numbers are two examples of such systems. The first was developed to meet needs in counting problems, the second to meet needs in measuring. Both of these needs became so pressing as civilization developed that the properties of these numbers became known long before there was appreciation of them as constituting a mathematical system. The structure of mathematical systems becomes evident as we compare different systems and note properties that they have in common. For reference we list below the fundamental properties of several systems we have studied.

The system of the natural numbers and zero is a set N of elements $a, b, c, \ldots$, an equivalence relation (equality, symbolized by $=$), together with two binary operations, $+$ and $\cdot$, and a relation, $>$, which satisfy the following conditions:

Closure:
  If $a \in N$ and $b \in N$, then $a + b \in N$.
  If $a \in N$ and $b \in N$, then $a \cdot b \in N$.
Associativity:
  If $a \in N$, $b \in N$, and $c \in N$, then $(a + b) + c = a + (b + c)$.
  If $a \in N$, $b \in N$, and $c \in N$, then $(a \cdot b) \cdot c = a \cdot (b \cdot c)$.

Identity:
There is a unique number, 0, in N such that $a + 0 = 0 + a = a$, for every
    $a \in N$.
There exists a unique number, 1, in N such that $a \cdot 1 = 1 \cdot a = a$, for every
    $a \in N$.
Commutativity:
If $a \in N$ and $b \in N$, then $a + b = b + a$.
If $a \in N$ and $b \in N$, then $a \cdot b = b \cdot a$.
Distributivity:
If $a \in N$, $b \in N$, and $c \in N$, then $a \cdot (b + c) = a \cdot b + a \cdot c$.
Operations are well defined:
If $a \in N$, $b \in N$, $c \in N$, and $a = b$, then $c + a = c + b$.
If $a \in N$, $b \in N$, $c \in N$, and $a = b$, then $c \cdot a = c \cdot b$.
Cancellation:
If $a \in N$, $b \in N$, $c \in N$, and $c + a = c + b$, then $a = b$.
If $a \in N$, $b \in N$, $c \in N$, $c \neq 0$, and $ca = cb$, then $a = b$.
    Note: The distributive, well-defined, and cancellation properties have been
        stated only on the left.   The corresponding properties on the right
        follow from the commutative property.
Trichotomy:
If $a \in N$, and $b \in N$, then exactly one of the following is true: $a = b$, or there
exists an $x \in N$, $x \neq 0$, such that $a + x = b$ and we write $a < b$ or $b > a$, or
there exists a $y \in N$, $y \neq 0$, such that $a = b + y$, and we write $a > b$ or $b < a$.
Finite Induction:
If S is a set that contains 0 and 1, and that contains $k + 1$ whenever it con-
tains the natural number k, then S contains all of N.

All of the above have been discussed in some detail and used in establishing
other properties of the natural numbers and zero, except for the final one.   This
principle was mentioned, without naming it, in Section 8-8 in the discussion of the
"successor" ordering of the natural numbers.

The system of nonnegative rationals is a set R of elements $x, y, z, \ldots$, subject
to all the conditions above (stated in terms of R) except the principle of induction,
together with the following property.

Multiplicative Inverse:
If $x \in R$, and $x \neq 0$, then there exists a unique element $y \in R$ such that
$x \cdot y = 1$.

It was shown in Chapters 11 to 17 how such a system could be constructed
from equivalence classes of ordered pairs of elements taken from the set of zero and
the natural numbers.   The notation used was $\frac{a}{b}$, where a was any element of the set
of zero and the natural numbers, but b was restricted to the natural numbers.
Because of the isomorphism $\frac{a}{1} \leftrightarrow a$, it was possible to identify $\frac{a}{1}$ with a, thus making

the set of zero and the natural numbers a subset of the nonnegative rationals. In particular, $\dfrac{0}{1} = 0$, and $\dfrac{1}{1} = 1$. In the statement of the multiplicative inverse, if $x = \dfrac{a}{b}$ and $x \neq 0$, then both $a \neq 0$, and $b \neq 0$, and $y = \dfrac{b}{a}$. That is, $\left(\dfrac{a}{b}\right)\left(\dfrac{b}{a}\right) = 1$.

The existence of the multiplicative inverse makes it possible to omit the cancellation property of multiplication from the basic list of properties of the rational numbers if desired, since if the former is assumed the latter follows as a theorem.

Suppose $x \in R$, $y \in R$, $z \in R$ but $z \neq 0$, and $x \cdot z = y \cdot z$.

Assume that z has a multiplicative inverse, which we may call z^*, so that $z \cdot z^* = 1$.

Since multiplication is well defined and associative, and 1 is the identity for multiplication we have,

$$(x \cdot z) \cdot z^* = (y \cdot z) \cdot z^*, \qquad x \cdot (z \cdot z^*) = y \cdot (z \cdot z^*), \qquad x \cdot 1 = y \cdot 1, \qquad \text{and } x = y$$

The system of integers is a set I of elements, $r, s, t, \ldots$, subject to all the conditions stated for zero and the natural numbers, except for a modification of the trichotomy principle and the exclusion of the principle of induction, together with the following property.

Additive Inverse:

If $r \in I$, then there exists a unique number $s \in I$ such that $r + s = 0$.

It was shown in Chapter 17 how such a system could be constructed from equivalence classes of ordered pairs of elements taken from the set of zero and the natural numbers. These equivalence classes separate into three types symbolized by ^+n, 0, and ^-n. Because of the isomorphism $^+n \leftrightarrow n$ it was possible to identify ^+n with n, thus making the natural numbers a subset of the integers. The pairs ^+n and ^-n, or 0 and 0, are additive inverses.

For the integers the trichotomy principle becomes as follows. If $r \in I$ and $s \in I$, then exactly one of the following is true: $r = s$, or there exists a positive integer ^+m such that $r + {}^+m = s$ or $s - r = {}^+m$ and we write $r < s$, or there exists a positive integer ^+n such that $r = s + {}^+n$ or $r - s = {}^+n$ and we write $r > s$. Since $r - s = -(s - r)$ there is another way to state the trichotomy principle. The positive elements ^+n of I form a distinguished subset P of I. For all $r \in I$ exactly one of these is true: $r = 0$, or $r \in P$, or $-r \in P$. Furthermore, P is closed for addition and multiplication so that if $r \in P$ and $s \in P$, then $r + s \in P$ and $rs \in P$.

a. Show that the existence of an additive inverse implies that the cancellation property of addition must always hold.

The system of rational numbers has all the properties common to the three systems above together with both additive inverses and multiplicative inverses for nonzero elements. The trichotomy principle is changed only by replacing "positive integer" by "positive rational number." It is an example of a mathematical system called an *ordered field*.

A full discussion of mathematical systems is properly a part of the study of algebra and cannot be given here. In particular, we must omit consideration of such important questions as to the extent to which the above assumptions define these systems *uniquely*. Two possibilities exist. One is that there be systems isomorphic to the above so that they differ essentially only in the names of the elements, operations, and relations. The other possibility is of systems that agree in the above properties but differ in still others.

We shall discuss a few of the many systems where some combination of part of these properties hold. Sometimes the definition of a binary operation on a set includes the requirement that the operation be closed on the set. From this point of view the systems with a minimum amount of structure would consist of a set of elements on which an operation has been defined. Such a system is known as a *groupoid*. As an example, let the set be the set I of all integers (positive, negative, and zero). The operation of subtraction is always defined on this set. This groupoid is not associative, since if a, b, and c are integers, it is not always true that $a - (b - c) = (a - b) - c$. It is also not commutative, since it is not always true that $a - b = b - a$. And there is no identity for this groupoid, since while $a - 0 = a$, it is not always true that $0 - a = a$. Since there is no identity, there can be no inverses.

b. If a, b, and c are integers, for what a, b, and c, if any, does $a - (b - c)$ $= (a - b) - c$?

c. If a and b are integers, for what a and b, if any, does $a - b = b - a$?

d. If a is an integer, for what a, if any, does $0 - a = a$?

Suppose we require that the operation defined on the set is associative. Such a groupoid is then known as a *semigroup*. A semigroup can be obtained from the set of all mappings of a set into itself, by taking the composition of these mappings as the operation for the system.

> **Example:** Let $P = \{a, b\}$. All of the possible mappings $P \rightarrow P$ are given below, and designated as α (alpha), β (beta), γ (gamma), and δ (delta). (The arrowheads used in Section 8-7 are omitted for simplicity.)

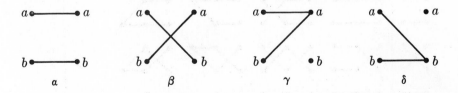

> The composition $x \circ y$ of a first mapping x and a second mapping y can be illustrated by the joining of the diagrams in the same left-to-right order. The operation of composition is not commutative. (In the first composition both a and b map to b, in the second they both map to a.)

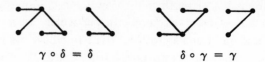

$$\gamma \circ \delta = \delta \qquad\qquad \delta \circ \gamma = \gamma$$

However, this operation is associative on this set of mappings.

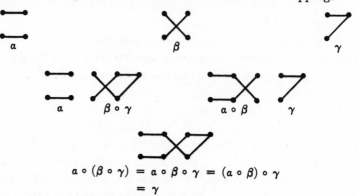

$$a \circ (\beta \circ \gamma) = a \circ \beta \circ \gamma = (a \circ \beta) \circ \gamma$$
$$= \gamma$$

Associativity requires that $x \circ (y \circ z) = (x \circ y) \circ z$ for each choice of x, y, and z from the set. We have only verified one of the 4^3 or 64 different cases. The reader should verify some other cases.

It is conventional in the study of mathematical systems to call all unusual binary operations by the common name of "multiplication." If the number of elements is small, all the possible "products" from applying the operation can be listed in a "multiplication" table. The table below is repeated, first using diagrams, and then the Greek letter names of the mappings. The composition $x \circ y$ appears at the intersection of the row designated as x, and the column designated as y.

$$S = \{\alpha, \beta, \gamma, \delta\}.$$

$\circ$	α	β	γ	δ
α	α	β	γ	δ
β	β	α	γ	δ
γ	γ	δ	γ	δ
δ	δ	γ	γ	δ

This semigroup is a *finite* mathematical system. The table shows a complete list of all 4^2 or 16 possibilities for the binary composition $x \circ y$ where x and y are members of $S = \{\alpha, \beta, \gamma, \delta\}$. Each entry in the table is one, and only one, member of the set. This shows that the operation is closed and well defined on the set.

For every $x \in S$, we have $x \circ \alpha = x$. This is shown in the table by the α column (the first) being identical to the side heading of the table, which lists the elements in turn. Also for every $x \in S$, we have $\alpha \circ x = x$. This is shown in the table by the α row (the first) being identical to the heading at the top of the table. Hence α is both a right and a left identity, or an identity, for the semigroup.

e. Is there another identity besides α for the system?

Not every element has an inverse. Thus there is no x where $x \in S$ such that $\gamma \circ x = \alpha$. If every element did have an inverse, the identity α would appear in each row and each column of the table. If this inverse were unique, it would appear exactly once in each row and each column.

f. What is the inverse element for α? for β? for δ?

Since $\gamma \circ \beta = \delta$ and $\gamma \circ \delta = \delta$ we have $\gamma \circ \beta = \gamma \circ \delta$. But $\beta \neq \delta$. Therefore the cancellation law fails.

As an example of a semigroup that does not have an identity we might take the set of natural numbers and the operation of addition. Addition is a closed associative operation on this set as required for a semigroup, but there is no identity, since zero is not a member of the set.

For the next example of a mathematical system, assume that the semigroup has both a unique identity, and a unique inverse for each element. This system is known as a *group*, and as the simple name suggests, was one of the first mathematical structures to be formulated. Our first two examples will be of *infinite* groups, that is, of groups with an infinite number of members in the set.

> **Example:** Let n be a variable whose range is the set of natural numbers, and consider the set S_1, which consists of all operators of the form $+ n$ or $- n$, together with the operator $+ 0$.
>
> $$S_1 = \{+ 0, + 1, - 1, + 2, - 2, + 3, - 3, \ldots\}$$
>
> The group operation is to be the composition of these operators. Since this is an infinite group, the table can only be suggestive of the properties that need to hold in general.

$\circ$	$+ 0$	$+ 1$	$- 1$	$+ 2$	$- 2$	$\cdot$
$+ 0$	$+ 0$	$+ 1$	$- 1$	$+ 2$	$- 2$	$\cdot$
$+ 1$	$+ 1$	$+ 2$	$+ 0$	$+ 3$	$- 1$	$\cdot$
$- 1$	$- 1$	$+ 0$	$- 2$	$+ 1$	$- 3$	$\cdot$
$+ 2$	$+ 2$	$+ 3$	$+ 1$	$+ 4$	$+ 0$	$\cdot$
$- 2$	$- 2$	$- 1$	$- 3$	$+ 0$	$- 4$	$\cdot$
$\cdot$	$\cdot$	$\cdot$	$\cdot$	$\cdot$	$\cdot$	$\cdot$

Return to the comments for the previous table on what must be true about a group table (closure, associative, identity, inverse). The operator $+0$ is the identity, and $+n$ and $-n$ are inverse pairs except that $+0$ is its own inverse. The operator -0 is not included in the set because we want the identity to be unique.

We cannot possibly check all cases needed to verify the associative property. But we can obtain some help here from the following isomorphism. Let $+0$ correspond to 0, $+n$ to ^+n, and $-n$ to ^-n. In other words, rename S_1 as being the set of integers. Then let $(-m) \circ (-n)$ correspond to $^-m + ^-n$. From this point of view we have the *additive group of the integers*. Since the addition of integers is known to be associative, we can infer that the composition of addition and subtraction operators is also associative.

Example: Let x be a variable whose range is the set of nonzero rational numbers, and consider the set S_2 ,which consists of all operators of the form $x(\ )$.

$$S_2 = \{1(\ ), -1(\ ), 2(\ ), -2(\ ), \tfrac{1}{2}(\ ), -\tfrac{1}{2}(\ ), \ldots\}$$

The group operation is again that of composition of these operators.

$\circ$	$1(\ )$	$-1(\ )$	$2(\ )$	$-2(\ )$	$\tfrac{1}{2}(\ )$	$-\tfrac{1}{2}(\ )$	$\cdot$
$1(\ )$	$1(\ )$	$-1(\ )$	$2(\ )$	$-2(\ )$	$\tfrac{1}{2}(\ )$	$-\tfrac{1}{2}(\ )$	$\cdot$
$-1(\ )$	$-1(\ )$	$1(\ )$	$-2(\ )$	$2(\ )$	$-\tfrac{1}{2}(\ )$	$\tfrac{1}{2}(\ )$	$\cdot$
$2(\ )$	$2(\ )$	$-2(\ )$	$4(\ )$	$-4(\ )$	$1(\ )$	$-1(\ )$	$\cdot$
$-2(\ )$	$-2(\ )$	$2(\ )$	$-4(\ )$	$4(\ )$	$-1(\ )$	$1(\ )$	$\cdot$
$\tfrac{1}{2}(\ )$	$\tfrac{1}{2}(\ )$	$-\tfrac{1}{2}(\ )$	$1(\ )$	$-1(\ )$	$\tfrac{1}{4}(\ )$	$-\tfrac{1}{4}(\ )$	$\cdot$
$-\tfrac{1}{2}(\ )$	$-\tfrac{1}{2}(\ )$	$\tfrac{1}{2}(\ )$	$-1(\ )$	$1(\ )$	$-\tfrac{1}{4}(\ )$	$\tfrac{1}{4}(\ )$	$\cdot$
$\cdot$	$\cdot$	$\cdot$	$\cdot$	$\cdot$	$\cdot$	$\cdot$	

The operator $1(\ )$ is the identity. The inverse pairs of elements are $\dfrac{a}{b}(\ )$ and $\dfrac{b}{a}(\ )$, both of which carry the same sign.

g. Do you see why the operator $0(\ )$ must be excluded from S_2?

There is again an opportunity to establish an important isomorphism. S_2' is

to be the set of nonzero ration-
als, by setting $\frac{a}{b}(\ ) \leftrightarrow \frac{a}{b}$.

·	1	− 1	2	− 2	$\frac{1}{2}$	$-\frac{1}{2}$	·
1	1	− 1	2	− 2	$\frac{1}{2}$	$-\frac{1}{2}$	·
− 1	− 1	1	− 2	2	$-\frac{1}{2}$	$\frac{1}{2}$	·
2	2	− 2	4	− 4	1	− 1	·
·	·	·	·	·	·	·	·

Let the group operation for S_2' be multiplication.

This gives us the multiplicative group for nonzero rational numbers. The additive group for the integers could also be extended to the rationals.

A number of analogies between signed numbers and operators have already been discussed and mention made of the usefulness of the operator concept both in computation and applications. The possibilities for identification of these two concepts arises from the two pairs of isomorphic groups given above.

A counter-example may be mentioned of a set of mathematical objects that is of reduced interest because of lack of structure for the set. In the expressions $a + b$, $a - b$, $a \times b$, and $a \div b$, the symbols $+$, $-$, $\times$ and $\div$ may be termed *binary opera-tors*. But the set $\{+, -, \times, \div\}$ seems to lack operations on or relations among its members. One can form the union of two of them, and write $a \pm b$ for "a plus b or a minus b" but this method of combination has not been found useful for other pairs. Until some sort of structure has been formulated for this set, the mathematical interest of its members will rest upon them as individuals but not as members of a system of operators.

Answers to Exercises

a. Assume z has an additive inverse z^*. Then $z + z^* = 0$. Then if $x + z = y + z$, $(x + z) + z^* = (y + z) + z^*$, $x + (z + z^*) = y + (z + z^*)$, $x + 0 = y + 0$, $x = y$. **b.** All a and b, $c = 0$. **c.** $a = b$. **d.** $a = 0$. **e.** No. **f.** α; β; there is none. **g.** It has no inverse.

Problems (166)

Just as multiplication has been used as a general name for binary operations, the symbol ○ will be used as a general symbol, and given a special definition for the occasion.

1. Let $x \circ y$ be symbolized by $\underline{xy}$, as a binary operation on set S.
   a. Write (as an equation) the condition that this operation be commutative.
   b. Write the condition that the operation be associative. Observe that the notation provides its own parentheses.
   c. Write the conditions that e be an identity for the operation.
   d. If e be an identity, write the conditions that each element have an inverse.
   e. Write the condition that the operation be well defined with respect to equality.
   f. Write the condition that the cancellation laws hold for the operation.

2. Follow the directions for problem 1, if the operation $x \circ y$ as defined on a set S, is symbolized by $\boxed{xy}$.

3. The condition that a first binary operation, represented by $x * y$, be left distributive with respect to a second binary operation, represented by $x \, \Delta \, y$, is that $x * (y \, \Delta \, z) = (x * y) \, \Delta \, (x * z)$. The condition that the operation represented by $x \, \Delta \, y$ be left distributive with respect to the operation represented by $x * y$ is that $x \, \Delta \, (y * z) = (x \, \Delta \, y) * (x \, \Delta \, z)$.

   a. Write the condition that the operation represented by $x * y$ be right distributive with respect to the operation represented by $x \, \Delta \, y$.

   b. Follow the directions for a., if the first operation is represented by $x \, \Delta \, y$, and the second by $x * y$.

   c. Write the condition that the operation represented by $\underline{xy}$ be left distributive for the operation represented by $\boxed{xy}$.

   d. Follow the directions for c. for right distributive.

   e. Write the condition that the operation represented by $\boxed{xy}$ be left distributive for the operation represented by $\underline{xy}$.

   f. Follow the directions for e. for right distributive.

   g. Write the conditions that the operation represented by $\boxed{xy}$ be distributive with respect to itself.

4. Let two operations on a set S be symbolized by $x \, || \, y$ and $\overline{xy}$. Complete the following conditions so that a distributive law holds.

   a. $x \, || \, \overline{yz} = ?$ c. $\overline{x \, (y \, || \, z)} = ?$ e. $\overline{x} \, \overline{yz} = ?$ g. $x \, || \, (y \, || \, z) = ?$

   b. $\overline{yz} \, || \, x = ?$ d. $\overline{(y \, || \, z)x} = ?$ f. $\overline{yz} \, \overline{x} = ?$ h. $(y \, || \, z) \, || \, x = ?$

5. Let $x \circ y$ be defined on the set S consisting of zero and the natural numbers, by $x \circ y = y$.

   a. Is this operation closed on S?   b. Is this a commutative operation?
   c. Is this an associative operation?   d. Is there an identity for this operation?
   e. If the answer to d. is yes, does each operation have an inverse?   f. Does cancellation on the left hold?   g. Does cancellation on the right hold?

6. Follow the directions for problem 5, if the operation defined on the set S is such that $x \circ y$ is the l.c.m. of x and y, and S is the set of natural numbers.

7. Follow the directions for problem 5, if the operation defined on the set S is given by $x \circ y = \dfrac{x + y}{2}$, and S is the set of nonnegative rationals.

8. Follow the directions for problem 5, if the operation defined on the set S is such that $x \circ y$ is x if $x = y$, and is the larger of x and y if $x \neq y$. Let S be the set of zero and the natural numbers.

9. Follow the directions for problem 5, if the operation defined on the set S is $x \circ y = x + 2y$, and S is the set of zero and the natural numbers.

10. Follow the directions for problem 5, if the operation defined on the set S is $x \circ y = |x + y|$, and S is the set of integers.

11. An operation on $S = \{a, b, c\}$ is defined by Table 1. It can be verified that the operation is associative so that the system is a semi-group.

Table 1

$\circ$	a	b	c
a	a	b	c
b	b	c	a
c	c	a	b

  a. Is the operation commutative?

  b. Is there an element y such that both $y \circ x = x$ and $x \circ y = x$, for all $x \in S$?

  c. Is there an element y such that both $y \circ x = y$ and $x \circ y = y$, for all $x \in S$?

  d. If possible, give an example where the following *fails* to hold. If $x \circ y = x \circ z$, then $y = z$.

  e. If possible, give an example where the following *fails* to hold. If $x \circ y = z \circ y$, then $x = z$.

  f. Is there an inverse for a? b? c?

  g. Is this system a group?

Table 2

$\circ$	a	b	c
a	a	a	a
b	a	b	c
c	a	c	a

12. Follow the directions for problem 11, using Table 2.

13. Let f and g be functions of a single variable, and define the composite function $f \circ g$ by $(f \circ g)(x) = f[g(x)]$ (see Section 10-4). For example if $f(x) = x^2$ and $g(x) = x - 1$, then $(f \circ g)(x) = f[x - 1] = (x - 1)^2$, and $(g \circ f)(x) = g[x^2] = x^2 - 1$. Let $S = \{f_1, f_2, f_3, f_4\}$, where $f_1(x) = x$, $f_2(x) = -x$, $f_3(x) = \dfrac{1}{x}$, and $f_4(x) = -\dfrac{1}{x}$, and let the operation be defined as above. Make entries in the table and answer these questions:

$\circ$	f_1	f_2	f_3	f_4
f_1				
f_2				
f_3				
f_4				

  a. Is the operation well defined?

  b. Is the operation closed on the set?

  c. Is there an identity?   **f.** Is the operation associative?

  d. Does each element have an inverse?   **g.** Do the cancellation laws hold?

  e. Is the operation commutative?   **h.** Is the system a group?

14. $S = \{a, b, c, d\}$. The first row and first column of the table have been entered so that a is an identity for $x \circ y$. What must be true in the table if:

$\circ$	a	b	c	d
a	a	b	c	d
b	b			
c	c			
d	d			

  a. $x \circ y$ is closed?

  b. $x \circ y$ is well defined?

  c. Each element has an inverse?

  d. This inverse is unique?

  e. $x \circ y$ is commutative?

  f. Cancellation on the left holds?   **g.** Cancellation on the right holds?

Complete the table so that all conditions hold. (There are just four ways to complete the table so that all the above conditions hold. All these systems are associative and therefore are groups, three of which are isomorphic.)

18-2. Divisibility of Integers

In this section we return to the set I of integers, to develop some tools for the further study of mathematical systems. To avoid being led too far afield, some basic theorems will be assumed without proof. They will be verified by example, but this leaves open the question whether the results would have been so fortunate if other choices of examples had been made. When statements that are to apply to all members of a system are to be justified, it is clear that the arguments must rest on the fundamental assumptions that characterize that system. One of the reasons for showing how the integers and the rational numbers can be constructed from the natural numbers is to make possible a chain of proofs that begin with the properties of the natural numbers. One of these, the finite induction principle, is of primary importance, since by its use an argument can begin with a statement about the number 1, then move to a statement about the successor of 1, and thus finally apply to "all the natural numbers." Such proofs, with full details, can be found in texts for the branch of mathematics known as the Theory of Numbers.

The statements made in Chapters 3 to 5 about the multiplicative structure of the natural numbers must be revised if they are to extend to the integers. *An integer a is said to be divisible by a nonzero integer b if there exists an integer c such that $a = bc$.* In this case we also say that b divides a and the relation $b \, R \, a$ where R represents "divides" may be written as $b \mid a$. If b does not divide a, we write $b \nmid a$. We also say that b is a divisor of a, and if $1 \leq b < a$, then b is a *proper* divisor of a.

If $b \mid a$, then a is a *multiple* of b. Let b be any integer, then the multiples of b are

$$0, \pm b, \pm 2b, \pm 3b, \ldots$$

that is, all numbers of the form kb where k is an integer. The two numbers $+b$ and $-b$, which are additive inverses and which have the same absolute value, are called *associates* when b is an integer. The definition of associates is usually given in this form: a and b are associates if both $a \mid b$ and $b \mid a$.

If $a \mid b$ and $b \mid a$ then by definition there exist integers c and d, such that $a = bc$, and $b = ad$, and hence $a = adc$.

By the cancellation law for multiplication, $dc = 1$, and hence d is 1 or -1 and c is 1 or -1.

Thus the only associates of a are a and $-a$, and of b are b and $-b$.

The equation $a = bc$, where b and c and hence a are integers, also reveals that both b and c are factors of a and is said to give a factorization of a. If $a = bc$ there is also the factorization $a = (-b)(-c)$, and for any integer a we have $a = 1 \cdot a$ and also $a = (-1) \cdot (-a)$.

If p is an integer greater than 1 whose only positive divisors are 1 and p itself, then p is a prime. This definition restricts the term prime to positive numbers. When necessary it can be extended by designating $-2, -3, -5, \ldots$ as *negative primes*. An integer greater than 1 that is not a prime is said to be composite.

Problems (167)

1. List all the integer divisors of 12.
2. List all the integer divisors of a prime p.

Proofs are to be given for the following, all of which follow directly from the definition of divisibility.   They should be compared with those given in Section 4-6 for the natural numbers.

3. If ha and ka are two multiples of an integer a, their sum is a multiple of a.
4. If ha and ka are two multiples of an integer a, their difference is a multiple of a.
5. If ha and ka are two multiples of an integer a, their product is a multiple of a.
6. If c_1 or ab_1 and c_2 or ab_2 are two numbers that are divisible by a, their sum is divisible by a.
7. If c_1 or ab_1 and c_2 or ab_2 are two numbers that are divisible by a, their difference is divisible by a.
8. If c_1 or ab_1 and c_2 or ab_2 are two numbers that are divisible by a, their product is divisible by a.
9. If $a \mid b$ then $a \mid bc$ for any integer c.
10. The relation "divides" is reflexive.
11. The relation "divides" is transitive.
12. The relation "divides" is antisymmetric, when a and b are positive.
13. The relation "divides" is a partial ordering, when a and b are positive.
14. If $a \mid b$, $a > 0$, and $b > 0$, then $a \leq b$.
15. If $a \mid b$ and $a \mid c$, then $a \mid (bx + cy)$ for any integers x and y.
16. If $a \neq 0$, then $a \mid 0$.
17. $1 \mid b$ and $-1 \mid b$ for all b.
18. If $a \mid b$, then $ma \mid mb$ for any nonzero integer m.
19. If $a \mid b$ and $a + b = c$, then $a \mid c$.
20. If $a \mid c$ and $a + b = c$, then $a \mid b$.
21. If $m \mid (15n + 13)$, and $m \mid (3n + 2)$, and $m > 1$, prove that $m = 3$.
22. If $m \mid (6n + 5)$, and $m \mid (4n + 3)$, prove that $m = \pm 1$.

For all rational numbers a and b we have $|ab| = |a| \cdot |b|$ as can be seen from consideration of the following possible cases:

Since $|0| = 0$, then $|ab| = |a| \cdot |b|$, if either $a = 0$, or $b = 0$, or both equal zero.

If $a > 0$ and $b > 0$,
   then $|a| = a, |b| = b, ab > 0, |ab| = ab = (a)(b) = |a| \cdot |b|$.

If $a > 0$ and $b < 0$,
   then $|a| = a, |b| = -b, ab < 0, |ab| = -(ab) = (a)(-b) = |a| \cdot |b|$.

If $a < 0$ and $b > 0$,

then $|a| = -a, |b| = b, ab < 0, |ab| = -(ab) = (-a)(b) = |a| \cdot |b|$.

If $a < 0$ and $b < 0$,

then $|a| = -a, |b| = -b, ab > 0, |ab| = ab = (-a)(-b) = |a| \cdot |b|$.

We can now show that if $a \neq 0$ and $c \mid a$, then $|c| \leq |a|$. For if $c \mid a$, then an integer k exists such that $ck = a$. But if $a \neq 0$, then $k \neq 0$. From above we have $|ck| = |c| \cdot |k|$. But since $k \neq 0$, then $|k| \geq 1$ and $|c| \leq |ck|$. Therefore $|c| \leq |a|$.

If a and b are positive and $a \mid b$ and $b \mid a$, then $a = b$. From the above we have $|a| \leq |b|$ and $|b| \leq |a|$. Since $a > 0$ and $b > 0$, the absolute value bars may be omitted and $a \leq b \leq a$. But this holds only when $a = b$. [See also problem 12 in set (167).]

Let a and b be any two integers, with not both zero. If c is an integer such that $c \mid a$ and $c \mid b$, then c is said to be a *common divisor* of a and b. Since every number is divisible by 1, there exists a common divisor c of a and b such that $c \geq 1$. But no common divisor c of a and b can be larger than the smaller of $|a|$ and $|b|$, since $|c| \leq |a|$ and $|c| \leq |b|$. From this finite set of common divisors of a and b the largest (which is certainly positive) is selected and termed the *greatest common divisor* (g.c.d.) of a and b.

The notation (a, b) is often used for the g.c.d. of a and b, in discussions where other uses of this symbol are not likely to arise. If $(a, b) = 1$, then a and b are said to be *relatively prime*. In this case the only common divisors of a and b are $+1$ and -1.

   a. To what integers are $+1$ and -1 relatively prime?
   b. Give a reason for not allowing both a and b to be zero in the definition of common divisor.
   c. To what integers is zero relatively prime?
   d. If p is a prime, to what integers is p relatively prime?

If a, b, m, and n are integers, the sum $ma + nb$ is called a *linear combination* of a and b (and also of m and n). Problem 15 in set (167) can now be restated as:

If $a \mid b$ and $a \mid c$, then a divides any linear combination of b and c.

The following theorem always holds:

Let a and b be any two integers such that $b \neq 0$. Then there are unique integers q and r for which $0 \leq r < |b|$ and such that

$$a = qb + r$$

In problem sets (21) and (22) q and r were to be found where a and b were from the set of natural numbers and zero, and in problem set (160) a and b were integers. The dividend a is thus expressed as a linear combination of the divisor b and the remainder r. Hence any common divisor of the divisor and the remainder is a divisor of the dividend.   But if $a = qb + r$, then $r = a - qb$.   The remainder r is now a linear combination of the dividend and the divisor so that any common divisor of the dividend and the divisor is a divisor of the remainder.   *Thus the common factors of dividend and divisor are always the same as those of divisor and remainder.*   The above conclusions should be checked out in the following example, which shows how the division algorithm can be used repeatedly as a method of computing the g.c.d. of two integers.

> **Example:** $(24, 90) = d$.   As a step in determining d, we use the integer with the largest absolute value as the dividend in the division algorithm. Then
>
> $$90 = (3)(24) + 18 \qquad \text{and} \qquad 18 = 90 - (3)(24)$$
>
> Any common divisor of 24 and 18 is a divisor of 90.
> Any common divisor of 24 and 90 is a divisor of 18.
> Hence any common divisor of 24 and 90 is also a common divisor of 24 and 18.
> We began our search for d knowing that $1 \le d \le 24$.   We now know that $1 \le d \le 18$, and can repeat the above step with a smaller pair of numbers, the divisor 24 and the remainder 18.
>
> $$24 = 1(18) + 6 \qquad \text{and} \qquad 6 = 24 - 1(18)$$
>
> We can now observe that $1 \le d \le 6$, since any common factor of 24 and 18 (or from above, of 24 and 90), is also a common factor of 18 and 6. At the next division, the remainder turns out to be zero.
>
> $$18 = 3(6)$$
>
> Hence $d = 6$, since $6 = (6, 18) = (18, 24) = (24, 90)$.
> Here are two suggested ways of arranging the computation:

A.

```
            3
     24 │  90
          72    1
          18 │  24
              18    3
               6 │  18
                    6
```

B.

	3	1	3
6	18	24	90
	18	18	72
0	6	18

$(24, 90) = 6$

Form **B** is suggested for recording the results of machine calculation.

The repeated use of the division algorithm to determine the g.c.d. of two numbers is called Euclid's Algorithm.   Euclid gave the method in geometrical terms in Book VII of the famous *Elements*.   Since $(a, b) = (-a, b) = (a, -b) = (-a, -b)$ the computation can be restricted to positive integers.   The next example illustrates the case where a and b are relatively prime.

Example: $(37, 127) = 1$

	5	3	2	3
1	5	16	37	127
	5	15	32	111
	0	1	5	16

$$127 = 3 \cdot 37 + 16$$
$$37 = 2 \cdot 16 + 5$$
$$16 = 3 \cdot 5 + 1$$
$$5 = 5 \cdot 1$$

$$a = q_1 b + r_1$$
$$b = q_2 r_1 + r_2$$
$$r_1 = q_3 r_2 + r_3$$
$$\cdots \cdots \cdots$$
$$r_{n-1} = q_{n+1} r_n$$

$$a \geq b > r_1 > r_2 > \cdots > r_n \geq 1,$$
$$\text{with } r_{n+1} = 0$$

$$(a, b) = r_n$$

By using the next to the last equation, the g.c.d., which is 1, can be expressed as a linear combination of 16 and 3. By solving for each remainder in turn, and substituting, it is possible to represent (a, b) as a linear combination of a and b. The remainders and the given numbers are underlined to help keep track of them.

$$1 = 16 - 3 \cdot 5$$
$$5 = 37 - 2 \cdot 16$$
$$16 = 127 - 3 \cdot 37$$

$$1 = \underline{16} - 3 \cdot \underline{5}$$
$$= \underline{16} - 3(\underline{37} - 2 \cdot \underline{16}) = \underline{16} - 3 \cdot \underline{37} + 6 \cdot \underline{16}$$
$$= 7 \cdot \underline{16} - 3 \cdot \underline{37} = 7 \cdot (\underline{127} - 3 \cdot \underline{37}) - 3 \cdot \underline{37} = 7 \cdot \underline{127} - 21 \cdot \underline{37} - 3 \cdot \underline{37}$$
$$= 7 \cdot \underline{127} - 24 \cdot \underline{37}$$

This representation is not unique. For example,

$$1 = (7 + 37) \cdot 127 - (24 + 127) \cdot 37$$
$$= 44 \cdot 127 - 151 \cdot 37$$

Note that the above change was made by adding $37 \cdot 127$, and subtracting $127 \cdot 37$.

The following theorem always holds: *The g.c.d. of two integers a and b is the least positive linear combination $ma + nb$ of a and b.* To adapt the above method of obtaining m and n, to the case where a and b are not relatively prime, we first divide both a and b by (a, b). Thus for the first example where $a = 90$ and $b = 24$, we have:

$$(24, 90) = 6 \qquad \frac{90}{6} = 15, \frac{24}{6} = 4 \qquad 15 = 3 \cdot 4 + 3 \qquad 3 = \underline{15} - 3 \cdot \underline{4}$$
$$4 = 1 \cdot 3 + 1 \qquad 1 = \underline{4} - 1 \cdot \underline{3}$$

$$1 = \underline{4} - 1 \cdot \underline{3} = \underline{4} - 1(\underline{15} - 3 \cdot \underline{4}) = \underline{4} - 1 \cdot \underline{15} + 3 \cdot \underline{4} = 4 \cdot 4 - 1 \cdot \underline{15}$$

$$1 = 4 \cdot 4 - 1 \cdot 15 \qquad 6 = 4 \cdot 4 \cdot 6 - 1 \cdot 15 \cdot 6 \qquad 6 = 4 \cdot 24 - 1 \cdot 90$$

ANSWERS TO EXERCISES

a. To every integer. **b.** a and b would have every integer as a common divisor, and the g.c.d. would not exist. **c.** Only to $+1$ and -1. **d.** To all nonzero integers that do not have p as a factor.

Problems (168)

1. Prove that $|a + b| \leq |a| + |b|$.

2. Let $S = \{1, 2, 3, 4, 5, 6, 7, 8, 9\}$. Arrange the members of S in the diagram so that:

$$P = \{x \mid x \in S \text{ and } (x, 2) = 1\},$$
$$Q = \{x \mid x \in S \text{ and } (x, 3) = 1\}.$$

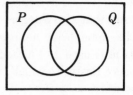

For problems 3 to 10, compute (a, b) and express (a, b) as a linear combination of a and b in two ways.

3. $a = 9, b = 25$ 6. $a = 11, b = 37$ 9. $a = 10, b = 6$

4. $a = 27, b = 16$ 7. $a = 8, b = 13$ 10. $a = 24, b = 15$

5. $a = 29, b = 13$ 8. $a = 21, b = 13$

11. Compute $(180, 66)$.   12. Compute $(492, 228)$.

13. Compute $(871, 1139)$ and write each number in prime factored form.

14. Compute $(1073, 1147)$ and write each number in prime factored form.

15. Compute the g.c.d. of 15, 21, and 35 and express it as a linear combination of 15, 21, and 35.

16. Compute the g.c.d. of 12, 20, and 30 and express it as a linear combination of 12, 20, and 30.

17. Express $(78,696, 19,332)$ as a linear combination of 78,696 and 19,332.

18. In the natural number sequence $1, 2, 3, 4, 5 \cdots$ circle every multiple of a, and underline every multiple of b. Interpret the significance of (a, b).

19. $S = \{x \mid 100 < x < 200, x \text{ is a multiple of } 13\}$. What is **a.** the least member of S? **b.** the greatest member of S? **c.** $n(S)$?

20. $S = \{x \mid 200 < x < 400, x \text{ is a multiple of } 17\}$. What is **a.** the least member of S? **b.** the greatest member of S? **c.** $n(S)$?

21. Determine integers x and y such that $5x + 7y = 1$. Determine integers a and b such that $25x + 35y = 5$.

22. Determine integers x and y such that $18x + 25y = 1$. Determine integers a and b such that $54x + 75y = 3$.

18-3. Congruences

The even integers are those integers that leave a remainder of 0 when divided by 2. Similarly, the odd integers are those that leave a remainder of 1 when divided by 2. Together, the even and odd integers constitute a partition of the set I of all integers. The corresponding equivalence relation is "has the same parity as" (Section 16-10). From the preceding section we know that when two integers n and m are given with $m \neq 0$, the integer n can be expressed uniquely in the form

$$n = qm + r, \text{ with } 0 \leq r < |m|$$

From this we see the possibility of separating all the integers into $|m|$ classes according to the remainders they yield when divided by m. The even and odd integers are the two equivalence classes given by $m = 2$.

We say that two integers are *congruent modulo m* if and only if these integers yield the same least nonnegative remainder upon being divided by m. The *modulus m* is used to "measure" the integers, and the remainders determine the equivalence classes to which the integers belong. The discussion will be limited to the case where $m \geq 2$.

Example: $m = 3$

$$I = \{\cdots \quad -5 \quad -4 \quad -3 \quad -2 \quad -1 \quad 0 \quad 1 \quad 2 \quad 3 \quad 4 \quad 5 \quad 6 \quad 7 \quad 8 \quad \cdots\}$$
$$[0] = \{\cdots \qquad\qquad\qquad -3 \qquad\qquad\quad \underline{0} \qquad\qquad 3 \qquad\qquad 6 \qquad\qquad \cdots\}$$
$$[1] = \{\cdots \quad -5 \qquad\qquad\qquad -2 \qquad\qquad \underline{1} \qquad\qquad 4 \qquad\qquad 7 \qquad \cdots\}$$
$$[2] = \{\cdots \qquad -4 \qquad\qquad\qquad -1 \qquad\qquad \underline{2} \qquad\qquad 5 \qquad\qquad 8 \quad \cdots\}$$

The set of integers congruent to a given integer for the modulus m constitutes a *residue class modulo m*. The least nonnegative remainder upon division by m is the standard representative of such residue classes.

The notation for "a is congruent to b modulo m" is

$$a \equiv b \bmod m$$

For this to be an equivalence relation on the set I of integers, as claimed, it is necessary and sufficient that

R. $a \equiv a \bmod m$
S. If $a \equiv b \bmod m$, then $b \equiv a \bmod m$
T. If $a \equiv b \bmod m$, and $b \equiv c \bmod m$
    then $a \equiv c \bmod m$

Each of these properties follow immediately from the uniqueness of the remainder in the division algorithm. Certainly a and a have the same remainder relative to m. If a and b have the same remainder, so do b and a. If a and b have the same remainder, and b and c have the same remainder, then a and c have the same remainder.

The zero residue class is noteworthy, since it consists of all the multiples of the modulus m. The definition of divisor (and factor) can be stated in language of congruences as: The positive integer m is a divisor of an integer a if and only if $a \equiv 0 \bmod m$.

From the previous definition of divisor we know that $m \mid a$ if and only if there exists an integer c such that

$$a = cm = cm + 0$$

Since $0 = 0m + 0$, then both a and 0 have the remainder 0 for any modulus m, and $a \equiv 0 \bmod m$.

An alternate characterization of congruence can be based on the concept of divisor. *The integer a is congruent to the integer b modulo m if and only if m is a divisor of a − b.* Alternatively, $a \equiv b$ mod m if and only if $a - b = km$ for some integer k.

To establish this, first let $a \equiv b$ mod m. Then

$$a = q_1 m + r$$

and $$b = q_2 m + r, \qquad 0 \le r < m, \qquad \text{by the definition of congruence}$$

Then $r = a - q_1 m$ and $r = b - q_2 m$

so that $a - q_1 m = b - q_2 m$

and $a - b = (q_1 - q_2)m = km,$ as required.

Conversely, if $a - b = km$, then $a = b + km$. Now

$$b = qm + r, \qquad 0 \le r < m, \qquad \text{by the division algorithm}$$

Hence $a = qm + r + km$

$$= (q + k)m + r, \qquad 0 \le r < m$$

Since r is the unique remainder when both a and b are divided by m, we have

$$a \equiv b \text{ mod } m$$

Examples: 37 is congruent to 22 modulo 5, since both 37 and 22 have a remainder of 2 when divided by 5.

The second definition is more direct here: 37 is congruent to 22 modulo 5 since $37 - 22 = 15$, and 15 is a multiple of (or is divisible by) 5.

$19 \equiv -2$ mod 7, since $19 + 2$ is divisible by 7.

$18 \not\equiv 2$ mod 3, since $18 - 2$ is not divisible by 3.

To find a value of x among the numbers 0, 1, 2, 3, 4, 5 such that $x^2 \equiv 4$ mod 6, we try in turn $0^2 - 4$, $1^2 - 4$, $2^2 - 4$, $3^2 - 4$ and $4^2 - 4$. Of these, $2^2 - 4$ or 0, and $4^2 - 4$ or 12 are multiples of 6. Hence $x = 2$ or 4. Verify that there is no x in the above list such that $x^2 \equiv 2$ mod 6.

Problems (169)

In problems 1 to 16, give all the numbers, if any, in the set $S = \{0, 1, 2, 3, 4, 5, 6\}$ that will give a true statement as a replacement for a.

1. $a \equiv 0$ mod 3	5. $a^2 \equiv 1$ mod 5	9. $2a \equiv 3$ mod 7	13. $a^2 \equiv 2$ mod 7
2. $a \equiv 1$ mod 3	6. $a^3 \equiv 1$ mod 5	10. $3a \equiv -2$ mod 7	14. $a^2 \equiv 3$ mod 7
3. $a \equiv 2$ mod 3	7. $3a \equiv -3$ mod 5	11. $6a \equiv 1$ mod 7	15. $a^3 \equiv 5$ mod 7
4. $2a \equiv 1$ mod 3	8. $4a \equiv 0$ mod 5	12. $a^2 \equiv 4$ mod 7	16. $a^3 \equiv 6$ mod 7

For problems 17 to 24, give two values of m for which the congruence is false, and two values of m for which it is true, including the largest value for which it is true.

17. $12 \equiv 2$ mod m	20. $2 \equiv 12$ mod m	23. $0 \equiv -9$ mod m
18. $12 \equiv 4$ mod m	21. $-5 \equiv -15$ mod m	24. $-2 \equiv 10$ mod m
19. $-5 \equiv 7$ mod m	22. $7 \equiv -1$ mod m	

The binary operations of addition, subtraction, and multiplication are all well defined with respect to the congruence relation. Hence congruences with the same modulus m have some properties similar to those of equations.

> Assume $a \equiv b \bmod m$, and $c \equiv d \bmod m$.
> Then $a - b = k_1 m$ and $c - d = k_2 m$.
> Then $(a - b) + (c - d) = k_1 m + k_2 m$,
> $(a + c) - (b + d) = (k_1 + k_2)m$, and $a + c \equiv b + d \bmod m$.
> Also $(a - b) - (c - d) = k_1 m - k_2 m$,
> $(a - c) - (b - d) = (k_1 - k_2)m$, and $a - c \equiv b - d \bmod m$.
> Furthermore, $a = b + k_1 m$ and $c = d + k_2 m$.
> Hence $ac = (b + k_1 m)(d + k_2 m)$
> $= bd + k_1 m d + b k_2 m + k_1 k_2 m^2$
> $= bd + (k_1 d + b k_2 + k_1 k_2 m)m$, and $ac \equiv bd \bmod m$.

However, the cancellation law for multiplication holds only with an important restriction.

Examples:

$$0 \cdot 3 \;\equiv\; 0 \cdot 5 \bmod 7, \qquad \text{but} \quad 3 \not\equiv 5 \bmod 7.$$
$$7 \cdot 2 \;\equiv\; 7 \cdot 3 \bmod 7, \qquad \text{but} \quad 2 \not\equiv 3 \bmod 7.$$
$$6 \cdot 6 \;\equiv\; 6 \cdot 2 \bmod 8, \qquad \text{but} \quad 6 \not\equiv 2 \bmod 8.$$
$$3 \cdot 16 \equiv 3 \cdot 2 \bmod 7, \qquad \text{and } 16 \equiv 2 \bmod 7.$$

The cancellation law is a central principle for the simplification of congruences. But the number cancelled must not only be nonzero, it must also be relatively prime to the modulus. That is,

$$\text{if } ca \equiv cb \bmod m, \text{ and } (c, m) = 1, \text{ then } a \equiv b \bmod m$$

To show this we need the following property of divisors: *If a number a divides a product bc, and a is relatively prime to b, then a divides c.* In symbols: If $a \mid bc$ and $(a, b) = 1$, then $a \mid c$.

> If $(a, b) = 1$, there exist integers x and y such that $ax + by = 1$.
> Then $cax + cby = c$.
> Since $a \mid bc$, then $a \mid cby$, and $a \mid cax + cyb$.
> Hence $a \mid c$.

We can now show that if $(c, m) = 1$, then if $ca \equiv cb \bmod m$ it will follow that $a \equiv b \bmod m$.

> If $ca \equiv cb \bmod m$, then $m \mid ca - cb$, or $m \mid c(a - b)$.
> But if m is relatively prime to c, then m must divide $a - b$.
> Hence $a \equiv b \bmod m$.

Since if $a \equiv b \bmod m$ and $c \equiv d \bmod m$, then $ac \equiv bd \bmod m$, as was shown above, it follows as a special case that if $a \equiv b \bmod m$, then $ak \equiv bk \bmod m$ for any integer k. And by multiplying repeatedly one can show that if $a \equiv b$ mod m, then $a^n \equiv b^n$ mod m for any natural number n.

The polynomial form $a_0 x^n + a_1 x^{n-1} + \cdots + a_{n-1} x + a_n$ is constructed from the variable x by using only the operations of adding, subtracting, multiplying, and raising to a positive integral power. We have seen above that all of these operations when applied to congruent numbers give congruent results. Hence, if $f(x)$ is specified by a polynomial in x where all the coefficients are integers, then if $a \equiv b$ mod m it will be true that $f(a) \equiv f(b)$ mod m.

> **Examples:** $26 \equiv 5$ mod 7 and $54 \equiv -2$ mod 7. Hence by adding the congruences we have $26 + 54 \equiv 5 - 2$ mod 7, or $80 \equiv 3$ mod 7.
>
> $7 \equiv 3$ mod 4. Hence $5 \cdot 7 \equiv 5 \cdot 3$ mod 4, or $35 \equiv 15$ mod 4.
> Furthermore, $7^2 \equiv 3^2$ mod 4, so that $49 \equiv 9$ mod 4.
> But since $9 \equiv 1$ mod 4, we have $7^2 \equiv 1$ mod 4.
>
> $3 \equiv -2$ mod 5. Suppose $f(x) = x^2 - 2x + 3$. Then $f(3) = 6$ and $f(-2) = 11$. Then $6 \equiv 11$ mod 5.
>
> $2^2 \equiv 1$ mod 3 $(2^2)^{20} \equiv 1^{20} \equiv 1$ mod 3
> Hence when 2^{40} (a very large number) is divided by 3, the remainder is 1.
>
> $2^2 \equiv 0$ mod 4 $(2^2)^{20} \equiv 0$ mod 4
> The number 2^{40} is exactly divisible by 4.
>
> $2^2 \equiv (-1)$ mod 5 $(2^2)^{20} \equiv (-1)^{20} \equiv 1$ mod 5
> There is a remainder of 1 when 2^{40} is divided by 5.
>
> $2^3 \equiv 1$ mod 7 $(2^3)^{13} \equiv 1^{13} \equiv 1$ mod 7 $2^{39} \equiv 1$ mod 7
> $2^{40} \equiv 2$ mod 7
> There is a remainder of 2 when 2^{40} is divided by 7.

Problems (170)

1. $5^1 \equiv 5$ mod 9, and $5^2 = 25 \equiv 7$ mod 9. Continue to find, with a minimum amount of labor, the remainders when each of the first 10 powers of 5 is divided by 9.
2. Find the remainders when the first 10 powers of 7 are divided by 11.
3. Find the remainder when 356^{16} is divided by 7.
4. Find the remainder when 37^{13} is divided by 17.
5. Verify that $30 \equiv 4$ mod 13, and $3 \equiv 16$ mod 13. Add, subtract in both orders, and multiply these congruences; verify your results.
6. Verify that $20 \equiv -2$, mod 11, and $-5 \equiv 28$ mod 11. Add, subtract, in both orders, and multiply these congruences; verify your results.
7. Show that $2^{11} - 1$ is divisible by 23.
8. Show that $2^{41} - 3$ is divisible by 23.
9. What is the remainder when $(21)(61)(-32)(17) + (65)^2$ is divided by 9?
10. Find, in turn, the smallest values of n such that $9n \equiv x$ mod 5 for $x = 0, 1, 2, 3$, and 4.

Since $10 \equiv 1 \bmod 9$, it follows from repeated multiplication of the members of this congruence that $10^2 \equiv 1 \bmod 9$, $10^3 \equiv 1 \bmod 9$, $10^4 \equiv 1 \bmod 9$, etc. We can now give a more adequate discussion of tests of divisibility than was presented in Section 4-7.

Every natural number N has a unique representation in the form

$$N = \cdots + N_3 \cdot 10^3 + N_2 \cdot 10^2 + N_1 \cdot 10 + N_0$$
$$\text{where } N_i \in \{0,\ 1,\ 2,\ 3,\ 4,\ 5,\ 6,\ 7,\ 8,\ 9\}$$

The uniqueness of this representation can be proven by repeated use of the division algorithm and depends directly on the uniqueness of q and r in the form $a = qb + r$. By making use of the above congruences we now have:

$$(\cdots + N_3 \cdot 10^3 + N_2 \cdot 10^2 + N_1 \cdot 10 + N_0) \equiv (\cdots + N_3 \cdot 1 + N_2 \cdot 1 + N_1 \cdot 1 + N_0)$$
$$\bmod 9$$

The test for divisibility by 9 (or 3, a divisor of 9) is the immediate: *A natural number, represented in decimal numeral form, is divisible by 9 (or 3) if, and only if, the sum of its digits is divisible by 9 (or 3).*

Furthermore, if the number is not exactly divisible by 9 or 3, the remainder from the division algorithm will be the same with the sum of the digits as a dividend, as with the number itself.

> **Example:** $238 \equiv x \bmod 9$. To solve for x such that $0 \leq x < 9$, observe that $238 \equiv 2 + 3 + 8 \equiv 13 \equiv 1 + 3 \equiv 4 \bmod 9$. Hence $x = 4$.

This idea can be readily extended to tests for divisibility when the natural number is represented in bases other than 10. For every natural number n we have $n \equiv 1 \bmod (n - 1)$, and hence by repeated multiplication we have for all natural numbers n and p,

$$n^p \equiv 1 \bmod (n - 1)$$

Examples:

$5 \equiv 1 \bmod 4$	$3 \equiv 1 \bmod 2$	$12 \equiv 1 \bmod 11$
$5^2 \equiv 1 \bmod 4$	$3^2 \equiv 1 \bmod 2$	$12^2 \equiv 1 \bmod 11$
$5^3 \equiv 1 \bmod 4$	$3^3 \equiv 1 \bmod 2$	$12^3 \equiv 1 \bmod 11$
etc.	etc.	etc.

The following theorem for representation of natural numbers in various bases can be shown to hold:

> *Let a be a natural number greater than 1. Then every natural number n can be uniquely represented in the form*
>
> $$n = r_k a^k + r_{k-1} a^{k-1} + \cdots r_1 a + r_0$$
>
> *where k is some nonnegative integer and $r_0, r_1 \cdots, r_k$ are nonnegative integers less than a, with $r_k \neq 0$.*

From the congruences above we have $a^k \equiv 1 \bmod (a - 1)$. Hence

$$n \equiv (r_k + r_{k-1} + \cdots r_1 + r_0) \bmod (a - 1)$$

Hence if a natural number is in the form $\cdots dcba_{\text{base } r}$ we can obtain the remainder when this number is divided by $r - 1$, by dividing $\cdots + d + c + b + a$ by $r - 1$.

Examples: To determine x in $1035_{(\text{six})} \equiv x \bmod 5$, with $0 \leq x < 5$.

$$1035_{(\text{six})} \equiv (1 + 0 + 3 + 5)_{(\text{six})} \equiv 13_{(\text{six})} \equiv (1 + 3)_{(\text{six})} \equiv 4 \bmod 5$$

Check: $1035_{(\text{six})} = 239_{(\text{ten})}$ $239 = (47)(5) + 4$.

$3t5e4_{(\text{twelve})}$ is exactly divisible by 11,
since $(3 + t + 5 + e + 4)_{(\text{twelve})}$ or $29_{(\text{twelve})}$ or $33_{(\text{ten})}$ is divisible by 11.

Divisibility by 11 can also be checked readily when a natural number is given in decimal numeral notation. When 11 is the modulus, the powers of 10 are congruent alternately to $+1$ and -1.

$$10^1 \equiv -1 \bmod 11 \qquad 10^2 \equiv (-1)^2 \equiv 1 \bmod 11 \qquad 10^3 \equiv -1 \bmod 11 \qquad \text{etc.}$$

Hence
$$(\cdots N_3 \cdot 10^3 + N_2 \cdot 10^2 + N_1 \cdot 10 + N_0) \equiv \cdots - N_3 + N_2 - N_1 + N_0) \bmod 11$$

In general,
$$(r_k a^k + r_{k-1} a^{k-1} + \cdots + r_1 a + r_0) \equiv (\cdots - r_5 + r_4 - r_3 + r_2 - r_1 + r_0)$$

when the modulus is $a + 1$ (one greater than the base).

Examples:

$$268759 \equiv [9 + 7 + 6 - (2 + 8 + 5)] \equiv 7 \bmod 11$$
$$957862 \equiv [2 + 8 + 5 - (9 + 7 + 6)] \equiv -7 \equiv 4 \bmod 11$$
$$12345_{(\text{six})} \equiv [5 + 3 + 1 - (2 + 4)]_{(\text{six})} \equiv 3 \bmod 7$$
$$\textit{Check: } 12345_{(\text{six})} = 1865_{(\text{ten})} = 266 \cdot 7 + 3$$

Congruences can be used to construct divisibility tests by any natural number for any natural number, as expressed in any base, but most of them would have little practical value. One more example is given. Since $10^3 + 1 = 1{,}001 = 7 \cdot 11 \cdot 13$ a test of the following type can be devised for 7, 11, or 13.

$1 \equiv 1 \bmod 1{,}001$	$10^3 \equiv -1 \bmod 1{,}001$	$10^6 \equiv 1 \bmod 1{,}001$
$10 \equiv 10 \bmod 1{,}001$	$10^4 \equiv -10 \bmod 1{,}001$	$10^7 \equiv 10 \bmod 1{,}001$ etc.
$10^2 \equiv 10^2 \bmod 1{,}001$	$10^5 \equiv -10^2 \bmod 1{,}001$	

Hence $N \equiv [\cdots + (N_8 \cdot 10^2 + N_7 \cdot 10 + N_6) - (N_5 \cdot 10^2 + N_4 \cdot 10 + N_3) + (N_2 \cdot 10^2 + N_1 \cdot 10 + N_0)]$, when the modulus is $7 \cdot 11 \cdot 13$.

Example: $847{,}963{,}207 \equiv (207 - 963 + 847) \equiv 91 \bmod 7 \cdot 11 \cdot 13$
$91 = 7 \cdot 13 = 8 \cdot 11 + 3$
The number given is exactly divisible by 7 and 13, and has a remainder of 3 when divided by 11.

Problems (171)

1. Give in turn the remainders when each of the following is divided by 9, 11, 7, or 13.

    a. 2,481　　**b.** 670,813　　**c.** 639,634,058　　**d.** 5,200,903

2. Give in turn the remainders when each of the following is divided by 9, 11, 7, or 13.

    a. 10,309　　**b.** 847,605　　**c.** 191,919　　**d.** 53,616,109,207

3. Solve for x in the following congruences, where $0 \le x < a$, for the modulus a.

    a. $3,422_{(five)} \equiv x \bmod 4$　　　　**e.** $17,123_{(eight)} \equiv x \bmod 7$

    b. $3,422_{(five)} \equiv x \bmod 6$　　　　**f.** $17,123_{(eight)} \equiv x \bmod 9$

    c. $45te_{(twelve)} \equiv x \bmod 11$　　　**g.** Verify **a.** to **f.** by doing the computations

    d. $45te_{(twelve)} \equiv x \bmod 13$　　　　　in base 10.

4. Solve for x in the following congruences, where $0 \le x < a$, for the modulus a.

    a. $5,324_{(seven)} \equiv x \bmod 6$　　　　**e.** $2,012_{(three)} \equiv x \bmod 2$

    b. $5,324_{(seven)} \equiv x \bmod 8$　　　　**f.** $2,012_{(three)} \equiv x \bmod 4$

    c. $3,045_{(six)} \equiv x \bmod 5$　　　　　**g.** Verify **a.** to **f.** by doing the computations

    d. $3,045_{(six)} \equiv x \bmod 7$　　　　　　in base 10.

5. $62 = 1 \cdot 3^4 - 1(3)^3 + 1(3)^2 + 0(3) - 1$

    $ = 1\underline{1}101_{(three)}$

    In the place value notation, the underlined digits have a negative face value. The computation at the right is based on the possibility for any two integers a and b of determining unique q and r such that

$$a = qb + r \text{ where } 0 \le |r| \le \left|\frac{b}{2}\right|.$$

```
3 | 6  2
3 | 2  1  ———(−1)
3 |    7  ———(0)
3 |    2  ———(1)
  |    1  ———(−1)
```

Obtain such representations for:

    a. $100_{(ten)}$ in base three　　**c.** $196_{(ten)}$ in base five

    b. $152_{(ten)}$ in base three　　**d.** $178_{(ten)}$ in base four

6. Any natural number can be expressed uniquely as the sum of terms of the form $a \cdot n!$, where $0 \le a \le n$.

    $423 = 3 \cdot 5! + 2 \cdot 4! + 2 \cdot 3! + 1 \cdot 2! + 1$

    Obtain such representations for:

    a. 100　　**b.** 153　　**c.** 119

    d. Continue this sequence for ten more numbers:

    1, 10, 11, 20, 21, 100, 101, . . .

```
2 | 4  2  3
3 | 2  1  1  ———(1)
4 |    7  0  ———(1)
5 |    1  7  ———(2)
  |       3  ———(2)
```

18-4. The Arithmetic of Residue Classes

For a given modulus m, the members of the m residue (equivalence) classes are as follows:

$$I = \begin{cases} \cdots & -2\,m, & -m, & 0, & m, & 2m, \cdots \\ \cdots & 1-2\,m, & 1-m, & 1, & 1+m, & 1+2m, \cdots \\ \cdots & 2-2\,m, & 2-m, & 2, & 2+m, & 2+2m, \cdots \\ \cdots & (m-1)-2m, & (m-1)-m, & m-1, & (m-1)+m, & (m-1)+2m, \cdots \end{cases}$$

As in Section 18-3, the notation for these classes will be $[0], [1], [2], \ldots, [m-1]$, Note that the symbol $[a]$ cannot be interpreted until m is known.

In set language, these residue classes would be as follows (remember the vertical bar here means "such that," and not "divides").

$$[0] = \{mn \mid m \text{ and } n \text{ are integers}, m \geq 2\}$$
$$[1] = \{mn + 1 \mid m \text{ and } n \text{ are integers}, m \geq 2\}$$
$$[2] = \{mn + 2 \mid m \text{ and } n \text{ are integers}, m \geq 2\}$$

$$[m-1] = \{mn + (m-1) \mid m \text{ and } n \text{ are integers}, m \geq 2\}$$

For a given modulus m, $[a] = [b]$, if and only if $a \equiv b \bmod m$. Since the operations of addition, subtraction, and multiplication are well defined for congruences, the following definitions of these operations are well defined for residue classes.

$$[a] + [b] = [a + b]$$
$$[a] - [b] = [a - b]$$
$$[a] \cdot [b] = [a \cdot b]$$
$$n \cdot [a] = [n \cdot a]$$

Suppose $[a] = [a']$ and $[b] = [b']$. Then $a \equiv a' \bmod m$, and $b \equiv b' \bmod m$

Hence $a + b \equiv a' + b' \bmod m$, and $[a + b] = [a' + b']$,
$\quad a - b \equiv a' - b' \bmod m$, and $[a - b] = [a' - b']$,
$\quad a \cdot b \equiv a' \cdot b' \bmod m$, and $[a \cdot b] = [a' \cdot b']$,
$\quad n \cdot a \equiv n \cdot a' \bmod m$, and $[n \cdot a] = [n \cdot a']$.

This shows that for these operations any member of a given class may be chosen as a representative without affecting the result. In the next problem set the reader will be invited to prove that the addition and multiplication operations defined above are commutative, associative, and possess identity elements, and also that multiplication is distributive with respect to addition. Since there are just m residue classes for a modulus m, "sums" and "products" may be displayed in tables of m^2 entries.

Addition				*Multiplication*			
Residue Classes mod 3				*Residue Classes mod 3*			
+	[0]	[1]	[2]	·	[0]	[1]	[2]
[0]	[0]	[1]	[2]	[0]	[0]	[0]	[0]
[1]	[1]	[2]	[0]	[1]	[0]	[1]	[2]
[2]	[2]	[0]	[1]	[2]	[0]	[2]	[1]

a. Verify in the table that addition is closed, well defined, and commutative.

b. Verify in the table that [0] is a unique additive identity, and that each element has a unique additive inverse.

c. Verify in the table that multiplication is closed, well defined, and commutative.   Verify in the table that [1] is a unique multiplicative identity, and that each element has a unique multiplicative inverse.

The two associative properties and the distributive property cannot be so readily checked by inspection of the tables.   They do hold, however, by the preceding theorems, which apply to the arithmetic of all systems of residue classes modulo m, and could be checked in all of the possible cases.

Problems (172)

1. Prove that $[a] + [b] = [b] + [a]$, by using the definition of addition.
2. Prove that $[a] \cdot [b] = [b] \cdot [a]$.
3. Prove that $([a] \cdot [b]) \cdot [c] = [a] \cdot ([b] \cdot [c])$.
4. Prove that $([a] + [b]) + [c] = [a] + ([b] + [c])$.
5. Prove that $[a] + [0] = [0] + [a] = [a]$.
6. Prove that $[1] \cdot [a] = [a] \cdot [1] = [a]$.
7. Prove that $[a] \cdot ([b] + [c]) = [a] \cdot [b] + [a] \cdot [c]$.
8. Prove that $([b] - [c]) \cdot [a] = [b] \cdot [a] - [c] \cdot [a]$.
9. Construct addition and multiplication tables for the residue classes modulo 2. Check for an analogy with the following statements:

   even + even = odd + odd = even   even · even = even · odd = even
   even + odd = odd   odd · odd = odd
10. Can you identify an isomorphism between addition modulo 2, and multiplication mod 3, if only nonzero elements are used in multiplication?

For problems 11 to 14, give a phase of everyday life that might be associated with the system.

11. addition mod 7   13. addition mod 24
12. addition mod 12   14. addition mod 365 (almost)

Thus far in this section we have considered systems whose structure was based on a set of m elements, with each element being a set consisting of an infinite number of integers. We now turn to some closely related *finite* systems. Let $Z_m = \{\overline{0}, \overline{1}, \overline{2}, \ldots, \overline{m-1}\}$. The overlined notation is used as a reminder that these decimal numerals do *not* represent zero and the natural numbers, or integers, or rational numbers, but rather are abstract objects whose properties will be assigned by definition. Two operations, denoted by $+_m$ and $\cdot_m$, will be defined by tables, for a given m.

These tables will be designed to preserve the following correspondence between the new systems and the arithmetic of residue classes of the integers modulo m.

$$[a] \leftrightarrow \overline{a} \qquad + \text{ (modulus known)} \leftrightarrow +_m \qquad \cdot \text{ (modulus known)} \leftrightarrow \cdot_m$$

Example:

Addition, Z_3

$+_3$	$\bar{0}$	$\bar{1}$	$\bar{2}$
$\bar{0}$	$\bar{0}$	$\bar{1}$	$\bar{2}$
$\bar{1}$	$\bar{1}$	$\bar{2}$	$\bar{0}$
$\bar{2}$	$\bar{2}$	$\bar{0}$	$\bar{1}$

Multiplication, Z_3

$\cdot_3$	$\bar{0}$	$\bar{1}$	$\bar{2}$
$\bar{0}$	$\bar{0}$	$\bar{0}$	$\bar{0}$
$\bar{1}$	$\bar{0}$	$\bar{1}$	$\bar{2}$
$\bar{2}$	$\bar{0}$	$\bar{2}$	$\bar{1}$

The system above is known as the *integers modulo 3* (in spite of the warning that $\bar{0}$, $\bar{1}$, and $\bar{2}$ are not integers!). With the residue classes mod 3, we could say that $[2] + [2] = [4]$, since [4] and [1] are the same residue class. But with the integers modulo 3 it is *not* true that $\bar{2} +_3 \bar{2} = 4$, since 4 is not a member of the system. However, it is true that $\bar{2} +_3 \bar{2} = \bar{2} \cdot_3 \bar{2}$.

The integers modulo m are isomorphic to the residue class of the integers mod m, so that all the properties that were verified for the residue classes mod 3 continue to hold. The following diagram will be useful for some further analysis, and suggests why a system of integers modulo m is sometimes known as a "clock arithmetic," or an example of "numbers on a circle."

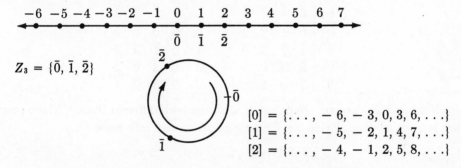

$Z_3 = \{\bar{0}, \bar{1}, \bar{2}\}$

$$[0] = \{\ldots, -6, -3, 0, 3, 6, \ldots\}$$
$$[1] = \{\ldots, -5, -2, 1, 4, 7, \ldots\}$$
$$[2] = \{\ldots, -4, -1, 2, 5, 8, \ldots\}$$

It can be verified from the table that $\bar{0}$ is a unique identity for $+_3$, and that $\bar{0}$ is its own additive inverse, while $\bar{1}$ and $\bar{2}$ are additive inverses. In the table for $\cdot_3$ we find that $\bar{1}$ is the unique identity, and that for the elements different from $\bar{0}$, that is, $\bar{1}$ and $\bar{2}$, each is its own multiplicative inverse. Hence the equation $a +_3 x = b$ always has a solution with a, b, and x in Z_3, so that "subtraction," which we might denote by $-_3$, could be defined in Z_3 in the usual way as the inverse of addition. Also the equation $a \cdot_3 x = b$ has a solution with a, b, and x in Z_3, provided that $a \neq \bar{0}$. This means that "division," which we might denote by $\div_3$, could be defined in Z_3 as the inverse of multiplication, provided that the divisor was not $\bar{0}$.

Examples: The equations $\bar{2} +_3 x = \bar{1}$, and $\bar{1} -_3 \bar{2} = x$, both have the solution $x = \bar{2}$.

The equations $\bar{2} \cdot_3 x = \bar{1}$, and $\bar{1} \div_3 \bar{2} = x$, both have the solution $x = \bar{2}$.

An important property, which is shared by the systems of natural numbers, integers, and rational numbers, is that a product of two numbers can be zero only if one or both of the factors is zero. That is, if $ab = 0$, then $a = 0$, or $b = 0$, or both a and b equal zero. This property of products is closely related to the cancellation law for multiplication; in fact, if either holds, then the other follows in the presence of other assumptions.

Suppose $a \cdot b = 0$. Then if $a = 0$, the theorem holds, but if $a \neq 0$, then $a \cdot 0 = 0$ and $a \cdot b = 0$ requires that $a \cdot b = a \cdot 0$. Hence, if the cancellation law holds we have $b = 0$.

Conversely, if $a \neq 0$ and $ab = ac$, then $ab - ac = 0$, and $a(b - c) = 0$. Hence if at least one factor must be zero, and $a \neq 0$, then $b - c = 0$, or $b = c$ as required by the cancellation law.

A check of the multiplication table for Z_3 shows that here also the product is not $\bar{0}$ when both factors are not $\bar{0}$. This will not be true in the next example of the integers modulo m.

Examples:

<table>
<tr><td colspan="5">Addition, Z_4</td><td colspan="5">Multiplication, Z_4</td></tr>
<tr><td>$+_4$</td><td>$\bar{0}$</td><td>$\bar{1}$</td><td>$\bar{2}$</td><td>$\bar{3}$</td><td>$\cdot_4$</td><td>$\bar{0}$</td><td>$\bar{1}$</td><td>$\bar{2}$</td><td>$\bar{3}$</td></tr>
<tr><td>$\bar{0}$</td><td>$\bar{0}$</td><td>$\bar{1}$</td><td>$\bar{2}$</td><td>$\bar{3}$</td><td>$\bar{0}$</td><td>$\bar{0}$</td><td>$\bar{0}$</td><td>$\bar{0}$</td><td>$\bar{0}$</td></tr>
<tr><td>$\bar{1}$</td><td>$\bar{1}$</td><td>$\bar{2}$</td><td>$\bar{3}$</td><td>$\bar{0}$</td><td>$\bar{1}$</td><td>$\bar{0}$</td><td>$\bar{1}$</td><td>$\bar{2}$</td><td>$\bar{3}$</td></tr>
<tr><td>$\bar{2}$</td><td>$\bar{2}$</td><td>$\bar{3}$</td><td>$\bar{0}$</td><td>$\bar{1}$</td><td>$\bar{2}$</td><td>$\bar{0}$</td><td>$\bar{2}$</td><td>$\bar{0}$</td><td>$\bar{2}$</td></tr>
<tr><td>$\bar{3}$</td><td>$\bar{3}$</td><td>$\bar{0}$</td><td>$\bar{1}$</td><td>$\bar{2}$</td><td>$\bar{3}$</td><td>$\bar{0}$</td><td>$\bar{3}$</td><td>$\bar{2}$</td><td>$\bar{1}$</td></tr>
</table>

Note that $\bar{2} \cdot_4 \bar{2} = \bar{0}$. Here are two factors, both different from $\bar{0}$, whose product is 0. The cancellation law for multiplication also fails since

$$\bar{2} \cdot_4 \bar{0} = \bar{0} = \bar{2} \cdot_4 \bar{2} \quad \text{but} \quad \bar{0} \neq \bar{2}$$

In both Z_3 and Z_4 the following hold for all a, b, and c in Z_m.

1. $a +_m b$ and $a \cdot_m b$ are in Z_m.
2. $(a +_m b) +_m c = a +_m (b +_m c)$, and $(a \cdot_m b) \cdot_m c = a \cdot_m (b \cdot_m c)$.
3. $\bar{0} +_m a = a = a +_m \bar{0}$, and $1 \cdot_m a = a = a \cdot_m 1$.
4. There exists an x in Z_m such that $a + x = \bar{0} = x + a$.
5. $a +_m b = b +_m a$, and $a \cdot_m b = b \cdot_m a$.
6. $a \cdot_m (b +_m c) = a \cdot_m b +_m a \cdot_m c$.

These properties qualify Z_3 and Z_4 as examples of a mathematical system known as a *commutative ring with identity*. But as seen above, Z_3 has an additional property:

4'. There exists a y in Z_m such that for $a \neq \bar{0}$ and all b, $a \cdot_m y = b$.

This makes Z_3 an example of a *field* (finite). In neither Z_3 nor Z_4 is there an order relation defined, so that Z_3 is not an ordered field, as the rational numbers are.

Problems (173)

1. **a.** In Z_5, give in turn the additive inverses of $\bar{0}, \bar{1}, \bar{2}, \bar{3}$, and $\bar{4}$.
   b. In Z_5, give in turn the multiplicative inverses of $\bar{1}, \bar{2}, \bar{3}$, and $\bar{4}$.
2. **a.** In Z_7, give in turn the additive inverses of $\bar{0}, \bar{1}, \bar{2}, \bar{3}, \bar{4}, \bar{5}$, and $\bar{6}$.
   b. In Z_7, give in turn the multiplication inverses of $\bar{1}, \bar{2}, \bar{3}, \bar{4}, \bar{5}$, and $\bar{6}$.
3. In Z_6, give an example of two factors, each different from $\bar{0}$, whose product is $\bar{0}$.
4. Follow the directions for problem 3, for Z_8.

In problems 5 and 6, compute with the modulus indicated. Assume that $a -_m b$ represents the sum of a and the additive inverse of b, and that $a \div_m b$ represents the product of a and the multiplicative inverse of b. If the expression is not defined, write "not defined."

5. **a.** $\bar{2} +_4 \bar{3}$ **c.** $\bar{5} -_8 \bar{7}$ **e.** $\bar{3} \div_6 \bar{4}$ **g.** $\bar{3} \cdot_7 (\bar{4} +_7 \bar{5})$ **i.** $\bar{1} -_4 (\bar{2} -_4 \bar{3})$
   b. $\bar{4} \cdot_6 \bar{3}$ **d.** $\bar{3} \div_5 \bar{4}$ **f.** $\bar{3} \div_5 \bar{0}$ **h.** $\bar{3} \cdot_7 \bar{4} + \bar{3} \cdot_7 \bar{5}$ **j.** $\bar{3} \div_6 \bar{5}$

6. **a.** $\bar{5} +_7 \bar{6}$ **c.** $\bar{2} -_6 \bar{4}$ **e.** $\bar{4} \div_6 \bar{3}$ **g.** $(\bar{2} -_7 \bar{6}) \cdot_7 \bar{3}$ **i.** $\bar{3} \cdot (\bar{5} \div_6 \bar{3})$
   b. $\bar{5} \cdot_6 \bar{5}$ **d.** $\bar{4} \div_7 \bar{5}$ **f.** $\bar{0} \div_3 \bar{2}$ **h.** $\bar{2} \cdot_7 \bar{3} - \bar{6} \cdot_7 \bar{3}$ **j.** $\bar{3} + (\bar{5} -_6 \bar{3})$

In problems 7 to 10 assume all numerals and operations are in Z_m. Determine all possible values for x where $0 \leq x < m$.

7. Z_7

   a. $x - 3 = 6$ **e.** $4x - 1 = 3$ **i.** $x^2 = 4$ **m.** $2x = 1$
   b. $4 - x = 5$ **f.** $3(x - 2) = 1$ **j.** $x^2 = 3$ **n.** $2x^2 = 1$
   c. $5x = 3$ **g.** $3(x - 2) = 0$ **k.** $3x^2 = 6$ **o.** $2x^2 = 0$
   d. $2x + 4 = 5$ **h.** $x^2 = 1$ **l.** $x^3 = 6$

8. Z_5

   a. $x - 4 = 4$ **e.** $4x = 5x - 2$ **i.** $x^2 = 2$ **m.** $x^3 = 2$
   b. $3 - x = 1$ **f.** $2(x - 3) = 4$ **j.** $x^2 + x = 2$ **n.** $3x^2 = 2$
   c. $4x = 2$ **g.** $2(x - 3) = 0$ **k.** $x^2 + x = 1$ **o.** $3x^2 = 0$
   d. $2x - 1 = 4$ **h.** $x^2 = 4$ **l.** $x^2 + x = 0$

9. Z_6

   a. $5x - 2 = 1$ **c.** $3x = 3$ **e.** $x^2 = 4$
   b. $3x = 2$ **d.** $4x = 0$ **f.** $x^2 = 5$

10. Z_{10}

   a. $7x - 5 = 3$ **c.** $6x = 6$ **e.** $x^2 = 4$
   b. $6x = 5$ **d.** $5x = 5$ **f.** $x^2 = 1$

For Further Study

Reference [S1], pp. 37–65, gives the properties of the different number systems in the same order they have been introduced in this text: natural numbers, nonnegative rationals, integers, and rationals.

There is an amusing and instructive introduction to the theory of groups in [D4], pp. 117–127.

For an excellent discussion of "multiplication tables" see [S14], pp. 137–154.

The following references are suggested for treatments of the Euclidean algorithm and the divisibility properties of the integers: [B1], pp. 43–61; [C4], pp. 220–249; [H2], pp. 216–227; [L5], pp. 21–36; [O3], pp. 41–49; [P1], pp. 128–135; and [Y1], pp. 123–136.

For supplementary reading on congruence relations, see [B1], pp. 78–91; [L5], pp. 52–60; [O1], pp. 324–352; [O3], pp. 209–233; [P1], pp. 143–149; and [S14], pp. 122–136.

Discussions of modular systems ranging from simple to more advanced can be found in [N6], pp. 1–35; [C4], pp. 256–295; [O1], pp. 314–324; [W3], pp. 272–282; [K2], pp. 34–41; [O2], pp. 73–74; and [W7], pp. 36–42. For a monograph on this subject, see [J2].

19

The Decimal Notation for Rational Numbers

19-1. Decimal Fractions, Decimals, and Decimal Numerals

Every rational number has an unlimited number of representations in the *common fraction notation*, that is, in the form $\frac{a}{b}$ where a is an integer and b is a nonzero integer. This representation can be made unique in the following way. Let a and b be relatively prime and given in decimal numeral form. Not more than one minus sign need be used, and if it is required, it can be placed at the left, thus allowing a and b to be free of plus and minus signs. These conventions provide for a unique representation of each and every rational number except zero, and zero could be standardized as $\frac{0}{1}$ if desired.

A proper subset of the rational numbers can be distinguished by selecting those that have a common fraction representation where the denominator b is a power of 10. *A decimal fraction is a rational number that has a common fraction notation where the denominator b has the form 10^n, where n is zero or a natural number.*

Examples: $\frac{7}{10}, \frac{37}{100}, \frac{37}{1000}, \frac{17}{10}, \frac{70}{100}, \frac{25}{100}.$

a. With this definition, would 7 be considered a decimal fraction?

Such numbers can be represented more compactly by the *decimal notation*, which for the examples given would be .7, .37, .037, 1.7, .70, and .25, respectively. It is common practice in the literature also to use the phrase "decimal fractions" when referring to such forms, and to shorten this further to "decimals" when referring either to the numeral or to the number represented. The term "decimal numeral" will be extended to include these forms; the common property being the continued use of powers of 10 to represent place value.   The next section introduces an operator that is useful in this connection.

ANSWER TO EXERCISE

a. Yes. $7 = \frac{7}{1} = \frac{7}{10^0}$. This is a convenient convention when stating computation rules for decimal fractions.

19-2. The Reciprocal Operator

In the following example the sequences can be extended to the left by: **a.** multiplying by 3; **b.** joining the operator $3 \cdot$; **c.** adding 1 to the exponent.

a. $\leftarrow$		27	9	3	1	$\rightarrow$?
b. $\leftarrow$	$3 \cdot 3 \cdot 3 \cdot 1$	$3 \cdot 3 \cdot 1$	$3 \cdot 1$	1		$\rightarrow$?
c. $\leftarrow$		3^3	3^2	3^1	3^0	$\rightarrow$?

Sequence **a.** can be extended to the right in a consistent manner by dividing by 3.   In **b.** note that $3 \cdot 3 \cdot 3 \cdot 1$ can be changed to $3 \cdot 3 \cdot 1$ either by removing the operator $3 \cdot$, or *joining the inverse operator* $\frac{1}{3}(\ )$, since

$$\frac{1}{3}(3 \cdot 3 \cdot 3 \cdot 1) = 3 \cdot 3 \cdot 1$$

In **c.** observe that 3^3 can be changed to 3^2, either by subtracting 1 from the exponent, or by *adding* -1, since $3 - 1 = 3 + (-1) = 2$.   The three sequences can thus be extended to the right in the manner shown.

a. $\leftarrow$		27	9	3	1	$\frac{1}{3}$	$\frac{1}{9}$ $\frac{1}{27}$ $\rightarrow$
b. $\leftarrow$	$3 \cdot 3 \cdot 3 \cdot 1$	$3 \cdot 3 \cdot 1$	$3 \cdot 1$	1	$\frac{1}{3}(1)$	$\frac{1}{3}\left(\frac{1}{3}(1)\right)$	$\frac{1}{3}\left(\frac{1}{3}\left(\frac{1}{3}(1)\right)\right)$ $\rightarrow$
c. $\leftarrow$		3^3	3^2	3^1 3^0	3^{-1}	3^{-2}	3^{-3} $\rightarrow$

The entries in **a.** and **b.** are already defined, and thus provide a guide as to how to define the negative exponents that arise in **c.**   The fact that 3^{-1} corresponds to $\frac{1}{3}$, which is the reciprocal of 3, suggests that $(\ )^{-1}$ be considered as the *reciprocal operator*, and we make this definition:

$$x \cdot x^{-1} = 1, \text{ for all } x \neq 0$$

The reciprocal operator is an exponential operator, and may be composed with other exponential operators to give a composite or double operator:

$$((\ )^2) \circ ((\ )^{-1}) = (\ )^{-2} = ((\ )^{-1}) \circ ((\ )^2)$$
$$((\ )^3) \circ ((\ )^{-1}) = (\ )^{-3} = ((\ )^{-1}) \circ ((\ )^3) \text{ etc.}$$

The composite operator $(\ )^{-m}$ calls for both taking the reciprocal and raising to the mth power. These two unary operations may be commuted

$$(3)^{-2} = ((3)^2)^{-1} = (9)^{-1} = \frac{1}{9}$$

$$= ((3)^{-1})^2 = \left(\frac{1}{3}\right)^2 = \frac{1}{9}$$

The exponent $-m$ can also be interpreted as the product $(-1)(m)$ and then used in an extension of $(A^m)^n = A^{mn}$ (see Section 4-3).

$$3^{-2} = 3^{(-1)(2)} = (3^{-1})^2 = \left(\frac{1}{3}\right)^2 = \frac{1}{9}$$

$$= 3^{(2)(-1)} = (3^2)^{-1} = (9)^{-1} = \frac{1}{9}$$

The desirability of the definition given, for exponents that are negative integers, is further verified by its use in still other principles of exponents, as originally developed for natural number exponents. As an instance of $A^m \cdot A^n = A^{m+n}$ set $A = x$ where $x \neq 0$, $m = 1$, and $n = -1$.

$$\text{Then } x^1 \cdot x^{-1} = x^{1+(-1)} = x^{1-1} = x^0 = 1$$

Since $m - n$ is now always defined, the identity $\dfrac{A^m}{A^n} = A^{m-n}$ may now be used without the former restriction that $m \geq n$.

$$\textbf{Examples: } \frac{1}{3^3} = \frac{3^0}{3^3} = 3^{0-3} = 3^{-3} = (3^{-1})^3 = \left(\frac{1}{3}\right)^3 = \frac{1}{3^3}$$

$$(7)^{-1} = \frac{1}{7} \qquad (-7)^{-1} = -\frac{1}{7} \qquad \left(\frac{3}{5}\right)^{-1} = \frac{5}{3} \qquad \left(-\frac{3}{5}\right)^{-2} = \frac{25}{9}$$

$$\left(\frac{1}{7}\right)^{-1} = 7 \qquad \left(-\frac{1}{7}\right)^{-1} = -7 \qquad \left(\frac{3}{5}\right)^{-2} = \frac{25}{9} \qquad \left(-\frac{3}{5}\right)^{-3} = -\frac{125}{27}$$

Problems (174)

Simplify the following, interpreting $(\ )^{-1}$ as "take the reciprocal."

1. $(11)^{-1}$	7. $\left(\dfrac{1}{3^2}\right)^{-1}$	13. $(5)^{-2}$	19. $\left(2\dfrac{1}{2}\right)^{-1}$	25. $\left(-\dfrac{1}{2}\right)^{-5}$
2. $(6)^{-1}$	8. $\left(\dfrac{1}{2^3}\right)^{-1}$	14. $\left(-\dfrac{2}{3}\right)^{-1}$	20. $((8)^{-1})^{-1}$	26. $(-5)^{-3}$
3. $\left(\dfrac{7}{2}\right)^{-1}$	9. $(9+3)^{-1}$	15. $\left(\dfrac{1}{4}\right)^{-3}$	21. $\left(1-\dfrac{1}{4}\right)^{-1}$	27. $\left(-\dfrac{1}{3}\right)^{-4}$
4. $\left(\dfrac{9}{4}\right)^{-1}$	10. $(5-2)^{-1}$	16. $\left(\dfrac{4}{5}\right)^{-2}$	22. $\left(2-\dfrac{2}{3}\right)^{-1}$	28. $-\left(\dfrac{3}{4}\right)^{-2}$
5. $(2^3)^{-1}$	11. $\left(-\dfrac{1}{5}\right)^{-1}$	17. $\left(\dfrac{8}{3}\right)^{-2}$	23. $\left(\left(\dfrac{3}{8}\right)^{-1}\right)^{-1}$	29. $-\left(\dfrac{1}{3}\right)^{-4}$
6. $(3^2)^{-1}$	12. $(-4)^{-1}$	18. $\left(-\dfrac{4}{5}\right)^{-3}$	24. $\left(1\dfrac{3}{4}\right)^{-2}$	30. $\left(-\dfrac{3}{4}\right)^2$

19-3. Place Value and the Decimal Point

The digit 7 in the numeral 1,957 is recognized as being in the ones or units place because it is the digit farthest to the right. Further emphasis can be given to the units place by placing a point just to its right.

$$1,957.$$

This point might well be called the units point, but is at present commonly called the *decimal point*. Let us now examine the representation of 1,957 as given, and after multiplication by 10.

$$\text{before} \quad 1,957.$$
$$\text{after} \quad 19,570.$$

The careless language of describing the above change by saying, "A zero was added, and the decimal point was moved one place to the right," should be avoided. If zero were actually added, the number would not change at all since $1,957 + 0 = 1,957$. Also it is better to think of the decimal point as remaining at a fixed position, while the digits 1, 9, 5, and 7 have each been shifted to a new place, which has 10 times its original place value.

0 has replaced 7 in the units place.
7 has been moved from the units place to the tens place.
5 has been moved from the tens place to the hundreds place.
9 has been moved from the hundreds place to the thousands place.
1 has been moved from the thousands place to the ten thousands place.

The polynomial notation reveals the central role of the distributive principle in this change.

$$1,957 = \quad 1(10)^3 + 9(10)^2 + 5(10)^1 + 7(10)^0$$
$$10[1,957] = \quad 10[1(10)^3 + 9(10)^2 + 5(10)^1 + 7(10)^0]$$
$$19,570 = 1(10)^4 + 9(10)^3 + 5(10)^2 + 7(10)^1 + 0(10)^0$$

In a more general sense, this can be considered an example of a number, expressed in a given base, multiplied by that base number.

Examples: In the base seven, seven is written as 10.
Hence $10[34062_{(\text{seven})}] = 340620_{(\text{seven})}$.
and $10^2[34062_{(\text{seven})}] = 3406200_{(\text{seven})}$.
In the second example, 10^2 represents $(\text{seven})^2$ or $49_{(\text{ten})}$.

The next chart indicates the extent to which place value has been used thus far. The rightmost digit is assumed to be in the ones or units place, and the place next to the left has the place value of the base number. For each shift to the left the place value is then multiplied by the base number.

(base)^4	(base)^3	(base)^2	base	unit
b^4	b^3	b^2	b	1

$\leftarrow$ $\rightarrow$

10^4	10^3	10^2	10	1
ten thousands	thousands	hundreds	tens	ones

To extend this notation system to the right, the units place is marked with a point, and new place values are created by dividing by the base number for each shift to the right. This provides a way of representing smaller and smaller fractional parts as places are introduced to the right, just as larger and larger groups can be designated by working to the left.

(base)^3	(base)^2	base	1.	$\dfrac{1}{\text{base}}$	$\dfrac{1}{(\text{base})^2}$	$\dfrac{1}{(\text{base})^3}$
b^3	b^2	b	1.	$\dfrac{1}{b}$	$\dfrac{1}{b^2}$	$\dfrac{1}{b^3}$
10^3	10^2	10	1.	$\dfrac{1}{10}$	$\dfrac{1}{10^2}$	$\dfrac{1}{10^3}$
10^3	10^2	10^1	10^0	10^{-1}	10^{-2}	10^{-3}
b^3	b^2	b^1	b^0	b^{-1}	b^{-2}	b^{-3}

$\leftarrow$ (on the 10^3 row) ... $\rightarrow$

The place values to the right remain positive and have zero as a lower bound. Zero is the greatest lower bound for this sequence of place values, since if any number greater than zero is selected, no matter how small, there is a place to the right such that this place and all others to its right have values smaller than the selected number.

The number 1 (but not the decimal point) may be taken as the center of this system to show the symmetry given by the reciprocal relation between place values on either side.

One is its own reciprocal.
Ten and one-tenth are reciprocals.
One hundred and one-hundredth are reciprocals, etc.

Note in the above chart that when place values that are reciprocals are written as powers of the base, the exponents are then additive inverses. For example, 10^2 and 10^{-2} are reciprocals.

The polynomial notation can now be extended to include negative powers of the base.

$$\cdots c_2b^2 + c_1b^1 + c_0b^0 + c_{-1}b^{-1} + c_{-2}b^{-2} + \ldots, \text{ with } 0 \le c_i < b$$

Examples:

750.	represents $7(10)^2 + 5(10)^1 + 0(10)^0$
75.	represents $\qquad\quad 7(10)^1 + 5(10)^0$
7.5	represents $\qquad\qquad\quad 7(10)^0 + 5(10)^{-1}$
.75	represents $\qquad\qquad\qquad\quad 7(10)^{-1} + 5(10)^{-2}$
.075	represents $\qquad\qquad\qquad\qquad 0(10)^{-1} + 7(10)^{-2} + 5(10)^{-3}$

Problems (175)

For problems 1 to 20, write as a polynomial in powers of 10, using positive integers, zero, and negative integers as required for exponents.

1. 63.	**5.** .63	**9.** .603	**13.** .0125	**17.** 1.414
2. 2.54	**6.** 1.01	**10.** 3.14	**14.** 1.732	**18.** 2.7182
3. 6.3	**7.** .063	**11.** 6.03	**15.** 9.99	**19.** 3.1416
4. .005	**8.** 7.	**12.** .333	**16.** 39.37	**20.** .7854

For problems 21 to 28, write as a polynomial in powers of the given base.

21. $3.4_{(five)}$	**23.** $.02_{(three)}$	**25.** $87.e5_{(twelve)}$	**27.** $11.0101_{(two)}$
22. $.01_{(four)}$	**24.** $.542_{(six)}$	**26.** $.0002_{(nine)}$	**28.** $2.0102_{(three)}$

For problems 29 to 36, write as a polynomial in two ways: **a.** using negative exponents, **b.** avoiding negative exponents.

29. .25	**31.** $.012_{(five)}$	**33.** $.555_{(eight)}$	**35.** $.1011_{(two)}$
30. .073	**32.** $.008_{(nine)}$	**34.** $.123_{(four)}$	**36.** $.0101_{(two)}$

The notation for decimal fractions can always be interpreted as an expression of the ratio (or quotient) of two integers. The following examples illustrate the steps by which this change of form can be accomplished.

Examples:

$$3.14 = 3(10)^0 + 1(10)^{-1} + 4(10)^{-2}$$
$$= 3(1) + 1\left(\frac{1}{10}\right) + 4\left(\frac{1}{100}\right)$$
$$= 3\left(\frac{100}{100}\right) + 1\left(\frac{10}{100}\right) + 4\left(\frac{1}{100}\right) = \frac{300}{100} + \frac{10}{100} + \frac{4}{100} = \frac{314}{100}$$

$$.037 = 0(10)^{-1} + 3(10)^{-2} + 7(10)^{-3}$$
$$= 0 \qquad + 3\left(\frac{1}{100}\right) + 7\left(\frac{1}{1000}\right)$$
$$= \qquad 3\left(\frac{10}{1000}\right) + 7\left(\frac{1}{1000}\right) = \frac{30}{1000} + \frac{7}{1000} = \frac{37}{1000}$$

By inspection, we see that the change from decimal fraction form to common fraction form can be made directly in the following manner:

N. To obtain the numerator, write down the numeral that results from ignoring the decimal point.

Thus from 3.14 we get 314, and from .037 we get 37.

D. The denominator is a power of 10, written as 1 followed by the same number of zeros as there were digits to the right of the decimal point.

3.12 has two such digits; the denominator is 100.

.037 has three such digits; the denominator is 1,000.

The digits to the right of the decimal points are often said to occupy *decimal places*, and the number of such digits is then said to be the number of decimal places in the numeral.   Both 3.12 and .037 have been represented by numerals of three digits, but 3.12 is called a two-place decimal, and .037 is called a three-place decimal.

We can also use negative exponents to obtain another variation in form whereby the quotient obtained above is replaced by a product.

$$3.12 = \frac{312}{100} = 312\left(\frac{1}{100}\right) = 312(10)^{-2}$$

$$.037 = \frac{37}{1000} = 37\left(\frac{1}{1000}\right) = 37(10)^{-3}$$

Note that the absolute value of the exponent for 10 agrees with the number of decimal places in the decimal numeral notation.

Problems (176)

In problems 1 and 2, change each decimal fraction to an equivalent common fraction.   Use the smallest possible power of 10 for the denominator, but do not reduce.

1. Use the odd-numbered problems 1 to 19, of set (175).
2. Use the even-numbered problems 2 to 20, of set (175).

In problems 3 and 4, express each number in the form $N(10)^n$ where both N and n are integers, and N is as small as possible.

3. Use the even-numbered problems 2 to 20, of set (175).
4. Use the odd-numbered problems 1 to 19, of set (175).

In problems 5 and 6, express each number in the form $N(b)^n$ where b is the given base, N and n are integers, and N is as small as possible.

5. Use the odd-numbered problems 21 to 27, of set (175).
6. Use the even-numbered problems 22 to 28, of set (175).

In problems 7 and 8, the common fraction forms are to be replaced by the equivalent decimal notation.

7. a. $\frac{25}{1}$ **b.** $\frac{25}{10}$ **c.** $\frac{25}{1000}$ **8. a.** $\frac{365}{100}$ **b.** $\frac{365}{10000}$ **c.** $\frac{365}{10}$

For problems 9 to 12, represent each number with a place value notation.

9. $\frac{1}{5} + \frac{2}{25} + \frac{3}{125}$ **10.** $2 + \frac{3}{4} + \frac{1}{16}$ **11.** $3 + \frac{1}{2} + \frac{1}{8}$ **12.** $\frac{1}{4} + \frac{1}{8}$

We have noted the simplicity of the computation when a number, expressed in place value notation for a given base, is multiplied by that base number.   This simplicity extends to all multipliers that are integral powers of the base.   The digits of the multiplicand retain their same face value and relative position to each other in the product, but their place value is changed as their position relative to the decimal point is changed. Note that if the multiplier is written as (base)^n, then the number of places in the resulting shift is the same as the absolute value of the exponent n, or is the same as the number of zeros in the form 10, 100, 1000, etc.

Examples:

$$(8.75)(1) = 8.75 \qquad (8.75)(100) = 875.$$
$$(8.75)(10)^0 = 8.75 \qquad (8.75)(10)^2 = 875.$$
$$(8.75)(10) = 87.5 \qquad \frac{8.75}{100} = .0875$$
$$(8.75)(10)^1 = 87.5$$
$$\frac{8.75}{10} = .875 \qquad (8.75)(10)^{-2} = .0875$$
$$(8.75)(10)^{-1} = .875$$

Problems (177)

For problems 1 and 2, compute the result in decimal form.

1. **a.** $(.061)(10)^2$ **c.** $(804)(10)^{-1}$ **e.** $(68.8)(10)^{-3}$ **g.** $(.0074)(10)^2$
   b. $(1.64)(10)^{-2}$ **d.** $(.72)(10)^3$ **f.** $(.80)(10)^{-1}$ **h.** $(34)(10)^{-2}$
2. **a.** $(.0002)(10)^3$ **c.** $(101)(10)^{-3}$ **e.** $(642)(10)^2$ **g.** $(3.92)(10)$
   b. $(82.6)(10)^{-2}$ **d.** $(38.8)(10)^{-1}$ **f.** $(.069)(10)^{-1}$ **h.** $(.0078)(10)^2$

For problems 3 and 4, supply the number (in decimal form) that would give a true statement.

3. **a.** $43.4 = (\ )(10)$ **d.** $53.6 = (\ )(10)^{-2}$ **g.** $(\ )(10)^{-1} = .003$
   b. $945. = (\ )(10)^2$ **e.** $.789 = (\ )(10)$ **h.** $2.38 = (\ )(10)^{-2}$
   c. $(\ )(10)^{-3} = .13$ **f.** $.020 = (\ )(10)^2$ **i.** $.707 = (\ )(10)^{-1}$
4. **a.** $(\ )(10)^{-1} = .006$ **d.** $3.33 = (\ )(10)^{-2}$ **g.** $.408 = (\ )(10)^{-3}$
   b. $.031 = (\ )(10)$ **e.** $.080 = (\ )(10)$ **h.** $374 = (\ )(10)^{-1}$
   c. $(\ )(10)^{-3} = 8.6$ **f.** $667. = (\ )(10)^2$ **i.** $.008 = (\ )(10)^{-2}$

19-4. Significant Digits and Rounding Off

The number 23 is 3 more than 20 or 2 tens. It is 7 less than 30 or 3 tens. Suppose that 23 is the count or measure of an amount that it is desirable to record only to the nearest multiple of 10. Since 23 is between 20 and 30, but is nearer to 20, it can be "rounded off" to 20. The numbers 21, 22, and 24 may likewise be "rounded down" by ignoring the amount by which they exceed 20.

The numbers 26, 27, 28, and 29 are all closer to 30 than to 20 (or to any other multiple of 10). Hence, they would be "rounded up" to 30 if an approximation to the nearest multiple of 10 was desired.

Since 25 is halfway between two multiples of 10, a choice must be made. A common but arbitrary convention for this is to require that the approximation end in an *even* digit. This means that

05, 25, 45, 65, and 85 are to be rounded *down* to
00, 20, 40, 60, and 80 respectively, while

15, 35, 55, 75, and 95 are to be rounded *up* to
20, 40, 60, 80, and 100, respectively.

When 23 has been rounded off to 20, the zero now serves only as a placeholder and 20 is said to have only one *significant digit* (the digit 2). The digit 2 is thus considered to give reliable information and hence is significant, but no such claim is made for the digit zero. To say that a digit is significant is to claim that any error present is not more than one half of the place value where the digit is used. Since in the example the significant digit 2 was in the tens place, the error is not to exceed one half of 10, or 5. If it is desired that the zero in 20 also be significant, then the number being approximated should not differ from 20 by more than .5, that is, by more than half of 1, the place value where the zero appears.

The same principles that were used to approximate to the nearest 10 can be extended to any other place value.

Examples:

47,824 is approximately 50,000 to one significant digit, or to ten thousands.

47,824 is approximately 48,000 to two significant digits, or to thousands.

47,824 is approximately 47,800 to three significant digits, or to hundreds.

47,824 is approximately 47,820 to four significant digits, or to tens.

When a count or measurement is represented by a numeral of n significant digits, it is said to have n-digit *accuracy*. Thus in the example 48,000 is accurate to two significant digits. The *precision* of a number is specified by the place value of the rightmost significant digit. Thus 48,000 is precise to thousands.

The following convention can be used to approximate numbers by rounding off to n significant digits, where n is less than the number of digits in the decimal numeral.

A. Do not change the digits to the left of the nth digit (counted from the left), except as noted below.

B. Do not change the nth digit if the digit to its right is less than 5.

C. Add 1 to the nth digit, if the digit to its right is more than 5, or if this digit is 5 and one of the digits to the right of it is not zero.

D. If the digit to the right of the nth digit is 5 and only zeros are to the right of it, then leave the nth digit as is, or add 1, whichever results in an even digit.

E. Replace the digits to the right of the nth digits with zeros as required for place holders.

Note: If the nth digit is 9, and the rule requires that we add 1, then it becomes zero, and 1 is added to the digit to its left.

Examples:

Number	n = 2	n = 3	n = 4
24,265	24,000	24,300	24,260
65,035	65,000	65,000	65,040
78,501	79,000	78,500	78,500
4,993	5,000	4,990	4,993

All nonzero digits are presumed to be significant, while zero digits may or may not be significant. In such a number as .00030800 the three zeros at the left are not significant while the zero between 3 and 8 is significant. The two zeros at the right are significant, since, if not, they would be left off.

Problems (178)

Round off to two, then to three, and then to four significant digits, if possible; otherwise omit. In each case, round off the original number.

1. 92,151	**5.** 42,996	**9.** 989,395	**13.** 6.0800	**17.** .001450
2. 47,283	**6.** 8,994	**10.** 34.913	**14.** .80005	**18.** .001356
3. 31,416	**7.** 107,060	**11.** 17.538	**15.** .0500	**19.** .10804
4. 35,858	**8.** 605,050	**12.** 7.2265	**16.** .00805	**20.** .80615

19-5. Scientific Notation

The numeral 4,500. has at least two significant digits, the 4 and the 5, but one or both of the zeros may also be intended to be significant. But without any other information at hand, it is not possible to decide whether 4,500. has two, three, or four significant digits. The following notation meets this difficulty.

4,500. is written as $4.5(10)^3$, if two digits are significant.
4,500. is written as $4.50(10)^3$, if three digits are significant.
4,500. is written as $4.500(10)^3$, if four digits are significant.

We shall see that this notation has other advantages as well, particularly for writing and computing with very large and very small numbers. It has become so common in scientific work that it is called the *scientific notation*, or the standard form. The specifications are that the number be written as

$$N \cdot 10^k \qquad \text{or} \qquad N(10)^k$$

where $1 \leq N < 10$, and k is an integer that is positive, negative, or zero.

To construct this form, the number should first be in decimal numeral notation. The significant digits are then used in their given order, but the decimal point is placed just to the right of the first significant digit, so that N is within the required bounds. This is then multiplied by 10^k, where k is the number of places from the new position of the decimal point to its former position, counting positive to the right, negative to the left. For simplicity, 10^1 may be written as 10, and 10^0 or 1 may be omitted from $N \cdot 10^k$.

Examples: $93{,}000{,}000 = 9.3(10)^7$, if two digits are significant.
$.00060 = 6.0(10)^{-4}$.

Problems (179)

In problems 1 and 2, write the numbers in scientific notation.   For these problems consider all zeros between the decimal point and the first nonzero digit to the left (as well as to the right) to be nonsignificant.

1. a. 371,000   **c.** 11 million   **e.** .060   **g.** 1,487,000
   b. .00094   **d.** 23 thousandths   **f.** 100   **h.** .0000389
2. a. .0066   **c.** 7 ten thousandths   **e.** 100   **g.** 31,600,000
   b. 98 billion   **d.** 6.02   **f.** 8   **h.** .00000613

In problems 3 and 4, change to the decimal numeral notation.

3. a. $5.6(10)^{-4}$ **c.** $2.9(10)^5$ **e.** $3(10)^7$ **g.** $5.00(10)^6$
   b. $6.04(10)^{-1}$ **d.** $7.66(10)^{-2}$ **f.** $1.07(10)^3$ **h.** $5.0(10)^6$
4. a. $9.1(10)^4$ **c.** $3.6(10)^{-5}$ **e.** $2(10)^5$ **g.** $4.000(10)^4$
   b. $1.93(10)$ **d.** $2.54(10)^3$ **f.** $3.12(10)^{-3}$ **h.** $4.00(10)^4$

The numbers in problems 5 and 6 are not correctly represented in scientific notation.   Rewrite them correctly in this way.

5. a. $53.4(10)^3$ **c.** $618.3(10)^{-1}$ **e.** $.024(10)^{-3}$ **g.** $514(10)^2$
   b. $.91(10)^{-2}$ **d.** $84.6(10)^{-2}$ **f.** $.831(10)^2$ **h.** $.514(10)^2$
6. a. $.26(10)^{-1}$ **c.** $.093(10)^{-3}$ **e.** $74.86(10)^3$ **g.** $40.0(10)^{-1}$
   b. $13.8(10)^2$ **d.** $427.4(10)^{-1}$ **f.** $.53(10)^{-2}$ **h.** $.030(10)^3$

Every number x that has a decimal numeral notation has a unique representation in the form $x = N(10)^k$ where both N and k are integers and N has the same significant digits as x.   The numbers for problems 7 and 8 are to be written in this form.

7. a. .32   **c.** $15.3(10)^2$ **e.** .0860   **g.** $.3700(10)^3$
   b. $.07(10)^{-2}$ **d.** $.14(10)^{-3}$ **f.** $2.753(10)^2$ **h.** 39.82
8. a. $.094(10)^2$ **c.** $8.00(10)^4$ **e.** 2.135   **g.** .0130
   b. $16.5(10)^{-2}$ **d.** $.002(10)$ **f.** $61.16(10)^{-1}$ **h.** $8.147(10)^2$

For problems 9 and 10 each pair of numbers are to be represented as follows: Write the first number in the form $N_1(10)^{k_1}$ and the second number in the form $N_2(10)^{k_2}$, with N_1, N_2, k_1, k_2 all integers, $k_1 = k_2$, and N_1 and N_2 are as small as possible.

9. a. 2.1, 3.05   **b.** 7.32, 4.   **c.** 9.2, 3.175   **d.** .003, .00070
10. a. 5., 7.276   **b.** 6.08, 4.4   **c.** 7.133, 9.9   **d.** .071, .0017

For Further Study

The extension of the concept of an exponent provides an example for study which is quite typical of the growth of mathematics. See [M1], pp. 236–237, 266–268, 279–281 for a detailed discussion; also [M9], pp. 143–148; and [W3], pp. 226–228.

For supplementary treatments of scientific notation, refer to [B2], pp. 294–297; [B5], pp. 194–196; and [L3], pp. 123–127.

20

Computations with Decimal Fractions

20-1. Equivalent Decimal Fractions

Does $5.2 = 5.20$? Does $5.20 = 5.200$? Are all three of these decimal fractions different notations (or names) for the same number? The answers are either yes or no, depending on the conditions under which these fractions are used.

$$5.2 = \frac{52}{10} \qquad 5.20 = \frac{520}{100} \qquad 5.200 = \frac{5,200}{1,000}$$

Until the previous chapter there had been no discussion of approximation and all numerals had been assumed to represent a number exactly. From this point of view, then

$$\frac{52}{10} = \frac{520}{100} = \frac{5,200}{1,000} \qquad \text{and} \qquad 5.2 = 5.20 = 5.200$$

However, decimal fractions are much used to report the results of measurement, and the concept of significant digits is then used to give some control over the amount of approximation that is present.

5.2 is precise to tenths of the unit, indicating that the measurement was recorded to the nearest tenth. The error is claimed not to exceed .05.

$$\frac{1}{2} \text{ of } \frac{1}{10} = \frac{1}{20} = \frac{5}{100} = .05$$

5.20 is precise to hundredths of the unit. The error is claimed not to exceed .005.

$$\frac{1}{2} \text{ of } \frac{1}{100} = \frac{1}{200} = \frac{5}{1000} = .005$$

445

5.200 is precise to thousandths of the unit.   The error is claimed not to exceed .0005.

$$\frac{1}{2} \text{ of } \frac{1}{1000} = \frac{1}{2000} = \frac{5}{10,000} = .0005$$

Summary: If the numbers are considered exact, or we ignore their different precision then 5.2, 5.20, and 5.200 are equivalent, and one form can be interchanged for another freely.   But if the criterion of significant digits is to be applied, then these decimal fractions contain quite different information.

The following procedure has been found effective for computations with decimal fractions.   During the computation proper all numbers are treated as though they were exact, thus admitting such equivalences as were noted above.   The question of significant digits, and in general, the broader question of reliability of information, is then made a matter of separate consideration.

20-2. Addition and Subtraction of Decimal Fractions

To add or subtract numbers that are written as decimal fractions, the numerals are written so that the decimal points, which mark the units place, are kept in a vertical line.   Then the digits of like place value will be in a convenient position to be combined.

If two such numbers as 5.3 and 1.265 are to be added or subtracted, one can begin by joining zeros at the right as required, so that both numerals will then terminate in the same decimal place.

		Add	*Subtract*
5.4	5.400	5.400	5.400
1.385	1.385	1.385	1.385
		6.785	4.015

There is usually little need to adjoin these extra zeros since their main value is just to help keep the columns in a straight line.   The vertical alignment of the decimal points (and hence of the place value positions) makes possible a direct application of the distributive principle.

$$5.4 \ \ = 5.400 = 5400(10)^{-3}$$
$$1.385 = 1.385 = 1385(10)^{-3}$$
$$5.4 + 1.385 = 5400(10)^{-3} + 1385(10)^{-3} = (5400 + 1385)(10)^{-3}$$
$$= (6785)(10)^{-3} = 6.785$$
$$5.4 - 1.385 = 5400(10)^{-3} - 1385(10)^{-3} = (5400 - 1385)(10)^{-3}$$
$$= 4015(10)^{-3} = 4.015$$

This analysis also illustrates an important aspect of computations with decimal fractions: These computations can be reduced to computations with integers, together with some device for controlling place value (locating the decimal point).

If $x = 5.4$ is an approximation with two significant digits, then

$5.35 \leq x \leq 5.45$, since both 5.35 and 5.45 round off to 5.4

If $y = 1.385$ is an approximation with four significant digits, then

$$1.3846 \leq y \leq 1.3854$$

Hence $x + y$ could be as small as $5.35 + 1.3846$, or 6.7346,

or as large as $5.45 + 1.3854$, or 6.8354.

The computation gave $x + y = 6.785$, but a study of the possible error gave $6.7346 \leq x + y \leq 6.8354$.   This indicates that in 6.785 the reliability of the digits 5 and 8 is certainly open to question, and possibly the 7 as well.   Hence we cannot be sure that the precision of the sum is any greater than the precision of least precise addend, which in this case was 5.4.

However, this observation may be best taken as a warning, rather than a command to round off 6.785 to 6.8, so that its precision (to tenths) agrees with 5.4. One would have to have much more information about how the numbers 5.4 and 1.385 were obtained before any reasonable estimate of the most probable value of the sum could be given.   Hence computers often retain one or more doubtful digits as being significant, because of a lack of good reason to discard them.

a. If $5.35 \leq x \leq 5.45$ and $1.3846 \leq y \leq 1.3854$ as above, determine the minimum N_1 and the maximum N_2 for $N_1 \leq x - y \leq N_2$.

The difference between an approximation and a "true" or accepted value of a number is called the *error*, or *discrepancy*.   If this error is defined as $E = A - T$, that is, the error equals the approximate value minus the true value, then the error will be positive if the approximation is larger than the true value and negative if it is smaller.   A signed number can thus record both the kind and amount of the error.

Answer to Exercise

a. $3.9646 \leq x - y \leq 4.0654$.   The precision of the result is again controlled principally by the least precise term.

Problems (180)

Give two results for the computations in problems 1 to 4: **i.** the first as though the numbers were exact; **ii.** the second rounded off to the precision of the least precise term.

1. a. $7.6 + 1.3$	**c.** $3.46 + 5.8271$	**e.** $.0746 - .0287$	**g.** $27.3 - 6.802$
b. $.027 + .6$	**d.** $5.00 + 8.21$	**f.** $43. - .87$	**h.** $351.17 - 78.6$
2. a. $3.46 + 1.25$	**c.** $16. + 2.51$	**e.** $5.6 - 2.46$	**g.** $1.06 - .8094$
b. $9.16 + 7.4$	**d.** $3.80 + 4.500$	**f.** $31.0 - 7.0$	**h.** $5.062 - 2.9$

3. a. $4. - .03 + .84$ **b.** $.0035 + .072 - .009$ **c.** $.008 - .026 + .011$
4. a. $7. - .07 - .70$ **b.** $.067 - .32 + .254$ **c.** $41.2 - 33.08 - 9.16$

For problems 5 and 6, compute the error, assuming that the first term is an approximation and the second term is the true value.

5. a. $100 - 98$ **b.** $41 - 40.8$ **c.** $56.0 - 56.47$ **d.** $.92 - .9245$
6. a. $100 - 103$ **b.** $41 - 41.4$ **c.** $.07 - .0618$ **d.** $.00 - .0032$

20-3. Multiplication of Decimal Fractions

To compute the product $(.24)(.3)$, first observe that $.24 = 24(10)^{-2}$ and $.3 = 3(10)^{-1}$.

$$(.24)(.3) = [24(10)^{-2}][3(10)^{-1}] = (24 \cdot 3)(10^{-2} \cdot 10^{-1})$$
$$= 72(10)^{-3}$$
$$= .072$$

$$\begin{array}{r} .24 \\ .3 \\ \hline .072 \end{array}$$

The digits for the product are determined just as though two natural numbers were being multiplied.   Then the number of decimal places in the product is equal to the sum of the numbers of decimal places in the factors.   Note in the preceding example how the exponents for 10 keep account of these places.

If $x = .24$ and $y = .3$ are approximations, then
$$.235 \leq x \leq .245, \text{ and } .26 < y < .34$$

Hence it is possible that xy might be as small as $(.235)(.26)$, or $.06110$; or that it might be as large as $(.245)(.34)$, or $.08330$.   In multiplication the reliability of the digits in a product is judged by the accuracy* as given by the number of significant digits.   This is in contrast to the precision point of view as used for sums and differences.   When the computed product of $.072$ is compared with the range of $.06110$ to $.08330$ we see that there can be little confidence that the number of significant digits in a product will be more than the number of significant digits in that factor which has the least number of significant digits.   Again a good working rule is to use one or two more digits than this, at least until the final result, when there is a series of computations.

A variety of symbols have been used in the literature to mean "is approximately equal to."   We shall use a dot placed over the equals sign.   Hence $(.24)(.3) \doteq .07$.

The computation below shows that $(.703)(245.) \doteq 172$.   The first digits of the product that are computed are 5, then 3, and then 2; but these are discarded in rounding off to 172.   Without these digits, or at least the number of them, the decimal point could not be located by the usual rule, since the places are counted from right to left.

---

* See additional discussion in Section 21-3.

$$
\begin{array}{r}
.703 \\
245. \\
\hline
3\ 515 \\
28\ 12 \\
140\ 6 \\
\hline
172.235 \\
172.
\end{array}
$$

When one makes a mental estimate, or when a slide rule is used, it is the digits at the left, the most significant digits, that are obtained.   One then needs a method for locating the decimal point by working from left to right.   This can be done by the help of the scientific notation.

$$.703 \doteq (7)(10)^{-1}$$
$$245. \doteq (2)(10)^{2}$$
$$(.703)(245) \doteq (7)(10)^{-1}(2)(10)^{2} = (7)(2)(10)^{-1}(10)^{2}$$
$$= 14(10)^{-1+2}$$
$$= 14(10) = 140$$

Each number is written in scientific notation, but at the same time is rounded off to 1 or 2 significant digits.   This gives a problem that is simple enough to do mentally, in fact, the entire process can be done this way after a little practice.   If this product were to be computed on a slide rule, one could obtain the first three digits, 172, and possibly the first four, or 1,722.   The approximation of 172 by 140 may seem a little rough at first, but it is certainly better than 17.20 or 1,720. Hence with its help, the choice of 172, or 172.2 could be made with confidence for the slide rule reading.

Examples:

$$(430)(.51) \doteq 4(10)^{2} \cdot 5(10)^{-1} = 20(10) = 200$$
$$(70.12)(23) \doteq 7(10) \cdot 2(10) = 14(10)^{2} = 1400$$
$$(2,315)(.004) \doteq 2(10)^{3} \cdot 4(10)^{-3} = 8(10)^{0} = 8$$
$$(483)(253) \doteq 5(10)^{2} \cdot 2(10)^{2} = 10(10)^{4} = 100,000$$

Problems (181)

For these problems, only the first three left-hand digits are given for the product as they might be read from a slide rule.   Use the above method to locate the decimal point.

1. $(4.29)(23.7) \doteq 102$
2. $(1.294)(.0133) \doteq 172$
3. $(.0748)(3.20) \doteq 240$
4. $(5.83)(132) \doteq 770$
5. $(48.3)(12.1) \doteq 584$
6. $(.0647)(.0374) \doteq 242$
7. $(836)(.0089) \doteq 744$
8. $(283)(780) \doteq 221$
9. $(.5784)(.2956) \doteq 171$
10. $(.1269)(.0497) \doteq 631$
11. $(.0982)(.0329) \doteq 383$
12. $(46.0)(416) \doteq 192$
13. $(54.7)(486) \doteq 264$
14. $(10.72)(.0595) \doteq 638$
15. $(522)(.0825) \doteq 431$
16. $(.0764)(860) \doteq 656$

17. $(.536)(.00725) \doteq 389$ 19. $(.00748)(4.96) \doteq 371$

18. $(.0347)(18.3) \doteq 635$ 20. $(.0917)(.605) \doteq 555$

For the following problems: **a.** Give an approximate answer of one or two significant digits. **b.** Compute as though the numbers were exact. **c.** Round off the result in **b.** so that the product has the same number of significant digits as that factor which has the least number of significant digits.

21. $(41.3)(1.8)$	24. $(79.2)(.38)$	27. $(.081)(.007)$	30. $(453)(6.409)$
22. $(2.6)(40.4)$	25. $(.748)(.32)$	28. $(.832)(.402)$	31. $(15.26)(.7)$
23. $(.61)(50.3)$	26. $(.048)(.23)$	29. $(.917)(.605)$	32. $(.044)(17.69)$

20-4. Division of Decimal Fractions

The procedure for this computation continues in the same pattern as for addition, subtraction, and multiplication. The digits for the result are obtained by computing with integers; the place values of these digits are determined by a device for locating the decimal point.

Examples:

$$\frac{.072}{.24} = \frac{72(10)^{-3}}{24(10)^{-2}} = \frac{72(10)^{-3} \cdot (10)^2}{24(10)^{-2} \cdot (10)^2} = \frac{72(10)^{-3+2}}{24(10)^0} = 3(10)^{-1} = .3$$

$$\frac{27.6}{1.2} = \frac{276(10)^{-1}}{12(10)^{-1}} = \frac{276(10)^{-1} \cdot (10)}{12(10)^{-1} \cdot (10)} = \frac{276(10)^{-1+1}}{12(10)^0} = 23(10)^0 = 23.$$

$$\frac{.276}{.12} = \frac{276(10)^{-3}}{12(10)^{-2}} = \frac{276(10)^{-3} \cdot (10)^2}{12(10)^{-2} \cdot (10)^2} = \frac{276(10)^{-3+2}}{12(10)^0} = 23(10)^{-1} = 2.3$$

$$\frac{27.6}{.012} = \frac{276(10)^{-1}}{12(10)^{-3}} = \frac{276(10)^{-1} \cdot (10)^3}{12(10)^{-3} \cdot (10)^3} = \frac{276(10)^{-1+3}}{12(10)^0} = 23(10)^2 = 2300.$$

$$\frac{.000276}{.12} = \frac{276(10)^{-6}}{12(10)^{-2}} = \frac{276(10)^{-6} \cdot (10)^2}{12(10)^{-2} \cdot (10)^2} = \frac{276(10)^{-6+2}}{12(10)^0} = 23(10)^{-4} = .0023$$

In each case the multiplier introduced for the dividend and the divisor is the smallest power of 10 that will free the divisor of decimal places (corresponding to a negative k in $N \cdot 10^k$). The cases should be checked for an understanding of the method and then compared with the usual algorithm, which is an efficient way of carrying out these same transformations.

Recommended procedure:

a. Count the number of decimal places in the divisor.

b. Count this many places to the right of the decimal point in the dividend, and then place a point directly above, for the quotient. It may be necessary to adjoin zeros to the dividend, in locating this point.

$$.24\overline{\smash{)}.07\,2}$$

with quotient $.3$ above and $7\,2$ below.

c. Divide, ignoring the decimal points in both dividend and divisor.

If there are k decimal places in the divisor, then ignoring the decimal point and thinking of the divisor as an integer amounts to multiplying the divisor by 10^k, where k is a nonnegative integer.   If the decimal point were moved k places to the right in the dividend, this would multiply the dividend by 10^k also, as required. But there is no need actually to shift the decimal point in either divisor or dividend, since the decimal point in the quotient can be located just as well without these changes.

A common suggestion (not recommended here) is that these changes to divisor and dividend be made and recorded with a symbol "$\wedge$" called a *caret*.   However, the necessary counting of places to locate the decimal point in the quotient can be done just as easily without any marks of any kind.   Furthermore, if both divisor and dividend are left as is, without the confusion of other marks, it is much easier to use a check (to be given below) after the division is complete.   Omitting any extra marks also makes it easier to get the remainder if this should be of interest. The procedure is illustrated below for the remaining four examples given below.

$$
\begin{array}{r}
2\,3. \\
\hline
1.2\,)\,27.6 \\
24 \\
\hline
3\,6 \\
3\,6 \\
\hline
\end{array}
\qquad
\begin{array}{r}
2.3 \\
\hline
.12\,)\,.27\,6 \\
24 \\
\hline
3\,6 \\
3\,6 \\
\hline
\end{array}
\qquad
\begin{array}{r}
2\,300. \\
\hline
.012\,)\,27.600 \\
24 \\
\hline
3\,6 \\
3\,6 \\
\hline
\end{array}
\qquad
\begin{array}{r}
.0023 \\
\hline
.12\,)\,.00\,0276 \\
24 \\
\hline
36 \\
36 \\
\hline
\end{array}
$$

The division being without remainder in these examples, the dividend is the product of the divisor and the quotient.   Hence, we may use the procedure for placing the decimal point in multiplication, as a check for its placement in division.   *The number of decimal places in the divisor added to the number of decimal places in the quotient equals the number of decimal places in the dividend.*   This check also applies when the remainder is not zero.

a. Verify that in the preceding four examples we have respectively:
$$1+0=1 \qquad 2+1=3 \qquad 3+0=3 \qquad \text{and} \qquad 2+4=6$$

This check on the decimal point is simple and effective in practice, but depends on the divisor and dividend remaining as they were given for the problem.   This is the principal reason for the advice against the use of carets, arrows, or similar marks for indicating shifts of the decimal point.

Most of the time in division with decimals the steps are continued until there is no remainder, or until the remainder is small enough to be ignored.   At times, however, the remainder may be useful information.   In the following examples, all decimal points are retained in the steps to make it easier to obtain the correct remainder.

Examples:

$$
\begin{array}{r}
.031 \\
\hline
12\,)\,.376 \\
.36 \\
\hline
.016 \\
.012 \\
\hline
.004 \\
\end{array}
\qquad
\begin{array}{l}
.376 = (.03)(12) + .016 \\[1em]
.376 = (.031)(12) + .004
\end{array}
$$

b. Read from the examples below the numbers sought for the following:

 i. $37.6 = (30.)(1.2) + (\ )$; $37.6 = (31.)(1.2) + (\ )$.

 ii. $.376 = (3.)(.12) + (\ )$; $.376 = (3.1)(.12) + (\ )$.

 iii. $.00376 = (.3)(.012) + (\ )$; $.00376 = (.31)(.012) + (\ )$.

i.	**ii.**	**iii.**
$\phantom{1.2\,\overline{)}}3\,1.$	$\phantom{.12\,\overline{)}}3.1$	$\phantom{.012\,\overline{)}}.31$
$1.2\,\overline{)\,37.6}$	$.12\,\overline{)\,.37\ 6}$	$.012\,\overline{)\,.003\ 76}$
36	$.36$	$.003\ 6$
1.6	$.01\ 6$	$.000\ 16$
1.2	$.01\ 2$	$.000\ 12$
$.4$	$.00\ 4$	$.000\ 04$

ANSWER TO EXERCISE

b. i. 1.6; .4. **ii.** .016; .004. **iii.** .00016; .00004.

Problems (182)

Compute the following:

1. $\dfrac{.1248}{.048}$ **3.** $\dfrac{49.056}{8.4}$ **5.** $\dfrac{8.7699}{.093}$ **7.** $\dfrac{.12987}{.481}$

2. $\dfrac{52.50}{.0014}$ **4.** $\dfrac{489.8}{.79}$ **6.** $\dfrac{6.2916}{.84}$ **8.** $\dfrac{1.462}{.0034}$

It is desirable for division problems to develop a method for making a quick mental estimate of the most significant digit (the leftmost digit) together with its position with respect to the decimal point so that its place value is determined. One such method is to follow the paper and pencil algorithm, by first multiplying dividend and divisor by 10^k (shifting decimal points k places), so that the divisor becomes an integer.

Examples: $\dfrac{8.44}{.37} = \dfrac{844}{37} \doteq \dfrac{800}{40} = 20.$, and $\dfrac{.0252}{.37} = \dfrac{2.52}{37} \doteq \dfrac{2.40}{40} = .06.$

Instead of always changing the form so that the divisor is an integer, it may be simpler to make the divisor a number between 1 and 10, rounded off to one digit. When the divisor is in this range then the first significant digit of the quotient will be in the same place (relative to the decimal point) as the first significant digit of the dividend, or it will be one place to the right.

Examples: $\dfrac{8.44}{.37} \doteq \dfrac{84.4}{3.7} \doteq \dfrac{80}{4} = 20.$, and $\dfrac{.0252}{.37} = \dfrac{.252}{3.7} \doteq \dfrac{.24}{4} = .06.$

The reader is urged to experiment with a variety of methods. In the next example, both numbers have been changed to scientific notation, together with an approximation, so that the division can be exact for one digit.

Examples:

$$\frac{8.44}{.37} \doteq \frac{8(10)^0}{4(10)^{-1}} = 2(10)^{0-(-1)} = 2(10)^1 = 20$$

$$\frac{.252}{374} \doteq \frac{2.4(10)^{-1}}{4(10)^2} = .6(10)^{-1-2} = .6(10)^{-3} = .0006$$

Problems (183)

For problems 1 to 16, obtain an approximation of one significant digit.

1. $(.851)(3.46)$ 5. $\dfrac{3.46}{.851}$ 9. $\dfrac{.0671}{.267}$ 13. $\dfrac{47.75}{.0638}$

2. $(2.915)(16.07)$ 6. $\dfrac{16.07}{2.915}$ 10. $\dfrac{.056}{36.12}$ 14. $\dfrac{.00785}{.354}$

3. $\dfrac{.851}{3.46}$ 7. $\dfrac{.267}{.0671}$ 11. $(47.75)(.0638)$ 15. $\dfrac{.0638}{47.75}$

4. $\dfrac{2.915}{16.07}$ 8. $\dfrac{36.12}{.056}$ 12. $(.00785)(.354)$ 16. $\dfrac{.354}{.00785}$

For problems 17 to 24, locate the decimal points for which the three significant digits at the left are given, as they might be read from a slide rule.

17. $\dfrac{.466}{15.44} \doteq 306$ 19. $\dfrac{4.75}{.0851} \doteq 558$ 21. $\dfrac{28.2}{507} \doteq 557$ 23. $\dfrac{505}{.634} \doteq 797$

18. $\dfrac{.869}{.0156} \doteq 557$ 20. $\dfrac{30.1}{747} \doteq 403$ 22. $\dfrac{.073}{320} \doteq 228$ 24. $\dfrac{94.}{.0808} \doteq 116$

For problems 25 to 34, the quotients can be computed exactly in decimal form.

25. $\dfrac{.1248}{.048}$ 27. $\dfrac{49.056}{8.4}$ 29. $\dfrac{8.7699}{.093}$ 31. $\dfrac{7.0000}{16}$ 33. $\dfrac{1.462}{.0034}$

26. $\dfrac{52.50}{.0014}$ 28. $\dfrac{489.8}{.79}$ 30. $\dfrac{12.328}{.023}$ 32. $\dfrac{16.740}{310.}$ 34. $\dfrac{3.000}{8}$

20-5. Approximation of Rational Numbers by Rational Numbers

The algorithms for computing with decimal fractions have many advantages over the corresponding methods of computing with the same numbers as given in common fraction form. Unfortunately, there are relatively few rational numbers that have exact representations as decimal fractions with a finite number of digits, while the others have decimal forms only in an approximate sense. The search for decimal fraction approximations for rational numbers is a special case of the following problem:

Given a rational number $\frac{a}{b}$, determine a rational number $\frac{c}{d}$, of a *specified form*, such that $\left| \frac{a}{b} - \frac{c}{d} \right|$ shall be less than a given number e, where $e > 0$. The particular forms we shall be seeking will be those where the denominator d of $\frac{c}{d}$ is p^n, where p and n are nonnegative integers and $p \geq 2$. If $p = 10$, then $\frac{c}{10^n}$ is a decimal approximation to $\frac{a}{b}$. The discussion will be limited to the case where $\frac{a}{b} > 0$, and $a < b$, since the extension to the other cases is immediate.

Example: Let $\frac{a}{b} = \frac{5}{8}$, and let $p = 3$. We seek integers c_1, c_2, c_3, ... such that $\frac{5}{8} \doteq \frac{c_1}{3} + \frac{c_2}{3^2} + \frac{c_3}{3^3} + \cdots$, where

$$\left| \frac{5}{8} - \sum_{k=1}^{r} \frac{c_k}{3^k} \right| < \frac{1}{3^r}$$

To meet this inequality it is necessary that $c_i < 3$ for all i. This is a polynomial in negative powers of 3, whose place value notation is $\frac{5}{8} \doteq \cdot c_1 c_2 c_3 \cdots \text{(three)}$. The method to be used is based on repeatedly multiplying $\frac{a}{b}$ by 1, in the form of $p\left(\frac{1}{p}\right)$.

Solution:

$$\frac{5}{8} = \frac{5}{8}(1) = \frac{5}{8}(3)\left(\frac{1}{3}\right) = \frac{15}{8}\left(\frac{1}{3}\right) = \frac{8+7}{8}\left(\frac{1}{3}\right) = \left(1 + \frac{7}{8}\right)\left(\frac{1}{3}\right) = \frac{1}{3} + \frac{7}{8}\left(\frac{1}{3}\right)$$

If $\frac{5}{8}$ is approximated by $\frac{1}{3}$, or $.1_{\text{(three)}}$, the error of $\frac{7}{8}\left(\frac{1}{3}\right)$ is less than $\frac{1}{3}$. To get a better approximation, the process is repeated on $\frac{7}{8}\left(\frac{1}{3}\right)$.

$$\frac{7}{8}\left(\frac{1}{3}\right) = \frac{7}{8}\left(\frac{1}{3}\right)(3)\left(\frac{1}{3}\right) = \left(\frac{21}{8}\right)\left(\frac{1}{3^2}\right) = \left(\frac{16+5}{8}\right)\left(\frac{1}{3^2}\right) = \left(2 + \frac{5}{8}\right)\left(\frac{1}{3^2}\right)$$

$$\frac{5}{8} = \frac{1}{3} + \frac{2}{3^2} + \frac{5}{8}\left(\frac{1}{3^2}\right)$$

If $\frac{5}{8}$ is approximated by $\frac{1}{3} + \frac{2}{3^2}$, or $\frac{5}{9}$, or $.12_{\text{(three)}}$, the error of $\frac{5}{8}\left(\frac{1}{3^2}\right)$ is less than $\frac{1}{3^2}$.

$$\frac{5}{8}\left(\frac{1}{3^2}\right) = \left(\frac{15}{8}\right)\left(\frac{1}{3^3}\right) = \left(1 + \frac{7}{8}\right)\left(\frac{1}{3^3}\right) = \frac{1}{3^3} + \frac{7}{8}\left(\frac{1}{3^3}\right)$$

$$\frac{5}{8} = \frac{1}{3} + \frac{2}{3^2} + \frac{1}{3^3} + \frac{7}{8}\left(\frac{1}{3^3}\right)$$

$\frac{5}{8} \doteq \frac{1}{3}$	$\frac{5}{8} \doteq \frac{1}{3}$	$\frac{5}{8} \doteq .1_{\text{(three)}}$
$\frac{5}{8} \doteq \frac{1}{3} + \frac{2}{3^2}$	$\frac{5}{8} \doteq \frac{5}{9}$	$\frac{5}{8} \doteq .12_{\text{(three)}}$
$\frac{5}{8} \doteq \frac{1}{3} + \frac{2}{3^2} + \frac{1}{3^3}$	$\frac{5}{8} \doteq \frac{16}{27}$	$\frac{5}{8} \doteq .121_{\text{(three)}}$

. . . .

The process above will not terminate, and give an exact representation of $\frac{5}{8}$ in the required form. However, at the rth stage the error is less that $\frac{1}{3^r}$, and hence can be made as small as desired.

If a decimal approximation is desired for $\frac{5}{8}$, the multiplier will be $(10)\left(\frac{1}{10}\right)$, and this can be handled readily in the division algorithm because of the following relations: $5. = 5(10)\left(\frac{1}{10}\right) = \frac{50}{10} = 5.0$; $5. = \frac{500}{100} = 5.00$; and so on. Joining an extra zero, which is to the right of the decimal point and also to the right of a non-zero digit, has the effect of multiplying both numerator and denominator by 10, in the common fraction form.

In the following example, the steps are given in detail both for the common fraction and the decimal fraction algorithm, so that a comparative study can be made.

Example:

$$\frac{5}{8} = \frac{5}{8}(1)$$

$$= \frac{5}{8}(10)\left(\frac{1}{10}\right) = \frac{50}{8}\left(\frac{1}{10}\right)$$

$$= \frac{48+2}{8}\left(\frac{1}{10}\right) = \frac{6}{10} + \frac{1}{8}\left(\frac{2}{10}\right)$$

$$= \frac{60}{100} + \frac{1}{8}\left(\frac{20}{100}\right)$$

$$= \frac{60}{100} + \frac{1}{8}\left(\frac{16+4}{100}\right)$$

$$= \frac{60}{100} + \frac{2}{100} + \frac{1}{8}\left(\frac{4}{100}\right)$$

$$= \frac{62}{100} + \frac{1}{8}\left(\frac{4}{100}\right)$$

$$= \frac{620}{1000} + \frac{1}{8}\left(\frac{40}{1000}\right)$$

$$= \frac{620}{1000} + \frac{5}{1000} = \frac{625}{1000}$$

Step

1. $8\,|\,5.$

2. $8\,|\,5.0$ (quotient .)

3.
$$\begin{array}{r} .6 \\ 8\,|\,5.0 \\ 4.8 \\ \hline .2 \end{array}$$

4.
$$\begin{array}{r} .60 \\ 8\,|\,5.00 \\ 4.80 \\ \hline .20 \end{array}$$

5.
$$\begin{array}{r} .02 \\ .60 \\ 8\,|\,5.00 \\ 4.80 \\ \hline .20 \\ .16 \\ \hline .04 \end{array}$$

6.
$$\begin{array}{r} .620 \\ 8\,|\,5.000 \\ 4.800 \\ \hline .200 \\ .160 \\ \hline .040 \end{array}$$

7.
$$\begin{array}{r} .005 \\ .620 \\ 8\,|\,5.000 \\ 4.800 \\ \hline .200 \\ .160 \\ \hline .040 \\ .040 \end{array}$$

Conventional Form

$$
\begin{array}{r}
.625 \\
8\overline{\smash{)}5.000} \\
4\,8 \\
\hline
20 \\
16 \\
\hline
40 \\
40 \\
\hline
\end{array}
$$

We return the first example where $\dfrac{5}{8}$ was to be approximated by what may be called a basimal fraction (base three). The compactness of the division algorithm can be made available in this case also, by first changing both 5 and 8 to base three, and then doing the computation in this base.

$$
5 = 12_{(three)}
$$

$$
8 = 22_{(three)}
$$

$$
\begin{array}{r}
.121 \\
22\overline{\smash{)}12.000_{(three)}} \\
2\,2 \\
\hline
2\,10 \\
1\,21 \\
\hline
120 \\
22 \\
\hline
21\ \text{etc.}
\end{array}
$$

$$
\frac{12}{22} \doteq .121_{(three)}
$$

The fraction $\dfrac{5}{8}$ was found to have an exact decimal equivalent of .625. If $\dfrac{a}{b}$ is a common fraction in lowest terms, it will have an exact decimal equivalent if and only if the denominator b does not have prime factors other than 2 or 5. The fraction $\dfrac{a}{b}$ (in lowest terms) can be expressed exactly in the form $\dfrac{c}{p^n}$ only when b has no other prime divisors than the prime divisors of p. Hence $\dfrac{5}{8}$ could only be approximated by the form $\dfrac{c}{3^n}$.

When a rational number has a common fraction form where the denominator has a prime factor other than 2 or 5, the decimal approximation never "comes out even" and a decision rule must be adopted for an acceptable approximation. Decimal approximations to a rational number can be given to a certain precision by stating the place value of the rightmost significant digit, or to a certain accuracy by specifying the number of significant digits. The last digit computed will be significant and hence we must be guided by our rounding off conventions when we record this digit.

Example:

$\frac{2}{35} \doteq .1$ That is, .1 is an approximation that is precise to tenths,

since $\frac{2}{35}$ is closer to .1 than to .0.   .1 is

also an approximation of one significant
digit, but the best approximation of one significant digit is .06.

$\frac{2}{35} \doteq .06$ .06 is precise to hundredths.

$\frac{2}{35} \doteq .057$ .057 is precise to thousandths, and accurate to two significant digits.

$\frac{2}{35} \doteq .0571$ .0571 is precise to ten thousandths and is accurate to
three significant digits.

$$\begin{array}{r} .0571 \\ 35\overline{\smash{\big)}2.0000} \\ \underline{1\,75} \\ 250 \\ \underline{245} \\ 50 \\ \underline{35} \\ 15 \end{array}$$

To be sure of the last statement, we must know that the next digit
for the quotient would be less than 5, and this is the case since the remainder of 15 is less than half of the divisor 35.   If the remainder were
18 or more (one half of 35 or more, then the next quotient digit would be
5 or more and we would round off to .0572.

Problems (184)

For problems 1 and 2, indicate the common multiplier for numerator and denominator that will give an equivalent fraction with a denominator that is a power
of 10.   Then give the decimal equivalent.

Example: $\frac{7}{40} = \frac{7}{2^3 \cdot 5} = \frac{7}{2^3 \cdot 5}\left(\frac{5^2}{5^2}\right) = \frac{7 \cdot 5^2}{2^3 \cdot 5^3} = \frac{175}{1000} = .175$

1. a. $\frac{3}{8}$ **b.** $\frac{11}{20}$ **c.** $\frac{7}{25}$ **d.** $\frac{11}{16}$ **e.** $\frac{5}{32}$ **f.** $\frac{11}{8}$ **g.** $\frac{19}{125}$

2. a. $\frac{7}{8}$ **b.** $\frac{9}{16}$ **c.** $\frac{7}{20}$ **d.** $\frac{11}{25}$ **e.** $\frac{13}{32}$ **f.** $\frac{7}{4}$ **g.** $\frac{3}{40}$

For problems 3 to 8, use the division algorithm to obtain decimal equivalents for
the following, all of which can be exact.

3. $\frac{15}{16}$ **4.** $\frac{33}{40}$ **5.** $\frac{39}{80}$ **6.** $\frac{5}{64}$ **7.** $2\frac{5}{8}$ **8.** $3\frac{3}{4}$

For problems 9 to 18, obtain basimal fraction equivalents in the base suggested,
all of which can be exact.   It is suggested that both of the methods used in the
example problems be tried.

9. $\frac{5}{8}$ (two) **11.** $\frac{5}{8}$ (four) **13.** $\frac{7}{9}$ (six) **15.** $\frac{3}{4}$ (eight) **17.** $\frac{19}{27}$ (three)

10. $\frac{13}{16}$ (two) **12.** $\frac{13}{16}$ (eight) **14.** $\frac{2}{9}$ (six) **16.** $\frac{3}{4}$ (twelve) **18.** $\frac{23}{32}$ (four)

For problems 19 to 30, give each of the following six approximations for each rational number:

A. To the nearest tenth (one decimal place).
B. To the nearest hundredth (two decimal places).
C. To the nearest thousandth (three decimal places).
D. To one significant digit.
E. To two significant digits.
F. To three significant digits.

19. $\dfrac{3}{7}$ 21. $\dfrac{2}{9}$ 23. $\dfrac{2}{31}$ 25. $\dfrac{12}{7}$ 27. $\dfrac{25}{14}$ 29. $\dfrac{4}{51}$

20. $\dfrac{6}{7}$ 22. $\dfrac{9}{13}$ 24. $\dfrac{3}{19}$ 26. $\dfrac{15}{11}$ 28. $\dfrac{35}{18}$ 30. $\dfrac{3}{47}$

For problems 31 to 38, an approximation to three significant digits is to be given by a basimal fraction for the specified base.

31. $\dfrac{2}{3}$ (four)   33. $\dfrac{3}{4}$ (five)   35. $\dfrac{1}{12}$ (three)   37. $\dfrac{4}{5}$ (eight)

32. $\dfrac{3}{11}$ (three)   34. $\dfrac{2}{3}$ (five)   36. $\dfrac{1}{4}$ (five)   38. $\dfrac{2}{12}$ (seven)

Methods have been given for approximating $\dfrac{5}{8}$ by $.121\cdots_{\text{(three)}}$, and for determining an exact representation of this common fraction by $.625_{\text{(ten)}}$ and $.101_{\text{(two)}}$. We now consider some possible algorithms for transforming any one of these forms into another.

Example: To transform .625 to $.121\cdots_{\text{(three)}}$.

.625 is multiplied by 3 repeatedly, each time isolating and recording the integral part of the product (if any), and continuing to multiply the fractional part by 3.

To see why this works, analyze the same computation as given below.

$$
\begin{array}{r}
.625 \\
3 \\
\hline
\boxed{1}.875 \\
3 \\
\hline
\boxed{2}.625 \\
3 \\
\hline
\boxed{1}.875
\end{array}
$$

$$.625 \doteq .121_{\text{(three)}}$$

$$.625 = .625\left(\frac{3}{3}\right) = (1.875)\left(\frac{1}{3}\right) = (1 + .875)\left(\frac{1}{3}\right) = \frac{1}{3} + .875\left(\frac{1}{3}\right)$$

$$= \frac{1}{3} + .875\left(\frac{3}{3^2}\right) = \frac{1}{3} + 2.625\left(\frac{1}{3^2}\right) = \frac{1}{3} + \frac{2}{3^2} + .625\left(\frac{1}{3^2}\right) \text{ etc.}$$

Example: To transform $.625$ to $.101_{(two)}$.

Note that a zero is recorded when the product has no integral part, that is, it is less than 1.

$$.625$$
$$2$$

$$\boxed{1}\,.250$$
$$2$$

$$\boxed{0}\,.500$$
$$2$$

$$\boxed{1}\,.000$$

$$.625 = .101_{(two)}$$

In both of these examples, we were working from the familiar base of 10 toward an unfamiliar base. We now wish to consider changes going the other way. If a rational number has an exact basimal representation, the polynomial form may be transformed as below for any base b.

$$\begin{aligned}.rstu_{(\text{base } b)} &= rb^{-1} + sb^{-2} + tb^{-3} + ub^{-4}\\ &= b^{-1}(r + sb^{-1} + tb^{-2} + ub^{-3})\\ &= b^{-1}(r + b^{-1}(s + tb^{-1} + ub^{-2}))\\ &= b^{-1}(r + b^{-1}(s + b^{-1}(t + b^{-1}u)))\end{aligned}$$

Begin with u. Then multiply by b^{-1}. Then add t. Then multiply by b^{-1}. Then add s. Then multiply by b^{-1}. Then add r. Then multiply by b^{-1}.

Examples: To transform $.625$ to $\dfrac{625}{1000}$.

$$5\left(\frac{1}{10}\right) = \frac{5}{10} \quad \frac{5}{10} + 2 = \frac{25}{10} \quad \frac{25}{10}\left(\frac{1}{10}\right) = \frac{25}{100} \quad \frac{25}{100} + 6 = \frac{625}{100} \quad \frac{625}{100}\left(\frac{1}{10}\right) = \frac{625}{1000}$$

To transform $.101_{(two)}$ to $\dfrac{5}{8}$.

$$1\left(\frac{1}{2}\right) = \frac{1}{2} \quad \frac{1}{2} + 0 = \frac{1}{2} \quad \frac{1}{2}\left(\frac{1}{2}\right) = \frac{1}{4} \quad \frac{1}{4} + 1 = \frac{5}{4} \quad \frac{5}{4}\left(\frac{1}{2}\right) = \frac{5}{8}$$

In all of the preceding examples we began with an exact form and worked toward either another exact form or an approximation. But a change from an exact form to an approximation is not reversible, unless of course there is some way to eliminate the error and thus replace the approximation by an exact form.

Example: To transform $.121\cdots_{(three)}$ to a common fraction approximation of $\dfrac{5}{8}$.

$$1\left(\frac{1}{3}\right) = \frac{1}{3} \quad \frac{1}{3} + 2 = \frac{7}{3} \quad \frac{7}{3}\left(\frac{1}{3}\right) = \frac{7}{9} \quad \frac{7}{9} + 1 = \frac{16}{9} \quad \frac{16}{9}\left(\frac{1}{3}\right) = \frac{16}{27}$$

$$\frac{16}{27} \doteq \frac{5}{8}, \text{ since } \frac{5}{8} \doteq .121_{(three)}, \text{ and } .121_{(three)} = \frac{16}{27}.$$

It is also possible to go directly from one basimal representation to another, even when both are in an unfamiliar base, by carrying out the computations in an unfamiliar base (the correct one!). We shall not discuss such methods, but the reader is challenged to discover them for himself, if interested. For example, try changing $.101_{(two)}$ directly to $.121 \cdots_{(three)}$.

Problems (185)

1. Transform .9375 to: **a.** base 8   **b.** base 6   **c.** base 12
2. Transform .6875 to: **a.** base 2   **b.** base 4   **c.** base 8
3. Express as a common fraction (with decimal numerals).
      a. $.201_{(three)}$ **b.** $.0204_{(five)}$ **c.** $.333_{(four)}$
4. Express as a common fraction (with decimal numerals).
      a. $.132_{(five)}$ **b.** $.222_{(three)}$ **c.** $.10101_{(two)}$

Note: An alternate method of transforming $.101_{(two)}$ to $\frac{5}{8}$ is as follows:

$$.101_{(two)} = \frac{.101_{(two)} \; 1000_{(two)}}{1000_{(two)}} = \frac{101._{(two)}}{1000_{(two)}} = \frac{5}{8}$$

5. Use this alternate method for problem 3.
6. Use this alternate method for problem 4.

In problems 7 and 8, the numerals are to be transformed to base 10 and given both a mixed number and an improper fraction form. A variety of methods are available. Three suggestions are:

A. Use face and place value to transform each digit separately, and combine.
B. Transform the integral and fractional parts separately.
C. Use the device suggested in the note following problem 4.

7. **a.** $21.12_{(three)}$ **b.** $132.21_{(four)}$ **c.** $3.104_{(five)}$ **d.** $101.011_{(two)}$
8. **a.** $42.3_{(six)}$ **b.** $2.22_{(five)}$ **c.** $10.32_{(four)}$ **d.** $11.1011_{(two)}$

20-6. Repeating Decimals

The rational number $\frac{3}{16}$ or $\frac{3}{2^4}$ has an exact decimal equivalent of .1875. The division algorithm yields a zero remainder at the fourth step. We say that .1875 is a *terminating* decimal. The rational number $\frac{3}{11}$ has a denominator with prime divisors other than 2 or 5; in this case no exact decimal equivalent exists, and the division process never produces a zero remainder. However, each remainder must be less than 11, and there are only 10 nonzero natural numbers that are less than 11. Hence, after not more than 10 divisions, the same remainders must start appearing again. And when this happens the digits in the quotient must start a cycle of repetition also. (This assumes that by this time all the nonzero digits in the original dividend have been used, which must happen eventually.)

In the example here the repetition occurs after only two stages of the division algorithm, and it is evident that further division will continue to pro- $\underline{.27272}$
duce the digits 2 and 7 over and over again.

The decimal $.27272 \cdots$ is an example of a *nonterminating* decimal. Because of the repetition of the digits 2 and 7, it is called a *repeating* decimal with a *repetend* of 27.   It may be represented by the notation $.\overline{27}$, with a bar over the repetend.

There are then two cases that arise when a decimal equivalent is sought for a rational number $\dfrac{N_1}{N_2}$ with N_1 and N_2 being relatively prime natural numbers.

$$
\begin{array}{r}
.27272 \\
11\overline{)3.00000} \\
2\,2 \\
\hline
80 \\
77 \\
\hline
30 \\
22 \\
\hline
80 \\
77 \\
\hline
30 \\
22 \\
\hline
8
\end{array}
$$

A. The division process will terminate only when $N_2 = 1$, or when N_2 has no prime divisors other than 2 or 5.

B. In all other cases, while the division will not terminate with a zero remainder, the digits in the quotient will eventually repeat, and the number of digits in the repetend will not be greater than $N_2 - 1$.

When a decimal equivalent is sought for $\dfrac{1}{3}$, the result is $.333 \cdots$, or $.\overline{3}$.   For a graphical model, we may consider the problem of locating the division point $\dfrac{1}{3}$ on a decimal scale (Ten equal subdivisions of the unit.)

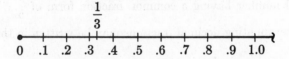

It is evident as we begin that $0 < \dfrac{1}{3} < 1$, and after one step of the division we find that $0 < .3 < \dfrac{1}{3} < .4 < 1$, as illustrated.

The division is carried a step further, with the following results as shown.   For clarity, only the portion of the scale between .3 or .30 and .4 or .40 is shown, and it has been magnified in scale by 10 times.

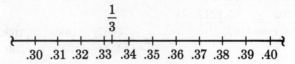

At this stage we have $0 < .3 < .33 < \dfrac{1}{3} < .34 < .4 < 1$.

We have now a pattern emerging of two sequences, both of which approach $\dfrac{1}{3}$ as a limit.   The sequence of approximations to $\dfrac{1}{3}$ given by .3, .33, .333, . . . is monotonic increasing with $\frac{1}{3}$ as an upper bound. The sequence of approxima-

tions given by .4, .34, .334, ... is monotonic decreasing with $\frac{1}{3}$ as a lower bound.

The differences between $\frac{1}{3}$ and the approximations to it are:

$$\frac{1}{3} - \frac{3}{10} = \frac{1}{30} \qquad\qquad\qquad \frac{4}{10} - \frac{1}{3} = \frac{2}{30}$$

$$\frac{1}{3} - \frac{33}{100} = \frac{1}{300} \qquad\qquad \frac{34}{100} - \frac{1}{3} = \frac{2}{300}$$

$$\frac{1}{3} - \frac{333}{1000} = \frac{1}{3000} \qquad \frac{334}{1000} - \frac{1}{3} = \frac{2}{3000}$$

$$\text{etc.} \qquad \text{etc.}$$

By continuing the sequence .3, .33, .333, ... the error in the approximation can never be made equal to zero, but it can be made less than any number e, as long as $e > 0$. The repeating decimal $.\overline{3}$ is accepted as another name for $\frac{1}{3}$, and we write

$$\frac{1}{3} = .\overline{3}.$$

We have found that every rational number has a decimal representation in either terminating or repeating form. We now show that every repeating decimal represents a rational number having a common fraction form of $\frac{a}{b}$. We have already indicated how terminating decimal fractions may be written in this form.

Example: To find the common fraction form for x, where $x = 4.5\overline{12}$.

$10^1 x = 45.\overline{12}$ This places the decimal point at the left of the first digit of the repetend.

$10^2(10x) = 4512.\overline{12}$ This shifts the decimal point as many places as the number of digits in the repetend.

While each of the two numbers thus obtained remains a repeating decimal (with an infinite sequence of digits), their difference terminates.

$$
\begin{aligned}
1000x &= 4512.1212\cdots\\
10x &= 45.1212\cdots\\
\hline
990x &= 4467.
\end{aligned}
\qquad x = \frac{4467}{990} = \frac{1489}{330} = 4\frac{169}{330}
$$

a. Solve the example, by working on the fractional part separately. That is, obtain a common fraction form for $.5\overline{12}$.

The method of the example can be applied in the general case. Let x be a positive number, less than 1, having a decimal representation of

$$.a_1a_2 \cdots a_m \overline{b_1b_2 \cdots b_n}$$

Then $10^m \cdot x = a_1a_2 \cdots a_m .\overline{b_1b_2 \cdots b_n}$

And $10^n \cdot 10^m \cdot x = a_1a_2 \cdots a_m b_1b_2 \cdots b_n .\overline{b_1b_2 \cdots b_n}$

Then, as in the example, the difference between these two numbers is a terminating decimal.

$$10^{m+n} \cdot x - 10^m \cdot x = a_1a_2 \cdots a_m b_1b_2 \cdots b_n - a_1a_2 \cdots a_m$$

$$(10^{m+n} - 10^m) \cdot x = a_1a_2 \cdots a_m b_1b_2 \cdots b_n - a_1a_2 \cdots a_m$$

$$x = \frac{a_1a_2 \cdots a_m b_1b_2 \cdots b_n - a_1a_2 \cdots a_m}{10^{m+n} - 10^m}$$

The extension of the result to include rationals that are integral, or negative, presents no difficulties. Every rational number also has, for a given base r, a basimal representation. If for a rational number $\frac{N_1}{N_2}$, the prime divisors of N_2 are also divisors of r, then this basimal fraction will terminate; otherwise it will repeat with a period of not more than $N_2 - 1$ digits. This basimal form can be computed by expressing N_1 and N_2 in the base r, and using the division algorithm.

Examples:

```
        .142857                    .125                        .1
    7 | 1.000000(ten)          7 | 1.000(nine)           10 | 1.0(seven)
        7                          7                          1 0
       ──                        ──                         
        30                         20                        .05
        28                         15                   11 | 1.00(six)
       ──                         ──                         55
        20                         40                          1
        14                         38                        
       ──                         ──
        60                          1
        56
       ──
        40
        35                         .1
       ──                      7 | 1.0(eight)
        50                         7
        49                        
       ──                          1
         1
```

Hence $\frac{1}{7} = .\overline{142857}_{(ten)} = .\overline{125}_{(nine)}$

$= .\overline{1}_{(eight)} = .1_{(seven)} = .\overline{05}_{(six)}$

b. What is the basimal representation of $\frac{1}{7}$ in base five? In base four? In base three? In base two?

It is possible to develop a theory for computing with rational numbers as expressed in the repeating decimal notation, but we shall not do this. One of the problems to be faced is the lack of uniqueness for some numbers. For example $\frac{1}{2} = .5\overline{0}$ and also $\frac{1}{2} = .4\overline{9}$. For practical computations with rational numbers the repeating decimal notation is not used.   Instead, a decision is made with regard to the allowable error and an approximation is chosen within this limit.   If an exact number is required, then the common fraction form can be used.

Sometimes an attempt is made to extend the possibilities for exact decimal equivalents by writing such a fraction as $\dfrac{4\frac{1}{3}}{100}$ in the form $.04\frac{1}{3}$.

Such so-called *complex* decimal fractions should be avoided.   They are not well adapted to computation, and are a source of error because of confusion regarding the place value to be assigned to the common fraction.   In the decimal fraction .043 the digit 3 is in the thousandths place.   That is, 3 here has a place value of 10^{-3} or $\dfrac{1}{1000}$.   In $.04\frac{1}{3}$ the fraction $\dfrac{1}{3}$ also seems to be in the third decimal place.   But since $\dfrac{1}{3}$ is not a digit, it is not assigned a place value of its own, but rather is given the place value of the digit at its left.   Since 4 is in the hundredths position in this example, then $\dfrac{1}{3}$ here represents $\dfrac{1}{3}$ of $\dfrac{1}{100}$.   Thus, $\dfrac{4\frac{1}{3}}{100}$ can be approximated by $\dfrac{4}{100}$ or .04 if the error is not too great and can be represented exactly by $\dfrac{(3)\left(4\frac{1}{3}\right)}{(3)(100)} = \dfrac{13}{300}$.   This can then be approximated, if desired, by .04, .043, .0433, and so on, according to the precision needed.

c. Since $.04\frac{1}{2}$ is the same as .045, does this mean that $\dfrac{1}{2}$ is the same as 5?

ANSWERS TO EXERCISES

a. $z = .5\overline{12}$, $10z = 5.\overline{12}$, $1000z = 512.\overline{12}$; $1000z - 10z = 990z = 512.\overline{12} - 5.\overline{12} = 507$; $z = \dfrac{507}{990} = \dfrac{169}{330}$.   **b.** $\dfrac{1}{7} = .\overline{032412}_{\text{(five)}} = .\overline{021}_{\text{(four)}} = .\overline{010212}_{\text{(three)}} = .\overline{001}_{\text{(two)}}$.   **c.** No.   Rather, $\dfrac{1}{2}\left(\dfrac{1}{100}\right) = 5\left(\dfrac{1}{1000}\right)$.

Problems (186)

For problems 1 to 18, transform each rational number to a repeating decimal fraction, placing a bar over the repetend.

1. $\dfrac{2}{3}$	4. $\dfrac{15}{11}$	7. $\dfrac{1}{13}$	10. $\dfrac{7}{9}$	13. $\dfrac{5}{999}$	16. $\dfrac{7}{18}$
2. $\dfrac{7}{11}$	5. $\dfrac{5}{37}$	8. $\dfrac{1}{41}$	11. $\dfrac{25}{99}$	14. $\dfrac{143}{999}$	17. $\dfrac{7}{90}$
3. $\dfrac{7}{3}$	6. $\dfrac{9}{37}$	9. $\dfrac{4}{9}$	12. $\dfrac{41}{99}$	15. $\dfrac{5}{12}$	18. $\dfrac{21}{990}$

For problems 19 to 28, represent each by a quotient of two natural numbers.

19. $.1\overline{2}$ **21.** $.\overline{12}$ **23.** $.0\overline{102}$ **25.** $.435\overline{91}$ **27.** $.007\overline{007}$

20. $.6\overline{0}$ **22.** $.0\overline{6}$ **24.** $.06\overline{03}$ **26.** $.\overline{037}$ **28.** $.555\overline{5}$

29. Find natural numbers x and y such that:

    a. $\dfrac{x}{y} = 2.\overline{15}$ **b.** $\dfrac{x}{y} = 2.1\overline{51}$

30. Find natural numbers x and y such that:

    a. $\dfrac{x}{y} = .5\overline{0}$ **b.** $\dfrac{x}{y} = .4\overline{9}$

31. Determine basimal fractions for $\dfrac{3}{5}$ in the following bases:

    a. nine   **b.** six   **c.** five   **d.** four   **e.** three

32. Determine basimal fractions for $\dfrac{1}{4}$ in the following bases:

    a. eight   **b.** five   **c.** four   **d.** three   **e.** two

33. Find natural numbers x and y (in decimal numeral form) such that:

    a. $\dfrac{x}{y} = .\overline{03}_{\text{(seven)}}$ **b.** $\dfrac{x}{y} = .\overline{21}_{\text{(five)}}$

34. Find natural numbers x and y (in decimal numeral form) such that:

    a. $\dfrac{x}{y} = .\overline{03}_{\text{(five)}}$ **b.** $\dfrac{x}{y} = .0\overline{3}_{\text{(five)}}$

35. Arrange the following numbers in increasing order of size:
$$.3\overline{9}, \ .4\overline{1}, \ .\overline{39}, \ .4\overline{1}$$

36. Express $.\overline{3} - .3$ as

    a. a common fraction   **b.** a repeating decimal

20-7. The Arithmetical Mean

Suppose we are given a set of n numbers $\{x_1, x_2, x_3, \ldots, x_n\}$ and wish to determine a single number $\bar{x}$ such that if each x_i be replaced by $\bar{x}$, then the sum $x_1 + x_2 + x_3 + \cdots + x_n$ is not changed. The condition to be met is that

$$\underbrace{\bar{x} + \bar{x} + \bar{x} + \cdots + \bar{x}}_{n \text{ terms}} = n\bar{x} = x_1 + x_2 + x_3 + \cdots x_n$$

Hence $\qquad \bar{x} = \dfrac{x_1 + x_2 + x_3 + \cdots x_n}{n} = \dfrac{1}{n}\sum_{i=1}^{i=n} x_i$

The number $\bar{x}$ (read "x-bar") is said to be the *arithmetical mean* of the set of numbers $\{x_1, x_2, x_3, \ldots, x_n\}$. It is also commonly referred to as the average of these numbers, but one should be aware that the word "average" is used with a variety of meanings, including others than the one given above. One of the meanings of average is that of being "typical." The definition of arithmetical mean shows that it is typical of a set of numbers in the sense that each member of the set can be replaced by the mean without disturbing the sum of the numbers.

For two numbers x_1 and x_2, we have $\bar{x} = \dfrac{x_1 + x_2}{2}$. A graphical model of this case shows that the word "mean" has somewhat the same meaning as "in the middle."

> **Example:** A boy rode his bicycle 7 miles during the first hour and then 3 more miles during the second hour. How many miles per hour did he average?

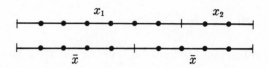

In some situations where an average is to be computed, the sum $S = x_1 + x_2 + x_3 + \cdots + x_n$ is known, so that the formula becomes $\bar{x} = \dfrac{S}{n}$.

Problems (187)

1. Complete the following, meeting the condition that both numbers supplied be the same.
   a. $13 + 23 = (\ ) + (\ )$
   b. $.0092 + .0018 = (\ ) + (\ )$
   c. $\dfrac{1}{8} + \dfrac{9}{16} = (\ ) + (\ )$

2. Show that the mean of x_1 and x_2, with $x_1 < x_2$, can be computed by:
   a. Adding half their difference to the smaller number.
   b. Subtracting half their difference from the larger number.

For problems 3 to 14, compute the arithmetical mean, considering all numbers to be exact.

3. 4, 6, 8, 10, 12   7. $\dfrac{1}{5}, \dfrac{1}{6}, \dfrac{1}{30}$ 11. .489, .498, .522, .527

4. 1, 5, 9, 13, 17   8. $\dfrac{1}{2}, \dfrac{1}{3}, \dfrac{1}{6}$ 12. 14.1, 14.3, 15.0, 15.1, 15.5

5. 0, 0, 0, 4   9. .03, .3, 3.   13. $-.1, +.3, -.4, +.9, -.7$

6. 1, 1000   10. .642, .6   14. $-30, -12, -18, -24, -11$

For the numbers $x_1, x_2, x_3, \ldots, x_n$, the amounts by which they differ from their mean $\bar{x}$ are the numbers

$$x_1 - \bar{x}, \ x_2 - \bar{x}, \ x_3 - \bar{x}, \ \ldots, \ x_n - \bar{x}$$

These quantities are called the *deviations* from the mean of the set of numbers. By adding the first and second terms separately we can conclude that the sum of all n deviations will always be zero.

a. In problems 3 and 11 of set (187), verify that the sum of the deviations is zero.

The above property of the sum of the deviations provides a check on the computation of the arithmetic mean, and suggests the following alternate computation.

For the numbers $x_1, x_2, x_3, \ldots, x_n$, let h be an estimate of $\bar{x}$, and let $y_i = x_i - h$ for $i = 1, 2, 3, \ldots, n$. By adding these n equations, we have

$$\sum_{i=1}^{i=n} y_i = \sum_{i=1}^{i=n} (x_i - h) = \left(\sum_{i=1}^{i=n} x_i \right) - nh$$

$$= n\bar{x} - nh$$

Hence $n\bar{x} = \sum_{i=1}^{i=n} y_i + nh$ and $\bar{x} = \dfrac{1}{n} \sum_{i=1}^{i=n} y_i + h.$

Let $\bar{y} = \dfrac{1}{n} \sum_{i=1}^{i=n} y_i.$ Then $\bar{x} = \bar{y} + h.$

For any assumed arithmetic mean h, add to this assumed mean the arithmetic mean of the deviations from it, to get the true mean.

Example: Let $x_1 = 70$, $x_2 = 75$, $x_3 = 76$, $x_4 = 89$, $x_5 = 100$, and suppose $h = 80$.

Then $y_1 = -10$, $y_2 = -5$, $y_3 = -4$, $y_4 = +9$, and $y_5 = +20$

$$\bar{y} = \frac{-10 - 5 - 4 + 9 + 20}{5} = \frac{10}{5} = 2 \qquad \bar{x} = 80 + 2 = 82$$

b. Compute the mean for the preceding example, using $h = 85$.

If a rectangle has a width of one, then its length and area are measured by the same number. This fact can be used to develop a graphical model for the arithmetic mean that is based on area.

Example: Find the arithmetic mean of 2, 7, and 3.

$$2 + 7 + 3 = 4 + 4 + 4 = 3 \cdot 4$$

Rectangles of lengths (and areas) of 2, 7, and 3 are placed side by side on a common base line. There are three numbers whose arithmetic mean is sought; the width of the diagram is 3. The total area is the sum of the numbers.

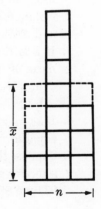

A rectangle has been constructed, also of width 3, and of such height that the area of the rectangle is the same as of the original diagram. This height of 4 is the arithmetic mean of the given numbers. There is a suggestion here of why averaging is sometimes considered to be a "leveling off" process.

Sometimes when the arithmetic mean of a set of numbers is computed, it is desired that some of the numbers be considered more important than others. One way of assigning such importance to a number is to use it more than once. The next diagram shows the arithmetic mean of two 2's, three 7's, and one 3.

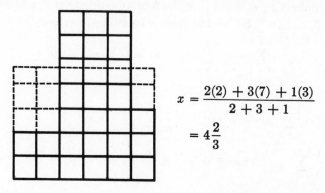

$$x = \frac{2(2) + 3(7) + 1(3)}{2 + 3 + 1}$$

$$= 4\frac{2}{3}$$

The 2, 3, and 1 give the relative importance or weight that has been assigned to each number and are called *weighting factors*. Thus, $4\frac{2}{3}$ is the weighted arithmetic mean of two, seven, and three, where two has a weight of 2, seven has a weight of 3, and three has a weight of 1.

To find a weighted arithmetic mean: *Form the product of each number by its weighting factor, and then divide the sum of these products by the sum of the weighting factors.*

Answers to Exercises

a. $(4 - 8) + (6 - 8) + (8 - 8) + (10 - 8) + (12 - 8) = 0$. $(.489 - .509) + (.498 - .509) + (.522 - .509) + (.527 - .509) = 0$. **b.** $y_1 = -15$, $y_2 = -10$, $y_3 = -9$, $y_4 = +4$, $y_5 = +15$; $\bar{y} = -3$; $\bar{x} = 85 - 3 = 82$.

Problems (188)

1. Compute the arithmetic mean of 1,461, 1,464, 1,467, 1,470, 1,462, and 1,460, using an assumed mean of 1,465.
2. Compute the arithmetic mean of .2406, .2424, .2388, .2433, .2454, .2426, .2436, and .2433, by using an assumed mean of .2430.
3. If $\bar{x}$ is the arithmetic mean of $\{x_1, x_2, x_3, \ldots, x_n\}$, what is the arithmetic mean of
   a. $\{cx_1, cx_2, cx_3, \ldots cx_n\}$?
   b. $\{x_1 + k, x_2 + k, x_3 + k, \ldots x_n + k\}$?
4. If $x_1, x_2, x_3, \ldots, x_n$ consists of k numbers each equal to y' and m numbers each equal to y'' where $k + m = n$, what is $\bar{x}$?
5. Suppose that in a certain class short quizzes are given a weight of 1, and a midsemester grade a weight of 3. What is the average of quiz grades of 71, 86, 93, and 88, and a midsemester grade of 81?

6. A small shop pays the following salaries: one foreman gets $200 a week, 5 workers get $140 a week, and 2 workers get $90 a week. What is the average weekly salary?

7. Assume that an *A* counts 4 points, a *B* counts 3 points, and a *C* counts 2 points. What is the grade point average of one *A*, two *B*'s, and two *C*'s?

8. On a ten-point quiz, two students get 10 points, three students get 9 points, one student gets 8 points, six students get 7 points, and two students get 5 points. What is the average grade (nearest tenth)?

For Further Study

Discussions of many of the topics in Chapters 19 and 20 of this text can be found under such headings as "approximate computation" and the "arithmetic of measurement." See [B2], pp. 279–293; [L1], pp. 223–242; [M1], pp. 100–104; [M2], pp. 360–367; [N5], pp. 44–58; [O1], pp. 301–313; [S5], pp. 1–18; [S17], pp. 233–247; [W3], pp. 259–271.

For repeating decimals, see [B4], pp. 73–81; [C4], pp. 396–399; [H3], pp. 142–149; [M6], pp. 44–61; [O3], pp. 311–325; and [R1], pp. 97–107.

Some interesting material on averages appears in [M3], pp. 113–123. Reference [R2], pp. 448–450, discusses the weighted arithmetic mean in an introductory section on statistics.

21

Percentage

21-1. Ratio Comparisons with Common and Decimal Fractions

The ratio comparison C, of a first number N_1 to a second number N_2, may be expressed as

$$\frac{N_1}{N_2} = C \quad \text{or as} \quad N_1 = CN_2$$

In the following examples the verbal statement parallels the second of these forms. Graphical models are also given, with the comparison number in both common and decimal fraction notation when it is not a natural number.

Examples: Eight is four times two. $\quad 8 = (4)(2)$

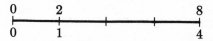

Eight is one fourth of thirty-two. $\quad 8 = \left(\frac{1}{4}\right)(32)$

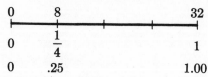

If two of the three numbers in $N_1 = CN_2$ are known, this is sufficient to determine the third, which is represented by X in the following:

If $X = CN_2$, then the multiplication that is denoted explicitly will determine X, or N_1.

If $N_1 = XN_2$, then $X = \dfrac{N_1}{N_2}$.   The division of the first number, N_1, by the second number, N_2, is implied for computing X, or C.

If $N_1 = CX$, then $X = \dfrac{N_1}{C}$.   The division of the first number, N_1, by the comparison number, C, is implied for computing X, or N_2.

A large number of the applications of arithmetic are based on these forms, so that mastery of the associated computations is essential.

Problems (189)

For problems 1 to 12, whenever the comparison number is given, it is in the form of a common fraction in lowest terms. Whenever it is unknown, it is to be determined and written in this form, or as a natural number in decimal numeral form.

1. $(\ ) = \left(\dfrac{1}{5}\right)(20)$ **5.** $9 = \left(\dfrac{3}{7}\right)(\ )$ **9.** $2.7 = (\ )(2.4)$

2. $15 = (\ )(40)$ **6.** $4.02 = \left(\dfrac{6}{5}\right)(\ )$ **10.** $(\ ) = \dfrac{23}{100}(310)$

3. $14 = (\ )(35)$ **7.** $(\ ) = \left(\dfrac{8}{5}\right)(30)$ **11.** $1.23 = \left(\dfrac{3}{2}\right)(\ )$

4. $(\ ) = \left(\dfrac{7}{6}\right)(42)$ **8.** $.56 = \left(\dfrac{7}{100}\right)(\ )$ **12.** $.021 = (\ )(.015)$

For problems 18 to 24, the comparison number is to be in decimal form. The numbers have been chosen so that approximations are not needed.

13. $(\ ) = (.4)(35)$ **17.** $32 = (.8)(\ )$ **21.** $.63 = (7)(\ )$
14. $.125 = (\ )(2.5)$ **18.** $21 = (\ )(140)$ **22.** $(\ ) = (1.75)(2.5)$
15. $7.5 = (\ )(25)$ **19.** $(\ ) = (2.25)(36)$ **23.** $36 = (\ )(.24)$
16. $(\ ) = (.21)(.6)$ **20.** $.65 = (.13)(\ )$ **24.** $10.2 = (\ )(8.5)$

For problems 25 to 30, first construct a mathematical model in the form of a conditional equation, and then solve.

25. If a person sleeps 9 hours out of 24, what fraction of the day is he awake?

26. Fred hopes to save $\dfrac{3}{10}$ of his salary. How much must he earn in order to save $360?

27. During a sale, a sport coat was offered for sale at $\dfrac{2}{3}$ of its former price. If the sale price was $28, what was the original price?

28. A man whose salary was $6,500 per year was promised an increase of $\dfrac{1}{10}$ of this amount. What would the new salary be?

29. A Community Chest drive yielded \$120,000, but this was announced as being only $\frac{4}{5}$ of the goal set. How much had they hoped to raise?

30. A football player missed only twice in 18 tries for a point after a touchdown. For what fraction of the total attempts was he successful?

21-2. Percentage Comparison

The constant use of ratio comparisons in business and commercial practice has led to the development of a special *percent* notation for ratios. We have already noted the superiority of decimal fractions over common fractions for most computations. The conventions for percentage are based on working with hundredths rather than ones as units, and the use of a special symbol for hundredths.

$$\frac{3}{4} = \frac{75}{100} = .75 = 75\%$$

The percent operator $\%$ is always written at the right, and has the effect of any one of the equivalent operators:

$$(\ )(.01), \text{ or } (\ )\left(\frac{1}{100}\right), \text{ or } \frac{(\ )}{100}$$

The $\%$ symbol is used for reference only, and is replaced by one of the above forms for computations.

$$80\% = (80)(.01) = .80 \quad \text{Also} \quad 80\% = 80\left(\frac{1}{100}\right) = \frac{80}{100} = \frac{4}{5}$$

To some extent the development of the percent notation reflects the considerable difficulty that man has experienced in computing with even the simplest common fractions. Thus the relatively large whole numbers appearing in 75% and 80% seem more accessible to the mind than the corresponding fractions of $\frac{3}{4}$ and $\frac{4}{5}$. Since $1 = \frac{100}{100} = 100\%$, the use of the percent notation for ratios has the effect of making 100 rather than 1 the standard of comparison. The use of hundredths gives a close tie between the percent and the decimal notations. The main difficulty stems from the fact that so relatively few ratios can be expressed both simply and exactly in terms of hundredths, so that approximations are often used.

The following are some examples of the changes of form that arise in practice.

$$12\% = (12)(.01) = .12 \qquad\qquad 12\% = \frac{12}{100} = \frac{3}{25}$$

$$450\% = (450)(.01) = 4.5 \qquad\qquad 450\% = \frac{450}{100} = \frac{9}{2} = 4\frac{1}{2}$$

$$.0325 = (3.25)(.01) = 3.25\%$$

$$\frac{3}{5} = \frac{60}{100} = .60 = 60\%$$

$$2.10 = (210)(.01) = 210\%$$

$$\frac{3}{7} \doteq .429 = 42.9\%$$

$$\frac{11}{400} = .0275 = (2.75)(.01) = 2.75\%$$

$$\frac{11}{400} = \frac{2\frac{3}{4}}{100} = 2\frac{3}{4}\%$$

$8\frac{1}{3}\%$ should not be expressed in decimal form.

$$8\frac{1}{3}\% = \frac{8\frac{1}{3}}{100} = \frac{25}{300} = \frac{1}{12}$$

The following examples illustrate the use of the percent notation in stating the ratio comparisons of a first number to a second.

Example: How does 4 compare to 5?

$$4 = \left(\frac{4}{5}\right)(5) \qquad 4 \text{ is } \frac{4}{5} \text{ of 5.}$$

$$4 = (.8)(5) \qquad 4 \text{ is .8 of 5.}$$

$$4 = (.80)(5) \qquad 4 \text{ is } 80\% \text{ of 5.}$$

4 compares to 5 as 80 does to 100, or as .80 does to 1.00.

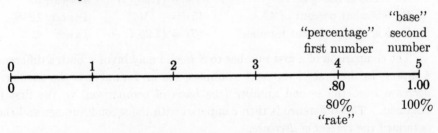

The second number is the basis or standard of comparison. It is commonly called the *base*, and is associated with 100%. Since 100% is another way of writing 1, we think of the base as being all of some quantity, with which another quantity is being compared.

The first number is termed the *percentage*, a name derived from its former use as so many "hundred parts." This name is somewhat unfortunate since the number called the percentage is not the number written with the percent symbol.

The multiplier, which the second number requires to give the first number, expresses the ratio comparison and is called the *rate*. The basic relation is $N_1 = CN_2$, with the comparison number given with percent notation rather than as a common or decimal fraction. For the above example the three typical problems are:

A. What is 80% of 5? $(\ ) = (.80)(5)$ *Answer:* 4.
B. 4 is what percent of 5? $4 = (\ )(5)$ *Answer:* 80%.
C. 4 is 80% of what number? $4 = (.80)(\ )$ *Answer:* 5.

When the first number is less than the second, the ratio multiplier will be less than 1, that is, less than 100%. If however the first number is the larger, the ratio will be greater than 100%.

Example: How does 5 compare to 4?

$$5 = \left(\frac{5}{4}\right)(4) \qquad \text{5 is } \frac{5}{4} \text{ times 4.}$$

$$5 = (1.25)(4) \qquad \text{5 is 1.25 times 4.}$$

$$5 = 125\% \text{ of 4.}$$

5 compares to 4 as 125 does to 100, or as 1.25 does to 1.00.

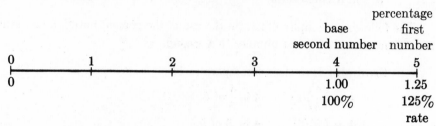

There are again three typical problems:

A. What is 125% of 4?   ( ) = (1.25)(4)   *Answer:* 5.
B. 5 is what percent of 4?   (5) = ( )(4)   *Answer:* 125%.
C. 5 is 125% of what number? (5) = (1.25)( )   *Answer:* 4.

The comparison of a first number to a second may involve both a difference and a ratio. In the first of the next examples, the first number is the smaller. The decrease from the second number (the basis of comparison) to the first is first obtained. This difference is then compared with the second number and the ratio is termed the *percent of decrease.*

Example: How does 4 compare to 5?

$$4 = 5 - 1 \qquad\qquad \text{4 is 1 less than 5.}$$

$$4 = 5 - \left(\frac{1}{5}\right)(5) \qquad \text{4 is } \frac{1}{5} \text{ of 5 less than 5.}$$

$$4 = (1.00)(5) - (.20)(5) \qquad \text{4 is 100\% of 5 minus 20\% of 5;}$$

4 is 5 minus 20% of 5;

4 is 20% of 5 less than 5;

4 is 20% less than 5.

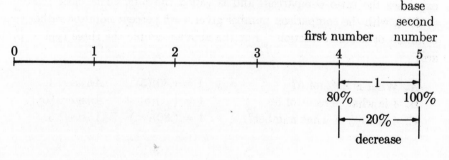

One should note carefully that the usual phrase of "20% less than 5" is an abbreviation of the more explicit "20% of 5 less than 5." While it is true that $\frac{1}{5} = .20 = 20\%$, these expressions are not interchangeable in all contexts. Thus "10 less $\frac{1}{5}$" could certainly mean $10 - \frac{1}{5}$, and if we really mean $10 - \frac{1}{5}(10)$, we should state "10 less $\frac{1}{5}$ of 10." By contrast, "10 less 20%" would always refer to "10 less 20% of 10," that is, $10 - (.20)(10)$. Hence when "20%" appears in a verbal statement, the wording of the sentence must make clear what the base is.

In the next example the first number is considered to represent an increase over the second number. This increase is compared with the second number, and the ratio is termed the *percent of increase*.

Example: How does 5 compare to 4?

$5 = 4 + 1$	5 is 1 more than 4.
$5 = 4 + \frac{1}{4}(4)$	5 is $\frac{1}{4}$ of 4 more than 4.

$5 = (1.00)(4) + (.25)(4)$ 5 is 100% of 4 plus 25% of 4;
                                          5 is 25% of 4 more than 4;
                                          5 is 25% more than 4.

Note that 4 is 20% less than 5, while 5 is 25% more than 4. This discrepancy between 20% and 25%, even though both are related to the same difference of 1, is due to the fact that one is 20% *of 5*, and the other is 25% *of 4*. This again emphasizes the importance of the base in the percent notation.

Problems (190)

In problems 1 to 12, the two alternate forms are to be supplied. If an approximate value is needed, round off to the nearest thousandth.

	Common Fraction	Decimal Fraction	Percent		Common Fraction	Decimal Fraction	Percent
1.		.35		**7.**		.124	
2.			4%	**8.**			.3%
3.	$1\frac{3}{4}$			**9.**	$\frac{3}{400}$		
4.		1.15		**10.**		.002	
5.			$3\frac{1}{4}\%$	**11.**			$\frac{1}{4}\%$
6.	$\frac{2}{3}$			**12.**	$\frac{7}{6}$		

For problems 13 to 32, supply the missing numbers for the line diagrams.

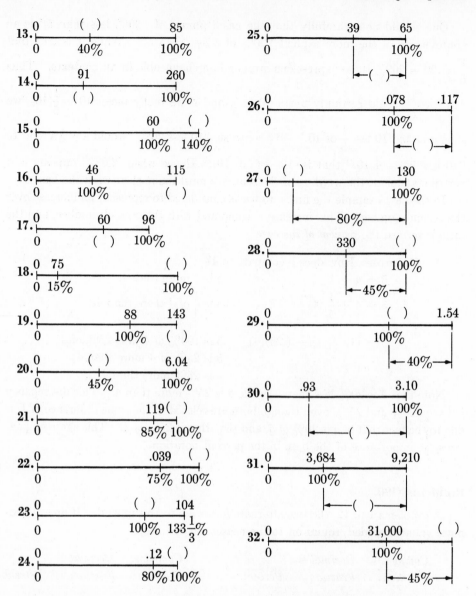

Line diagrams, such as those used in problems 13 to 32, are often useful in analyzing applications of percentage as well as other problems built around ratio comparisons, even when done only as rough sketches, which are only approximately to scale. The quantities being compared, which go on the upper scale, can usually be recognized in verbal problems by the dimensions given for them such as dollars, pounds, and so on.

The lower scale locates the comparison numbers or percents, and these are dimensionless; 100% is always assigned to the base number.

After a line diagram has been sketched, the next step should be construction of an equation model for the problem. Careful attention to these two planning stages is possibly the best cure for a common error in percentage problems, that of solving the wrong problem!

Problems (191)

For problems 1 to 20, use the data from problems 13 to 32 in set (190).   In each case give **a.** a verbal statement of the problem; **b.** a conditional equation model.

1. #13	**5.** #17	**9.** #21	**13.** #25	**17.** #29
2. #14	**6.** #18	**10.** #22	**14.** #26	**18.** #30
3. #15	**7.** #19	**11.** #23	**15.** #27	**19.** #31
4. #16	**8.** #20	**12.** #24	**16.** #28	**20.** #32

Solve for x in problems 21 to 30.   Then give a verbal statement of the problem in the language of percent.   (Percents are given by the decimal fractions.)

21. $x = 84 - (.80)(84)$ **27.** $77 = x + (.10)(x)$

22. $18 = x + (.50)(x)$ **28.** $700 = (1.75)(x)$

23. $x = 36 + (.25)(36)$ **29.** $75 - 65 = (x)(65)$

24. $x = 3100 - (.15)(3100)$ (in percent form, to the nearest tenth)

25. $56 = x - (.30)(x)$ **30.** $75 - 65 = (x)(75)$

26. $x = 8000 + (.005)(8000)$ (in percent form, to the nearest tenth)

31. A lawnmower with a price of $70 was offered for sale at a discount of 15%. What was the cost to a purchaser if there was a sales tax of 4%?

32. If water increases in volume by 9% on freezing, how many cubic feet of water is needed to make 245 cubic feet of ice?   (nearest tenth)

33. a. A man with a salary of $6,000 a year was given a 10% cut.   Later his salary was increased 10%.   What was his salary after the increase?

  b. A man with a salary of $6,000 a year was given a 10% raise.   Later his salary was decreased 10%.   What was his salary after the decrease?

34. The total cost to a dealer for a bicycle was $48.

  a. At what price should he sell to make a profit of 20% on the cost price?

  b. At what price should he sell to make a profit of 20% on the sale price?

35. Twelve grams of salt are dissolved in 68 grams of water.   What is the percent strength of the salt solution?

36. How many grams of salt are there in 60 grams of a salt solution of 15% strength?

37. How many grams of water and how many grams of salt would you use to prepare 80 grams of a solution of 5% strength?

38. How many grams of salt would have to be dissolved in 60 grams of water to produce a solution of 25% strength?

39. Some goods were marked so that the sales price would show a profit of 40%. If the selling price were to be reduced by 20%, what percent of the reduced price would be profit?

40. a. 7,920 is 10% more than what number?

  b. 7,920 is 10% less than what number?

21-3. Absolute and Relative Errors

The error, which was defined in Section 20-1 as the difference between an approximation of a quantity and its true or accepted value, will henceforth be called the *absolute error*. The absolute error for a measurement reported as 5.2 lb is assumed not to be greater than .05 lb. The precision is judged by the maximum absolute error. The absolute error is always expressed in terms of the same unit as the given measurement.

The ratio of the absolute error to the measurement itself is known as the *relative error*. Thus a measurement of 5.2, with an absolute error of .05, would have a relative error of $\dfrac{.05}{5.2}$, or .0096 approximately. This is a dimensionless number, since both .05 and 5.2 have the same dimension. If this ratio is expressed in percent notation, it is then known as the *percent of error*. A relative error of .0096 is thus an error of .96 percent, or slightly less than 1%.

Now consider a measurement of 5.20, where the maximum absolute error is assumed to be .005. The relative error is now $\dfrac{.005}{5.20}$, or .00096. This gives a percent error of .096%, or one tenth that of the previous example. The size of the relative error is taken as the index of the accuracy of an approximation, while the precision is given by the absolute error, as noted above. The contrast between precision and accuracy can be summarized as follows:

Let n_1 and n_2 be two approximate numbers, with absolute errors of e_1 and e_2, and relative errors of r_1 and r_2, respectively.

Then n_1 is more precise than n_2 if $e_1 < e_2$, and n_1 is more accurate than n_2 if $r_1 < r_2$.

For numbers expressed in decimal notation, the position of the most significant digit determines the precision, while the number of significant digits is a rough but convenient indication of the accuracy.

Problems (192)

1. The following are assumed to be approximate numbers having a maximum absolute error of one half of the place value next to the right of the significant digit farthest to the right. Give the absolute error, the relative error to two significant digits, and the percent of error.

    a. .4   c. .40   e. .040   g. .31   i. .065
    b. 4.0   d. .04   f. .400   h. .031   j. .650

2. An approximation is given, followed by the true value. In each case find the absolute error, the relative error to two significant digits, and the percent of error; and state the precision and accuracy in terms of significant digits.

    a. 3.15, 3.14   c. .001, .000   e. .000786, .000783
    b. 360, 365   d. 31.5, 31.4   f. 30, 20

For Further Study

For a sound and comprehensive treatment of percent and its applications in the field of business, refer to [B5], Chapters 12, 13, 17, and 18.

22

Irrational Numbers

22-1. The Square Root Operator

The operator that transforms the number x into its square, x^2, is the exponential operator, $(\ )^2$, with the parentheses being used only if needed to extend the reach of the exponent. We have had available no command to "undo" such a transformation, and turn now to the consideration of such a possible operator.

For any number N, if $x^2 = N$, then x is said to be a *square root of N*.

> **Examples:** Since $7^2 = 49$, 7 is a square root of 49.
>
> Since $\left(\dfrac{2}{3}\right)\left(\dfrac{2}{3}\right) = \dfrac{4}{9}$, $\dfrac{2}{3}$ is a square root of $\dfrac{4}{9}$.
>
> Since $(.03)(.03) = .0009$, .03 is a square root of .0009.

Note that the above definition speaks of "*a* square root," rather than "*the* square root." This is necessary since if the universe for a discussion includes the negative numbers, then not only is 7 a square root of 49 but so also is -7 a square root of 49, since $(-7)(-7) = 49$. In general, if there is a number x such that $(x)(x) = N$, then $(-x)(-x) = N$, also. Of these two square roots, the positive one is selected as the one likely to have the greater usage, and hence the positive square root is called the *principal* square root, or *the* square root when the discussion is limited to positive numbers.

The symbol $\sqrt{\ }$, known as the square root operator, or more precisely as the principal square root operator, is defined as follows:

If there is an x such that $x \geq 0$, and $x^2 = N$, then $\sqrt{N} = x$.

> **Examples:** $\sqrt{100} = 10$, since $10 > 0$, and $10^2 = 100$.
>
> $\sqrt{\dfrac{25}{36}} = \dfrac{5}{6}$, since $\dfrac{5}{6} > 0$, and $\left(\dfrac{5}{6}\right)^2 = \dfrac{25}{36}$.
>
> $\sqrt{2.25} = 1.5$, since $1.5 > 0$, and $(1.5)^2 = 2.25$.

Now if $p > 0$, we have $\sqrt{p^2} = p = p^1$. Hence in this instance we observe that $(\ )^2 \circ \sqrt{\ } = (\ )^1$. Since the composition of the operators $(\ )^2$ and $\sqrt{\ }$ here gives the identity operator $(\ )^1$, there is the suggestion that we consider the square and the square root operators as being a pair of inverse operators. But the next several examples will show some restrictions that must be placed on such a usage.

Examples:

   A. $\sqrt{(5)^2} = 5$

   With 5 as an operand, $(\ )^2$ produces 25. The principal square root of 25 is 5, which brings us back to the original number.

   B. $(\sqrt{5})^2 = ?$

   The same operators are used as in **A**, but in the opposite order, and a difficulty arises that was not present in example **A**. Does 5 even have a square root? This question requires additional discussion, and will be returned to later.

   C. $\sqrt{(-5)^2} = 5$, since $5 > 0$ and $5^2 = (-5)^2$

   With -5 as an operand, $(\ )^2$ produces 25. The principal square root of 25 is 5. But this does not bring us back to the original number, which was -5.

   D. $(\sqrt{-5})^2 = ?$

   This is similar to example **C**, but the operators are given in the opposite order. The first step now requires that we produce a number whose square is negative. (By definition, a square root of -5 must be a number x such that $(x)(x) = -5$.) But none of the kinds of numbers we have discussed have this possibility, since the squares of both positive and negative rationals are positive.

The above examples show that the order of applying the operators $(\ )^2$ and $\sqrt{\ }$ may affect the result and hence must be considered. The difficulty in **D** may be met by constructing a new kind of numbers, called the *complex* numbers, which have the needed properties. This important extension of the number concept lies beyond the scope of this text and will not be given. Henceforth our use of the operator $\sqrt{\ }$ will be limited to operands that are nonnegative, and expressions as in **D** will remain undefined.

We observed in Chapter 5 that a natural number is a square if and only if in its prime factored form every factor has an even number for an exponent. Hence if $p > 0$, and k is a natural number, then

$$\sqrt{p^{2k}} = p^k. \quad \text{This follows from } (p^k)(p^k) = p^{k+k} = p^{2k}.$$

The square roots of such numbers can therefore be obtained readily from inspection of the prime factored form. Furthermore, with such operands we see that the operator $\sqrt{\ }$ distributes over both products and quotients.

$$\sqrt{p^{2k}q^{2j}} = \sqrt{p^{2k}}\sqrt{q^{2j}} = p^k q^j, \text{ follows from } (p^k)(q^j)(p^k)(q^j) = p^{2k}q^{2j}$$

$$\sqrt{\frac{p^{2k}}{q^{2j}}} = \frac{\sqrt{p^{2k}}}{\sqrt{q^{2j}}} = \frac{p^k}{q^j}, \text{ follows from } \left(\frac{p^k}{q^j}\right)\left(\frac{p^k}{q^j}\right) = \frac{p^{2k}}{q^{2j}}$$

Examples:

$$\sqrt{64} = \sqrt{2^6} = 2^3 = 8$$
$$\sqrt{144} = \sqrt{2^4 \cdot 3^2} = 2^2 \cdot 3 = 12$$
$$\sqrt{\frac{36}{625}} = \sqrt{\frac{2^2 \cdot 3^2}{5^4}} = \frac{2 \cdot 3}{5^2} = \frac{6}{25}$$

Problems (193)

Compute the following square roots by first obtaining the prime factored forms.

1. $\sqrt{225}$ 3. $\sqrt{8,281}$ 5. $\sqrt{27,225}$ 7. $\sqrt{\dfrac{1,089}{1,225}}$

2. $\sqrt{5,929}$ 4. $\sqrt{12,544}$ 6. $\sqrt{36,864}$ 8. $\sqrt{\dfrac{1,521}{3,025}}$

The definition of $\sqrt{N}$ requires that it be a nonnegative number x such that $x^2 = N$. Since $2^2 = 4$, it is evident at a glance that $x = 2$ is a solution of the equation $x^2 = 4$, so that $\sqrt{4} = 2$. But it is not at all clear what the solutions of $x^2 = 5$, or $x^2 = 3$ might be, or even whether the numbers we have at our command are adequate to provide a solution at all. The need for such numbers became evident centuries ago, and this was particularly true because of problems that arose in measurement.

Example: The square with solid outline is assumed to have sides of length 1, and hence an area of 1 unit square.

This square has been divided into two triangles, each of area $\dfrac{1}{2}$, and four of these triangles are joined to make the larger square, which is shown in outline. Its area is therefore $4\left(\dfrac{1}{2}\right)$ or 2. This requires that the length of a side (represented by x) be such that $x^2 = 2$, that is, $x = \sqrt{2}$.

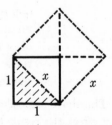

In problems 1, 7, and 9 of set (194), the reader is asked to verify that there are both common and decimal fractions whose squares differ from 2 by only a small amount. But none of the given numbers has a square that is exactly 2. One of the great achievements of the ancient Greek mathematicians was the discovery that there is no rational number whose square is 2.

One way of proving the above statement depends on the following property of even and odd numbers: The square of an even number is even and the square of an odd number is odd.

All even natural numbers have the form $2n$, where n is a natural number. But if $x = 2n$, then $x^2 = (2n)(2n) = 2(2n^2)$. Since $2n^2$ is a natural number, x^2 is even. All odd natural numbers have the form $2n - 1$, where n is a natural number. Now if $y = 2n - 1$, then $y^2 = (2n - 1)(2n - 1)$. Then $y^2 = 4n^2 - 4n + 1 = 2(2n^2 - 2n) + 1$. Now $2n^2 - 2n = 2n(n - 1)$ so that $2n^2 - 2n$ is either zero or an even natural number. In either case y^2 is an odd number, as was to be shown.

Every positive rational number has a fraction representation of the form $\dfrac{p}{q}$ where p and q are natural numbers. If we divide both p and q by their g.c.d. we get an equivalent fraction $\dfrac{a}{b}$ where a and b are relatively prime. In particular, a and b cannot then both be even, since this would mean they then have a common divisor of two, and would not be relatively prime.

Now suppose there is a rational number $\dfrac{p}{q}$ whose square is 2. That is $\left(\dfrac{p}{q}\right)\left(\dfrac{p}{q}\right)$ $= 2$, or $\dfrac{p^2}{q^2} = 2$. Then $\dfrac{p}{q}$ can be replaced by $\dfrac{a}{b}$, as above, and $\dfrac{a^2}{b^2} = 2$, where a and b are not both even. But if $\dfrac{a^2}{b^2} = 2$, then $a^2 = 2b^2$. Then since b is a natural number, so also is b^2 so that a^2 is even. But if a^2 is even, so must a be even, since an odd number has an odd square. Since a is even it has the form $2m$ where m is a natural number, and $a^2 = (2m)(2m) = 4m^2$. But if $a^2 = 2b^2$ and also $a^2 = 4m^2$, then $2b^2 = 4m^2$ and $b^2 = 2m^2$. Hence b^2 is even and therefore b is even.

We began with a and b not both even and now find they must be both even. It is impossible that a and b be both even and not both even. But we have shown that this impossible requirement must be met if $\dfrac{a}{b}$ is a rational number whose square is 2. We conclude that there can be no such number.

A variety of proofs that $\sqrt{2}$ cannot be a rational number have been found. One more is given below, and it also is based on showing that any proposed rational number $\dfrac{p}{q}$ such that $\dfrac{p^2}{q^2} = 2$ must satisfy an impossible condition. Again let $\dfrac{p}{q}$ be replaced, if necessary, by $\dfrac{a}{b}$ where $\dfrac{p}{q} = \dfrac{a}{b}$ and $\dfrac{a}{b}$ is in lowest terms. This means there is no fraction $\dfrac{c}{d}$ such that $\dfrac{p}{q} = \dfrac{a}{b} = \dfrac{c}{d}$, and such that c and d are smaller natural numbers than a and b respectively. Now if $\dfrac{a^2}{b^2} = 2$, then $\dfrac{a}{b} = \sqrt{2}$. By checking $1^2 = 1$, and $2^2 = 4$, we see that $1 < \sqrt{2} < 4$. Therefore the numerator a of $\dfrac{a}{b}$ is greater than b, but less than twice b. From $\dfrac{a^2}{b^2} = 2$, or $a^2 = 2b^2$, we have $a^2 - ab = 2b^2 - ab$, or $a(a - b) = b(2b - a)$. Then since $a > b$ and $a < 2b$, we have both $a - b$ and $2b - a$ are positive. Hence from $a(a - b) = b(2b - a)$ we have $\dfrac{a}{b} = \dfrac{2b - a}{a - b}$. Since $a < 2b$, then $a - b < b$. This means that the fraction

$\dfrac{2b - a}{a - b}$ equals $\dfrac{a}{b}$, but has a smaller denominator. But this is not possible, since

$\dfrac{a}{b}$ is already in lowest terms.

Problems (194)

For problems 1 to 10, express the difference as a signed number.

1. a. $(1)(1) - 2$ **c.** $\left(\dfrac{7}{5}\right)\left(\dfrac{7}{5}\right) - 2$ **e.** $\left(\dfrac{41}{29}\right)\left(\dfrac{41}{29}\right) - 2$

     b. $\left(\dfrac{3}{2}\right)\left(\dfrac{3}{2}\right) - 2$ **d.** $\left(\dfrac{17}{12}\right)\left(\dfrac{17}{12}\right) - 2$ **f.** $\left(\dfrac{99}{70}\right)\left(\dfrac{99}{70}\right) - 2$

2. a. $(1)(1) - 3$ **c.** $\left(\dfrac{5}{3}\right)\left(\dfrac{5}{3}\right) - 3$ **e.** $\left(\dfrac{19}{11}\right)\left(\dfrac{19}{11}\right) - 3$

     b. $(2)(2) - 3$ **d.** $\left(\dfrac{7}{4}\right)\left(\dfrac{7}{4}\right) - 3$ **f.** $\left(\dfrac{26}{15}\right)\left(\dfrac{26}{15}\right) - 3$

3. a. $2^2 - 5$ **b.** $\left(\dfrac{9}{4}\right)^2 - 5$ **c.** $\left(\dfrac{38}{17}\right)^2 - 5$

4. a. $\left(\dfrac{5}{2}\right)^2 - 6$ **b.** $\left(\dfrac{22}{9}\right)^2 - 6$ **c.** $\left(\dfrac{49}{20}\right)^2 - 6$

5. a. $\left(\dfrac{5}{2}\right)^2 - 7$ **b.** $\left(\dfrac{8}{3}\right)^2 - 7$ **c.** $\left(\dfrac{37}{14}\right)^2 - 7$

6. a. $3^2 - 10$ **b.** $\left(\dfrac{19}{6}\right)^2 - 10$ **c.** $\left(\dfrac{117}{37}\right)^2 - 10$

7. a. $(1.4)^2 - 2.00$ **c.** $(1.41)^2 - 2.0000$ **e.** $(1.414)^2 - 2.000000$
    b. $(1.5)^2 - 2.00$ **d.** $(1.42)^2 - 2.0000$ **f.** $(1.415)^2 - 2.000000$

8. a. $(1.7)^2 - 3.00$ **c.** $(1.73)^2 - 3.0000$ **e.** $(1.732)^2 - 3.000000$
    b. $(1.8)^2 - 3.00$ **d.** $(1.74)^2 - 3.0000$ **f.** $(1.733)^2 - 3.000000$

9. a. $\left(1 + \dfrac{1}{2}\right)^2 - 2$ **c.** $\left(1 + \dfrac{1}{2} - \dfrac{1 \cdot 1}{2 \cdot 4} + \dfrac{1 \cdot 1 \cdot 3}{2 \cdot 4 \cdot 6}\right)^2 - 2$

    b. $\left(1 + \dfrac{1}{2} - \dfrac{1 \cdot 1}{2 \cdot 4}\right)^2 - 2$ **d.** $\left(1 + \dfrac{1}{2} - \dfrac{1 \cdot 1}{2 \cdot 4} + \dfrac{1 \cdot 1 \cdot 3}{2 \cdot 4 \cdot 6} - \dfrac{1 \cdot 1 \cdot 3 \cdot 5}{2 \cdot 4 \cdot 6 \cdot 8}\right)^2 - 2$

10. In each case determine the natural number n so that the fraction resulting is the best possible approximation to $\sqrt{2}$, with the given denominator.

     a. $\dfrac{n}{1}$ **b.** $\dfrac{n}{2}$ **c.** $\dfrac{n}{3}$ **d.** $\dfrac{n}{4}$ **e.** $\dfrac{n}{5}$ **f.** $\dfrac{n}{6}$ **g.** $\dfrac{n}{7}$ **h.** $\dfrac{n}{8}$ **i.** $\dfrac{n}{9}$

22-2. Real Numbers

Thus far for $\sqrt{2}$, we have established what it is *not*. It is not rational. For $\sqrt{2}$ to be a number, the concept of number must be extended to include *irrational* numbers. When only the natural numbers and zero are available, the equation $3x = 2$ has no root. But by using pairs of numbers selected from the natural numbers and zero, the nonnegative rationals can be constructed, and this set of numbers includes $\frac{2}{3}$, which is a root of $3x = 2$. However, the nonnegative rationals do not contain a root for the equation $x + 3 = 2$. By again using pairs of numbers the number system can be extended once more, this time to the rational numbers, and one of these, -1, is a root of $x + 3 = 2$.

The above contructions of new kinds of numbers have been carried out in previous chapters. Now we need a root for the equation $x^2 = 2$, but this time the device of using pairs of numbers is not adequate for the task of devising such a number. The square root of 2 is an instance of a *real* number. The rational numbers are a proper subset of the real numbers, and the real numbers that are not rational are termed irrational.

The construction of the real numbers from the rational numbers is considerably more involved than the constructions we have given and is reserved for more advanced texts. However, it is very desirable to develop some intuition for the nature of the real numbers, and we shall indicate three ways in which this may be done. The first of these, which is the most arithmetical in character, is that of considering the real numbers to be those numbers that have decimal fraction representations.

The discussion in Chapter 20 revealed that all terminating decimals (finite numbers of digits) represent rational numbers and that the remaining rational numbers have repeating decimal forms. But the possibility is evident of forming decimal fractions with an infinite number of digits but which are not repeating decimals.

> **Example:** $x = .24681012 \cdots$
>
>   The pattern of choice for successive digits can be seen (consecutive even numbers), but there is no repetend of fixed length. x is an example of an irrational number. Other examples can be created at will by simply avoiding any periodic pattern in the choice of the digits.

Only a few digits of the infinite decimal were given for x in the example, but they yield considerable information about this number.

Thus,

$$.2 < x < .3$$
$$.24 < x < .25$$
$$.246 < x < .247$$
$$.2468 < x < .2469$$
$$.24681 < x < .24682$$
$$.246810 < x < .246811$$

etc.

The left members of these inequalities form a monotonic increasing sequence with x as an upper bound. The right members form a monotonic decreasing sequence with x as a lower bound. The results of problem 7 in set (194) give the same sort of information about the irrational number $\sqrt{2}$. Thus we have

$$1.4 < 1.41 < 1.414 < \sqrt{2} < 1.415 < 1.42 < 1.5$$

In the next section a method will be given for continuing the determination of the successive digits in the infinite decimal for $\sqrt{2}$. With this at hand we will have a sense in which it may be said that we "know" the number $\sqrt{2}$.

A second way of thinking about the real numbers is geometric and consists of conceiving of the real numbers as all the points on a line of infinite length. Let O and U be distinct points on such a line and let zero correspond to the point O and let 1 correspond to the point U.

The constructions of elementary geometry provide for constructing line segments of equal length and for dividing a line segment into n segments of equal length. These enable one to determine the point to be associated with any rational number $\frac{a}{b}$. For an irrational number such as the $\sqrt{2}$, the point to be associated with it cannot be located in this manner. Yet we have seen above the need for such a point on the scale so that the line segment from zero to this point would have a length equal to that of the diagonal of a unit square. Hence we are led to the following assumption:

> *Corresponding to each point of the line there is one and only one real number, and to each real number there corresponds one and only one point on the line, moreover, if the point zero is to the left of the point 1, we assume that if A and B are any two points of the line, and a and b are the corresponding real numbers, then A is to the left of B if and only if a < b.*

In more advanced discussions proofs are given of the consistency of these two points of view; that is, the real numbers are the same mathematical objects whether they be considered those numbers with decimal representations, or those numbers that can be put in one-to-one correspondence with the points on a line. The following sequence of diagrams indicates something of their relation to each other for the real number, $\sqrt{2}$. Each successive scale is magnified by 10 times over the preceding one. An arrow locates the approximate position of $\sqrt{2}$ within each interval.

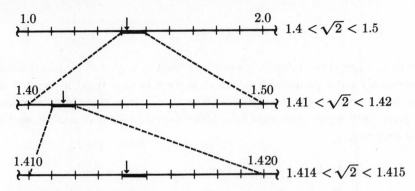

Our beginning study of sequences in Sections 6-3 and 8-7 was limited to *finite* sequences, where the domain of definition was some finite subset of the integers. An *infinite* sequence is a function whose domain is the set of all integers grearte than, or equal to, some specified integer.   The set of all ordered pairs

$$\left\{\left(n, \frac{1}{n^2}\right) \mid n \text{ is a positive integer}\right\}$$

is an example of such a sequence. This sequence is also given by

$$\left\{(1, 1), \left(2, \frac{1}{4}\right), \left(3, \frac{1}{9}\right), \ldots, \left(n, \frac{1}{n^2}\right), \ldots\right\}$$

When it is understood that the domain is the set of positive integers, the range of the function is by itself referred to as the sequence.   In this case we would have

$$\left\{1, \frac{1}{4}, \frac{1}{9}, \ldots, \frac{1}{n^2}, \ldots\right\}$$

as the sequence. This can then be further abbreviated to $\left\{\frac{1}{n^2}\right\}$.

A distinct but closely related idea is that of an *infinite series*.   This is an array of numbers and plus signs of the form

$$U_1 + U_2 + U_3 + \cdots + U_n + \cdots, \text{ where } \{U_n\} \text{ is a sequence.}$$

Since the terms need not be nonnegative, a series such as

$$1 + \left(-\frac{1}{4}\right) + \frac{1}{9} + \left(-\frac{1}{16}\right) + \cdots + \frac{(-1)^{n+1}}{n^2} + \cdots$$

would be written as

$$1 - \frac{1}{4} + \frac{1}{9} - \frac{1}{16} + \cdots$$

It is often convenient to use the summation symbol for the representation of infinite series and this may be done as follows.   Let $\{a_n\}$ be a sequence.   Then the infinite series $a_1 + a_2 + a_3 + \cdots + a_n + \cdots$ is abbreviated by

$$\sum_{n=1}^{\infty} a_n = a_1 + a_2 + a_3 + \cdots a_n + \cdots$$

The symbol, ∞, read as "infinity," is not here used as a symbol for a real number and is definitely not a permissible substitution for n in a_n. What it does tell us is that the list of addends for this indicated sum never comes to an end. Examples will be given both where such an infinite series does define a real number, and also where it does not.

Example A: Let $a_n = \dfrac{3}{10^n}$. Then

$$\sum_{n=1}^{\infty} a_n = \frac{3}{10} + \frac{3}{10^2} + \frac{3}{10^3} + \cdots + \frac{3}{10^n} + \cdots$$

Here the infinite series proves to be a disguise for an infinite decimal.

$$\sum_{n=1}^{\infty} a_n = .3 + .03 + .003 + \cdots = .333 \cdots$$

which is the repeating decimal form for the rational number, $\dfrac{1}{3}$.

Example B: Let $a_n = \dfrac{1}{(n-1)!}$, and

$$\sum_{n=1}^{\infty} a_n = \frac{1}{0!} + \frac{1}{1!} + \frac{1}{2!} + \frac{1}{3!} + \cdots$$

The computation for the first ten addends is given below (note the use of division in obtaining any given addend from the one preceding it).

$$1.000000 \leq 1 \leq 1.000000$$
$$1.000000 \leq 1 \leq 1.000000 \text{ (Now divide by 2)}$$
$$.500000 \leq \frac{1}{2!} \leq .500000 \text{ (Now divide by 3)}$$
$$.166666 \leq \frac{1}{3!} \leq .166667 \qquad \text{etc.}$$
$$.041666 \leq \frac{1}{4!} \leq .041667$$
$$.008333 \leq \frac{1}{5!} \leq .008334$$
$$.001388 \leq \frac{1}{6!} \leq .001389$$
$$.000198 \leq \frac{1}{7!} \leq .000199$$
$$.000024 \leq \frac{1}{8!} \leq .000025 \text{ (Now divide by 9)}$$
$$.000002 \leq \frac{1}{9!} \leq .000003$$

Adding, we have the result:

$$2.718277 \leq \sum_{n=1}^{10} \frac{1}{(n-1)!} \leq 2.718282$$

In order for the series to define a real number, it is necessary that for all k, the digit in the kth decimal place eventually "settle down" and remain fixed no matter how many more terms are added. Although we have not given a proof of this, the evidence seems strong that $2.7182\cdots$ will prove to be in this sense an approximation to some real number.

Example C:

$$a_n = 1 \qquad \sum_{n=1}^{\infty} a_n = 1 + 1 + 1 + \cdots + n + \cdots$$

$$b_n = (-1)^{n+1}, \quad \sum_{n=1}^{\infty} b_n = 1 - 1 + 1 - 1 + \cdots + (-1)^{n+1} + \cdots$$

In both cases, the infinite series does *not* define a number.

Example D: In this example, the infinite series also fails to define a number, but this is not so evident as in **C**.

$$a_n = \frac{1}{n} \qquad \sum_{n=1}^{\infty} a_n = 1 + \frac{1}{2} + \frac{1}{3} + \frac{1}{4} + \cdots + \frac{1}{n} + \cdots$$

Note that

$$\frac{1}{3} + \frac{1}{4} > \frac{1}{4} + \frac{1}{4} = \frac{1}{2}$$

and that

$$\frac{1}{5} + \frac{1}{6} + \frac{1}{7} + \frac{1}{8} > \frac{1}{8} + \frac{1}{8} + \frac{1}{8} + \frac{1}{8} = \frac{1}{2}$$

Furthermore, the next 8 terms total to more than $\frac{1}{2}$, as so also do the next 16, the next 32, and so on. By adding a sufficient number of terms the sum can be made greater than any fixed amount.

Problems (195)

For problems 1 to 8, give the rational number represented in common fraction form, in lowest terms.

1. $\displaystyle\sum_{n=1}^{\infty} \frac{4}{10^n}$ 3. $\displaystyle\sum_{n=1}^{\infty} \frac{21}{10^{2n}}$ 5. $\displaystyle\sum_{n=1}^{\infty} \frac{11}{10^{2n}}$ 7. $\displaystyle\sum_{n=1}^{\infty} \frac{123}{10^{3n}}$

2. $\displaystyle\sum_{n=1}^{\infty} \frac{6}{10^n}$ 4. $\displaystyle\sum_{n=1}^{\infty} \frac{73}{10^{2n}}$ 6. $\displaystyle\sum_{n=1}^{\infty} \frac{6}{10^{2n}}$ 8. $\displaystyle\sum_{n=1}^{\infty} \frac{185}{10^{3n}}$

For problems 9 to 20, continue the computation until you feel confident of three significant digits.

9. $\sum\limits_{n=1}^{\infty} \dfrac{n}{10^n}$ **12.** $\sum\limits_{n=1}^{\infty} \dfrac{(-1)^{n+1}}{n(10)^n}$ **15.** $\sum\limits_{n=1}^{\infty} \dfrac{n}{10^{2n}}$ **18.** $\sum\limits_{n=1}^{\infty} \dfrac{(-1)^{n+1}}{(2n-1)!}$

10. $\sum\limits_{n=1}^{\infty} \dfrac{n^2}{10^n}$ **13.** $\sum\limits_{n=1}^{\infty} \dfrac{n}{5^n}$ **16.** $\sum\limits_{n=1}^{\infty} \dfrac{n^2}{10^{2n}}$ **19.** $\sum\limits_{n=1}^{\infty} \dfrac{1}{(2n-2)!}$

11. $\sum\limits_{n=1}^{\infty} \dfrac{(-1)^{n+1}(n)}{10^{n-1}}$ **14.** $\sum\limits_{n=1}^{\infty} \dfrac{(-1)^{n+1}}{5^{n+1}}$ **17.** $\sum\limits_{n=1}^{\infty} \dfrac{1}{2^{n-1}(n-1)!}$ **20.** $\sum\limits_{n=1}^{\infty} \dfrac{(-1)^{n+1}}{(n+1)!}$

21. A real number can be defined by using a_n where $\begin{cases} a_1 = .4 \\ a_{k+1} = a_k + .8(.5 - a_k) \\ \quad \text{for } k \geq 1 \end{cases}$

Here the successive terms of the sequence approach a real number as a limit. Give five approximations to this number.

22. A real number is defined by $\sum\limits_{n=1}^{\infty} a_n$ where $\begin{cases} a_1 = 2 \\ a_{2k} = (.2)a_{2k-1} & \text{for } k \geq 1 \\ a_{2k-1} = (.1)a_{2k-2} & \text{for } k > 1 \end{cases}$

Give five approximations to this number.

22-3. Rational Approximations for Square Roots

The symbol $\sqrt{}$, which we have termed the principal square root operator, is also called a *radical* sign, and expressions such as $\sqrt{2}$ are called *radicals*. The operand for the square root operator is then known as the *radicand*. If n is a natural number, then $\sqrt{n}$ will be rational only when n is the square of a natural number. If n is a positive rational number, it can be written in the form $\dfrac{a}{b}$, where a and b are relatively prime natural numbers. In this case $\sqrt{n}$ is rational only when both a and b are squares of natural numbers.

An irrational number, such as $\sqrt{10}$, cannot be represented exactly in decimal form, since its decimal form has an infinite number of digits with no periodic pattern of repetition. However, one can obtain rational numbers that approximate such a number to any desired degree of accuracy, and such numbers will often be required in computations. We shall seek for such approximations in decimal fraction form.

Appendix 3 contains a table giving to four significant digits the square roots of the natural numbers from 1 to 100. Sometimes it is possible to extend the range of use of such a table by the following procedure, which takes advantage of the square root operator being distributive over a product. The first step is to express the radicand as a product, one of the two factors being the largest possible square.

Example:

$$\sqrt{348} = \sqrt{4 \cdot 87} = \sqrt{4}\sqrt{87} = 2\sqrt{87}$$
$$= 2(9.327) \quad \text{since } \sqrt{87} = 9.327 \text{ from the table}$$
$$= 18.654$$

The equals sign was used in reporting the above result, but it must be remembered that what we have is an approximation only. Note that the product of two radicals, as $\sqrt{4}\,\sqrt{87}$, or the product of a decimal numeral and a radical can be indicated by placing them side by side without any symbol for multiplication.

Problems (196)

In problems 1 to 4, list the set of numbers that satisfy all the conditions, as a replacement for n.

1. $\begin{cases} n \text{ is a natural number} \\ 100 < n < 200 \\ \sqrt{n} \text{ is a rational number} \end{cases}$

2. $\begin{cases} n \text{ is a natural number} \\ n < 100 \\ \sqrt{2n} \text{ is a rational number} \end{cases}$

3. $\begin{cases} n \text{ is a natural number.} \\ \dfrac{n}{49} \text{ is a proper fraction} \\ \sqrt{\dfrac{n}{49}} \text{ is a rational number.} \end{cases}$

4. $\begin{cases} n \text{ is a natural number.} \\ \dfrac{36}{n} \text{ is an improper fraction.} \\ \sqrt{\dfrac{36}{n}} \text{ is a rational number.} \end{cases}$

For problems 5 to 16, use the table in Appendix 3 and the above method of searching for a divisor that is a square, to compute an approximation.

5. $\sqrt{175}$ 7. $\sqrt{153}$ 9. $\sqrt{212}$ 11. $\sqrt{3,700}$ 13. $\sqrt{468}$ 15. $\sqrt{368}$
6. $\sqrt{275}$ 8. $\sqrt{147}$ 10. $\sqrt{164}$ 12. $\sqrt{9,300}$ 14. $\sqrt{396}$ 16. $\sqrt{464}$

The following variation of the scientific notation is also useful as a means of extending the use of a table of square roots. For the first step in computing $\sqrt{n}$, the number n is written in the form of $m(10)^{2k}$. In order that 10 always have an even exponent (positive, zero, or negative), it is sufficient to extend the range of m to $1 \leq m < 100$.

Examples: 1,600 is written as $16(10)^2$, instead of $1.6(10)^3$
$$\sqrt{1600} = \sqrt{16 \cdot 10^2} = 4 \cdot 10 = 40$$
.0016 is written as $16(10)^{-4}$, instead of $1.6(10)^{-3}$
$$\sqrt{.0016} = \sqrt{16 \cdot 10^{-4}} = 4 \cdot 10^{-2} = .04$$
90,000 is written as $9(10)^4$
$$\sqrt{90,000} = \sqrt{9 \cdot 10^4} = 3 \cdot 10^2 = 300$$
.009 is written as .0090, and then as $90(10)^{-4}$
$$\sqrt{.009} = \sqrt{90 \cdot 10^{-4}} = 9.487(10)^{-2} = .09487$$

We can think of a table for $\sqrt{n}$ where $1 \leq n \leq 99$ as one for use with any n where one or two significant digits are known. Where n has more than two significant digits we can still round n off to one or two significant digits, and thus a square root with one or more correct digits can be obtained. We also know the place value of these digits, which is important.

Examples:

$$413,689 \doteq 41(10)^4$$
$$\sqrt{413,689} \doteq \sqrt{41(10)^4} = 640.3$$

Since the correct result is 643.2, we find our approximation gave 2 significant digits.

$$.0756 \doteq 8(10)^{-2}$$
$$\sqrt{.0756} \doteq \sqrt{8(10)^{-2}} = .2828$$

Since the correct root is .27496, the approximation of .28 would be in error in the second digit.

Problems (197)

Obtain approximations for the following:

1. $\sqrt{300}$	7. $\sqrt{.03}$	13. $\sqrt{8300}$	19. $\sqrt{269,000}$
2. $\sqrt{70,000}$	8. $\sqrt{7,000}$	14. $\sqrt{.0056}$	20. $\sqrt{1,386}$
3. $\sqrt{3,000}$	9. $\sqrt{.003}$	15. $\sqrt{830}$	21. $\sqrt{.00041}$
4. $\sqrt{.0007}$	10. $\sqrt{.070}$	16. $\sqrt{.056}$	22. $\sqrt{871,000}$
5. $\sqrt{30,000}$	11. $\sqrt{.30}$	17. $\sqrt{.417}$	23. $\sqrt{6,074}$
6. $\sqrt{700}$	12. $\sqrt{.70}$	18. $\sqrt{.444}$	24. $\sqrt{.0208}$

It is evident that even with the extensions suggested, a much larger table of square roots would be required for computations where more significant digits are desired. A method will now be discussed whereby, if a positive number n is given in decimal numeral form, then an approximation to $\sqrt{n}$ can be computed to any desired number of significant digits.

Since for $n > 0$, we have $\dfrac{n}{\sqrt{n}} = \sqrt{n}$ by definition, we see that if a positive number is divided by its square root, the quotient is also the square root.

Now for any positive number n, let x be a positive number that is any approximation to $\sqrt{n}$. We now prove that if the approximation to $\sqrt{n}$ is too small, that is, if $x < \sqrt{n}$, then the quotient $\dfrac{n}{x}$ will be greater than $\sqrt{n}$; but if the approximation x is larger than $\sqrt{n}$, then the quotient $\dfrac{n}{x}$ will be less than $\sqrt{n}$.

Proof:

Assume $n > 0$, $x > 0$, and $x < \sqrt{n}$

Then $x\sqrt{n} < \sqrt{n}\sqrt{n}$,   (1)

And $x\sqrt{n} < n$ (2)

Hence $\sqrt{n} < \dfrac{n}{x}$, or $\dfrac{n}{x} > \sqrt{n}$ (3)

Now assume $n > 0$, $x > 0$, and $x > \sqrt{n}$

Then $x\sqrt{n} > \sqrt{n}\sqrt{n}$ (4)

And $x\sqrt{n} > n$ (5)

Hence $\sqrt{n} > \dfrac{n}{x}$, or $\dfrac{n}{x} < \sqrt{n}$ (6)

a. Give reasons in support of the above argument.

In summary, we can say that if n and x are any two positive numbers and $\dfrac{n}{x} = x$, then $x = \sqrt{n}$. But if $\dfrac{n}{x} \neq x$, then one of these two numbers, $\dfrac{n}{x}$ and x, is less than $\sqrt{n}$ and the other is greater than $\sqrt{n}$. It seems reasonable that the arithmetic mean of x and $\dfrac{n}{x}$ might be a better approximation to $\sqrt{n}$ than either x or $\dfrac{n}{x}$, and this proves to be the case. Hence to get a decimal approximation to $\sqrt{n}$ (n should be already in decimal numeral form), start with some approximation x_1, and compute successive approximations where

$$x_2 = \frac{1}{2}\left(x_1 + \frac{n}{x_1}\right)$$

$$x_3 = \frac{1}{2}\left(x_2 + \frac{n}{x_2}\right)$$

and in general,

$$x_{k+1} = \frac{1}{2}\left(x_k + \frac{n}{x_k}\right)$$

Example: To compute $\sqrt{5}$, correct to four significant digits.

Let $x_1 = 2$ (the first approximation). Then $x_2 = \dfrac{1}{2}\left(2 + \dfrac{5}{2}\right)$.

```
       2.5              2.5
  2 ) 5.0              2.
       4           2 ) 4.5
      ---              ----
      1 0              2.25
      1 0              2.2
```

The quotient was computed to two significant digits, one of which agreed (in face and place value) with a digit of the divisor. The average of the divisor and the quotient was rounded to two significant digits.

The second approximation of 2.2 was used as a divisor. The quotient was computed to four significant digits, two of which agree with digits of the divisor. The average of divisor and quotient was rounded to four significant digits. Our third approximation to $\sqrt{5}$ is 2.236, and all four digits can be verified as correct.

```
         2.272               2.272
 2.2 ) 5.0000                2.2
         4 4            2 ) 4.472
        ----                -----
          60                2.236
          44
         ----
         160
         154
         ----
          60
          44
         ----
```

Since many of the divisions would not terminate, there is need for a cut-off rule. Experience shows that one can expect approximately to double the number of correct digits with each new approximation. Hence if the quotient agrees with the divisor for the first k digits, carry the division out to a quotient of $2k$ digits, and round the average off to the same number of digits.

If the number whose square root is sought is not already in the range from 1 to 100, then as previously suggested, it should be rewritten in the form $m \cdot 10^{2k}$ where $1 \le m < 100$. The square root is then given by $\sqrt{m} \cdot 10^{k}$. For a number m of this size a satisfactory first approximation of 1 or 2 digits can then be given mentally, or can be obtained from a small table. Two or three repetitions of the divide-average steps then usually provide an approximation of sufficient accuracy.

ANSWER TO EXERCISE

a. (1) Both members multiplied by the positive number, $\sqrt{n}$. Monotonic law. (2) Definition of a square root. (3) Both members multiplied by the positive number, $\frac{1}{x}$. Monotonic law. (4), (5), and (6) Same as (1), (2), and (3).

Problems (198)

For problems 1 to 10, compute approximations to four significant digits.

1. $\sqrt{190}$ 3. $\sqrt{563}$ 5. $\sqrt{.563}$ 7. $\sqrt{.002372}$ 9. $\sqrt{378,486}$

2. $\sqrt{730}$ 4. $\sqrt{.9823}$ 6. $\sqrt{.00055}$ 8. $\sqrt{755,555}$ 10. $\sqrt{3.1416}$

For problems 11 to 14, compute approximations to three significant digits.

11. $\sqrt{3+\sqrt{2}}$ 12. $\sqrt{2+\sqrt{3}}$ 13. $\sqrt{\sqrt{5}-\sqrt{3}}$ 14. $\sqrt{\sqrt{3}+\sqrt{5}}$

For problems 15 to 18, compute a decimal approximation to three significant digits after first changing the common fraction to decimal fraction form. Then determine the common fraction form, with the same denominator as the given number, which is the best approximation to the square root.

15. $\sqrt{8\frac{1}{4}}$ 16. $\sqrt{11\frac{3}{8}}$ 17. $\sqrt{\frac{19}{32}}$ 18. $\sqrt{5\frac{5}{6}}$

22-4. Other Exponential Operators

If n is a natural number and $x^n = N$, then x is said to be a nth root of N.

Example: Since $2^6 = 64$, 2 is a 6th root of 64.

Since $(.3)(.3)(.3)(.3) = .0081$, .3 is a 4th root of .0081.

Since $\left(\frac{2}{5}\right)\left(\frac{2}{5}\right)\left(\frac{2}{5}\right) = \frac{8}{125}$, $\frac{2}{5}$ is a 3rd root, or cube root, of $\frac{8}{125}$.

The symbol $\sqrt[n]{}$ is known as the principal nth root operator. When $n = 2$, then we write $\sqrt{}$ as has been the practice thus far, rather than $\sqrt[2]{}$. Hence, referring to the above examples, we have $\sqrt[6]{64} = 2$, $\sqrt[4]{.0081} = .3$, and $\sqrt[3]{\frac{8}{125}} = \frac{2}{5}$.

The expression $\sqrt[n]{b}$ is a *radical*, which represents the principal nth root of b, where b is the *radicand* and n is the *index*. Where n is an even number, and b is a negative number, we define no principal nth root, since no such real number exists. We have already noted this for the square root, that is, when $n = 2$. When b is negative and n is odd then the principal nth root is negative. Thus $\sqrt[3]{-64} = -4$, since $(-4)(-4)(-4) = -64$. When b is positive, then the principal nth root is a unique positive real number.

The radical notation for roots was standard in the past, but is now being replaced by the notation to be introduced below.

Two diagrams are shown. The first is a review of the kinds of exponents we have already used. The second suggests a still different way to define an exponential operator.

$$\longleftarrow \quad 27 \qquad 9 \qquad 3 \quad \boxed{1} \quad \frac{1}{3} \qquad \frac{1}{9} \qquad \frac{1}{27} \qquad \longrightarrow$$
$$ 3^3 \qquad 3^2 \qquad 3^1 \quad \phantom{\boxed{}}3^0 \quad 3^{-1} \qquad 3^{-2} \qquad 3^{-3}$$

$$\longleftarrow \quad 6{,}561 \qquad 81 \qquad 9 \quad \boxed{3} \quad \sqrt[2]{3} \quad \sqrt[4]{3} \quad \sqrt[8]{3}$$
$$ 3^8 \qquad 3^4 \qquad 3^2 \quad \phantom{\boxed{}}3^1 \quad 3^{\frac{1}{2}} \quad 3^{\frac{1}{4}} \quad 3^{\frac{1}{8}} \quad \longrightarrow$$

In the upper row of the first diagram, we find 1, the identity for multiplication, at the center. One can start at any number and move to the left by multiplying by 3, or to the right by dividing by 3. In the lower row of the first diagram, we find zero, the identity for addition used as an exponent at the central position. One can start at any number in this row and move to the left by adding 1 to the exponent, or to the right by subtracting 1 from the exponent.

The introduction of zero and negative exponents, as suggested in the first diagram, made it possible to extend the use of $\dfrac{A^m}{A^n} = A^{m-n}$, to cases where $m \leq n$, as well as when $m > n$. The opposite nature of positive and negative numbers makes it possible, when such numbers are used as exponents, to call for the inverse operations of multiplying and dividing.

We turn now to the second diagram and note that the upper row now has 3 at the center. Movement to the left is by squaring; to the right is by taking the square root. The reader should verify that this holds true no matter where we start. On the lower row we find 1 used as an exponent at the center. To move to the left the exponent is multiplied by 2; to move to the right the exponent is divided by 2.

The pattern brought out in the second diagram suggests that the operators $\sqrt{}$ or $\sqrt[2]{}$ and $()^{\frac{1}{2}}$ be identified as being equivalent, and hence we define in general that

$$\sqrt[n]{b} = b^{\frac{1}{n}}$$

This makes possible a wider use of $(A^m)^n = A^{mn}$. In particular, we now have for $A > 0$,

$$(A^n)^{\frac{1}{n}} = A^{\frac{n}{n}} = A^1 = A$$

and $$(A^{\frac{1}{n}})^n = A^{\frac{n}{n}} = A^1 = A$$

and more generally

$$(A^{\frac{1}{n}})^m = A^{\frac{m}{n}} = (A^m)^{\frac{1}{n}}$$

Exponents as first introduced were limited to the use of natural numbers or zero. The first extension was to negative integers, and now we have an interpretation for any rational number used as an exponent. Further development of exponents is reserved to courses in algebra. A few examples will be given as a suggestion of the possibilities.

Examples:

A. $8^{-\frac{2}{3}} = ?$

The operator $(\ )^{-\frac{2}{3}}$ can be thought of as a composite of 3 different operators. Three unary operations are called for: taking the reciprocal, squaring, and taking the principal cube root. These transformations can be accomplished in any order.

$$8^{-\frac{2}{3}} = \left(\frac{1}{8}\right)^{\frac{2}{3}} = \left(\frac{1}{64}\right)^{\frac{1}{3}} = \frac{1}{4} \qquad 8^{-\frac{2}{3}} = \left(\frac{1}{8}\right)^{\frac{2}{3}} = \left(\frac{1}{2}\right)^2 = \frac{1}{4}$$

$$8^{-\frac{2}{3}} = (64)^{-\frac{1}{3}} = \left(\frac{1}{64}\right)^{\frac{1}{3}} = \frac{1}{4} \qquad 8^{-\frac{2}{3}} = (64)^{-\frac{1}{3}} = (4)^{-1} = \frac{1}{4}$$

$$8^{-\frac{2}{3}} = (2)^{-2} = \left(\frac{1}{2}\right)^2 = \frac{1}{4} \qquad 8^{-\frac{2}{3}} = (2)^{-2} = 4^{-1} = \frac{1}{4}$$

B. $(3^{-2} + 4^{-2})^{\frac{1}{2}} = ?$

The important observation here is that the operator $(\ )^{\frac{1}{2}}$ does not distribute over a sum, so that the operations must be performed in the order specified, until we have a quotient or a product. Then the operator may be distributed.

$$(3^{-2} + 4^{-2})^{\frac{1}{2}} = \left(\frac{1}{3^2} + \frac{1}{4^2}\right)^{\frac{1}{2}} = \left(\frac{3^2 + 4^2}{3^2 \cdot 4^2}\right)^{\frac{1}{2}}$$

$$= \frac{(3^2 + 4^2)^{\frac{1}{2}}}{(3^2 \cdot 4^2)^{\frac{1}{2}}}$$

$$= \frac{(25)^{\frac{1}{2}}}{(3^2 \cdot 4^2)^{\frac{1}{2}}} = \frac{5}{3 \cdot 4} = \frac{5}{12}$$

Problems (199)

Transform to a form without exponents.

1. a. $27^{\frac{1}{3}}$ **b.** $27^{\frac{2}{3}}$ **c.** $27^{\frac{3}{3}}$ **d.** $27^{\frac{4}{3}}$ **e.** $27^{\frac{5}{3}}$

2. a. $16^{\frac{1}{4}}$ **b.** $16^{\frac{1}{2}}$ **c.** $16^{\frac{3}{4}}$ **d.** 16^{1} **e.** $16^{\frac{5}{4}}$

3. a. $25^{\frac{1}{2}}$ **b.** 25^{0} **c.** $25^{-\frac{1}{2}}$ **d.** 25^{-1} **e.** $25^{-\frac{3}{2}}$

4. a. $64^{\frac{2}{3}}$ **b.** $64^{\frac{1}{3}}$ **c.** 64^{0} **d.** $64^{-\frac{1}{3}}$ **e.** $64^{-\frac{2}{3}}$

5. $32^{-\frac{4}{5}}$ **9.** $(.0001)^{\frac{1}{4}}$ **13.** $(5^2 - 3^2)^{-\frac{1}{4}}$ **17.** $\left(\dfrac{1}{9}\right)^{-\frac{1}{2}}$

6. $81^{-\frac{3}{4}}$ **10.** $(-.008)^{\frac{1}{3}}$ **14.** $(2^3 - 2^2)^{-\frac{1}{2}}$ **18.** $\left(\dfrac{1}{4}\right)^{-\frac{3}{2}}$

7. $(2^{10})^{-\frac{3}{5}}$ **11.** $(5^2 + 12^2)^{-\frac{1}{2}}$ **15.** $\dfrac{1}{2^{-2}}$ **19.** $(2^{-1} - 3^{-1})^{-1}$

8. $(2^{-6})^{\frac{2}{3}}$ **12.** $(13^2 - 12^2)^{\frac{1}{2}}$ **16.** $\left(\dfrac{8}{125}\right)^{-\frac{1}{3}}$ **20.** $(16^{\frac{1}{2}} + 25^{\frac{1}{2}})^{\frac{1}{2}}$

22-5. Axioms for the Real Numbers

A third way of characterizing the real numbers is by a list of the properties that identify them as a mathematical system.   Previously we have been concerned with models for these numbers, and have thereby associated the real numbers first with infinite decimals and then with points on a line.   A list of properties does not furnish another such model and hence may seem more abstract.   But to the user of these numbers this approach may actually be more direct, since we lay down a precise set of conditions that must be observed.   Such a set of assumed properties for a mathematical system is known as a set of *axioms* or *postulates*.

The real numbers consist of a set $R = \{a, b, c, \ldots\}$ of elements, together with an equivalence relation, two binary operations, and an order relation.   Axioms for each of these will be stated and discussed in turn.

The equivalence relation is the "equals" relation, symbolized by $=$.   The symbol representing an object may be thought of as a name for the object.   We assume for the elements of R that we have a way of deciding whether two elements are different or not.   That is, if a and b are names of elements of R, and if both names refer to the same element, then we write $a = b$, but if they refer to different elements, then we write $a \neq b$.   Stated as an axiom this becomes

E_1.   For all a and b in R, either $a = b$, or $a \neq b$.   Equality is *determinative*.

The next three axioms characterize all equivalence relations.

E_2. For all a in R, $a = a$. Equality is reflexive. In any context the same symbol must not name different objects.

E_3. For all a and b in R, if $a = b$, then $b = a$. Equality is symmetric.

E_4. For all a, b, and c in R, if $a = b$ and $b = c$, then $a = c$. Equality is transitive. This is often translated as, "things equal to the same thing are equal to each other."

Finally, it is convenient to assume for equality what may be called the *substitution principle*.

E_5. For all a and b in R, if $a = b$ then either may be substituted for the other in any statement about the real number they name.

Axioms for the real numbers are given in many places in the literature, and the above axioms are often omitted from the list. Many authors prefer to think of the equality axioms as having their origin in the background of logic within which the discussion lies. It is indeed true that these same assumptions are made in many contexts other than for the real numbers. It may be verified that all of the above follow from the assumption that the equation $a = b$ is a true statement if and only if a and b are names for the same object.

The next axioms are for the binary operation of addition. They do not tell us how to "add." Neither do they tell us what addition is, beyond a statement of the conditions that must be satisfied. In this sense addition is one of the undefined terms in the discussion just as are set, element, and equality.

A_1. For every ordered pair (a, b) of elements of R there is a unique element of R, designated as $a + b$, and called the sum of a and b. The real numbers are closed under addition. This axiom (and M_1 to follow) could be omitted from the list by agreeing to use the word "operation" only in the sense of closed operation.

A_2. For every triple, a, b, and c in R, $(a + b) + c = a + (b + c)$. Addition is associative. There is a further left-to-right reading convention, so that $a + b + c = (a + b) + c$. Hence we may observe that parentheses are not needed when $+$ is the only operation.

A_3. For every pair, a and b in R, $a + b = b + a$. Addition is commutative.

A_4. There is a unique member of R, designated by 0, and called zero or the additive identity, such that for every a in R, $a + 0 = a = 0 + a$.

A_5. For every a in R, there is a unique member of R, designated by $-a$, and called the additive inverse of a, such that $a + (-a) = 0 = (-a) + a$.

The reader will recognize the above as the same kind of assumptions that have been used for various other mathematical systems throughout the text. Section 18-1 in particular should be reviewed for a comparative study.

One of the properties assumed for the natural numbers was that addition be well

defined.   The above axioms ensure that this property also holds for the real numbers.   Thus if a and c are in R, we know from A_1 that $a + c$ is a real number.   Then
$a + c = a + c$ by E_2.   If it is given that $a = b$, it follows from E_5 that $a + c$
$= b + c$ as required.

The existence of an additive inverse for each real number makes it possible to
prove that the cancellation law for addition holds.   We want to show that if
$a, b,$ and c are any real numbers such that $a + b = a + c$, then $b = c$.

Proof: $b = 0 + b = (-a + a) + b = -a + (a + b) = -a + (a + c)$
$= (-a + a) + c = 0 + c = c.$

Sometimes an argument can be arranged in the above manner.   The
reader is asked to focus his attention on the left and right member of
each equality in turn, and to give the reason or reasons which support this
assertion.   In particular one should note at what stage the hypothesis
that $a + b = a + c$ is used.

It is well to begin the study and construction of such proofs by using
only one reason at a time.   But this soon becomes tedious to the point of
boredom, once the understanding is secure.   For example, in all but the
most elementary discussions the changes resulting from the use of the
equivalence axioms, E_1 to E_5, are combined with other changes, and
rarely are mentioned in the proof.

a. Supply reasons for the above proof.

A fair question that may be asked about a set of axioms is whether the list could
be shortened.   Are all statements essential, or could some be proved once others are
assumed?   In practice, an absolute minimum set of axioms may not be the most
convenient or useful.   For example, the word "unique" could have been omitted
from the statements of A_4 and A_5, since it can be shown that only one member of R
meets the specifications in each case.

Suppose that both 0 and $0'$ are additive identities.   Then
$$0' = 0' + 0 = 0 + 0' = 0$$
Hence $0'$ and 0 are the same number.

b. Supply reasons for the above proof.

Given any number a in R, there is no number x, other than $-a$, for which
$a + x = 0$.
If $a + x = 0$, then since $a + (-a) = 0$, we have $a + x = a + (-a)$.
Then $x = -a$.

c. Supply reasons for the above proof.

The following axioms for the binary operation of multiplication are similar to
the corresponding ones for addition, except for restrictions on the number zero.

M_1. For every ordered pair (a, b) of elements of R there is a unique element of R, designated as $a \cdot b$, $(a)(b)$, or ab, called the product of a and b. The real numbers are closed under multiplication.

M_2. For every triple a, b, and c in R, $(a \cdot b) \cdot c = a \cdot (b \cdot c)$. Multiplication is associative. Parentheses are not needed when the only operation is multiplication.

M_3. For every pair, a and b in R, $a \cdot b = b \cdot a$. Multiplication is commutative.

M_4. There is a unique member of R, different from zero, designated as 1, and called one or the multiplicative identity, such that for every a in R, $1 \cdot a = a = a \cdot 1$.

M_5. For every a in R that is different from zero, there is a unique member of R, designated by a^{-1}, and called the multiplicative inverse of a, such that $a \cdot a^{-1} = 1 = a^{-1} \cdot a$.

d. Show that multiplication is well defined.

e. Show that the cancellation law for multiplication holds. (See **a.** above.)

f. Show that uniqueness need not be assumed in M_4. (See **b.** above.)

g. Show that uniqueness need not be assumed in M_5. (See **c.** above.)

The next axiom links together the two binary operations.

D. For every triple a, b, and c of R, $a(b + c) = ab + ac$ and $(b + c)a = ba + ca$. Multiplication is distributive over (or with respect to) addition.

The statement of D includes both the left-distributive and the right-distributive laws. But in the presence of the commutative axioms, A_3 and M_3, the assumption of either of the distributive laws will mean that the other holds also. (See A_4, A_5, M_4, and M_5 as well.)

Any mathematical system that satisfies the axioms thus far listed is called a *field*. In Chapter 18 examples were given of a field of an infinite number of elements (the rational numbers), and of a field with a finite number of elements (integers modulo 3). Many simple but important results can now be proved, and the reader is invited to supply the reasons or construct the entire proof for some of these in the next problem set.

Answers to Exercises

a. A_4; A_5; A_2; $a + b = a + c$; A_2; A_5; A_4. E_5 was used repeatedly, as well as E_3. **b.** A_4; A_3; A_4. **c.** A_5, and the cancellation law for addition. **d.** $a \cdot c$ is a real number by M_1. $a \cdot c = a \cdot c$ by E_2. If $a = b$ is given, then $a \cdot c = b \cdot c$ by E_5. **e.** If $a \cdot b = a \cdot c$, we have

$$b = 1 \cdot b = (a^{-1} \cdot a) \cdot b = a^{-1} \cdot (a \cdot b) = a^{-1} \cdot (a \cdot c) = (a^{-1} \cdot a) \cdot c = 1 \cdot c = c$$

$$M_4; \ M_5; \ M_2; \ a \cdot b = a \cdot c; \ M_2; \ M_5; \ M_4$$

f. Suppose 1 and $1'$ are both multiplicative identities.

$$1' = 1' \cdot 1 = 1 \cdot 1' = 1. \qquad M_4, \ M_3, \ M_4.$$

g. Let x be a member of R such that $a \cdot x = 1$. Then $a \cdot a^{-1} = 1$, by M_5. Hence $a \cdot x = a \cdot a^{-1}$, and $x = a^{-1}$ by the cancellation law for multiplication.

Problems (200)

1. Zero is the "annihilator" for multiplication. For every a in R, $a \cdot 0 = 0$.
   Proof: $a \cdot a + a \cdot 0 = a(a + 0)$?   Supply reasons.
   $$= a \cdot a \qquad ?$$
   $$= a \cdot a + 0 \quad ?$$
   $$a \cdot 0 = 0 \qquad ?$$

2. A product is zero only if one of its factors is zero. For every pair, a and b in R, if $a \cdot b = 0$, then $a = 0$ or $b = 0$.
   Proof: Assume $a \cdot b = 0$. If $b = 0$, the statement is satisfied.
   But if $b \neq 0$, we have
   $$a = a \cdot 1 \qquad ? \qquad \text{Supply reasons.}$$
   $$= a \cdot (b \cdot b^{-1}) \quad ?$$
   $$= (a \cdot b) \cdot b^{-1} \quad ?$$
   $$= 0 \cdot b^{-1} \qquad ?$$
   $$= 0 \qquad ?$$

3. Every real number is the additive inverse of its additive inverse. For every a in R, $-(-a) = a$.
   Proof: $-a + a = 0$?   Supply reasons.
   $$= -a + [-(-a)] \quad ?$$
   $$a = -(-a) \qquad ?$$

4. Every nonzero real number is the multiplicative inverse of its multiplicative inverse. Prove that if a is a nonzero member of R (so that it has a multiplicative inverse), then $(a^{-1})^{-1} = a$.

5. The real number 1 is its own multiplicative inverse. $1^{-1} = 1$
   Proof: $1 \cdot 1^{-1} = 1$?   Supply reasons.
   $$1 \cdot 1 = 1 \qquad ?$$
   Then $1 \cdot 1^{-1} = 1 \cdot 1$, by E_5.
   $$1^{-1} = 1 \quad ?$$

6. Prove that the real number zero is its own additive inverse. That is, $-0 = 0$.

7. The additive inverse of a product is the product of one factor and the additive inverse of the other. For every pair, a and b in R, $-(ab) = (a)(-b)$.
   Proof: $ab + a(-b) = a(b + (-b))$?   Supply reasons.
   $$= a \cdot 0 \qquad ?$$
   $$= 0 \qquad ?$$
   $$ab + [-(ab)] = 0 \qquad ?$$
   $$-(ab) = a(-b) \qquad ?$$
   Now prove that $-(ab) = (-a)b$.

8. The product of two real numbers is equal to the product of their additive inverses. For every pair, a and b in R, $(-a)(-b) = ab$.

Proof: $-(ab) + (-a)(-b) = (-a)(b) + (-a)(-b)$?   Supply reasons.

$$= (-a)(b + (-b))$$?
$$= (-a) \cdot 0$$?
$$= 0$$?
$$-(ab) + ab = 0$$?
$$(-a)(-b) = ab$$?

9. The multiplicative inverse of a nonzero product is the product of the multiplicative inverses of the factors. For every pair, a and b in R, with $a \neq 0$ and $b \neq 0$, $(ab)^{-1} = a^{-1} \cdot b^{-1}$.

Proof: $(ab)(a^{-1} \cdot b^{-1}) = (ab)(b^{-1} \cdot a^{-1})$?

$$= [(ab)b^{-1}] \, a^{-1}$$?
$$= a(b \cdot b^{-1})a^{-1}$$?
$$= (a \cdot 1)a^{-1}$$?
$$= a \cdot a^{-1}$$?
$$= 1$$?
$$(ab)(ab)^{-1} = 1$$?
$$(ab)^{-1} = a^{-1} \cdot b^{-1}$$?

10. Prove that the additive inverse of a sum is the sum of the additive inverses. That is, for every pair, a and b in R, $-(a + b) = (-a) + (-b)$. (Analogous to problem 9.)

The results in problem set (200) include the "laws of signs," which we met first in the discussion of operators, and then were derived for the integers by the use of equivalence classes. We now show that two fundamental equations always have solutions in the set of real numbers. One of these equations had a central role in the extension of the natural numbers to the positive rationals, and the other was basic in the extension of the natural numbers to the integers.

For any pair, a and b in R, there exists in R a unique solution of the equation $x + b = a$, namely, $x = a + (-b)$.

Proof: We first verify that $x = a + (-b)$ is a solution, by substituting $a + (-b)$ for x in $x + b$.

$$x + b = (a + (-b)) + b$$
$$= a + ((-b) + b)$$?
$$= a + 0$$?
$$= a, \text{ as required}$$?

Next assume that x is a solution of $x + b = a$.

$-b$ is the additive inverse of b.   ?
$$(x + b) + (-b) = a + (-b)$$?
$$x + (b + (-b)) = a + (-b)$$?
$$x + 0 = a + (-b)$$?
$$x = a + (-b)$$?

a. Supply reasons for the above proof.

For any pair, a and b in R with $b \neq 0$, there exists in R a unique solution of the equation $x \cdot b = a$, namely, $x = a \cdot b^{-1}$.

b. Construct a proof for the above.

We are now in a position to define two new binary operations in R. This will be done indirectly, that is, in terms of the two operations already assumed in axioms A_1 and M_1.

> **Definition:** *For every ordered pair (a, b) of elements of R, $a - b$ is defined to be the unique solution of $x + b = a$. That is, $a - b = a + (-b)$. $a - b$ is called the difference of a and b (or of b from a), and the operation which assigns $a - b$ to the ordered pair (a, b) is called subtraction.*

> **Definition:** *For every ordered pair (a, b) of elements of R with $b \neq 0$, $\frac{a}{b}$ is defined to be the unique solution of $x \cdot b = a$. That is, $\frac{a}{b} = a \cdot b^{-1}$. $\frac{a}{b}$ is called the quotient of a and b (or of a by b), and the operation which assigns $\frac{a}{b}$ to the ordered pair (a, b) is called division.*

ANSWERS TO EXERCISES

a. A_2; A_5; A_4; A_5; addition is well defined; A_2; A_5; A_4.   **b.** $x \cdot b = (a \cdot b^{-1})b = a(b^{-1} \cdot b) = a \cdot 1 = a$. Substitution; M_2; M_5; M_4. $x \cdot b = a$, $(x \cdot b)b^{-1} = a \cdot b^{-1}$, $x(b \cdot b^{-1}) = a \cdot b^{-1}$, $x \cdot 1 = a \cdot b^{-1}$, $x = a \cdot b^{-1}$. Solution, multiplication is well defined; M_2; M_5; M_4.

Problems (201)

1. For all a in R, $0 - a = -a$.
   Proof: $0 - a = 0 + (-a)$?   Supply reasons.
   $\qquad\qquad = -a$?

2. Prove that for all nonzero a in R, $\frac{1}{a} = a^{-1}$.

3. For all a in R, $\frac{a}{1} = a$.

   Proof: $\frac{a}{1} = a \cdot 1^{-1}$?   Supply reasons.

   $\qquad\quad = a \cdot 1$?
   $\qquad\quad = a$?

4. Prove that for all a in R, $a - 0 = a$.

5. If $a + b = 0$, then $b = -a$.
   Proof: If $a + b = 0$,
   $\qquad$ Then $-a + (a + b) = -a + 0$?   Supply reasons.
   $\qquad\qquad (-a + a) + b = -a + 0$?
   $\qquad\qquad\qquad 0 + b = -a + 0$?
   $\qquad\qquad\qquad\qquad b = -a$?

6. Prove that if $a \cdot b = 1$, and $a \neq 0$, then $b = \dfrac{1}{a}$.

7. For all a and b in R with $a \neq 0$, $\left(\dfrac{b}{a}\right) a = b$.

   Proof: $\left(\dfrac{b}{a}\right) a = (b \cdot a^{-1})a$?   Supply reasons.

$$= b(a^{-1} \cdot a) \qquad ?$$
$$= b \cdot 1 \qquad ?$$
$$= b \qquad ?$$

8. Prove that for all a and b in R, $(b - a) + a = b$.

9. For all a, b, and c in R, $a - (b + c) = (a - b) - c$.

   Proof: $a - (b + c) = a + [-(b + c)]$?   Supply reasons.

$$= a + [(-b) + (-c)] \qquad ?$$
$$= [a + (-b)] + (-c) \qquad ?$$
$$= (a - b) - c \qquad ?$$

10. Prove that for all a, b, and c in R with $b \neq 0$ and $c \neq 0$, $\dfrac{a}{bc} = \left(\dfrac{a}{b}\right)\dfrac{1}{c}$.

11. $a - b = c - d$ if and only if $a + d = b + c$.

   Proof: If $a + d = b + c$,

$$\text{Then } (a + d) + (-d) = (b + c) + (-d) \qquad ? \text{ Supply reasons.}$$
$$a + (d + (-d)) = b + (c + (-d)) \qquad ?$$
$$a + 0 = b + (c - d) \qquad ?$$
$$a = c - d + b \qquad ?$$
$$a + (-b) = (c - d + b) + (-b) \qquad ?$$
$$a - b = c - d + (b + (-b)) \qquad ?$$
$$= c - d + 0 \qquad ?$$
$$= c - d \qquad ?$$

If $a - b = c - d$,

$$\text{Then } (a - b) + b = (c - d) + b \qquad ?$$
$$(a + (-b)) + b = b + (c - d) \qquad ?$$
$$a + ((-b) + b) = b + (c - d) \qquad ?$$
$$a + 0 = b + (c - d) \qquad ?$$
$$a = b + (c - d) \qquad ?$$
$$a + d = b + (c - d) + d \qquad ?$$
$$= b + (c + (-d)) + d \qquad ?$$
$$= b + c + ((-d) + d) \qquad ?$$
$$= b + c + 0 \qquad ?$$
$$= b + c \qquad ?$$

12. Prove that for $b \neq 0$ and $d \neq 0$, $\dfrac{a}{b} = \dfrac{c}{d}$ if and only if $ad = bc$.

13. a. Prove that for all a, b, c, and d in R,

$$(a - b) + (c - d) = (a + c) - (b + d)$$

     b. Part **a.** is a theorem about sums and differences. State and prove an analogous theorem about products and quotients.

14. a. Prove that for all a, b, c, and d in R, with b, c, and d not zero,

$$\frac{\dfrac{a}{b}}{\dfrac{c}{d}} = \frac{ad}{bc}$$

     b. Part **a.** is a theorem about quotients and products. State and prove an analogous theorem about differences and sums.

The next axioms to be added to the list are those of order. These axioms, together with the preceding ones, which defined a field, now define an ordered field. The rational numbers are an example of such a mathematical system (see Section 18-1).

The set R has a subset P, called the positive members of R, such that:

O_1. If $a \in P$ and $b \in P$, then $a + b \in P$. The set P is closed under addition.

O_2. If $a \in P$ and $b \in P$, then $a \cdot b \in P$. The set P is closed under multiplication.

O_3. For every member x of the set R, exactly one of the following statements is true:

     i. $x \in P$ **ii.** $x = 0$ **iii.** $-x \in P$

Axiom O_3 is one form of the law of trichotomy, which was one of the assumptions for the rational numbers. The set R can be partitioned into three sets P, $\{0\}$, and N, where N is defined by

$$N = \{x \mid x \in R \text{ and } -x \in P\}$$

N is said to be the set of negative members of R. The following definition relates the sets P and N to the relation $<$, which was used in the previous developments of number systems.

     Definition: *If a and b are members of R, then $a > b$, or $b < a$, is defined to mean that $a - b$, or $a + (-b)$, is a member of P.*

It is now possible to use the three order axioms above together with the previous axioms for R and thereby derive order properties that were assumed in the previous chapters. This project will not be carried out here in detail, but some basic properties will be established as examples.

     Examples:

         A. If a is positive (a member of P), then $-a$ is negative (a member of N).

         Proof: If a is positive, then $-(-a)$ is positive.

                                                 Problem 3 in set (200).

         Then $-a$ is negative by definition.

B. A member a of R is positive if and only if $a > 0$.

   Proof: $a - 0 = a$.   Problem 4 of set (201).

   $a - 0$ is positive by definition if and only if $a > 0$.

   Hence a is positive if and only if $a > 0$.

C. A member a of R is negative if and only if $a < 0$.

   Proof: $0 - a = -a$.   Problem 1 of set (201).

   If $-a$ is positive then $-(-a)$, or a, is negative by Example **A,** and Problem 3 of set (200).

   $0 > a$, or $a < 0$ if and only if $0 - a$ is positive.

                                                                       Definition.

   $a < 0$ if and only if $-a$ is positive.

   $a < 0$ if and only if a is negative.   From above.

D. For any a and b of R, one and only one of the following holds:

$$a > b \qquad a = b \qquad a < b$$

   Proof: There are for $a - b$ these three possibilities:

       $a - b$ is positive ($a - b$ is a member of P),

       $a - b = 0$,

       $-(a - b)$ is positive ($a - b$ is a member of N). O_3

   i. If $a - b$ is positive, then $a > b$ by definition.

   ii. If $a - b = 0$, then $a - b + b = 0 + b$, since addition is well defined.   Then $a = b$ by A_2, A_5, and A_4.

   iii. If $-(a - b)$ is positive,

       then $-(a - b) > 0$ **a.** Supply reasons.

           $-(a + (-b)) > 0$

           $-((-b) + a) > 0$

           $-(-b) - a > 0$

           $b - a > 0$

           $b > a$, or $a < b$

E. If a, b, and c are in R, and $a > b$ and $b > c$, then $a > c$.

   Proof: If $a > b$, and $b > c$,

       then $a - b$ and $b - c$ are positive.   **b.** Supply reasons.

       $(a - b) + (b - c)$ is positive.

       $(a + (-b)) + (b + (-c))$ is positive.

       $a - c$ is positive.

       $a > c$

F. If $a > b$ and c is in R, then $a + c > b + c$.

   Proof: $(a + c) - (b + c) = a - b$ **c.** Supply reasons.

       If $a > b$, then $a - b$ or $(a + c) - (b + c)$ is positive, and $a + c > b + c$.

G. If $a > b$ and c is positive, then $ac > bc$.

Proof: If $a > b$, then $a - b$ is positive. **d.** Supply reasons.

Then if c is positive, $c(a - b)$ is positive.

$c(a + (-b))$ is positive.

$ca + c(-b)$ is positive.

$ac - bc$ is positive.

$ac > bc$

Answers to Exercises

a. Example **B**; definition; A_3; problem 10 of set (200); problem 3 of set (200); definition.
b. Definition; O_1; definition; A_2, A_5, A_4, and definition; definition. **c.** $(a + c) - (b + c) =$ $a - b$ since $a + c + b = b + c + a$, by problem 11 of set (201), A_2, and A_3; definition; definition.
d. Definition; O_2; definition; D; problem 7 of set (200); definition.

Problems (202)

1. 1 is a positive number

Proof: $1 \neq 0$?   Supply reasons.

Suppose 1 were negative.

Then -1 would be positive.   ?

Then $-1 > 0$?

Then $(-1)(-1) > 0(-1)$?

Then $1 > 0$?

Then 1 is positive.   ?

But 1 cannot be both negative and positive.   ?

Therefore 1 is positive.   ?

2. Prove that if a is a nonzero member of R, then a^2 is positive.

3. $1 > 0$

Proof: $1 \neq 0$?   Supply reasons.

$1^2 > 0$?

$1^2 = 1$?

$1 > 0$

4. Use result of problem 3 to prove that for all a in R, $a + 1 > a$.

5. If a is positive and b is negative, their product ab is negative.

Proof: If b is negative, then $-b$ is positive.   ?   Supply reasons.

Then for positive a, $a(-b)$ is positive.   ?

Then $-(ab)$ is positive.   ?

Then $-(-(ab))$ or ab is negative.   ?

6. Prove that if a and b are both negative, their product ab is positive.

7. If a is positive, then the multiplicative inverse (reciprocal) of a is positive.

Proof: If a is positive, it is not zero.   ?   Supply reasons.

If a is not zero, then a^{-1} is its multiplicative inverse. ?

Then $a \cdot a^{-1} = 1$?

Suppose $a^{-1} = 0$, then $a \cdot a^{-1} = a \cdot 0 = 0$?

This contradicts $a \cdot a^{-1} = 1$, so that $a^{-1} \neq 0$

       Suppose a^{-1} is negative, then $a \cdot a^{-1}$ is negative.   ?
       But $a \cdot a^{-1} = 1$, and 1 is not negative.   ?
       Hence a^{-1} must be positive.   ?

8. If each of the following statements is true, give the reasons; if false, give an example.

  a. The set P of R is closed under addition.

  b. The set P of R is closed under subtraction.

  c. The set P of R is closed under multiplication.

  d. The set P of R is closed under division.

The discussion of real numbers was begun in Section 22-2 by showing a need for numbers that are not rational. The axioms we have thus far given for the real numbers are still all satisfied by the rational numbers. The extension of the reals to a broader class of numbers that includes irrationals as well as rationals comes from the next and final axiom. It is stated in the language of upper bounds and of least upper bounds, an introduction to which was given in Section 13-3.

    C. Every nonempty set of R (the real numbers) that has an upper bound has a least upper bound that is a member of R, and every nonempty set of R that is bounded below has a greatest lower bound in R.

This axiom is often called the Axiom of Completeness. It can now be shown, by proofs beyond the scope of this text, that the real numbers now include numbers corresponding to each infinite decimal, for which we found the rational numbers inadequate. The real numbers also include a unique number for each point on the real line. Because of this some equivalent forms of axiom C are called the axiom of continuity.

Some sets of rational numbers do have rational numbers for a least upper bound. Thus in Section 13-3, the rational numbers given by $\dfrac{n}{2n+1}$ for n, a natural number, were considered. It was shown there that each of this infinite set of rational numbers was less than $\dfrac{1}{2}$, so that the rational number $\dfrac{1}{2}$ was an upper bound for the set. Furthermore $\dfrac{1}{2}$ was shown to be the least upper bound. But suppose we consider the rational numbers whose square is less than 2. These numbers are bounded above, since each is clearly less than 2, for example. But it can be shown that there is no rational number that is the least upper bound for this set. The axiom of completeness assures of the existence of an irrational number for this least upper bound, and this number can be proved to be the real number we have designated as $\sqrt{2}$.

The fact that every irrational number turns out to be the least upper bound of a set of rational numbers is of very great importance for computation with irrational numbers, since we can therefore approximate any irrational number as closely as we please by a rational number.   Hence a characterization of the real numbers can be given as being those numbers that can be approximated by rational numbers to any specified precision.

For Further Study

The discussion of square root in [S17], pp. 219–232, includes not only the division method as given in this text, but also gives an analysis of the traditional algorithm.

The following list of references includes a variety of elementary introductions to the real numbers: [A1], pp. 263–271; [H2], pp. 229–245; [K1], pp. 227–232; [W7], pp. 116–124.

The uniqueness of prime factorization of natural numbers is used in [S14], pp. 53–65, to establish that certain numbers are irrational.

For help with the theorems for an ordered field, see [F1], pp. 148–189; [H1], pp. 41–58; [K2], pp. 8–13; [N4], pp. 96–103; and [O2], pp. 1–14.

References [F2] and [R3] are short monographs that give good summaries of the development of the elementary number systems.

For a careful treatment of the foundations of arithmetic, as given fifty years ago, refer to [H4].

23

Arithmetic and Geometry

23-1. Geometry as a Mathematical System

The mathematical systems that have thus far been considered have been arithmetical or algebraical systems. This designation applies because the usual interpretation for the elements of the set, on which the relations and operations are defined, has been a set of numbers. Geometry is also a mathematical system, whose structure can be built on a set S, called the set of *points* of space. Certain subsets of S are then called *lines* and still other subsets of S are called *planes*. Axioms are then stated for relations on these sets such as for *on*, *contains*, *equal*, *congruent*, and so on. Various concepts are then introduced by definitions, and the implications of these assumptions are derived logically and stated as a body of theorems. Such a study of geometry as an axiomatic system is reserved for courses of that title. Our concern for geometry will be that it is a principal field for the applications of arithmetic, so that our approach will be factual with most of the connecting logical argument omitted.

23-2. Measure

An important link between arithmetic and geometry comes from the idea of measure. We have already referred to measurement many times in previous chapters. The more careful statements to be given about measure concern properties that have been assumed without explicit mention thus far.

We have been using the words "count" and "measure" in a way that has emphasized their differences. Thus we have counted to determine the cardinal number of a set, but measurement has referred to the use of some unit for determining the ratio comparison of this unit to the quantity being measured. We now use the term "measure" in a broader way, so that counting can be considered as a special case of measurement. The advantage of this point of view lies in the possibility of observing the general properties we shall want for all measures, by studying the simple case of a measure for a finite set.

In the broadest sense, to "measure" is to assign a number to an object. Let the objects be a set S together with all of its subsets, and let $m(A)$ refer to the measure of the subset A, as obtained by counting the number of elements in A.

1. One of the subsets of S is the empty set $\varnothing$, and

$$m(\varnothing) = 0$$

2. For any other subset A of S, $m(A)$ is a natural number and hence is nonnegative. That is, for all A, including $A = \varnothing$,

$$m(A) \geq 0$$

3. The count of the elements in the union of two sets can be obtained directly from the count of each separate set provided that the intersection of these sets is empty. Hence

$$\text{if } A \cap B = \varnothing, \text{ then } m(A \cup B) = m(A) + m(B)$$

4. If A is a subset of B, then A cannot have a greater number of elements than B does.

$$\text{if } A \subseteq B, \text{ then } m(A) \leq m(B)$$

Properties 2, 3, and 4 are known as the nonnegative, finitely additive, and monotone properties, respectively. Experience has shown that these properties are the ones that should be assumed for all measures including such typical ones as lengths of line segments, areas of regions, volumes and masses of solid bodies, and so on. For the measure of length of line segments we assume that:

A. The empty set has measure zero. A point is considered to be a degenerate or limiting case of a line segment, and has a length of zero.
B. The length of a line segment is a nonnegative real number.
C. The length of the line segment formed by placing two line segments end to end is the sum of the lengths of the given line segments.
D. As an example of property 4, where equality holds even when A is a proper subset of B consider the line segments determined by the following intervals from a linear scale.

$$A = \{x \mid 3 \leq x < 5\}$$
$$B = \{x \mid 3 \leq x \leq 5\}$$

Here $m(A) = 2 = m(B)$, even though $A \subset B$.

23-3. Measurement of Angles

The term "angle" has several related but different connotations. There is the idea of a geometric angle, which is a geometric figure or set of points, to be defined below. But we also speak of an angle of rotation, which is a measure of turning.

Consider a wheel turning about the point C as a center, and in the direction indicated, which is called counterclockwise, since it is opposite to the motion of the hands of a clock. A scale for the measurement of rotation can then be devised as follows. Let a point on the wheel correspond to a point in the fixed background.

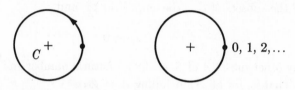

This gives the zero position of the wheel. After one complete turn the points again correspond, and repeated revolutions can be designated by 2, 3, ... Revolutions in the opposite direction can be assigned negative numbers. The turning of rotating machinery is often measured in revolutions. Thus the crankshaft of an engine may make 4,000 revolutions per minute (r.p.m.).

A circular scale may be constructed as below for measuring fractional parts of a revolution. But the awkwardness of common fractions for this purpose would soon be apparent.

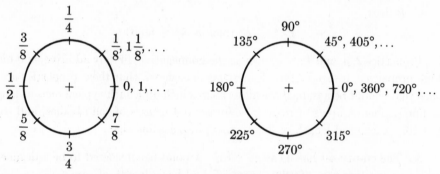

Many centuries ago the Babylonians decided to assign the number 360 to the measure of one turn or revolution. It is not known exactly why they made this choice; but it can be seen that, while quite large numbers would be needed for several turns, many of the most used fractional parts of a turn would now be measured by natural numbers, since 360 has so many exact divisors.

Geometric figures are to be conceived of as being sets of points. If P and Q are two distinct points, the unique line that contains both of the points will be designated by either $\overleftrightarrow{PQ}$ or $\overleftrightarrow{QP}$. Again if P and Q are distinct points, the line segment $\overline{PQ}$ (or $\overline{QP}$) is the set of points consisting of P, Q, and all points between them. And if P and Q are distinct points, the set of points of the segment $\overline{PQ}$ together with all the points X such that Q is between P and X is called a ray or half-line $\overrightarrow{PQ}$.

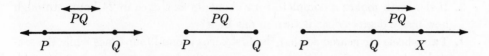

As a geometric figure, an angle is a point set that is the union of two rays that have a common end point and do not lie in the same straight line.   In the figure the rays of $\overrightarrow{AB}$ and $\overrightarrow{AC}$ form the *sides* of the angle, and the common end point A is called the *vertex* of the angle.   The angle may be designated either as the angle BAC or the angle CAB.

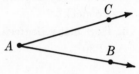

The connection between an angle as a set of points and as a measure of rotation can be established as follows.   Given the angle BAC as above, a circle is now drawn with a center at A and with a convenient radius, which intersects the ray $\overrightarrow{AB}$ at M and the ray $\overrightarrow{AC}$ at N.   Now think of A as being the center of a wheel, with $\overline{AM}$ being a spoke of this wheel.   Imagine that the wheel is revolved counterclockwise, as indicated by the curved

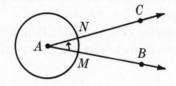

arrow.   If $\overline{AM}$ then comes to rest at position $\overline{AN}$, we say that the spoke, and the wheel, has turned through the angle MAN (which is the same angle as BAC). Thus it is possible to speak of the measure or size of the angle in terms of degrees or revolutions.   If $\overline{AM}$ has made $\frac{1}{12}$ of a turn, then m (angle BAC) = 30°.

Note that the definition of an angle as a point set does not admit "zero angles," that is, angles with a measure of zero.   Neither does it admit so-called "straight angles," which have a measure of $\frac{1}{2}$ turn or 180°.   Such angles are useful in some applications but can be ignored in the study of simple geometric figures where they are limiting cases of little interest.

Problems (203)

For problems 1 and 2 consider each fraction as specifying a number of revolutions.   Compute its equivalent in degrees.

1. a. $\dfrac{1}{2}, \dfrac{3}{2}, \dfrac{5}{2}$ c. $\dfrac{1}{6}, \dfrac{5}{6}, \dfrac{7}{6}$ e. $\dfrac{1}{20}, \dfrac{11}{20}, \dfrac{23}{20}$

   b. $\dfrac{1}{5}, \dfrac{2}{5}, \dfrac{3}{5}, \dfrac{4}{5}$ d. $\dfrac{1}{12}, \dfrac{5}{12}, \dfrac{7}{12}$ f. $\dfrac{1}{24}, \dfrac{19}{24}$

2. a. $\dfrac{1}{3}, \dfrac{2}{3}, \dfrac{7}{3}$ **c.** $\dfrac{1}{8}, \dfrac{3}{8}, \dfrac{5}{8}$ **e.** What other divisors does 360 have that were not used in problems 1 **a.** to **f.**, and 2 **a.** to **d.**?

     b. $\dfrac{1}{4}, \dfrac{3}{4}, \dfrac{5}{4}$ **d.** $\dfrac{1}{9}, \dfrac{2}{9}, \dfrac{4}{9}$

3. If the earth makes a complete turn about its axis once in 24 hours, through how many degrees does it turn in one hour?

4. Two wheels are geared so that the first turns around four times while the second turns once. If the first is turned one-third of the way around, through how many degrees does the second turn?

5. How many degrees are there in the angle made by the hands of a clock at 2 o'clock?

6. How many degrees are there in the angle made by the hands of a clock at 12:30?

23-4. Triangles and Measurement

If three distinct points A, B, and C do not lie on a line, they may be said to form a triangular array. The three possible pairs of these points determine the three line segments, $\overline{AB}$, $\overline{BC}$, and $\overline{CA}$. The union of these three line segments is called a *triangle*. The points A, B, and C are known as the *vertices* of the triangle, and the three segments are the *sides* of the triangle.

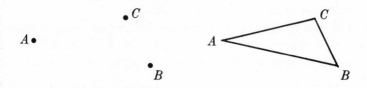

A measure, in units of length, can be given for each of these sides. The *perimeter* is the sum of these three lengths.

$$P = m(\overline{AB}) + m(\overline{BC}) + m(\overline{CA})$$

If two of these lengths are equal, the triangle is said to be *isosceles*. If all three are equal, the triangle is *equilateral*. If no two sides have the same length, the triangle is *scalene*.

Three angles, ABC, BCA, and CAB are determined, whose vertices are at B, C, and A, respectively. These are referred to as the three angles of the triangle. However, it is clear that any of these angles, as a point set, is not a subset of the points that constitute the triangle. For example, the rays $\overrightarrow{AC}$ and $\overrightarrow{AB}$ whose union is the angle CAB do not terminate at C and B respectively, but extend without limit and thus include points that are not part of the triangle.

The classical (and simplest) axioms for geometry are those given by the Greek geometer Euclid. By their use, it can be established that the sum of the measures

in degrees of the three angles of a triangle is 180°.
An angle of one quarter of a turn, or 90 degrees,
is called a right angle.   It follows that a triangle
can have at most one angle of this size.   Triangle
ABC here has a right angle at A, and hence may
be called a right-angled triangle, or a right triangle.

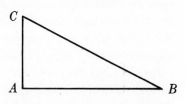

Two lines or line segments that determine a right angle are said to be *perpendicu-lar*, as are $\overline{AC}$ and $\overline{AB}$ in the right triangle.   Any side of a triangle and the angle
whose vertex is not a point of that side are said to be *opposite* each other.   In a right
triangle, the side opposite the vertex of the right angle is called the *hypotenuse* and
the other two sides are called the *legs*.   For any triangle, the perpendicular segment
from any vertex to the line determined by the opposite side is called an *altitude*.   In
the right triangle ABC above the segment $\overline{AC}$ is an altitude from the vertex C to
the opposite side $\overline{AB}$.   The side $\overline{AB}$ is then termed the *base*.   In this same triangle,
if $\overline{AC}$ is the base, then $\overline{AB}$ is the corresponding altitude.

If X and Y are two points of a triangle but X and Y are not on the same side of
the triangle, then all points of the segment $\overline{XY}$ between point X and point Y lie in
the *interior* of the triangle.   The set of all the interior points of a triangle, together
with the points of the triangle, constitutes a triangular region, having the triangle
itself as a *boundary*.   A measure, called area, can be assigned to a triangular region
and a discussion of this problem is given in the next section.

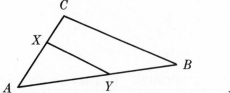
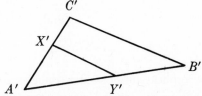

In triangles ABC and $A'B'C'$ suppose that each side and angle measure of triangle ABC is equal to the corresponding side and angle measure of triangle $A'B'C'$.

$$m(\overline{AB}) = m(\overline{A'B'})$$
$$m(\overline{BC}) = m(\overline{B'C'})$$
$$m(\overline{CA}) = m(\overline{C'A'})$$
$$m(\text{angle } ABC) = m(\text{angle } A'B'C')$$
$$m(\text{angle } BCA) = m(\text{angle } B'C'A')$$
$$m(\text{angle } CAB) = m(\text{angle } C'A'B')$$

The triangles ABC and $A'B'C'$ are then said to be *congruent*.   The congruence relation may be defined more generally as follows: Two subsets, S and T, of the points
of a plane are congruent, if there is a one-to-one correspondence between S and T
such that if X and Y are points of S and X' and Y' are the corresponding points of
T, then $m(\overline{XY}) = m(\overline{X'Y'})$.

It is proved in courses in geometry that if certain of the above six equations hold, then the remaining equations must also be true. Thus if the corresponding sides are equal in length, then the corresponding angles must have the same measure also. But it is possible for the measures of the corresponding angles to be equal, when the measures of the corresponding sides are not equal. The triangles will then not be congruent, but they will be *similar*. The definition of similarity, as applied to various pairs of geometric figures, requires not only that corresponding angles have the same measure, but also that corresponding line segments have measures that are proportional. For triangles, if corresponding angles have the same measure, then the proportionality of the sides must also hold, although a proof of this is not elementary.

Let ABC and $A'B'C'$ be similar triangles, with the same letter used to indicate corresponding vertices. Let the lengths of the sides opposite these vertices be represented by a, b, c and a', b', c'.

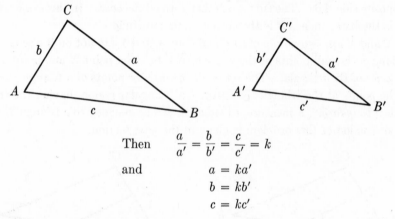

Then $\quad \dfrac{a}{a'} = \dfrac{b}{b'} = \dfrac{c}{c'} = k$

and
$$a = ka'$$
$$b = kb'$$
$$c = kc'$$

The applications of similar triangles are very extensive. We have already referred to one in Section 9-3 when discussing the ratio interpretation of multiplication. We give one further simple but very useful example, which makes use of two similar right triangles.

Angles ABC and ADE are both right angles. Angle CAB is common to both triangle ABC and triangle ADE. Because of the constant of 180° for the sum of the measures of the three angles of any triangle, angle ACB must have the same measure as angle AED. Hence the two

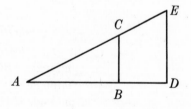

right triangles are similar, and corresponding sides are proportional in length. In particular,

$$\frac{m(\overline{AB})}{m(\overline{AD})} = \frac{m(\overline{BC})}{m(\overline{DE})} = k$$

For example, let $k = .7$. The assertion is that if the length of $\overline{AB}$ is .7 of the length $\overline{AD}$, then the length of $\overline{BC}$ is .7 of that of $\overline{DE}$. We now show how such a pair of similar triangles can be used in connection with a table of values such as for $\sqrt{n}$ in Appendix 3.

The pairs $(n, \sqrt{n})$ for $n = 0, 10, 20, 30, \ldots, 90, 100$ have been entered on the graph below, and the points given by these pairs have been connected with a smooth curve.

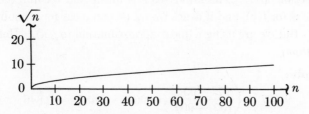

The above graph was constructed by selecting only every tenth entry from the table in the Appendix. Suppose now that these values had been the only ones given. What we wish to consider is a possible means of *interpolation*, that is, of estimating intermediate values of the function when only certain ones are known. A suggestion for such a method lies in this observation of the graph: While the graph nowhere coincides with a straight line exactly, the curvature appears very small for small differences in n, particularly for larger values of n. Hence if the actual graph between two known points is replaced by a straight line, we might have a reasonably good approximation. But the straight line provides similar triangles whose dimensions are easily computed. The diagram below is a study of the region from $n = 90$ to $n = 100$, with certain features exaggerated for greater clarity.

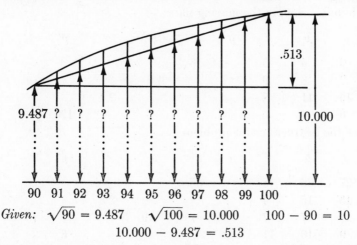

Given: $\sqrt{90} = 9.487$ $\sqrt{100} = 10.000$ $100 - 90 = 10$

$$10.000 - 9.487 = .513$$

The base of the larger of the similar triangles 10, and its altitude is .513. The interpolated values of $\sqrt{n}$ are computed as below, to the nearest thousandth, and compared with the value from the table in Appendix 3.

			Table
$n = 91$	$(.1)(.513) = .051$	$9.487 + .051 = 9.538$	9.539
$n = 92$	$(.2)(.513) = .103$	$9.487 + .103 = 9.590$	9.592
$n = 93$	$(.3)(.513) = .154$	$9.487 + .154 = 9.641$	9.644

a. The interpolated values for $n = 90, 91$, and 92 show errors of $-.001, -.002$, and $-.003$, respectively. Compute the interpolated values for $94, 95, \ldots$, 99 and give the error by comparison with the table.

Another way to picture the above result is by the use of two adjacent scales as was done in Section 11-1. The lower scale is linear and records the values of n. The upper scale is for $f(n)$, and if exact would be nonlinear for a nonlinear function such as $\sqrt{n}$ is. But we are using a linear approximation to $f(n)$. Hence the name, *linear interpolation*.

Example:

$$9.487 + \left(\frac{97 - 90}{100 - 90}\right)(10.000 - 9.487) = 9.846$$

$f(n)$ 9.487   9.846   10.000

n 90   97   100

ANSWER TO EXERCISE

a. $9.692, -.003; 9.744, -.003; 9.795, -.003; 9.846, -.003; 9.897, -.002; 9.949, -.001$.

Problems (204)

1. The data given are for two similar triangles, ABC and $A'B'C$. Corresponding sides are $a, a'; b, b';$ and c, c'. The perimeters are given by $p = a + b + c$, and $p' = a' + b' + c'$. The measures given are assumed to have a common length unit. Supply the missing data:

	a	b	c	p	a'	b'	c'	p'
a.	3	4	5	6				
b.	.7	.8	.9		4.0			
c.	15	11	8				2.4	
d.	6	4	5					120

2. Follow the instructions for problem 1.

	a	b	c	p	a'	b'	c'	p'
a.	27	36	48	36				
b.	15	15	4				2.8	
c.	7	7	7		.19			
d.	9	10	11					6

3. Given that $\sqrt{70} = 8.367$ and $\sqrt{80} = 8.944$, use linear interpolation to compute the square roots of $71, 72, 73, \ldots, 79$ to the nearest thousandth and give the error by comparison with the table in Appendix 3.

4. Given that $\sqrt{30} = 5.477$ and $\sqrt{40} = 6.325$, use linear interpolation to compute the square roots of $31, 32, 33, \ldots, 39$ to the nearest thousandth and give the error by comparison with the table in Appendix 3.

5. Use linear interpolation to compute an approximation, with the same precision as the data.
   a. $f(4.0) = .4014, f(5.0) = .4041, f(4.3) = ?$
   b. $f(.10) = .9075, f(.20) = .9088, f(.14) = ?$
   c. $f(20) = 7,980, f(30) = 8,239, f(28) = ?$
   d. $f(2.0) = 35.74, f(3.0) = 35.41, f(2.8) = ?$
   e. $f(13) = 48, f(21) = 72, f(18) = ?$
6. Use linear interpolation to compute an approximation, with the same precision as the data.
   a. $g(20) = .3491, g(25) = .4363, g(23) = ?$
   b. $g(3) = 4.173, g(32) = 4.147, g(8) = ?$
   c. $g(.8355) = .5818, g(.8371) = .5789, g(.8365) = ?$
   d. $g(.3) = -5, g(.8) = 20, g(.5) = ?$
   e. $g(-2) = 31, g(13) = -14, g(1) = ?$

23-5. Quadrilaterals and Measurement

Let $P_1, P_2, P_3, \ldots P_n$ with $n \geq 3$ be points in a plane, and let the n segments $\overline{P_1P_2}, \overline{P_2P_3}, \ldots, \overline{P_{n-1}P_n}, \overline{P_nP_1}$ be such that

A. No two segments with a common endpoint lie on the same line,

B. No two segments intersect except possibly at their endpoints,

then the union of these n segments is called a *polygon*. The n points are called the vertices and the n segments are the sides of the polygon. The points of the polygon, together with the points in its interior constitute a *polygonal region*. If n is 4, the polygon is called a *quadrilateral*.

Two lines in the same plane that do not intersect are said to be parallel. If lines $\overleftrightarrow{AB}$ and $\overleftrightarrow{CD}$ are parallel, then the line segments $\overline{AB}$ and $\overline{CD}$ are parallel.

Two sides of a quadrilateral that have exactly one point in common are *adjacent* sides; if they have no points in common they are *opposite* sides. A pair of opposite sides of a quadrilateral may or may not be parallel; if at least one pair of opposite sides is parallel, the quadrilateral is called a *trapezoid*,* if both pairs of opposite sides are parallel it is called a *parallelogram*. A *rectangle* is a parallelogram whose adjacent sides are perpendicular. If all sides of a rectangle have the same length it is a *square*. If the adjacent sides of a parallelogram have the same length it is a *rhombus*.

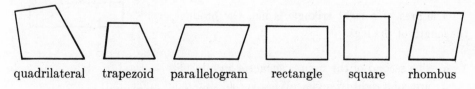

quadrilateral   trapezoid   parallelogram   rectangle   square   rhombus

* Some authors require that a trapezoid have exactly one pair of parallel sides.

A line segment that joins two nonadjacent vertices of a polygon is called a *diagonal*. If a polygon has four or more sides, then diagonals may be used to partition the polygonal region into triangular regions whose union is the polygonal region and whose intersection is empty or at most a vertex or a side. This dissection process will be much used in relating the area measures of various regions.

An area measure is a function from the set of polygonal regions to the set of nonnegative real numbers with the following properties, which should be compared with those in Section 23-2.

A. The area measure associates with every polygonal region a unique positive number in such a way that the number assigned to some square (called the unit square) is 1. The area measure of points and line segments is zero.

B. If two triangles are congruent, then relative to any unit square the corresponding triangular regions have the same area.

C. If two polygonal regions intersect only in edges or vertices (or not at all), then relative to a unit square the area of the union of the regions is the sum of the areas.

D. The unit square has sides whose length measure is 1. If this unit length is used to measure the length of two consecutive sides of a rectangle, then the area of the rectangular region is the product of these lengths. The two consecutive sides may be considered as a base and the altitude to it. Briefly, the area of a rectangle is the product of its base and altitude.

The following conventions will be used to simplify the continuing discussion of area. The area of a polygonal region will be referred to as the area of the polygon. The notation ABC will refer to the number giving the area measure of triangle ABC, and BC will refer to the number giving the length measure of line segment $\overline{BC}$. Proofs will be omitted but diagrams will be given that are suggestive of how the proofs can be constructed.

A diagonal of a rectangle is a common side of two congruent right triangles.

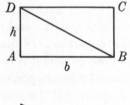

$$ABD = BCD$$
$$ABD + BCD = ABCD$$
$$ABCD = 2ABD$$
$$ABD = \frac{1}{2}bh$$

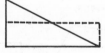

The area of a right triangle is half the product of the length of the legs.

a. The second of the figures suggests an alternate method for determining the area of a right triangle. What verbal statement and equation are suggested?

In a right triangle the altitude may be one of the sides of the triangle.   In other cases the altitude to a base may fall within or outside the triangle.

$$ADC = \frac{1}{2}b_1h, \; DBC = \frac{1}{2}b_2h$$

$$ABC = ADC + DBC$$

$$b_1 + b_2 = b$$

$$ABC = \frac{1}{2}b_1h + \frac{1}{2}b_2h$$

$$= \frac{1}{2}h(b_1 + b_2) = \frac{1}{2}bh$$

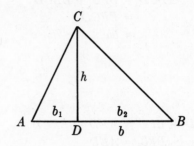

$$DAC = \frac{1}{2}b_1h, \; DBC = \frac{1}{2}(b_1 + b)h$$

$$DBC = DAC + ABC$$

$$ABC = DBC - DAC$$

$$= \frac{1}{2}(b_1 + b)h - \frac{1}{2}b_1h$$

$$= \frac{1}{2}b_1h + \frac{1}{2}bh - \frac{1}{2}b_1h$$

$$= \frac{1}{2}bh$$

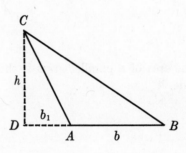

The area of a triangle is half the product of a base times the corresponding altitude.

The diagrams shown can be varied in many ways.   Additional line segments are constructed with the objective of expressing the desired area as either the sum or the difference of areas that can be determined from previous results.   One must be careful to consider all possible cases, since true statements for one diagram may be nonsense when the figure is changed in shape.   This is quite evident in the follow-ing analysis of three parallelograms.

$$ABCD = ABD + BCD$$

$$ABD = BCD = \frac{1}{2}bh$$

$$ABCD = \frac{1}{2}bh + \frac{1}{2}bh$$

$$= bh$$

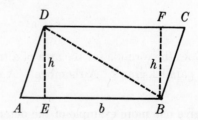

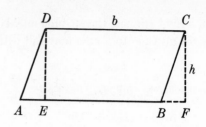

$$ABCD = AED + EBCD$$
$$ADE = BFC$$
$$ABCD = BFC + EBCD$$
$$= EFCD$$
$$= bh$$

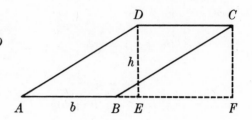

$$ABCD + BFC = AED + EFCD$$
$$BFC = AED$$
$$ABCD = EFCD$$
$$= bh$$

The area of a parallelogram is the product of a base times the corresponding altitude.

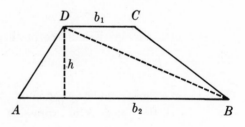

$$ABCD = ABD + BCD$$
$$ABD = \frac{1}{2}b_2h, \ BCD = \frac{1}{2}b_1h$$
$$ABCD = \frac{1}{2}b_2h + \frac{1}{2}b_1h$$
$$= \frac{1}{2}(b_1 + b_2)h$$

The area of a trapezoid is half the product of the altitude and the sum of the bases.

b. Does the formula for the area of a trapezoid hold true when the trapezoid is a parallelogram? A rhombus? A rectangle? A square? A triangle?

We give one more example of the determination of area by the partitioning of polygonal regions. The vertices of the polygon are located with reference to coordinate axes.

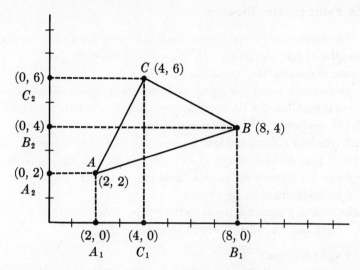

Example: What is the area of the triangle ABC whose vertices are $(2, 2)$, $(8, 4)$, and $(4, 6)$?

Let A_1, C_1, and B_1 have coordinates of $(2, 0)$, $(4, 0)$, and $(8, 0)$ respectively.

$$ABC = A_1C_1CA + C_1B_1BC - A_1B_1BA$$

$$= \frac{2}{2}(2 + 6) + \frac{4}{2}(6 + 4) - \frac{6}{2}(2 + 4)$$

$$= 8 + 20 - 18 = 10$$

Alternate Solution: Let A_2, B_2, and C_2 have coordinates $(0, 2)$, $(0, 4)$, and $(0, 6)$ respectively.

$$ABC = A_2ABB_2 + B_2BCC_2 - A_2ACC_2$$

$$= \frac{2}{2}(2 + 8) + \frac{2}{2}(8 + 4) - \frac{4}{2}(2 + 4) = 10 + 12 - 12 = 10$$

ANSWERS TO EXERCISES

a. The area of a right triangle is the product of the length of one leg times half the length of other leg. $A = h\left(\dfrac{b}{2}\right)$ or $A = b\left(\dfrac{h}{2}\right)$.   **b.** Yes, in all cases.   A triangle may be considered as a degenerate trapezoid, with an upper base of a single point whose length measure is zero.

Problems (205)

Compute the area of the following polygons. Their vertices are to be located with reference to coordinate axes as in the preceding example. Their sides are the segments determined by consecutive pairs of vertices.

1. $(1, 3)$; $(8, 2)$; $(3, 6)$; $(1, 3)$.   **5.** $(1, 2)$; $(4, 3)$; $(6, 7)$; $(1, 2)$.

2. $(1, 1)$; $(5, 4)$; $(4, 7)$; $(1, 1)$.   **6.** $(1, 3)$; $(8, 1)$; $(6, 7)$; $(3, 6)$; $(1, 3)$.

3. $(1, 4)$; $(4, 1)$; $(7, 3)$; $(1, 4)$.   **7.** $(1, 5)$; $(5, 1)$; $(8, 6)$; $(4, 4)$; $(1, 5)$.

4. $(1, 8)$; $(2, 4)$; $(6, 1)$; $(1, 8)$.   **8.** $(1, 2)$; $(4, 1)$; $(8, 3)$; $(6, 6)$; $(2, 5)$; $(1, 2)$.

23-6. The Pythagorean Theorem

There is a property of all right triangles that is very important for the measurement of lengths of line segments. *In any right triangle, the square of the length of the hypotenuse is equal to the sum of the squares of the lengths of the other two sides.* This famous theorem bears the name of Pythagoras, a Greek mathematician, to whom a proof is attributed. Scores of proofs, using a variety of methods, have been given over the centuries. We shall assume the theorem without proof. However, we shall indicate how diagrams might be used to explain the content of the theorem and to make it plausible for simple cases. In this manner the students in elementary school can be introduced to this basic concept some years before a correct proof could be understood or appreciated.

Since the area of a square is equal to the square of the length of a side, the theorem can be given an equivalent form in terms of areas.

For any right triangle:

A. Construct a square that has the hypotenuse of the triangle for a side.

B. Construct a second square that has a leg of the triangle for a side.

C. Construct a third square that has the other leg of the triangle for a side.

Then the area of the first square will be the sum of the areas of the other two squares.

The following exercise should be done on squared paper so that lengths and areas can be obtained simply by counting. First locate the vertices of the triangle ABC on lattice points, that is, where the rulings on the paper cross. Let $a = m(\overline{CA})$, $b = m(\overline{AB})$, $c = m(\overline{BC})$. It will be found that the vertices $D, E, F, G, H,$ and I of the three squares $EACD$, $FGBA$, and $BHIC$ will also fall on lattice points. The area of the square on the hypotenuse is c^2; the areas of the squares on the legs are a^2 and b^2. Our project is to verify for a particular case that $c^2 = a^2 + b^2$.

> **Example:** Suppose $a = 3$, and $b = 5$. Then by counting unit squares we have $a^2 = 9$, $b^2 = 25$, and $a^2 + b^2 = 34$. The slanting lines that cut across the squares on the paper present a problem on how to get c^2 by counting the squares in $BHIC$. But the dotted lines show how to get around this since they follow the lines on the paper.
>
> The rectangle $ABSC$ has an area of $3 \cdot 5$ or 15.
>
> The triangle BSC is half as large; its area is $7\frac{1}{2}$.

There are four triangles of this size in the square $BHIC$, and a small square $RSTU$ of area 2^2 or 4.

Hence $c^2 = 4\left(7\frac{1}{2}\right) + 4 = 30 + 4 = 34$, as was to be shown.

It is also possible to obtain c^2 in another manner.

The square $ALMN$ has an area of $(5 + 3)^2$ or 64.

From this we subtract the areas of the four triangles ABC, BLH, HMI, and CIN, all of which are congruent.

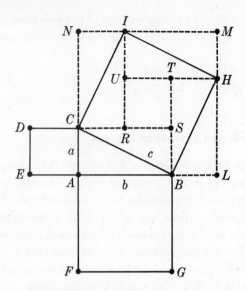

$$c^2 = (5 + 3)^2 - 4\left(\frac{3 \cdot 5}{2}\right) = 64 - 30 = 34$$

Hence $c = \sqrt{34}$, or 5.83 approximately.

In general, if two sides of a right triangle are known, this theorem enables one to compute the third side by one of the following formulas:

$$c^2 = a^2 + b^2 \qquad c = \sqrt{a^2 + b^2}$$
$$b^2 = c^2 - a^2 \qquad b = \sqrt{c^2 - a^2}$$
$$a^2 = c^2 - b^2 \qquad a = \sqrt{c^2 - b^2}$$

Problems (206)

For problems 1 to 6, make the constructions as in the example above, using squared paper as suggested, for the given choices of a and b and thus verify that $a^2 + b^2 = c^2$.

1. $a = 4, b = 7$ 3. $a = 5, b = 5$ 5. $a = 4, b = 1$
2. $a = 3, b = 6$ 4. $a = 1, b = 6$ 6. $a = 6, b = 6$

In problems 7 to 18, a, b, and c are the sides of a right triangle such that $a^2 + b^2 = c^2$. Determine the length of the side not given. Give four significant digits when approximations are required.

7. $a = 5, b = 12$ 11. $b = 35, c = 37$ 15. $b = 50, c = 150$
8. $a = 8, b = 15$ 12. $b = 63, c = 65$ 16. $b = 80, c = 160$
9. $a = 7, c = 25$ 13. $a = .16, b = .30$ 17. $a = .09, c = .12$
10. $a = 20, c = 29$ 14. $a = .14, b = .50$ 18. $a = .11, c = .13$

For problems 19 to 24, give the perimeters of the polygons. Leave the result in radical form, but as simple as possible. The numbers refer to problems in set (205).

19. #1   **21.** #4   **23.** #6
20. #2   **22.** #5   **24.** #7

23-7. Measurement of Curvilinear Figures

The discussion in previous sections has shown that polygons are reasonably accessible to measurement. The polygonal regions can always be divided up into triangular regions for area computations and the boundaries are sums of lengths of straight lines. We now consider the much more difficult problem of assigning measures to geometric figures (point sets) that are not composed of line segments. The circle is a familiar but not necessarily simple example.

Let P be a point of a plane and let r be a positive real number. The *circle* with *center* P and *radius* r is the set of all points Q of the plane whose distance from P is equal to r.

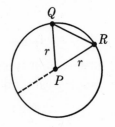

If Q is any point on the circle, then the segment $\overline{PQ}$ is a radius of the circle. Note that the word radius is thus used to mean both the segment and the number that measures its length. If Q and R are two distinct points of a circle, the segment $\overline{QR}$ is called a *chord* of the circle, and the line $\overleftrightarrow{QR}$ is called a *secant*. A chord that contains the center of the circle is called a *diameter*. The same word is also used to refer to the length of the diameter, for example, when we assert that the diameter is $2r$. Two circles with the same center are said to be *concentric*, and two circles with the same radius are *congruent*. The set of all points in the plane whose distance from P is less than the radius r is called the *interior* of a circle. The set of all points in the plane whose distance from P is greater than r is called the *exterior* of the circle. The circular region, which is the union of the interior of a circle and the points of the circle itself, is sometimes called a *disk*.

We speak of a circle as being a curved line. The idea of a curve is particularly difficult to define. In fact, no one has thus far found a definition of a curve that is simple enough to be understood by a beginner in the study and also precise enough to be of much use in a mathematical argument. Hence one points to examples of a curve, such as a circle. The usual practice in mathematics is to count lines (straight) and line segments as special cases of curves, but our meaning in this section of the words "curve" and "curved" is the more common one of "not straight."

Let Q and R be two points of a circle, with $\overline{QR}$ not a diameter, and let S be any other point of the circle. The radius $\overline{SP}$ may intersect the chord $\overline{QR}$. All points S that meet this condition, together with Q and R as endpoints form the *minor arc* $\overset{\frown}{QR}$

of the chord $\overline{QR}$. The radius $\overline{SP}$ may not intersect the chord $\overline{QR}$. All points S that meet this condition together with Q and R as endpoints form the *major arc* $\overset{\frown}{QR}$ of the chord $\overline{QR}$. If Q and R are endpoints of a diameter there are two arcs, called semicircles with Q and R as endpoints. To distinguish them, a third point must be named on the arc.

Since a chord is a line segment, we can speak of its length. In what sense can one speak of the length of an arc? Any chord and either of its arcs have only the endpoints in common. It seems intuitively clear that the length measure of the arc should be greater than that for the chord, although possibly in some cases the length of the chord might be a satisfactory approximation to the length of the arc. One can also anticipate difficulties with area measurement when the boundary is not made up of straight line segments. One can think of a "close fit" if the unit square is small, but that is not the exactness we would desire. These are indeed difficult problems and many major advances in mathematics have come from efforts to resolve them. We give some examples to illustrate a beginning attack upon them. The first will be to attempt to assign an area measure to a region bounded on three sides by line segments and on a fourth side by a curve. The curve is not an arc of a circle, but has been chosen to simplify the computation that arises.

Example A: The region $STQP$ is bounded above by points of the graph of the function $f(x) = \dfrac{1}{x}$. Hence P is the point $(1, 1)$ and Q is $\left(2, \dfrac{1}{2}\right)$. This function is defined for all real numbers x in the interval $1 \leq x \leq 2$. Therefore for each point of this interval there is a point on the graph of $f(x)$ and these points constitute the curve PQ. What is desired is an area measure, if possible, for the region $STQP$.

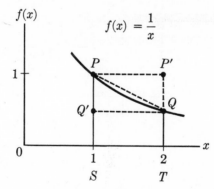

The function $f(x) = \dfrac{1}{x}$ can be shown to be monotonic decreasing as x ranges from 1 to 2. Hence our first assumption about the area A is that it should be less than that of the rectangle $STP'P$ and greater than that of the rectangle $STQQ'$. Even this innocent-sounding claim is not easy to defend carefully. The area of $STP'P$ is $1 \cdot 1$ or 1, and that of $STQQ'$

is $1 \cdot \frac{1}{2}$ or $\frac{1}{2}$. Hence $\frac{1}{2} < A < 1$. This gives us a lower and an upper

bound for A. Our next approximation will be the arithmetic mean of

these. $\frac{1}{2}\left(1 + \frac{1}{2}\right) = \frac{3}{4}$. But $\frac{3}{4}$ is the area of the trapezoid $STQP$ that

results from using the chord $\overline{PQ}$ as the upper boundary. Again we
appeal to the diagram as evidence that this approximation to A, although

still too large, should be much better than 1 or $\frac{1}{2}$. From the right tri-

angle $Q'QP$ we find the length of $\overline{PQ}$ to be $\sqrt{1^2 + \left(\frac{1}{2}\right)^2}$, or approximately

1.12, which provides a lower bound for the length of the curve PQ.
Unfortunately, there is no equally simple way of obtaining an upper
bound for this same length, so we lack evidence as to the magnitude of
the error in this approximation.

Example B: Another way to approximate A is to use for an approximat-

ing rectangle one whose height is the value of $f(x)$ at $x = 1\frac{1}{2}$, which is

the midpoint of the interval. The length of $\overline{MR}$ is $\dfrac{1}{1\frac{1}{2}} = \dfrac{2}{3}$. This gives

$\frac{2}{3}$ (1), or .67 approximately, as an estimate for A.

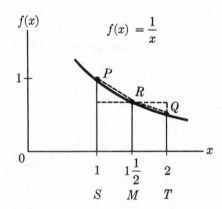

Another estimate comes from the trapezoids formed by chords $\overline{PR}$
and $\overline{RQ}$.

$$\left(\frac{1}{2}\right)\left[\left(1 + \frac{2}{3}\right) + \left(\frac{2}{3} + \frac{1}{2}\right)\right]\left(\frac{1}{2}\right) = .71 \text{ approximately}$$

The sum of the lengths of the chords $\overline{PR}$ and $\overline{RQ}$ should be a better
approximation to the length of the curve than the length of chord $\overline{PQ}$
was.

$$\sqrt{\left(\frac{1}{3}\right)^2 + \left(\frac{1}{2}\right)^2} + \sqrt{\left(\frac{1}{2}\right)^2 + \left(\frac{1}{6}\right)^2} = 1.13 \text{ approximately}$$

We can now see the possibility of obtaining better and better approximations by calculating the values of the function at more points between S and T. The increased number of trapezoids gives promise of a "better fit" to the curve for both the area and the length measures.

Example C: It turns out that we can get a still better approximation to the area A without computing $f(x)$ at any more points. It can be shown that a weighted mean of the three values we already have will be an excellent approximation for many situations. We have $m(\overline{PS}) = 1$, $m(\overline{RM}) = \frac{2}{3}$, and $m(\overline{QT}) = \frac{1}{2}$. The following is a weighted mean in which the central value has been given a weight of 4, compared to a weight of 1 for the endpoints. (See Section 20-7 for weighted means.)

$$\frac{1 + 4\left(\frac{2}{3}\right) + \frac{1}{2}}{1 + 4 + 1} = \frac{25}{36} = .694 \text{ approximately}$$

By using the methods of integral calculus it is possible to prove that there is a number which the above approximations approach as a limit. Hence it is natural to take this number as a definition of the area of the region $STQP$. To five significant figures this number is .69315.

Summary: In Example **A**, by using a single rectangle at a time, we obtained a low estimate of .5 and a high estimate of 1.0 for the area. With a trapezoid there was a high estimate of .75.

In Example **B**, a single rectangle with its height computed at the midpoint of the interval gave a low estimate of .67. With two trapezoids, a high estimate of .71 resulted.

The weighted mean method in Example **C** gave a still better estimate that was correct to two significant digits.

$$.50 < .67 < .69315 < .694 < .71 < .75 < 1.0$$

The classical problems of this type were those of determining the area of a circle, or more correctly, the area of the circular region for which the circle is a boundary, and the length of the circle. The latter problem is commonly called finding the *circumference* of the circle. Completely satisfactory solutions to these problems took centuries to attain. Yet rough upper and lower bounds for the numbers sought in both problems can be obtained quite readily. Let r be the radius of the circle. Then a square built on a radius as a side will have an area of r^2. The first diagram makes it quite apparent that four such squares have an area greater than the circle. Let the Greek letter π (pronounced "pie") represent the ratio of the area of the circle to the area of the square on the radius.   Thus far we have $\pi < 4$, that is, the area A of the circle is less than $4r^2$.   A glance at the second diagram shows that two of the squares on the radius together have an area considerably less than that of the circle.   Hence $\pi > 2$, or $A > 2r^2$.

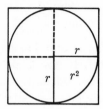  

For the next estimate let us try 3, the arithmetic mean of 2 and 4.   By making a cardboard model one can verify that 3 squares, each of area r^2, can be cut in pieces and fitted with a little to spare inside a circle of radius r.   Thus we now have $3 < \pi < 4$, or $3r^2 < A < 4r^2$.

To get much improvement on this estimate requires some sort of an approximation scheme that can be refined systematically.   One way of doing this is to increase the number of sides for the polygons that are fitted inside and around the circle. This approach can be found in geometry texts.   In problems 3 and 4 of the next set methods are suggested that are similar to those used in the above example.

Let us now turn to the circumference problem.   Let R be the ratio of the circumference C to the diameter d.   In other words, R is to represent the ratio of the distance around a circle compared to the distance across it.   The first of the three diagrams makes it evident that $R < 4$, or $C < 4d$, since $d = 2r$ and the perimeter of the square is $8r$.   From the second diagram it can be seen that $R > 2$, or $C > 2d$. And the third diagram reveals that $R > 3$, or $C > 3d$.   Note that these bounds on R are the same as were arrived at for π.   This is not nearly enough evidence to jump to the conclusion that R and π are the same number.   This however does prove to be true.   (Other diagrams can be drawn that make this more plausible, but a correct proof requires more advanced mathematics.)

The number π is an irrational number whose decimal form to nine significant digits is 3.14159265.   For computations, such as for the basic formulas $A = \pi r^2$ and $C = \pi d$, an approximation is chosen that is at least as accurate as the other approximate numbers being used.

Since $3\frac{1}{7} = 3.\overline{142857}$, its choice as an approximation to π is appropriate for accuracy of only two or three significant digits.   However, a common fraction that would be a more accurate approximation requires a considerably larger numerator and denominator.

The following problem set marks the end of our brief study of some of the links between arithmetic and geometry.   A further step, which we omit, could be a study of volume measure for sets of points in three-dimensional space.   Such problems are somewhat harder to picture than the corresponding ones for length and area meas-ure and the computations tend to be more complex.   Otherwise the difficulties are not essentially different than those we have encountered in this chapter.   Already we see the need for sharper tools for many tasks.   The continuing study of mathe-matics can provide a wealth of them.

Problems (207)

It is recommended that diagrams for the following problems be constructed on coordinate paper, using as large a scale as is convenient.   Each problem is stated in terms of finding the area under a curve, for some function $f(x)$ over an interval $x_1 < x < x_2$.   The lower boundary will be the x axis, and the graph of the function gives the upper boundary.   The left and right boundaries are vertical lines at $x = x_1$ and $x = x_2$, and intermediate vertical lines are to be used as suggested.

1. $f(x) = x^2 + 1$, for $0 \leq x \leq 1$.

    a. Approximate with a single rectangle whose height is computed at $x = 0$.

    b. Same as a. using $x = 1$.

    c. Same as a., but using the midpoint, where x equals $\dfrac{1}{2}$.

    d. Approximate with a single trapezoid.   Bases at $x = 0$, and $x = 1$.

    e. Approximate with two trapezoids.   Use $x = 0$, $x = \dfrac{1}{2}$, and $x = 1$.

    f. Use the weighted mean as in part C. of the example in the text, for $x = 0$, $x = \dfrac{1}{2}$, and $x = 1$.

    g. The approximation by f. is exact in this case.   Arrange the results of a. to f. in increasing order.

2. Refer to the example in the text and continue to refine the approximation as suggested.

    a. Divide the interval $1 \leq x \leq 2$ into four equal subintervals by the points where x is equal to 1, $1\frac{1}{4}$, $1\frac{1}{2}$, $1\frac{3}{4}$, and 2.   Approximate with four trape-zoids.

    b. Divide the interval as in a.   Use the weighted mean approximation twice (on half of the entire area at a time).

3. $f(x) = \dfrac{1}{x^2 + 1}$ for $0 \leq x \leq 1$.

    The area of this region can be shown to be $\dfrac{\pi}{4}$ or .7854 approximately.   Divide the interval into five equal parts and approximate with trapezoids.   Keep four decimal places in your computation, and round off the final result to three places.

4. $f(x) = \sqrt{4 - x^2}$, for $0 \leq x \leq 2$.

This graph is of a quarter circle, whose radius is 2. Hence its area is $\left(\dfrac{1}{4}\right)(\pi)(2)^2$, or π.

Divide the interval into five equal parts. Approximate with five rectangles whose altitudes are computed at the midpoint of the subintervals. Give the result to three significant digits.

For Further Study

Chapter 12 of [W3] is recommended for a beginning study of the mathematical theory of measurement.

References [M10] and [W10] are excellent recent texts on the foundations of geometry.

For additional discussion of interpolation, see [R2], pp. 319–321; [M1], pp. 188–190; and [K5], pp. 28–34.

Chapter 1 of [W5] is a classic from the literature of psychology. Its theme is based on finding the area of a parallelogram.

A fascinating study of π appears in [D3], pp. 55–81. See also [P1], pp. 229–230 and 256–263.

Chapter 10 of [C4] is recommended for supplementary reading. A good compact review of elementary geometry is given in [D2], pp. 84–107.

Appendix 1

Bibliography

A1 Adler, Irving, *A New Look at Arithmetic*, John Day, New York, 1964.

A2 Adler, Irving, *The New Mathematics*, John Day, New York, 1958.

A3 Ashby, W. Ross, *An Introduction to Cybernetics*, Wiley, New York, 1958.

B1 Ball, Richard W., *Principles of Abstract Algebra*, Holt, Rinehart and Winston, New York, 1963.

B2 Banks, J. Houston, *Elements of Mathematics*, Allyn and Bacon, Boston, 1961.

B3 Banks, J. Houston, *Learning and Teaching Arithmetic*, 2nd ed., Allyn and Bacon, Boston, 1964.

B4 Beiler, Albert H., *Recreations in the Theory of Numbers*, Dover, New York, 1964.

B5 Bell, Clifford, Clela D. Hammond, and Robert B. Herrera, *Fundamentals of Arithmetic for Teachers*, Wiley, New York, 1962.

B6 Bowers, Henry, and Joan E. Bowers, *Arithmetical Excursions*, Dover, New York, 1961.

C1 Carter, Hobart C., *Modern Basic Mathematics*, Appleton-Century-Crofts, New York, 1964.

C2 Clifford, William Kingdon, *The Common Sense of the Exact Sciences*, Knopf, New York, 1946.

C3 Committee on the Undergraduate Program, *Elementary Mathematics of Sets with Applications*, Mathematical Association of America, Ann Arbor, Michigan, 1958.

C4 Crouch, Ralph, George Baldwin, and Robert J. Wisner, *Preparatory Mathematics for Elementary Teachers*, Wiley, New York, 1965.

D1 Dantzig, Tobias, *Number: The Language of Science*, Doubleday, Garden City, New York, 1956.

D2 Daus, Paul H., John M. Gleason, and William M. Whyburn, *Basic Mathematics for War and Industry*, Macmillan, New York, 1944.

D3 Davis, Philip J., *The Lore of Large Numbers*, Random House, New York, 1961.

D4 Denbow, Carl H., and Victor Goedicke, *Foundations of Mathematics*, Harper, New York, 1959.

D5 Deskins, W. E., *Abstract Algebra*, Macmillan, New York, 1964.
D6 Dinkines, Flora, *Elementary Concepts of Modern Mathematics*, Appleton-Century-Crofts, New York, 1964.
D7 Dubisch, Roy, *Introduction to Abstract Algebra*, Wiley, New York, 1965.
D8 Dubisch, Roy, *Lattices to Logic*, Blaisdell, New York, 1964.
D9 Dubisch, Roy, *The Nature of Number*, Ronald Press, New York, 1952.

E1 Eves, Howard, *An Introduction to the History of Mathematics*, Holt, Rinehart and Winston, New York, 1964.
E2 Eves, Howard, and Carroll V. Newsom, *An Introduction to the Foundations and Fundamental Concepts of Mathematics*, Holt, Rinehart and Winston, New York, 1965.

F1 Fine, Nathan J., *An Introduction to Modern Mathematics*, Rand McNally, Chicago, 1965.
F2 Freitag, Herta T., and Arthur H. Freitag, *The Number Story*, National Council of Teachers of Mathematics, Washington, D.C., 1960.
F3 Freund, John E., *A Modern Introduction to Mathematics*, Prentice-Hall, Englewood Cliffs, New Jersey, 1956.

G1 Gardner, Martin, *Logic Machines and Diagrams*, McGraw-Hill, New York, 1958.
G2 Goodstein, R. L., *Fundamental Concepts of Mathematics*, Pergamon Press, Oxford, 1962.

H1 Haag, Vincent H., *Structure of Algebra*, Addison-Wesley, Reading, Massachusetts, 1964.
H2 Hacker, Sidney G., Wilfred E. Barnes, and Calvin T. Long, *Fundamental Concepts of Arithmetic*, Prentice-Hall, Englewood Cliffs, New Jersey, 1963.
H3 Hafstrom, John E., *Basic Concepts in Modern Mathematics*, Addison-Wesley, Reading, Massachusetts, 1961.
H4 Halstead, George Bruce, *On the Foundation and Technic of Arithmetic*, Open Court, Chicago, 1912.
H5 Harkin, Duncan, *Fundamental Mathematics*, Prentice-Hall, New York, 1941.

J1 Jones, Burton W., *Elementary Concepts of Mathematics*, 2nd ed., Macmillan, New York, 1963.
J2 Jones, Burton W., *Modular Arithmetic*, Blaisdell, New York, 1964.

K1 Keedy, Mervin L., *A Modern Introduction to Basic Mathematics*, Addison-Wesley, Reading, Massachusetts, 1963.
K2 Keesee, John W., *Elementary Abstract Algebra*, Heath, Boston, 1965.
K3 Kemeny, John G., J. Laurie Snell, and Gerald Thompson, *Introduction to Finite Mathematics*, Prentice-Hall, Englewood Cliffs, New Jersey, 1957.
K4 Kline, Morris, *Mathematics: A Cultural Approach*, Addison-Wesley, Reading, Massachusetts, 1962.
K5 Kovach, Ladis D., *Computer-Oriented Mathematics*, Holden-Day, San Francisco, 1964.

L1 Larsen, Harold D., and H. Glenn Ludlow, *Arithmetic for Colleges*, 3rd ed., Macmillan, New York, 1963.
L2 Lay, L. Clark, *Arithmetic: An Introduction to Mathematics*, Macmillan, New York, 1961.
L3 Leonhardy, Adele, *Introductory College Mathematics*, Wiley, New York, 1954.

L4   Levens, A. S., *Graphics in Engineering and Science*, Wiley, New York, 1954.
L5   Long, Calvin T., *Elementary Introduction to Number Theory*, Heath, Boston, 1965.

M1   May, Kenneth O., *Elementary Analysis*, Wiley, New York, 1952.
M2   May, Kenneth O., *Elements of Modern Mathematics*, Addison-Wesley, Reading, Massachusetts, 1959.
M3   McKay, Herbert, *Odd Numbers*, Macmillan, New York, 1944.
M4   McKay, Herbert, *The World of Numbers*, Macmillan, New York, 1946.
M5   Menger, Karl, *The Basic Concepts of Mathematics*, Illinois Institute of Technology, 1957.
M6   Merrill, Helen Abbott, *Mathematical Excursions*, Dover, New York, 1957.
M7   Meyer, Lester, *High-Speed Mathematics*, Van Nostrand, New York, 1947.
M8   Miller, Norman, *Limits*, Blaisdell, New York, 1964.
M9   Mitchell, Benjamin E., and Haskell Cohen, *A New Look at Elementary Mathematics*, Prentice-Hall, Englewood Cliffs, New Jersey, 1965.
M10   Moise, Edwin E., *Elementary Geometry from an Advanced Standpoint*, Addison-Wesley, Reading, Massachusetts, 1963.
M11   Mueller, Francis J., *Arithmetic: Its Structure and Concepts*, Prentice-Hall, Englewood Cliffs, New Jersey, 1964.

N1   National Council of Teachers of Mathematics, *Twenty-fourth Yearbook, Growth of Mathematical Ideas, Grades K-12*, NCTM, Washington, D.C., 1959.
N2   National Council of Teachers of Mathematics, *Twenty-seventh Yearbook, Enrichment Mathematics for the Grades*, NCTM, Washington, D.C., 1963.
N3   Newman, James R., *The World of Mathematics*, Vols. 1, 2, 3, 4, Simon and Schuster, New York, 1956.
N4   Newsom, Carroll V., *Mathematical Discourses*, Prentice-Hall, Englewood Cliffs, New Jersey, 1964.
N5   Newsom, Carroll V., and Howard Eves, *Introduction to College Mathematics*, Prentice-Hall, New York, 1954.
N6   Norton, M. Scott, *Finite Mathematical Systems*, Webster, St. Louis, 1963.

O1   Ohmer, Merlin, Clayton V. Aucoin, and Marion J. Cortez, *Elementary Contemporary Mathematics*, Blaisdell, New York, 1964.
O2   Olmstead, John M. H., *The Real Number System*, Appleton-Century-Crofts, New York, 1962.
O3   Ore, Oystein, *Number Theory and Its History*, McGraw-Hill, New York, 1948.

P1   Peterson, John A., and J. Hashisaki, *Theory of Arithmetic*, Wiley, New York, 1963.
P2   Polya, G., *How to Solve It*, Doubleday, New York, 1957.

R1   Reichmann, W. J., *The Fascination of Numbers*, Essential Books, Fair Lawn, New Jersey, 1957.
R2   Richardson, M., *Fundamentals of Mathematics*, 3rd ed., Macmillan, New York, 1966.
R3   Ringenberg, Lawrence A., *A Portrait of 2*, National Council of Teachers of Mathematics, Washington, D.C., 1956.
R4   Rule, John T., and Earle F. Watts, *Engineering Graphics*, McGraw-Hill, New York, 1951.

S1   Sanders, Paul, *Elementary Mathematics: A Logical Approach*, International Textbook Co., Scranton, Pennsylvania, 1963.

S2   Sawyer, W. W., *Mathematician's Delight*, Penguin Books, New York, 1946.

S3   Sawyer, W. W., ed., *Mathematics in Theory and Practice*, Odhams Press, London, n.d.

S4   Sawyer, W. W., *Vision in Elementary Mathematics*, Penguin Books, Baltimore, Maryland, 1964.

S5   Scarborough, James B., *Numerical Mathematical Analysis*, 5th ed., Johns Hopkins Press, Baltimore, Maryland, 1962.

S6   Schaaf, William L., *Basic Concepts of Elementary Mathematics*, Wiley, New York, 1965.

S7   Scheid, Francis J., *Elements of Finite Mathematics*, Addison-Wesley, Reading, Massachusetts, 1962.

S8   School Mathematics Study Group, *Studies in Mathematics*, Vol. IX, Stanford University, Stanford, California, 1963.

S9   Selby, Samuel, and Leonard Sweet, *Sets, Relations, Functions*, McGraw-Hill, New York, 1963.

S10 Shupe, Hollie W., and Paul Machovina, *Engineering Geometry and Graphics*, McGraw-Hill, New York, 1956.

S11 Smeltzer, Donald, *Man and Number*, Adam and Charles Black, London, 1953.

S12 Smith, David Eugene, *History of Mathematics*, Vols. 1 and 2, Ginn, Boston, 1923.

S13 Smith, David Eugene, and Jethukiel Ginsburg, *Numbers and Numerals*, National Council of Teachers of Mathematics, Washington, D.C., 1937.

S14 Stein, Sherman K., *Mathematics: The Man-Made Universe*, W. H. Freeman, San Francisco, 1963.

S15 Stoddard, Edward, *Speed Mathematics Simplified*, Dial Press, New York, 1962.

S16 Suppes, Patrick, *Introduction to Logic*, Van Nostrand, Princeton, New Jersey, 1957.

S17 Swain, Robert L., and Eugene D. Nichols, *Understanding Arithmetic*, Holt, Rinehart and Winston, New York, 1965.

W1   Waismann, Friedrich, *Introduction to Mathematical Thinking*, Frederick Ungar, New York, 1951.

W2   Ward, M., and C. E. Hardgrove, *Modern Elementary Mathematics*, Addison-Wesley, Reading, Massachusetts, 1964.

W3   Webber, G. Cuthbert, and John A. Brown, *Basic Concepts of Mathematics*, Addison-Wesley, Reading, Massachusetts, 1963.

W4   Weiss, Marie J., and Roy Dubisch, *Higher Algebra for the Undergraduate*, Wiley, New York, 1962.

W5   Wertheimer, Max, *Productive Thinking*, Harper, New York, 1945.

W6   Whitehead, Alfred North, *An Introduction to Mathematics*, Oxford University Press, New York, 1958.

W7   Whitesitt, J. Eldon, *Principles of Modern Algebra*, Addison-Wesley, Reading, Massachusetts, 1964.

W8   Witter, G. E., *Mathematics: The Study of Axiom Systems*, Blaisdell, New York, 1964.

W9   Wren, F. Lynwood, *Basic Mathematical Concepts*, McGraw-Hill, New York, 1965.

W10 Wylie, C. R., Jr., *Foundations of Geometry*, McGraw-Hill, New York, 1964.

Y1   Youse, Bevan K., *Arithmetic: A Modern Approach*, Prentice-Hall, Englewood Cliffs, New Jersey, 1963.

Appendix 2

Factors and Primes

Every natural number greater than 1 is either a prime or a unique product of primes.

		10	20	30	40	50	60	70	80	90
0		$2 \cdot 5$	$2^2 \cdot 5$	$2 \cdot 3 \cdot 5$	$2^3 \cdot 5$	$2 \cdot 5^2$	$2^2 \cdot 3 \cdot 5$	$2 \cdot 5 \cdot 7$	$2^4 \cdot 5$	$2 \cdot 3^2 \cdot 5$
1		11	$3 \cdot 7$	31	41	$3 \cdot 17$	61	71	3^4	$7 \cdot 13$
2	2	$2^2 \cdot 3$	$2 \cdot 11$	2^5	$2 \cdot 3 \cdot 7$	$2^2 \cdot 13$	$2 \cdot 31$	$2^3 \cdot 3^2$	$2 \cdot 41$	$2^2 \cdot 23$
3	3	13	23	$3 \cdot 11$	43	53	$3^2 \cdot 7$	73	83	$3 \cdot 31$
4	2^2	$2 \cdot 7$	$2^3 \cdot 3$	$2 \cdot 17$	$2^2 \cdot 11$	$2 \cdot 3^3$	2^6	$2 \cdot 37$	$2^2 \cdot 3 \cdot 7$	$2 \cdot 47$
5	5	$3 \cdot 5$	5^2	$5 \cdot 7$	$3^2 \cdot 5$	$5 \cdot 11$	$5 \cdot 13$	$3 \cdot 5^2$	$5 \cdot 17$	$5 \cdot 19$
6	$2 \cdot 3$	2^4	$2 \cdot 13$	$2^2 \cdot 3^2$	$2 \cdot 23$	$2^3 \cdot 7$	$2 \cdot 3 \cdot 11$	$2^2 \cdot 19$	$2 \cdot 43$	$2^5 \cdot 3$
7	7	17	3^3	37	47	$3 \cdot 19$	67	$7 \cdot 11$	$3 \cdot 29$	97
8	2^3	$2 \cdot 3^2$	$2^2 \cdot 7$	$2 \cdot 19$	$2^4 \cdot 3$	$2 \cdot 29$	$2^2 \cdot 17$	$2 \cdot 3 \cdot 13$	$2^3 \cdot 11$	$2 \cdot 7^2$
9	3^2	19	29	$3 \cdot 13$	7^2	59	$3 \cdot 23$	79	89	$3^2 \cdot 11$

	100	110	120	130	140	150	160	170	180	190
0	$2^2 \cdot 5^2$	$2 \cdot 5 \cdot 11$	$2^3 \cdot 3 \cdot 5$	$2 \cdot 5 \cdot 13$	$2^2 \cdot 5 \cdot 7$	$2 \cdot 3 \cdot 5^2$	$2^5 \cdot 5$	$2 \cdot 5 \cdot 17$	$2^2 \cdot 3^2 \cdot 5$	$2 \cdot 5 \cdot 19$
1	101	$3 \cdot 37$	11^2	131	$3 \cdot 47$	151	$7 \cdot 23$	$3^2 \cdot 19$	181	191
2	$2 \cdot 3 \cdot 17$	$2^4 \cdot 7$	$2 \cdot 61$	$2^2 \cdot 3 \cdot 11$	$2 \cdot 71$	$2^3 \cdot 19$	$2 \cdot 3^4$	$2^2 \cdot 43$	$2 \cdot 7 \cdot 13$	$2^6 \cdot 3$
3	103	113	$3 \cdot 41$	$7 \cdot 19$	$11 \cdot 13$	$3^2 \cdot 17$	163	173	$3 \cdot 61$	193
4	$2^3 \cdot 13$	$2 \cdot 3 \cdot 19$	$2^2 \cdot 31$	$2 \cdot 67$	$2^4 \cdot 3^2$	$2 \cdot 7 \cdot 11$	$2^2 \cdot 41$	$2 \cdot 3 \cdot 29$	$2^3 \cdot 23$	$2 \cdot 97$
5	$3 \cdot 5 \cdot 7$	$5 \cdot 23$	5^3	$3^3 \cdot 5$	$5 \cdot 29$	$5 \cdot 31$	$3 \cdot 5 \cdot 11$	$5^2 \cdot 7$	$5 \cdot 37$	$3 \cdot 5 \cdot 13$
6	$2 \cdot 53$	$2^2 \cdot 29$	$2 \cdot 3^2 \cdot 7$	$2^3 \cdot 17$	$2 \cdot 73$	$2^2 \cdot 3 \cdot 13$	$2 \cdot 83$	$2^4 \cdot 11$	$2 \cdot 3 \cdot 31$	$2^2 \cdot 7^2$
7	107	$3^2 \cdot 13$	127	137	$3 \cdot 7^2$	157	167	$3 \cdot 59$	$11 \cdot 17$	197
8	$2^2 \cdot 3^3$	$2 \cdot 59$	2^7	$2 \cdot 3 \cdot 23$	$2^2 \cdot 37$	$2 \cdot 79$	$2^3 \cdot 3 \cdot 7$	$2 \cdot 89$	$2^2 \cdot 47$	$2 \cdot 3^2 \cdot 11$
9	109	$7 \cdot 17$	$3 \cdot 43$	139	149	$3 \cdot 53$	13^2	179	$3^3 \cdot 7$	199

Appendix 3

Powers and Roots

n	n^2	n^3	$\sqrt{n}$	$\sqrt[3]{n}$	n	n^2	n^3	$\sqrt{n}$	$\sqrt[3]{n}$
0	0	0	0.000	0.000	50	2 500	125 000	7.071	3.684
1	1	1	1.000	1.000	51	2 601	132 651	7.141	3.708
2	4	8	1.414	1.260	52	2 704	140 608	7.211	3.733
3	9	27	1.732	1.442	53	2 809	148 877	7.280	3.756
4	16	64	2.000	1.587	54	2 916	157 464	7.348	3.780
5	25	125	2.236	1.710	55	3 025	166 375	7.416	3.803
6	36	216	2.449	1.817	56	3 136	175 616	7.483	3.826
7	49	343	2.646	1.913	57	3 249	185 193	7.550	3.849
8	64	512	2.828	2.000	58	3 364	195 112	7.616	3.871
9	81	729	3.000	2.080	59	3 481	205 379	7.681	3.893
10	100	1 000	3.162	2.154	60	3 600	216 000	7.746	3.915
11	121	1 331	3.317	2.224	61	3 721	226 981	7.810	3.936
12	144	1 728	3.464	2.289	62	3 844	238 328	7.874	3.958
13	169	2 197	3.606	2.351	63	3 969	250 047	7.937	3.979
14	196	2 744	3.742	2.410	64	4 096	262 144	8.000	4.000
15	225	3 375	3.873	2.466	65	4 225	274 625	8.062	4.021
16	256	4 096	4.000	2.520	66	4 356	287 496	8.124	4.041
17	289	4 913	4.123	2.571	67	4 489	300 763	8.185	4.062
18	324	5 832	4.243	2.621	68	4 624	314 432	8.246	4.082
19	361	6 859	4.359	2.668	69	4 761	328 509	8.307	4.102
20	400	8 000	4.472	2.714	70	4 900	343 000	8.367	4.121
21	441	9 261	4.583	2.759	71	5 041	357 911	8.426	4.141
22	484	10 648	4.690	2.802	72	5 184	373 248	8.485	4.160
23	529	12 167	4.796	2.844	73	5 329	389 017	8.544	4.179
24	576	13 824	4.899	2.884	74	5 476	405 224	8.602	4.198
25	625	15 625	5.000	2.924	75	5 625	421 875	8.660	4.217
26	676	17 576	5.099	2.962	76	5 776	438 976	8.718	4.236
27	729	19 683	5.196	3.000	77	5 929	456 533	8.775	4.254
28	784	21 952	5.292	3.037	78	6 084	474 552	8.832	4.273
29	841	24 389	5.385	3.072	79	6 241	493 039	8.888	4.291
30	900	27 000	5.477	3.107	80	6 400	512 000	8.944	4.309
31	961	29 791	5.568	3.141	81	6 561	531 441	9.000	4.327
32	1 024	32 768	5.657	3.175	82	6 724	551 368	9.055	4.344
33	1 089	35 937	5.745	3.208	83	6 889	571 787	9.110	4.362
34	1 156	39 304	5.831	3.240	84	7 056	592 704	9.165	4.380
35	1 225	42 875	5.916	3.271	85	7 225	614 125	9.220	4.397
36	1 296	46 656	6.000	3.302	86	7 396	636 056	9.274	4.414
37	1 369	50 653	6.083	3.332	87	7 569	658 503	9.327	4.431
38	1 444	54 872	6.164	3.362	88	7 744	681 472	9.381	4.448
39	1 521	59 319	6.245	3.391	89	7 921	704 969	9.434	4.465
40	1 600	64 000	6.325	3.420	90	8 100	729 000	9.487	4.481
41	1 681	68 921	6.403	3.448	91	8 281	753 571	9.539	4.498
42	1 764	74 088	6.481	3.476	92	8 464	778 688	9.592	4.514
43	1 849	79 507	6.557	3.503	93	8 649	804 357	9.644	4.531
44	1 936	85 184	6.633	3.530	94	8 836	830 584	9.695	4.547
45	2 025	91 125	6.708	3.557	95	9 025	857 375	9.747	4.563
46	2 116	97 336	6.782	3.583	96	9 216	884 736	9.798	4.579
47	2 209	103 823	6.856	3.609	97	9 409	912 673	9.849	4.595
48	2 304	110 592	6.928	3.634	98	9 604	941 192	9.899	4.610
49	2 401	117 649	7.000	3.659	99	9 801	970 299	9.950	4.626
					100	10 000	1 000 000	10.000	4.642

Appendix 4

Answers to Odd-Numbered Problems

(1) **1.** 15, 16, 17 **3.** 14, 16, 18, 20 **5.** 27, 29, 31, 33, 35 **7. a.** 1243 **b.** 4312
   9. 456, 465, 546, 564, 645, 654

(2) **1.** 60 **3.** 88 **5.** $9 + 1, 8 + 2, 7 + 3, 6 + 4$ **7.** $13 - 1, 14 - 2, 15 - 3$
   9. 899 **11.** 297 **13.** $1 + 19, 3 + 17, 5 + 15, 7 + 13, 9 + 11$
   15. $1 + 3 + 5 + 11, 1 + 3 + 7 + 9$ **17.** $3 + 3 + 3 + 3$ **19.** $2 + 4 + 6$ **21.** 13-1

(3) **1.** $7 + 5 = 12$ **3.** $20 = 14 + 6$ **5.** $15 - 8 = 7$ **7.** $8 = 9 - 1$ **9.** $34 = 21 + 13$
   11. $7 = 37 - 30$ **13.** $19 + 36 = 55$ **15.** $8 = 16 - 8$ **17.** $30 - 10 = 20$

(4) **1.** E **3.** E **5.** I **7.** I **9.** E **11.** I **13.** E **15.** I **17.** I

(5) **1.** $9 - 3 = 6$ **3.** $4 = 8 - 4$ **5.** $3 + 4 = 7$ **7.** $32 - 16 = 16$
   9. $225 - 40 = 185$ **11.** $37 = 19 + 18$

(6) **1.** E, $6 + 4 = 10$ **3.** I, $7 + 2 = 9$ **5.** I, $3 + 4 = 7$ **7.** E, $16 - 6 = 10$
   9. I, $12 - 8 = 4$ **11.** I, $20 - 7 = 13$ **13.** E, $14 = 8 + 6$ **15.** I, $24 = 9 + 15$
   17. I, $10 = 6 + 4$ **19.** E, $11 = 15 - 4$ **21.** I, $9 = 14 - 5$ **23.** I, impossible
   25. E, impossible **27.** I, impossible **29.** I, $35 = 15 + 20$ **31.** I, $17 + 0 = 17$
   33. I, $31 = 47 - 16$ **35.** I, impossible

(7) **1.** 27 **3.** 27 **5.** 21 **7.** 7 **9.** 7 **11.** 21 **13.** none **15.** 8 **17.** none **19.** 2
   21. none **23.** 2 **25.** 57 **27.** 57 **29.** 27 **31.** 3 **33.** 7 **35.** 27

(8) **1.** $N = 1913 + 38$ **3.** $60 - 45 = N$ **5.** $35 + 12 = N$ **7.** $N = 30 - 21$
   9. $12 + 23 - 8 = N$ **11.** $7 + 5 + 4 = N$ **13.** $N = 8 - 2 + 1$
   15. $N = 300 - (130 + 75)$ **17.** $75 + 50 - 15 = N$ **19.** $72 - 10 - 25 = N$
   21. $4000 - (2,257 - 243) = N$

(9) **7. a** to **b,** commutative; **b** to **c,** associative; **c** to **d,** commutative;
   d to **e,** commutative; **e** to **f,** associative; **f** to **g,** commutative;
   g to **h,** associative; **h** to **i,** commutative; **i** to **j,** commutative;
   j to **k,** commutative; **k** to **l,** associative.

(10) **1.** $70 + 92$ **3.** $200 + 62$ **5.** $155 + 100$ **7.** $23 + 50$ **9.** $20 + 42$
     11. $30 + 41$ **13.** $200 + 636$ **15.** $836 + 1000$

(11) **1.** $27 - 20$ **3.** $255 - 100$ **5.** $105 - 50$ **7.** $697 - 300$ **9.** $39 - 10$
     11. $95 - 20$ **13.** $48 - 20$ **15.** $548 - 100$

(12) **1.** E, $N = 63$ **3.** E, $N = 36$ **5.** I, $N = 28$ **7.** E, $N = 120$ **9.** I, $N = 120$
     11. I, $N = 225$ **13.** E, $N = 0$

(13) **1.** 120 **3.** 192 **5.** 6, 7, 8 **7.** $(7)(11)(13)$ **9. a.** $3 \cdot 7$ **b.** $5 \cdot 7$ **c.** $2 \cdot 11$
     d. $5 \cdot 13$ **e.** $7 \cdot 11$ **11.** 4, 5

(14) **1.** 14 **3.** 20 **5.** 10 **7.** 14 **9.** 296 **11.** 100 **13.** 26 **15.** 176 **17.** 57 **19.** 336
     21. 15 **23.** 168 **25.** 29 **27.** 77 **29.** 31 **31.** 80 **33.** 17 **35.** 63

(15) **1.** sum **3.** product **5.** sum **7.** product **9.** difference **11.** product
     13. difference **15.** product **17.** sum **19.** product **21.** difference **23.** product
     25. sum **27.** product **29.** sum **31.** product **33.** sum **35.** product

(16) **9. a** to **b,** associative; **b** to **c,** commutative; **c** to **d,** commutative;
     d to **e,** commutative; **e** to **f,** associative; **f** to **g,** commutative;
     g to **h,** commutative; **h** to **i,** commutative; **i** to **j,** associative;
     j to **k,** commutative; **k** to **l,** commutative **11. a** to **b,** commutative;
     b to **c,** associative; **c** to **d,** commutative; **d** to **e,** commutative;
     e to **f,** associative.

(17) **1.** $(6)(5) + (6)(3)$ **3.** $(4 + 6)(7)$ **5.** $(9)(6) + (4)(6)$ **7.** $(6)(8 + 2)$
     9. $8 \cdot 10 + 8 \cdot 4$ **11.** $10 \cdot (15 + 2)$ **13.** $(17 + 3) \cdot 5$ **15.** $(7)5 + (3)5$
     17. $5(200) + 5(30) + 5(4)$ **19.** $9 \cdot (5 + 3 + 2)$ **21.** $(1)5 + (2)5 + (3)5$
     23. $5(5 + 5)$ or $(5 + 5)5$ **25.** $(4)(13) - (4)(3)$ **27.** $6(14 - 4)$ **29.** $12 \cdot 7 - 5 \cdot 7$
     31. $(9 - 2) \cdot 6$ **33.** $5 \cdot 18 + 5 \cdot 7 - 5 \cdot 5$ **35.** $(2 + 4 - 3)3$
     37. a to **b,** distributive; **b** to **c,** distributive; **c** to **d,** addition is commutative;
     d to **e,** inverse of distributive; **e** to **f,** inverse of distributive.

(18) **1.** $N = (140)(320)$ **3.** $(2)(35)(9) = N$ **5.** $2 \cdot 30 + 2 \cdot 25 = N$
     7. $N = 10(36 - 29)$ **9.** $1805 - (39)(44) = N$ **11.** $7(60) + 37 = N$
     13. $N = 16 + 3 - 5$ **15.** $(21)(17) - (21 + 17) = N$ **17.** $N = 13(13 - 7)$

(19) **1.** $5 = 12 - 7, 7 = 12 - 5$ **3.** $13 = 8 + 5, 5 = 13 - 8$ **5.** $6 = \dfrac{42}{7}, 7 = \dfrac{42}{6}$
     7. $72 = (4)(18), 4 = \dfrac{72}{18}$ **9.** $16 = 7 + 9, 9 = 16 - 7$ **11.** $52 = (4)(13), 13 = \dfrac{52}{4}$

(20) **1.** E, 4 **3.** I, 9 **5.** E, 125 **7.** I, impossible **9.** I, 0 **11.** I, 252
     13. E, impossible **15.** I, impossible **17.** I, 3

(21) **1.** $43 = (8)(5) + [3]$ **3.** $15 = (5)(3) + [0]$ **5.** $2 = (0)(10) + [2]$
     7. $7 = (7)(1) + [0]$ **9.** $11 = (1)(11) + [0]$ **11.** $40 = (5)(7) + [5]$

(22) **1.** $Q = 9$ $R = 0$ **3.** $Q = 11, R = 4$ **5.** $Q = 0, R = 8$ **7.** $Q = 0, R = 0$
     9. $Q = 49, R = 0$ **11.** $Q = 680, R = 19$

(23) **1.** $(8)(15)$ **3.** no **5.** no, yes **7.** $1 \cdot 27$ **9.** $N \cdot 1$

(24) **1.** $\dfrac{16}{4} + \dfrac{12}{4}$ **3.** $\dfrac{35 + 15}{5}$ **5.** $\dfrac{40 - 16}{8}$ **7.** $\dfrac{32}{4} - \dfrac{20}{4}$ **9.** $\dfrac{42 + 24}{2 \cdot 3}$
   11. $\dfrac{60}{3 + 7} - \dfrac{20}{3 + 7}$ **13.** $\dfrac{4 \cdot 9}{7 + 5} + \dfrac{3 \cdot 16}{7 + 5}$ **15.** $\dfrac{(27 + 3) - (30 - 10)}{10}$

(25) **1.** 43   **3.** 47   **5.** 19

(26) **1.** 6, quotient   **3.** 3, quotient   **5.** 4, difference   **7.** 38, sum   **9.** 30, difference
   11. 21, difference   **13.** 180, product   **15.** 6, quotient   **17.** 24, product

(27) **1.** 55, no   **3.** 13, yes   **5.** 17, yes   **7.** 5, no   **9.** 15, yes   **11.** 8, no

(28) **1.** $N = \dfrac{120}{5}$ **3.** $N = \dfrac{6 \cdot 30}{3}$ **5.** $21{,}000 - (16{,}500 + 2400) = N$ **7.** $\dfrac{\frac{1500}{6}}{10} = N$
   9. $N = \dfrac{24 - 12}{3}$ **11.** $\dfrac{12 \cdot 15}{3} = N$ **13.** $N = 3\left(\dfrac{40}{10}\right)$ **15.** $N = 10 + (10)(10 - 4)$
   17. $5 \cdot 12 - (12 - 5) = N$ **19.** $\dfrac{9 \cdot 6}{9 - 6} = N$ **21.** $8N = 96$ **23.** $\dfrac{21}{N} = 7$
   25. $\dfrac{N}{24} = 12$

(30) **1. a.** 12   **b.** 12   **c.** 81   **d.** 64   **3. a.** 10   **b.** 10   **c.** 32   **d.** 25

(31) **1.** power, 625   **3.** power, 16   **5.** power, 1024   **7.** quotient, 4   **9.** power, 27
   11. sum, 56   **13.** difference, 120   **15.** product, 27   **17.** product, 32   **19.** product, 90
   21. difference, 24   **23.** power, 4   **25.** sum, 24   **27.** difference, 24   **29.** product, 75
   31. power, 900   **33.** power, 729   **35.** product, 720   **37.** product, 80
   39. difference, 28   **41.** sum, 102   **43.** sum, 90   **45.** quotient, 50   **47.** product, 48

(32) **1.** 2^6 **3.** 5^4 **5.** 7^3 **7.** $2^2 \cdot 11^2$ **9.** 7^{10} **11.** $(4 + 2)^0$

(33) **1.** 124   **3.** 58   **5.** 124   **7.** 257   **9.** 140   **11.** 38,057

(34) **1.** $6(10) + 7(1)$ **3.** $1(10)^3 + 4(10)^2 + 8(10) + 3(1)$
   5. $8(10)^5 + 4(10)^4 + 0(10)^3 + 2(10)^2 + 1(10) + 9(1)$
   7. $1(10)^4 + 2(10)^3 + 3(10)^2 + 4(10) + 5(1)$ **9.** $7(10) + 0(1)$
   11. $6(10)^3 + 0(10)^2 + 3(10) + 0(1)$ **13.** $1(10)^2 + 9(10) + 0(1)$
   15. $3(10)^4 + 4(10)^3 + 1(10)^2 + 0(10) + 0(1)$

(35) **1.** (1) If A is a divisor of B, then by definition there exists a natural number R
       such that $AR = B$.
   (2) Hence $(AR)M = BM$ since multiplication is well defined.
   (3) $A(RM) = BM$ by the associative property of multiplication.
   (4) Since R and M are natural numbers, RM is a natural number because the
       natural numbers are closed under multiplication.
   (5) By definition, A is a divisor of BM, as was to be proved.
   3. (1) If A is a divisor of B and of C there exist natural numbers R and S such that
       $AR = B$ and $AS = C$.
   (2) $AR + AS = B + C$ since addition is well defined.
   (3) $A(R + S) = B + C$ by the distributive property of multiplication.
   (4) $R + S$ is a natural number by the closure property of addition.
   (5) By definition, A is a divisor of $B + C$, as was to be proved.

5. (1) If A is a divisor of B and of $B + C$ there exist natural numbers R and S such that $AR = B$ and $AS = B + C$.
   (2) Then $AS = AR + C$ by substituting AR for B in $AS = B + C$.
   (3) $AS - AR = C$ by the definition of subtraction.
   (4) $A(S - R) = C$ since multiplication is distributive over subtraction.
   (5) $S - R$ is a natural number by the assumption allowed in the statement of the problem.
   (6) By definition, A is a divisor of C, as was to be proved.

(36) 1. $3176 = 3(10)^3 + 1(10)^2 + 7(10) + 6$
$$= [3(10)^2 + 1(10) + 7] \cdot 10 + 6$$
$$= [3(10)^2 + 1(10) + 7] \cdot 2 \cdot 5 + 6$$
3. $673 = 6(10)^2 + 7(10) + 3$
$$= 6(11 \cdot 9 + 1) + 7(1 \cdot 9 + 1) + 3$$
$$= 6 \cdot 11 \cdot 9 + 6 + 7 \cdot 1 \cdot 9 + 7 + 3$$
$$= (6 \cdot 11 + 7 \cdot 1) \cdot 9 + 6 + 7 + 3$$
$$= (6 \cdot 11 + 7 \cdot 1) \cdot 3 \cdot 3 + (6 + 7 + 3)$$
5. $61{,}712 = 6(10)^4 + 1(10)^3 + 7(10)^2 + 1(10) + 2$
$$= [6(10)^2 + 1(10) + 7] \cdot 100 + 1(10) + 2$$
$$= [6(10)^2 + 1(10) + 7] \cdot 4 \cdot 25 + 12$$
7. A natural number, whose decimal numeral has four or more digits, is divisible by 8 or 125 if, and only if, the number formed by its three right-hand digits is divisible by 8 or 125.
9. **a.** 2 **b.** 3 **c.** 3, 9 **d.** 5 **e.** 2, 4 **f.** 2, 5, 10 **g.** 2, 4, 5, 10 **h.** 3, 9 **i.** 2, 3, 9
   j. 2, 3 **k.** 2, 3, 5, 10 **l.** 2, 3, 4, 5, 10 **m.** none **n.** 5 **o.** 3, 9 **p.** 2, 4
   q. 2, 3, 4, 5, 9, 10 **r.** none **s.** 2 **t.** 3

(37) 1. $2^2 - 1^2$ 3. $4^2 - 3^2$ 5. $5^2 - 4^2$ 7. $4^2 - 2^2$ 9. $8^2 - 7^2, 4^2 - 1^2$
11. $9^2 - 8^2$ 13. $6^2 - 4^2$ 15. $12^2 - 11^2$ 17. $13^2 - 12^2$ 19. $8^2 - 6^2$
21. $16^2 - 15^2$ 23. $17^2 - 16^2, 7^2 - 4^2$ 25. $1^2 + 3^2, 1^2 + 1^2 + 2^2 + 2^2$
27. $1^2 + 6^2, 1^2 + 2^2 + 4^2 + 4^2$ 29. $3^2 + 3^2, 1^2 + 1^2 + 4^2, 1^2 + 2^2 + 2^2 + 3^2$
31. $2^2 + 7^2, 1^2 + 4^2 + 6^2$ 33. $5^2 + 6^2, 3^2 + 4^2 + 6^2, 2^2 + 4^2 + 4^2 + 5^2$
35. $3^2 + 6^2, 2^2 + 4^2 + 5^2, 2^2 + 3^2 + 4^2 + 4^2, 1^2 + 2^2 + 2^2 + 6^2$
37. $1^2 + 1^2 + 6^2, 2^2 + 3^2 + 5^2, 2^2 + 3^2 + 3^2 + 4^2$
39. $4^2 + 6^2, 1^2 + 1^2 + 1^2 + 7^2, 1^2 + 1^2 + 5^2 + 5^2, 2^2 + 4^2 + 4^2 + 4^2$
41. $2^2 = 1^3 + 1^3 + 1^3 + 1^3, 3^2 = 2^3 + 1^3, 4^2 = 2^3 + 2^3, 5^2 = 1^3 + 2^3 + 2^3 + 2^3,$
   $6^2 = 3^3 + 2^3 + 1^3, 7^2 = 3^3 + 2^3 + 2^3 + 1^3 + 1^3 + 1^3 + 1^3 + 1^3 + 1^3$
43. $1^3 = 1, 2^3 = 3 + 5, 3^3 = 7 + 9 + 11, 4^3 = 13 + 15 + 17 + 19,$
   $5^3 = 21 + 23 + 25 + 27 + 29$

(38) 1. $N = 7^2 + 10^2$ 3. $(8 - 6)^3 = N$ 5. $2^2 + 4^2 + 6^2 = N$ 7. $N = (6 \cdot 10)^2$
9. $N = (8 + 2)^2 - (8^2 + 2^2)$ 11. $[(6 + 4)(6 - 4)]^2 = N$

(40) 1. $7 + 23, 11 + 19, 13 + 17$ 3. $3 + 29, 13 + 19$ 5. $3 + 31, 5 + 29, 11 + 23,$
   $17 + 17$ 7. $3 + 73, 5 + 71, 17 + 59, 23 + 53, 29 + 47$ 9. $5 + 73, 7 + 71,$
   $11 + 67, 17 + 61, 19 + 59, 31 + 47$

(41) 1. $1, 2, 2^2, 5, 2^3, 2 \cdot 5, 2^4, 2^2 \cdot 5, 2^3 \cdot 5, 2^4 \cdot 5$ 3. $1, 3, 3^2, 3^3, 3^4$ 5. $1, 2, 41, 2 \cdot 41$
7. $1, 83$ 9. $1, 2, 3, 2^2, 2 \cdot 3, 7, 2^2 \cdot 3, 2 \cdot 7, 3 \cdot 7, 2^2 \cdot 7, 2 \cdot 3 \cdot 7, 2^2 \cdot 3 \cdot 7$
11. $1, 5, 17, 5 \cdot 17$ 13. $1, 2, 43, 2 \cdot 43$ 15. $1, 2, 2^2, 2^3, 11, 2 \cdot 11, 2^2 \cdot 11, 2^3 \cdot 11$

(42) **1.** (1)($2^2 \cdot 5^2$), (2)($2 \cdot 5^2$). (2^2)(5^2), (5)($2^2 \cdot 5$), ($2 \cdot 5$)($2 \cdot 5$)   **3.** (1)(101)
      5. (1)($2 \cdot 3 \cdot 17$), (2)($3 \cdot 17$). (3)($2 \cdot 17$), ($2 \cdot 3$)(17)   **7.** (1)(103)
      9. (1)($2^3 \cdot 13$), (2)($2^2 \cdot 13$), (2^2)($2 \cdot 13$), (2^3)(13)
      11. (1)($3 \cdot 5 \cdot 7$), (3)($5 \cdot 7$), (5)($3 \cdot 7$), (7)($3 \cdot 5$)

(43) **1.**

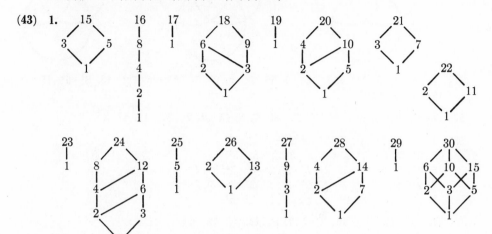

(44) **1.** 5   **3.** $2 \cdot 3$ **5.** $7 \cdot 19$ **7.** $2^4 \cdot 11$ **9.** 2^4 **11.** 2^2 **13.** 2^6 **15.** $3 \cdot 5 \cdot 7^2$ **17.** 17

(45) **1.** $2^4 \cdot 3^2$ **3.** $3 \cdot 7^2$ **5.** $2^3 \cdot 3^2 \cdot 5$ **7.** $2^4 \cdot 5^2$ **9.** $2^6 \cdot 7^3$ **11.** $2^4 \cdot 3^2 \cdot 7^2$ **13.** $2^2 \cdot 3^7$
      15. $19 \cdot 23^2$ **17.** $2 \cdot 5 \cdot 19$ **19.** $2 \cdot 3 \cdot 31$ **21.** $2 \cdot 3^2 \cdot 17^2$ **23.** $3 \cdot 7^3$

(46) **1.** $1, 2$ **3.** $1, 13$ **5.** $1, 5, 5^2$ **7.** $1, 2, 11, 2 \cdot 11$ **9.** 1
      11. $1, 2, 3, 2 \cdot 3, 7, 2 \cdot 7, 3 \cdot 7, 2 \cdot 3 \cdot 7$ **13.** $1, 3, 3^2$ **15.** 1   **17.** $1, 17$
      19. $1, 3, 19, 3 \cdot 19$ **21.** $1, 3, 3^2, 3^3$ **23.** 7   **25.** $3 \cdot 5 \cdot 11$ **27.** 2

(47) **1.** 11, 13, 17, 19   **3.** 1, 3, 7, 9   **5.** (26, 21), (26, 15), (15, 14)   **7.** 2

(48) **1. a.** $2^2 \cdot 5 \cdot 7$ **b.** $5^2 \cdot 7$ **c.** $2 \cdot 3 \cdot 5 \cdot 7$ **d.** $5 \cdot 7^2$ **e.** $2^3 \cdot 5 \cdot 7$
      3. a. $2^2 \cdot 5 \cdot 13^2$ **b.** $2^2 \cdot 5^2 \cdot 13^2$ **c.** $2 \cdot 5^3 \cdot 13^2$ **d.** $2^2 \cdot 3 \cdot 5^2 \cdot 13^2$ **e.** $2^2 \cdot 5 \cdot 13^3$
      f. $2 \cdot 13^2$ **g.** $2^2 \cdot 5^2 \cdot 13^4$ **h.** 13^2 **i.** $2 \cdot 5^2 \cdot 13^3$ **j.** $2 \cdot 13$

(49) **1. a.** $3 \cdot 5 \cdot 7, 2 \cdot 3 \cdot 5 \cdot 7, 3^2 \cdot 5 \cdot 7$ **b.** $2 \cdot 3 \cdot 5 \cdot 11, 2^2 \cdot 3 \cdot 5 \cdot 11, 2 \cdot 3^2 \cdot 5 \cdot 11$
      c. $3^3, 2 \cdot 3^3, 3^4$ **d.** $2 \cdot 5 \cdot 7, 2^2 \cdot 5 \cdot 7, 2 \cdot 3 \cdot 5 \cdot 7$ **e.** $2^3 \cdot 11^2, 2^4 \cdot 11^2, 2^3 \cdot 3 \cdot 11^2$
      3. a. $2^2 \cdot 3$ **b.** $5^2 \cdot 13^2$ **c.** $2 \cdot 3 \cdot 5 \cdot 7$ **d.** $3 \cdot 5^4$ **e.** $2^2 \cdot 3$ **f.** $2 \cdot 3 \cdot 7$
      5. a. 2401   **b.** 120   **c.** 112   **d.** 900
      7. a. $7 \cdot 13$, not possible   **b.** $1, 1$ **c.** $3^3 \cdot 11^2$, not possible   **d.** $1, 7^2$

(50) **1.**   **3.**   **5.**

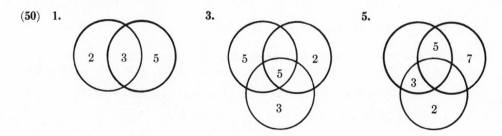

7.   **9.**   **11.**

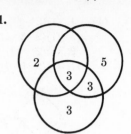

(51) **1.** $2^2 \cdot 3^4$ **3.** 5^4 **5.** $2^6 \cdot 3^4$ **7.** $2^8 \cdot 7^2$ **9.** $2^2 \cdot 7^2$ **11.** $(5 \cdot 7)^3$ **13.** $3^2 \cdot 5^2 \cdot 7^2$
     15. $(5^2 \cdot 7 \cdot 13^3)^2$

(52) **1.** $2^2 \cdot 26$ **3.** $3^2 \cdot 105$ **5.** $2^2 \cdot 23$ **7.** $6^2 \cdot 5$ **9.** $2^2 \cdot 57$ **11.** $8^2 \cdot 3$

(53) **1.** $2^2 \cdot 5^2,\ 2^4 \cdot 5^2,\ 2^2 \cdot 3^2 \cdot 5^2,\ 2^6 \cdot 5^2,\ 2^2 \cdot 5^4$
     3. $2^2 \cdot 3^4,\ 2^4 \cdot 3^4,\ 2^2 \cdot 3^6,\ 2^6 \cdot 3^4,\ 2^2 \cdot 3^4 \cdot 5^2$
     5. $5^2 \cdot 7^2,\ 2^2 \cdot 5^2 \cdot 7^2,\ 3^2 \cdot 5^2 \cdot 7^2,\ 2^4 \cdot 5^2 \cdot 7^2,\ 5^4 \cdot 7^2$
     7. $2^2 \cdot 3^4 \cdot 5^2,\ 2^4 \cdot 3^4 \cdot 5^2,\ 2^2 \cdot 3^6 \cdot 5^2,\ 2^6 \cdot 3^4 \cdot 5^2,\ 2^2 \cdot 3^4 \cdot 5^4$
     9. $2^6 \cdot 3^2,\ 2^8 \cdot 3^2,\ 2^6 \cdot 3^4,\ 2^{10} \cdot 3^2,\ 2^6 \cdot 3^2 \cdot 5^2$
     11. $\dfrac{26^2}{13}$ **13.** $\dfrac{18^2}{6}$ **15.** $\dfrac{30^2}{6}$ **17.** p **19.** pq **21.** pqr

(54) **1.** $3^3 \cdot 75$ **3.** no **5.** $7^3 \cdot 245$ **7.** $3^3 \cdot 7^3$ **9.** 11^3 **11.** $2^3 \cdot 3^3 \cdot 5^3$ **13.** $\dfrac{13^3}{13}$
     15. $\dfrac{105^3}{147}$ **17.** $\dfrac{15^3}{25}$

(55) **1.** $2 \cdot 3 \cdot 5 \cdot 7 + 1 = 211$, which is prime. $2 \cdot 3 \cdot 5 \cdot 7 \cdot 11 + 1 = 2{,}311$, which is prime.
     $2 \cdot 3 \cdot 5 \cdot 7 \cdot 11 \cdot 13 + 1 = 30{,}031 = 59 \cdot 509$.
     $2 \cdot 3 \cdot 5 \cdot 7 \cdot 11 \cdot 13 \cdot 17 + 1 = 510{,}511 = 19 \cdot 97 \cdot 277$

(56) **1. a.** $20 + 7$ **b.** $70 + 3$ **c.** $80 + 5$ **d.** $230 + 6$ **3. a.** $8 \cdot 100$ **b.** $3 \cdot 100$
     c. $9 \cdot 100$ **d.** $28 \cdot 100$ **e.** $9 \cdot 100$ **5.** $1 + 11, 2 + 10, 3 + 9, 4 + 8, 6 + 6$
     7. 30 **9.** 484 **11. a.** $2 \cdot 24 = 6 \cdot 8$ **b.** $1 \cdot 35 = 5 \cdot 7$ **c.** $5 \cdot 10 = 5 \cdot 10$
     d. $4 \cdot 24 = 8 \cdot 12$. The product of the g.c.d. and the l.c.m. of two numbers is
     equal to the product of the two numbers. **13.** $N = 23(23 - 7)$
     15. $\left(35 + \dfrac{35}{7}\right)^2 = N$ **17.** $N = 10^3 - (10 - 5)^3$ **19.** $\dfrac{18 - 3}{5} + 18 - 3 + 18 = N$
     21. $N = (5 + 8) + 3 \cdot 5$

(57) **1.** $3 \cdot 7 + \dfrac{10}{2}$ **3.** $\dfrac{45}{3} - 3^2$ **5.** $\dfrac{17 + 3}{6 - 2}$ **7.** $\dfrac{\dfrac{60}{2}}{\dfrac{14}{7}}$ **9.** $\dfrac{14}{7}(3 + 12)$ **11.** $(3 + 4)^2$
     13. $3(4 + 1)^2$ **15.** M_5 **17.** $x(x - 2)$ **19.** $\dfrac{2^{4-1}}{4}$

(58) **1.** $A + B \equiv B + A$, $(A:a + b, B:c)$ **3.** $A \equiv A$, $(A:r + 3s)$
     5. $A + B \equiv (A + C) + (B - C)$, $(A:18, B:7, C:2)$ **7.** $A(B + C) \equiv AB + AC$,
     $(A: m + n, B:s, C:t)$ **9.** $1 \cdot A \equiv A$, $(A: p + q)$ **11.** $AB \equiv \dfrac{A}{C}(CB)$,
     $(A:16, B:25, C:4)$ **13.** $(a + b) - b \equiv a$, $(a:t, b: x - y)$
     15. $\dfrac{A^m}{A^n} \equiv A^{m-n}$, $(A:5,\ m:9,\ n:3)$ **17.** $AB \equiv BA$, $(A:M_1, B:M_2)$
     19. $A^m \cdot A^n \equiv A^{m+n}$, $(A: a + b,\ m:x,\ n:y)$

(59) **1.** $A = 5,250$ **3.** $P = 15,700$ **5.** $A = 204$ **7.** $V = 384$ **9.** $S = 540$
11. $P = 147$ **13.** $S = 3,600$

(60) **1.** 1, 3, 5, 7, 9 **3.** 5, 10, 15, 20, 25 **5.** 1, 9, 25, 49, 81 **7.** 7, 9, 11, 13, 15
9. 1, 8, 27, 64, 125 **11.** 4, 21, 50, 91, 144 **13.** 4, 8, 16, 32, 64
15. 0, 0, 2, 8, 22 **17.** 4, 14, 36, 76, 140

(61) **1.** t_3 **3.** t^3 **5.** x_{2-1} **7.** x^{2-2} **9.** $y_5 = y_{5-1} + 2$ **11.** $y_{1+1} = (y_1)^2 + 1$
13. 1, 2, 4, 8, 16 **15.** 6, 9, 12, 15, 18 **17.** 1, 4, 9, 16, 25
19. 6, 4, 24, 80, 288 **21.** 2; 4; 16; 256; 65,536

(62) **1.** 1; 1; 2; 6; 24; 120; 720; 5,040; 40,320; 362,880 **3.** 5 **5.** 15 **7.** 2,450
9. 24 **11.** 720 **13.** 96 **15.** 60

(63) **1.** 15 **3.** 40 **5.** 20 **7.** 120 **9.** 32 **11.** 15 **13.** $\sum_{k=1}^{k=4} k^3$ **15.** $\sum_{k=1}^{k=3} k(k+1)$
17. $\sum_{k=2}^{k=5} k^2 - 2$

(64) **1.** $b = 12$ **3.** $D = 32$ **5.** $n = 10$ **7.** $R = 75$

(65) **1.** $9 = 15 - 6, 6 = 15 - 9$ **3.** $3 = \dfrac{48}{16}, 16 = \dfrac{48}{3}$ **5.** $5 = 4 \cdot 7 - 23, 4 = \dfrac{23 + 5}{7}$,
$7 = \dfrac{23 + 5}{4}$ **7.** $37 = 5 \cdot 6 + 7, 7 = 37 - 5 \cdot 6, 5 = \dfrac{37 - 7}{6}, 6 = \dfrac{37 - 7}{5}$
9. $33 = 5 + 4 \cdot 7, 4 = \dfrac{33 - 5}{7}, 7 = \dfrac{33 - 5}{4}$ **11.** $24 = 4(9 - 3), 4 = \dfrac{24}{9 - 3}$
$9 = \dfrac{24}{4} + 3, 3 = 9 - \dfrac{24}{4}$ **13.** $6 = \dfrac{13 + 17}{5}, 13 = 5 \cdot 6 - 17, 17 = 5 \cdot 6 - 13$
15. $\dfrac{48 - 8}{10} = 4, 48 = 4 \cdot 10 + 8, 8 = 48 - 4 \cdot 10$ **17.** $24 = \dfrac{3 \cdot 40}{5}, 3 = \dfrac{5 \cdot 24}{40}$,
$40 = \dfrac{5 \cdot 24}{3}, 5 = \dfrac{3 \cdot 40}{24}$ **19.** $3 = \dfrac{4 \cdot 9}{12}, 12 = \dfrac{4 \cdot 9}{3}, 4 = \dfrac{3 \cdot 12}{9}, 9 = \dfrac{3 \cdot 12}{4}$
21. $3 = \dfrac{21}{5 + 2}, 5 = \dfrac{21}{3} - 2, 2 = \dfrac{21}{3} - 5$ **23.** $10 = 4(8 - 5) - 2$,
$2 = 4(8 - 5) - 10, 8 = \dfrac{2 + 10}{4} + 5, 5 = 8 - \dfrac{2 + 10}{4}$

(66) **1.** $s = rt, t = \dfrac{s}{r}$ **3.** $r = \dfrac{t + u}{s}, s = \dfrac{t + u}{r}, t = rs - u, u = rs - t$
5. $r = \dfrac{s + t}{u}, s = ru - t, t = ru - s$ **7.** $u = rs - t, r = \dfrac{t + u}{s}, s = \dfrac{t + u}{r}$
9. $r = t(s + u), s = \dfrac{r}{t} - u, u = \dfrac{r}{t} - s$ **11.** $r = s - \dfrac{t}{u}, t = u(s - r), u = \dfrac{t}{s - r}$
13. $r = u(s - t), s = \dfrac{r}{u} + t, t = s - \dfrac{r}{u}, u = \dfrac{r}{s - t}$
15. $s = \dfrac{r}{t + u}, t = \dfrac{r}{s} - u, u = \dfrac{r}{s} - t$ **17.** $r = u(s - t), s = \dfrac{r}{u} + t, t = s - \dfrac{r}{u}$

(67) **1.** $N = 60 + 20 - 12$ **3.** $N = 2(30 - 17)$ **5.** $N = \dfrac{36}{3 \cdot 4}$ **7.** $N = 4 \cdot 12 + 4 \cdot 8$
9. $N = 7 + 11 - 13$ **11.** $N = \dfrac{15}{3} - 2$ **13.** $N = \dfrac{12}{6}(15)$ **15.** $N = \dfrac{2 \cdot 6}{6 - 2}$

(68)

1. $\begin{cases} L = A - S_1 - S_2 \\ S_2 = \dfrac{A - S_1}{2} \\ A = 20 \\ S_1 = 2 \end{cases}$

$$L = 20 - 2 - \frac{20 - 2}{2}$$

3. $\begin{cases} C = E_2 - E_1 \\ E_1 = \dfrac{B}{N_1} \\ E_2 = \dfrac{B}{N_2} \\ N_2 = N_1 - N_H \\ N_H = 2 \\ N_1 = 6 \\ B = 60 \end{cases}$

$$C = \frac{60}{6 - 2} - \frac{60}{6}$$

5. $\begin{cases} R = R_2 - R_1 \\ D_1 = R_1 T_1 \\ D_2 = R_2 T_2 \\ D = D_1 + D_2 \\ D = 255 \\ D_1 = 120 \\ T_1 = 3 \\ T_2 = 3 \end{cases}$

$$R = \frac{255 - 120}{3} - \frac{120}{3}$$

(69) **1.** $7(10)^2 + 5(10) + 7$ **3.** $1(10)^3 + 5(10)^2 + 6(10) + 7$ **5.** $9(10)^2 + 1(10) + 8$
7. $1(10)^3 + 0(10)^2 + 0(10) + 0$ **9.** $1(10)^3 + 3(10)^2 + 2(10) + 0$
11. $6(7)^2 + 2(7) + 4$ **13.** $4(7)^2 + 6(7) + 2$ **15.** $1(5)^3 + 0(5)^2 + 4(5) + 3$
17. $2(3)^3 + 0(3)^2 + 2(3) + 0$ **19.** $1(2)^3 + 1(2)^2 + 0(2) + 1$
21. $1(2)^4 + 1(2)^3 + 1(2)^2 + 1(2) + 0$

(71) **1.** $4(7) + 3(1)$ **3.** $3(9) + 4(1)$ **5.** $1(2)^4 + 1(2)^3 + 1(2)^2 + 1(2) + 1(1)$

(72) **1. a.** 50 **b.** 27 **c.** 103 **d.** 91 **e.** 170 **f.** 618 **g.** 8 **h.** 186
3. 191, $2(3)^4 + 1(3)^3 + 0(3)^2 + 0(3) + 2(1)$, 21002 **5.** 7625, $2(60)^2 + 7(60) + 5$,
symbols for 10 to 59 require more than 1 place. **7.** 542, $3(12)^2 + 9(12) + 2$
9. three **11.** five

(73) two: 1, 10, 11, 100, 101, 110, 111, 1000, 1001, 1010, 1011, 1100
five: 1, 2, 3, 4, 10, 11, 12, 13, 14, 20, 21, 22
twelve: 1, 2, 3, 4, 5, 6, 7, 8, 9, t, e, 10.

(74) **1.** 2, 4, 11, 13, 20, 22, 24, 31, 33.   Rule holds for even bases.
3. 5, 14, 23, 32, 41, 50, 55, . . .   Similar to nine in base ten.
5. 34, 40, 41, 42, 43, 44, 100, 101, 102, 103
7. 2012, 2011, 2010, 2002, 2001, 2000, 1222, 1221, 1220, 1212
9. 203, 201, 133, 131, 123, 121, 113, 111, 103, 101
11. 198, 196, 194, 192, 190, 18t, 188, 186, 184, 182
13. 198, 195, 192, 18e, 188, 185, 182, 17e, 178, 175
15. 198, 189, 17t, 16e, 160, 151, 142, 133, 124, 115

(75) **1.** $111120_{(three)}$ **3.** $1178_{(twelve)}$
5. $1101001_{(three)} = 1(729) + 1(243) + 0(81) + 1(27) + 0(9) + 0(3) + 1(1)$
7. a. $11 = 23_{(four)}$ **b.** $13 = 1101_{(two)}$ **9. a.** $4^4 = 256$ **b.** $5^3 = 125$ **c.** 100, 1000
11. $123_{(four)} = 27$

(76) **1. a.** 7 **b.** 11 **c.** 43 **d.** 82 **e.** 1102 **f.** 222 **g.** 100001

3. a.
$$3(10)^2 + 14(10) + 16(1)$$
$$\underline{2(10)^2 + 7(10) + 9(1)}$$
$$1(10)^2 + 7(10) + 7(1)$$

$$4(10)^2 + 15(10) + 16(1)$$
$$\underline{3(10)^2 + 8(10) + 9(1)}$$
$$1(10)^2 + 7(10) + 7(1)$$

b.
$$2(4)^2 + 2(4) + 5(1)$$
$$\underline{1(4)^2 + 2(4) + 2(1)}$$
$$1(4)^2 + 0(4) + 3(1)$$

$$2(4)^2 + 3(4) + 5(1)$$
$$\underline{1(4)^2 + 3(4) + 2(1)}$$
$$1(4)^2 + 0(4) + 3(1)$$

c. $2(2)^5 + 1(2)^4 + 0(2)^3 + 1(2)^2 + 2(2) + 2(1)$
$\underline{1(2)^5 + 1(2)^4 + 0(2)^3 + 1(2)^2 + 1(2) + 1(1)}$
$1(2)^5 + 0(2)^4 + 0(2)^3 + 0(2)^2 + 1(2) + 1(1)$

$1(2)^6 + 2(2)^5 + 1(2)^4 + 1(2)^3 + 2(2)^2 + 3(2) + 2(1)$
$\underline{1(2)^6 + 1(2)^5 + 1(2)^4 + 1(2)^3 + 2(2)^2 + 2(2) + 1(1)}$
$1(2)^5 + 0(2)^4 + 0(2)^3 + 0(2)^2 + 1(2) + 1(1)$

5. a. 312   **b.** 4,134   **c.** 21   **d.** 434tt
7. a. five   **b.** six   **c.** seven, or more
9. $45,665_{(\text{seven})}$

(77) **1. a.** $3(10) + 2(1)$ **b.** $7(10) + 2(1)$ **c.** $1(10)^2 + 2(10) + 3(1)$
$\underline{3}$ $\underline{4}$ $\underline{7}$
$9(10) + 6(1)$ $2(10)^2 + 8(10) + 8(1)$ $8(10)^2 + 6(10) + 1(1)$

d. $2(9) + 3(2)$ **e.** $4(8) + 2(1)$ **f.** $3(5)^2 + 4(5) + 2(1)$
$\underline{2}$ $\underline{3}$ $\underline{4}$
$4(9) + 6(1)$ $1(8)^2 + 4(8) + 6(1)$ $3(5)^3 + 0(5)^2 + 2(5) + 3(1)$

3. a. $312_{(\text{four})}$ **b.** $1023_{(\text{five})}$ **c.** $3114_{(\text{eight})}$ **d.** $12332_{(\text{six})}$ **e.** $38t06_{(\text{twelve})}$
f. $12001112_{(\text{three})}$ **g.** $10101101111_{(\text{two})}$ **h.** $64500_{(\text{seven})}$

(78) **1.** $\dfrac{2(10) + 8(1)}{2} = \dfrac{2(10)}{2} + \dfrac{8(1)}{2} = 1(10) + 4(1) = 14$

3. $\dfrac{1(10)^2 + 1(10) + 6(1)}{4} = \dfrac{8(10) + 36(1)}{4} = \dfrac{8(10)}{4} + \dfrac{36(1)}{4} = 2(10) + 9(1) = 29$

5. $\dfrac{30(10)^2 + 20(10) + 10(1)}{5} = \dfrac{30(10)^2}{5} + \dfrac{20(10)}{5} + \dfrac{10(1)}{5} = 6(10)^2 + 4(10) + 2(1)$
$= 642$

7. $\dfrac{3(5) + 9(1)}{3} = 1(5) + 3(1) = 13_{(\text{five})}$

9. $\dfrac{9(4)^2 + 3(4) + 6(1)}{3} = 3(4)^2 + 1(4) + 2(1) = 312_{(\text{four})}$

11. $2\,\underline{|\,1201}$ **13.** $t\,\underline{|\,47e8}$
$212_{(\text{three})}$ $572_{(\text{twelve})}$

(81) **1. a.** bevy of quail   **b.** clutch of eggs   **c.** legal code of laws   **d.** army of soldiers
e. pride of lions   **f.** brace of ducks.
3. $\{1\}, \{2\}, \{3\}, \{1, 2\}, \{2, 3\}, \{1, 3\}, \{1, 2, 3\}$ **5.** $\{2, 3, 5, 7\}$
7. $\{4, 8, 12, 16\}$ **9.** $\{a_0, a_1, a_2\}$ **11.** 64   **13.** $\{0\}$ **15.** $\{\emptyset\}$
17. a. $\{2\}$ **b.** $\{1, 2, 3\}$ **c.** $\{1\}$ **d.** $\{3\}$ **e.** $\{1, 3, 4\}$ **f.** $\{4\}$ **g.** $\{1, 3\}$
h. $\{2\}$ **i.** $\{2\}$ **j.** $\{1, 2, 3\}$ **k.** $\{1, 3, 4\}$ **l.** $\{1, 2, 3, 4\}$ **m.** $\{2, 4\}$
n. $\{1, 3, 4\}$ **o.** $\{4\}$ **p.** $\{1, 3, 4\}$ **q.** $\{1, 2, 3, 4\}$ **r.** $\{\ \ \}$.

(82) **1. a.** $\{0, 2, 4, 6, 8\}$ **b.** $\{2, 3, 5, 7\}$ **c.** $\{0, 1, 2\}$ **d.** $\{3, 6\}$ **e.** $\{8, 7, 6, 5\}$
f. $\{4, 5, 6, 7, 8\}$ **g.** $\{0, 1\}$ **h.** $\{2, 3, 4, 5, 6, 7, 8, 9, 10\}$
3. a. F   **b.** F   **c.** T   **d.** T   **e.** T   **f.** F   **g.** F   **h.** T   **i.** T

(83) **a.** $\{2, 3, 4\}, B$ **b.** $\{2, 3\}$ **c.** $\{2, 3\}$ **d.** $\{3\}$ **e.** $\{3\}$ **f.** $\emptyset$ **g.** $\emptyset$ **h.** $\{3, 4\}, C$
i. $\{3, 4\}, C$ **j.** $\{4\}$ **k.** $\{4\}$ **l.** $\emptyset$

3.

∩	∅	A	B	S
∅	∅	∅	∅	∅
A	∅	A	∅	A
B	∅	∅	B	B
S	∅	A	B	S

a. *S.* Column and row duplicates the power set.

b. ∅. Column and row all of ∅'s.

c. Symmetry about the diagonal from upper left to lower right.

d. $A \cap A = A = A \cap S$, but $A \neq S$.

5.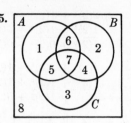

(84) **1. a.** {3, 4}, *C*   **b.** {1, 2, 3, 4}   **c.** {1, 2, 3, 4}   **d.** {1, 2, 3, 4, 5}
   e. {1, 2, 3, 4, 5}   **f.** {2, 3}   **g.** {2, 3, 4}, *B*   **h.** {2, 3, 4}, *B*   **i.** {4}
   j. {2, 3}   **k.** {2, 3, 4}, *B*   **l.** {4}

3.

∪	∅	A	B	S
∅	∅	A	B	S
A	A	A	S	S
B	B	S	B	S
S	S	S	S	S

a. ∅. Column and row duplicates the power set.

b. Symmetry about the diagonal from upper left to lower right.

c. $A \cup S = S = B \cup S$, but $A \neq B$.

5. 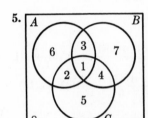   7. 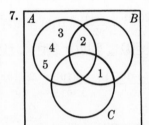   9.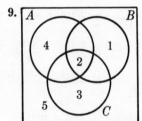

(85) **1.**

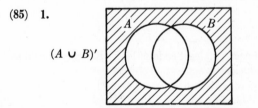

$(A \cup B)'$ $A' \cap B'$

The complement of a union is the intersection of the complements.

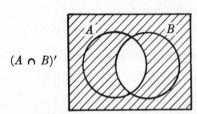

$(A \cap B)'$ $A' \cup B'$

The complement of an intersection is the union of the complements.

3. a. $\{1\}$, or A **b.** $\{1, \{1\}\}$, or B **c.** $\{1\}$ **d.** $\{\{1\}\}$ **e.** $\{2\}$ **f.** $\emptyset$
g. $\{\{1, \{1\}\}\}$ **h.** $\emptyset$ **i.** T   **j.** T   **k.** T   **l.** F   **m.** F   **n.** T   **o.** F   **p.** F
5. a. $1, 2$ **b.** $3, 4$ **c.** $1, 3$ **d.** $2, 4$ **e.** 1 **f.** $2, 3, 4$ **g.** $1, 2, 3$ **h.** 4 **i.** $1, 2, 4$
j. $1, 3, 4$ **k.** 3 **l.** 2 **m.** $1, 2, 3, 4$ **n.** none   **o.** $2, 3$ **p.** $1, 4$

(86) **1.** $\{\{\{x, y, z\}\}, \{\{x, y\}, \{z\}\}, \{\{x, z\}, \{y\}\}, \{\{y, z\}, \{x\}\}, \{\{x\}, \{y\}, \{z\}\}\}$
3. a. $\{\{2, 4, 6, 8, 10\}, \{1, 3, 5, 7, 9\}\}$ **b.** $\{\{1\}, \{2, 3, 5, 7\}, \{4, 6, 8, 9, 10\}\}$
c. $\{\{3, 6, 9\}, \{2, 5, 8\}, \{1, 4, 7, 10\}\}$ **d.** $\{\{1, 4, 9\}, \{2, 3, 5, 6, 7, 8, 10\}\}$
e. $\{\{4\}, \{1, 9\}, \{2, 6, 8, 10\}, \{3, 5, 7\}\}$ **f.** $\{\{2\}, \{4, 6, 8, 10\}, \{1\},$
$\{3, 5, 7\}, \{9\}\}$ **g.** $\{\{1\}, \{3\}, \{2, 5\}, \{7\}, \{6, 9\}, \{8\}, \{4, 10\}\}$
h. $\{\{9\}, \{6\}, \{3\}, \{2, 8\}, \{5\}, \{4\}, \{1\}, \{10\}, \{7\}\}$

(87) **1. a.** 1-1 correspondence, and hence both 1-1 and onto.   **b.** Not a mapping; F has
no image.   **c.** Into, but not onto since D is not an image.   **d.** Not a mapping
since F has two images.   **e.** Not a mapping; G has no image but H has two
images.

3.			**5.**			**7.**			**9.**			**11.**	
10	23		1	2		2	1		1	3		5	3
20	43		3	54		3	4		2	7			
30	63		5	250		4	18						
						5	96						

(88) **1. a.** 1   **b.** 32   **c.** 120   **3. a.** 5   **b.** 7   **c.** 15   **d.** 9   **e.** 10   **5. a.** 5   **b.** 12
7. $n(A \cup B) = n(A) + n(B) - n(A \cap B)$.   Check on a Venn diagram.
9. a. $(1, 18), (2, 15), (3, 9)$ **b.** $(3, 6), (4, 3)$ **c.** $(1, 2), (2, 27)$
11. 10   **13. a.** 15   **b.** 11

(89) **1. a.** $\{$(Dodge, sedan), (Dodge, truck), (Ford, sedan), (Ford, truck),
(Chevrolet, sedan), (Chevrolet, truck)$\}$ **b.** $\{$(box 1, black ball),
(box 1, white ball), (box 1, red ball), (box 2, black ball), (box 2, white ball),
(box 2, red ball), (box 3, black ball), (box 3, white ball), (box 3, red ball)$\}$
c. $\{$(true, true), (true, false), (false, true), (false, false)$\}$
d. $\{(0, 1), (0, 2), (0, 3), (1, 1), (1, 2), (1, 3)\}$ **e.** $\emptyset$
3. $\{(0, 0, 0), (0, 0, 1), (0, 1, 0), (0, 1, 1), (1, 0, 0), (1, 0, 1), (1, 1, 0), (1, 1, 1)\}$
5. $\{(1, 1), (2, 2), (3, 3), (4, 4)\}$ **b.** $\{(1, 1), (2, 4)\}$
c. $\{(1, 4), (2, 3), (3, 2), (4, 1)\}$ **d.** $\{(2, 1), (3, 2), (4, 3)\}$
e. $\{(3, 1), (3, 2), (3, 3), (3, 4)\}$ **f.** $\{(1, 2), (2, 2), (3, 2), (4, 2)\}$
g. $\{(1, 2), (2, 4)\}$ **h.** $\{(2, 1), (3, 2), (3, 1), (4, 3), (4, 2), (4, 1)\}$
i. $\{(1 , 2), (1, 3), (1, 4), (2, 1), (2, 3), (2, 4), (3, 1), (3, 2), (3, 4), (4, 1), (4, 2), (4, 3)\}$
7. a. $(A \otimes B) \otimes C$
$\{((1, 1), 1), ((1, 2), 1), ((1, 3), 1), ((2, 1), 1), ((2, 2), 1), ((2, 3), 1)\}$
b. $A \otimes (B \otimes C)$
$\{(1, (1, 1)), (1, (2, 1)), (1, (3, 1)), (2, (1, 1)), (2, (2, 1)), (2, (3, 1))\}$
c. $A \otimes B \otimes C$
$\{(1, 1, 1), (1, 2, 1), (1, 3, 1), (2, 1, 1), (2, 2, 1), (2, 3, 1)\}$

(90) **1. a.** $6 \cdot 5$ **b.** $7 \cdot 6 \cdot 5$ **c.** $5 \cdot 4 \cdot 3 \cdot 2 \cdot 1$ **d.** $5 \cdot 5 \cdot 5 \cdot 5 \cdot 5$
3. a. $(8)_4$ **b.** 8^4 **c.** $(6)_6$ or $6!$ **d.** $(7)_5$ or $V_{7, 5}$
5. a. $\dfrac{6!}{4!}$ **b.** $\dfrac{7!}{4!}$ **c.** $\dfrac{5!}{0!}$ **d.** $\dfrac{100!}{88!}$ **e.** $\dfrac{25!}{23!}$ **f.** $\dfrac{9!}{8!}$
7. a. 360   **b.** 30   **c.** 210   **d.** 840   **e.** 24

(91) **1. a.** 15 **b.** 15 **c.** 4950 **d.** 32

   3. 45, 46, 47, 54, 56, 57. 64, 65, 67, 74, 75, 76; $4(4 - 1) = (4)_2 = 12$ **5.** $(4)_2 = 12$

   7. (H, H, H), (H, H, T), (H, T, H), (H, T, T), (T, H, H), (T, H, T), (T, T, H), (T, T, T); $2^3 = 8$

   9. $\{1\}, \{2, 3, 4, 5\}; \{2\}, \{1, 3, 4, 5\}; \{3\}, \{1, 2, 4, 5\}; \{4\}, \{1, 2, 3, 5\}; \{5\},$
   $\{1, 2, 3, 4\}; \{1, 2\}, \{3, 4, 5\}; \{1, 3\}, \{2, 4, 5\}; \{1, 4\}, \{2, 3, 5\}; \{1, 5\},$
   $\{2, 3, 4\}; \{2, 3\}, \{1, 4, 5\}; \{2, 4\}, \{1, 3, 5\}; \{2, 5\}, \{1, 3, 4\}; \{3, 4\},$
   $\{1, 2, 5\}; \{3, 5\}, \{1, 2, 4\}; \{4, 5\}, \{1, 2, 3\}.$ $\binom{5}{1} + \binom{5}{2} = 15$

   11. $\{1, 5\}, \{1, 10\}, \{1, 25\}, \{1, 50\}, \{5, 10\}, \{5, 25\}, \{5, 50\}, \{10, 25\},$
   $\{10, 50\}, \{25, 50\}.$ $\binom{5}{2} = 10$

(92) **1. a.** Addition is commutative. **b.** Addition is associative. **c.** Zero is the identity for addition. **d.** and **e.** have no analogy for addition.

   3.

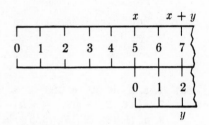

(93) **1.** If $n(A \cap B) = 0$, $n(A - B) = 6$. If $n(A \cap B) = 1$, $n(A - B) = 5$.
   If $n(A \cap B) = 2$, $n(A - B) = 4$. If $n(A \cap B) = 3$, $n(A - B) = 3$.

   3. a., b. The ordered pairs are $(5, 8)$, $(4, 7)$, $(3, 6)$, $(2, 5)$, $(1, 4)$, $(0, 3)$;
   $(0, 8)$, $(1, 7)$, $(2, 6)$, $(3, 5)$, $(4, 4)$, $(5, 3)$; $(5, 0)$, $(6, 1)$, $(7, 2)$, $(8, 3)$.

   5. a. $N = (\ ) + [\ ]$ **b.** $(\ ) + N = [\ ]$ **c.** $[\ ] - (\ ) = N$
   d. $N = (\ ) - [\ ]$ **e.** $N - (\ ) = [\ ]$ **f.** $(\ ) - N = [\ ]$
   g. $N + (\ ) = [\ ]$ **h.** $[\ ] - N = (\ )$ **i.** $N - [\ ] = (\ )$
   j. $N = (\ ) - [\ ]$

(94) **1. a.** Multiplication is commutative. **b.** Multiplication is associative. **c.** Multiplication is distributive with respect to addition. **d.** No analogy, since addition is not distributive with respect to multiplication. **e.** If zero is a factor, the product is always zero. **f.** One times any factor equals that factor. **g.** No analogy.

   3. a.

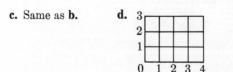

   c. Same as **b.** **d.**

  e.

f.

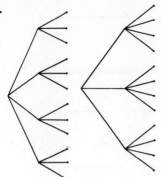

g.
$$a_{11}\ a_{12}\ a_{13}$$
$$a_{21}\ a_{22}\ a_{23}$$
$$a_{31}\ a_{32}\ a_{33}$$
$$a_{41}\ a_{42}\ a_{43}$$

$$(1, 3)\quad (2, 3)\quad (3, 3)\quad (4, 3)$$
$$(1, 2)\quad (2, 2)\quad (3, 2)\quad (4, 2)$$
$$(1, 1)\quad (2, 1)\quad (3, 1)\quad (4, 1)$$

h.

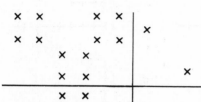

i.

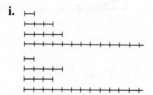

j.

5. a., d., e., f., g., h., i., j. cannot show a zero factor.

b., c. $\begin{cases} 0 & 1 & 2 & 3 & 4 & 5 \\ \updownarrow \\ 0 \end{cases}$ or $\begin{cases} 0 & 1 & 2 & 3 & 4 & 5 \\ \updownarrow & & & & & \updownarrow \\ 0 & & & & & 1 \end{cases}$

(95) **1. a.** $\{\{a, b, c, d\}, \{e, f, g, h\}, \{i, j, k, l\}\}$
$\{\{a, b, c\}, \{d, e, f\}, \{g, h, i\}, \{j, k, l\}\}$

b.
$$\frac{x}{y}$$
$$\begin{cases} 0 & & 1 & & 2 & & 3 \\ \updownarrow & & \updownarrow & & \updownarrow & & \updownarrow \\ 0 & 1 & 2 & 3 & 4 & 5 & 6 & 7 & 8 & 9 & 10 & 11 & 12 \\ & & & y & & & & & & & & & x \end{cases}$$

$$\begin{cases} 0 & & 1 & & 2 & & 3 & & 4 \\ \updownarrow & & \updownarrow & & \updownarrow & & \updownarrow & & \updownarrow \\ 0 & 1 & 2 & 3 & 4 & 5 & 6 & 7 & 8 & 9 & 10 & 11 & 12 \\ & & \frac{x}{y} & & & & & & & & & & x \end{cases}$$

where the lower left labels are $\frac{y}{}$ and $\frac{x}{y}$.

c. Similar to **b.**

d.

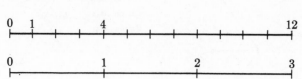

e.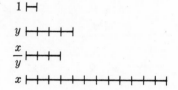

f.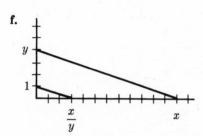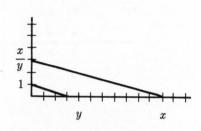

3. a. $N = (\ )[\ \ ]$ **b.** $N \cdot (\ ) = [\ \ ]$ **c.** $\dfrac{(\ )}{[\ \ ]} = N$ **d.** $\dfrac{N}{(\ )} = [\ \ ]$

  e. $[\ \ ] \cdot N = (\ )$ **f.** $N = \dfrac{[\ \ ]}{(\ )}$ **g.** $\dfrac{N}{[\ \ ]} = (\ )$ **h.** $\dfrac{N}{[\ \ ]} = \dfrac{(\ )}{1}$

  i. $\dfrac{[\ \ ]}{N} = \dfrac{(\ )}{1}$ **j.** $\dfrac{(\ )}{[\ \ ]} = S$ **k.** $\dfrac{N}{(\ )} = [\ \ ]$ **l.** $L \cdot [\ \ ] = (\ )$

  m. $\dfrac{N}{1} = \dfrac{(\ )}{[\ \ ]}$ **n.** $\dfrac{N}{(\ )} = \dfrac{[\ \ ]}{1}$

(96) 1. a. $\{\{(a, 0), (b, 0)\}, \{(a, 0), (b, 1)\}, \{(a, 0), (b, 2)\}, \{(a, 1), (b, 0)\},$
  $\{(a, 1), (b, 1)\}, \{(a, 1), (b, 2)\}, \{(a, 2), (b, 0)\}, \{(a, 2), (b, 1)\},$
  $\{(a, 2), (b, 2)\}\}$

  b. $\{(r, r), (r, s), (r, t), (s, r), (s, s), (s, t), (t, r), (t, s), (t, t)\}$

  c. $\boxed{1 \ \ 2} \boxed{} \boxed{}\ ,\ \boxed{1} \boxed{2} \boxed{}\ ,\ \boxed{1} \boxed{} \boxed{2}\ ,$

  $\boxed{2} \boxed{1} \boxed{}\ ,\ \boxed{} \boxed{1 \ \ 2} \boxed{}\ ,\ \boxed{} \boxed{1} \boxed{2}\ ,$

  $\boxed{2} \boxed{} \boxed{1}\ ,\ \boxed{} \boxed{2} \boxed{1}\ ,\ \boxed{} \boxed{} \boxed{1 \ \ 2}\ .$

3. 4^0 4^1 4^2 etc.

```
  *              *  *         *  *    *  *
                 *  *         *  *    *  *

                              *  *    *  *
                              *  *    *  *
```

(97) **1.** $1\,1\,\underline{1}, 1\,1\,0, 1\,1\,1, 1\,\underline{1\,1\,1}, 1\,1\,\underline{1}\,0, 1\,\underline{1\,1}\,1, 1\,1\,0\,\underline{1}, 1\,1\,\underline{1}\,0\,0, 1\,\underline{1}\,0\,1, 1\,1\,1\,\underline{1}$

3. a. $1^2 + 1 = 2, 2^2 + 1 = 5, 4^2 + 1 = 17, 6^2 + 1 = 37, 10^2 + 1 = 101$

b. $2^2 - 1 = 3$

c. $N^2 - 1 = (N + 1)(N - 1)$. If $N^2 - 1$ is a prime, then $N - 1 = 1, N = 2$. Hence 3 is the only prime of this form.

5. a. Must satisfy tests for 2, 3, and 5.   **b.** Must satisfy tests for 5 and 8.

c. Must satisfy tests for 5 and 9.   **d.** Must satisfy tests for 8 and 9.

7. a. L, N, R, T **b.** R, T

9.

D	D'	D	D'	D	D'	D	D'	D	D'	D	D'	D	D'	D	D'
2	12	5	15	9	11	13	4	14	7	10	1	3	6	16	8

(98) **1. a.** 16 **b.** 10 **c.** 16 **d.** 8 **e.** 15

3. {8, 12, 15}, g.c.d. 1, l.c.m. 120; {8, 12, 16}, g.c.d. 4, l.c.m. 48; {8, 15, 16}, g.c.d. 1, l.c.m. 240; {12, 15, 16}, g.c.d. 1, l.c.m. 240.

5. $\{(\varnothing, \{p, q\}), (\{p\}, \{q\}), (\{q\}, \{p\}), (\{p, q\}, \varnothing)\}$

7. a. 9 **b.** 6 **c.** 36 **d.** 362,880

(99) **1. a.** $5(9), 45$ **b.** $5(0), 0$ **c.** $5(2 + 8), 50$ **d.** $5(11 - 4), 35$

e. $5(3 \cdot 7), 105$ **f.** $5\left(\dfrac{12}{3}\right), 20$ **g.** $5(5^3), 625$ **h.** $5\left(\dfrac{18}{4 + 5}\right), 10$

3. a. $\dfrac{15}{5}, 3$ **b.** $\dfrac{0}{5}, 0$ **c.** $\dfrac{8}{5}$, undefined **d.** $\dfrac{12 + 3}{5}, 3$ **e.** $\dfrac{28 - 3}{5}, 5$

f. $\dfrac{5^4}{5}, 125$ **g.** $\dfrac{7 \cdot 15}{5}, 21$ **h.** $\dfrac{\frac{20}{4}}{5}, 1$

(100) **1. a.** $8 + 3, 11$ **b.** $0 + 3, 3$ **c.** $11 + 4 + 3, 18$ **d.** $11 - 4 + 3, 10$

e. $7 \cdot 11 + 3, 80$ **f.** $\dfrac{16}{2} + 3, 11$ **g.** $11 - 3, 8$ **h.** $2 - 3$, undefined

i. $14 + 2 - 3, 13$ **j.** $10 - 1 - 3, 6$ **k.** $5^0 - 3$, undefined **l.** $13 + 3 - 3, 13$

m. $\dfrac{7 + 3}{5} - 1, 1$ **n.** $\dfrac{4 \cdot 6 + 3}{3}, 9$ **o.** $3\left(\dfrac{20}{4} - 2\right), 9$ **p.** $4(17 - 2) + 5, 65$

q. $7\left(\dfrac{6 \cdot 5}{3}\right), 70$ **r.** $\dfrac{\frac{60}{2}}{3}, 10$ **s.** $\dfrac{18 - 5}{3}$, undefined **t.** $\dfrac{18}{3} - 5, 1$

u. $\dfrac{18 + 2}{5}, 4$ **v.** $\dfrac{18}{5} + 2$, undefined **w.** $3 + 2 - 4, 1$ **x.** $3 - 4 + 2$, undefined

3. a. $19; -4, \dfrac{}{3}, +3$ **b.** $4; +12, -4, \dfrac{}{6}$ **c.** $8; 5\,\cdot, +2, \dfrac{}{6}$ **d.** not possible

e. $30; \dfrac{}{2}, \dfrac{}{5}, 8(\ )$ **f.** not possible

(101) **a.** $1 \cdot$ or $\dfrac{}{1}$ **b.** $+0$ or -0 **c.** $1 \cdot$ or $\dfrac{}{1}$ **d.** $+0$ or -0

3. a. $7; (\ )^2, -4, \dfrac{}{9}$ **b.** $4; +2, (\ )^3, \dfrac{}{12}$ **c.** $10; \dfrac{}{2}, -2, (\ )^2$

d. not possible **e.** $6; (\ )^2, \dfrac{}{9}, (\ )^3$

(102) **1.** $+5$ **3.** $35(\ )$ **5.** $5(\ )$ **7.** $\overline{}$ **9.** $1(\ )$ **11.** $(\ )^{10}$ **13.** $2\cdot$ **15.** -9

17. $(\ )^9$ **19.** $+2$ **21.** $4(\ )$ **23.** $\dfrac{(\ )}{3}$ **25.** $343\cdot$ **27.** $6(\ )$ **29.** $(\ )^6$

31. $\dfrac{(\ )}{8}$ **33.** $48N$ **35.** N^8 **37.** N **39.** $\dfrac{N}{15}$ **41.** $+4$ **43.** -18 **45.** $100(\ )$

47. $7(\ )$ **49.** $+7$ **51.** $\overline{}_{7}$ **53.** A decrease of 8. **55.** An increase of 9.

57. a. $n \to \dfrac{n+2}{2}$ **b.** $n \to (n+2)^2$ **c.** $n \to \left(\dfrac{n}{2}\right)^2$ **d.** $n \to \dfrac{n^2}{2}$ **e.** $n \to n^2 + 2$

f. $n \to \dfrac{n}{2} + 2$ **59.** $n \to n + 2$ **61.** $n \to 3n$ **63.** $n \to n^{12}$ **65.** $n \to 6(n+5)$

67. $n \to [6(n+5)]^3$

(103) **1. a.**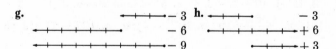

c.    **d.**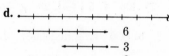

e.   **f.**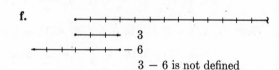

3 − 6 is not defined

g. 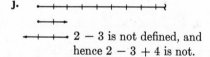 **h.**

i.   **j.**

2 − 3 is not defined, and
hence 2 − 3 + 4 is not.

3. a. 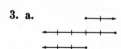   **b.**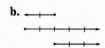

(104) **1.** After ⊢──────────────────┤   **3.** After ⊢──────┤
       Before ⊢─────┤   Before ⊢────────────────────┤

(105)

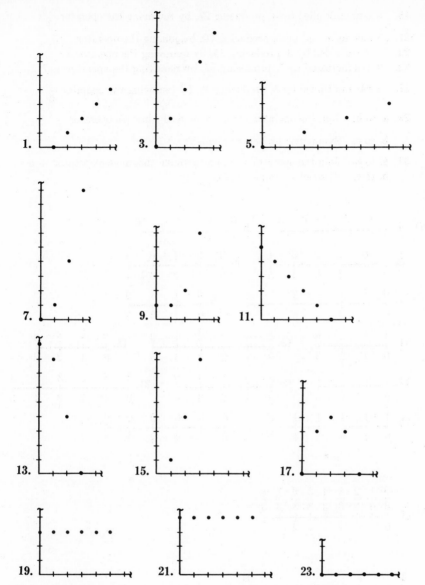

(106) **5.** 17 was decreased by 5, producing 12, by removing the operator $+ 5$

7. 10 was decreased by 3, producing 7, by joining the operator $- 3$

9. 56 was divided by 7, producing 8, by removing the operator $7 \cdot$

11. 24 was divided by 6, producing 4, by joining the operator $\dfrac{}{6}$

13. 21 was increased by 4, producing 25, by joining the operator $+ 4$

15. 10 was increased by 7, producing 17, by removing the operator $- 7$

17. 15 was multiplied by 4, producing 60, by joining the operator $4 \cdot$

19. 9 was multiplied by 3, producing 27, by removing the operator $\dfrac{\;}{3}$

21. 75 was decreased by 5, producing 70, by joining the operator $- 5$

23. 75 was divided by 3, producing 25, by removing the operator $3 \cdot$

25. 70 was increased by 7, producing 77, by removing the operator $- 7$

27. 6 was multiplied by 5, producing 30, by removing the operator $\dfrac{\;}{5}$

29. a. to b. Join the operator $\cdot\, t$ and remove the inverse operator $\dfrac{\;}{t}$

    b. to c. Symmetric property of equality.

31. a. to b. Join the operator $- u$, and remove the inverse operator $+ u$.

    b. to c. Symmetric property of equality.

(107) 1. a.   0 2 4 6 8   b.   0 4 8 12 16

3.
```
0  1  2  3  4
0  1  2  3  4  5
```
5.
```
0  2  4  6  8
0  1  2  3  4
```

7.
```
0     1      2      3
0     3      6      9
```
9.
```
0  1  4  9
0  1  2  3
```

11.
```
1  1  2  6
0  1  2  3
```
13.
```
5  4  3  2  1  0
0  1  2  3  4  5
```
15.
```
9  8  5  0
0  1  2  3
```

17.
```
1  4  7
0  1  2  3
```
19.
```
0  3  4  3  0
0  1  2  3  4
```
21.
```
3  3  3  3  3  3
0  1  2  3  4  5
```

23.
```
4  4  4  4  4  4
0  1  2  3  4  5

0  0  0  0  0  0
0  1  2  3  4  5
```

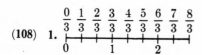

(108) 1.
```
0  1  2  3  4  5  6  7  8
3  3  3  3  3  3  3  3  3
0        1        2
```

3.   **i**   **ii**

```
0          1            0          1
|----------|            |----------|

0  1/4     1            0     1     2     3
|--+---+---|            |-----+-----+-----|

0  1/4  3/4  1          0   3/4  1  2     3
|--+---+---+|           |----+--+---+--+--|
```

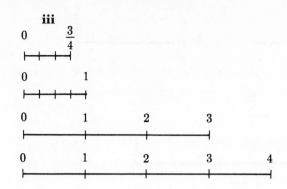

5.

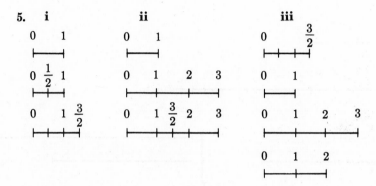

(109) **1. a.** 4 **b.** $6x = 24$ **c.** $x = 4$ **3. a.** 6 **b.** $18x = 108$ **c.** $x = 6$

5. a. 30 **b.** $24x = 720$ **c.** $x = 30$. **7. a.** $\dfrac{10}{2}$ **b.** $\dfrac{35}{7}$ **c.** $\dfrac{95}{19}$ **d.** $\dfrac{505}{101}$ **e.** $\dfrac{5}{1}$

9. a. $\dfrac{30}{6}$ **b.** $\dfrac{85}{17}$ **c.** $\dfrac{1000}{200}$ **d.** $\dfrac{555}{111}$

(110) **1.** $\dfrac{11}{2}, \dfrac{10+1}{2}, \dfrac{10}{2} + \dfrac{1}{2}, 5 + \dfrac{1}{2}, 5\dfrac{1}{2}$ **3.** $\dfrac{23}{4}, \dfrac{20+3}{4}, \dfrac{20}{4} + \dfrac{3}{4}, 5 + \dfrac{3}{4}, 5\dfrac{3}{4}$

5. $\dfrac{67}{9}, \dfrac{63+4}{9}, \dfrac{63}{9} + \dfrac{4}{9}, 7 + \dfrac{4}{9}, 7\dfrac{4}{9}$ **7.** $\dfrac{200}{13}, \dfrac{195+5}{13}, \dfrac{195}{13} + \dfrac{5}{13}, 15 + \dfrac{5}{13}, 15\dfrac{5}{13}$

9. $3\dfrac{2}{5}, 3 + \dfrac{2}{5}, \dfrac{15}{5} + \dfrac{2}{5}, \dfrac{15+2}{5}, \dfrac{17}{5}$ **11.** $1\dfrac{5}{7}, 1 + \dfrac{5}{7}, \dfrac{7}{7} + \dfrac{5}{7}, \dfrac{7+5}{7}, \dfrac{12}{7}$

13. $10\dfrac{1}{3}, 10 + \dfrac{1}{3}, \dfrac{30}{3} + \dfrac{1}{3}, \dfrac{30+1}{3}, \dfrac{31}{3}$ **15.** $15\dfrac{1}{2}$ **17.** $\dfrac{25}{3}$ **19.** $\dfrac{75}{2}$

21. $A = C\left(\dfrac{A}{C}\right)$ and $B = C\left(\dfrac{B}{C}\right)$ $A + B = C\left(\dfrac{A}{C}\right) + C\left(\dfrac{B}{C}\right) = C\left(\dfrac{A}{C} + \dfrac{B}{C}\right)$

$\dfrac{A+B}{C} = \dfrac{A}{C} + \dfrac{B}{C}$

(111) **1.** 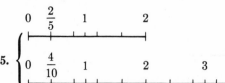 **3.**

5.

7.

9. 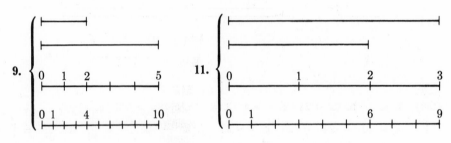 **11.**

13. $\dfrac{7}{11}$ **15.** $\dfrac{3}{1}$ **17.** $\dfrac{7^2}{5}$ **19.** $\dfrac{5}{7}$ **21.** $\dfrac{7}{2^3}$ **23.** $\dfrac{5}{11}$ **25.** $\dfrac{2\cdot3}{3\cdot7}$ **27.** $\dfrac{2\cdot5}{5\cdot7}$ **29.** $\dfrac{2\cdot3\cdot11}{3\cdot7\cdot11}$

31. $\dfrac{2\cdot3\cdot7}{3\cdot7^2}$ **33.** $\dfrac{2\cdot3^2}{3\cdot5\cdot7}$ **35.** $\dfrac{2\cdot5\cdot7}{3\cdot5\cdot7}$ **37.** $\dfrac{2^3\cdot13}{2^2\cdot3\cdot13}$ **39.** $\dfrac{a^3c}{a^2bc}$

41. (0, $\frac{1}{3}$, $\frac{3}{5}$, 1)

43. (0, $\frac{1}{2}$, $\frac{2}{3}$, $\frac{3}{4}$, 1) **45.** (0, $\frac{3}{4}$, $\frac{5}{6}$, 1)

47. $\dfrac{2\cdot5}{3\cdot5}, \dfrac{2^2\cdot3}{3\cdot5}$ **49.** $\dfrac{2\cdot3}{3^3}, \dfrac{5}{3^3}$ **51.** $\dfrac{5^2}{2^4\cdot3\cdot5}, \dfrac{2^2\cdot19}{2^4\cdot3\cdot5}$ **53.** $\dfrac{5\cdot13}{2^2\cdot3^2\cdot5}, \dfrac{3\cdot19}{2^2\cdot3^2\cdot5}$

(112) **1.** $\dfrac{10}{2} = 5,\ 10 = 2\cdot5$ $\dfrac{12}{3} = 4,\ 12 = 3\cdot4$ $3\cdot10 = 3\cdot2\cdot5 = (2\cdot3)\cdot5$

$12\cdot2 = 3\cdot4\cdot2 = (2\cdot3)\cdot4$ $3\cdot10 + 12\cdot2 = (2\cdot3)\cdot5 + (2\cdot3)\cdot4$

$$3 \cdot 10 + 12 \cdot 2 = (2 \cdot 3)(5 + 4) \qquad \frac{3 \cdot 10 + 12 \cdot 2}{2 \cdot 3} = 5 + 4$$

$$\frac{10}{2} + \frac{12}{3} = \frac{3 \cdot 10 + 12 \cdot 2}{2 \cdot 3}$$

3. If $\frac{a}{b} = x$, then $a = bx$, and $ad = bxd = bdx$.

If $\frac{c}{d} = y$, then $c = dy$, and $bc = bdy$. If ad is greater than or equal to bc, then

$ad - bc = bdx - bdy = bd(x - y)$.

Then $x - y = \dfrac{ad - bc}{bd}$ and $\dfrac{a}{b} - \dfrac{c}{d} = \dfrac{ad - bc}{bd}$

5. In $\dfrac{0}{a}$, let a be any natural number. $\dfrac{0}{a} + \dfrac{c}{d} = \dfrac{0 \cdot d + ac}{ad} = \dfrac{ac}{ad} = \dfrac{c}{d}$

$$\frac{c}{d} + \frac{0}{a} = \frac{ac + d \cdot 0}{da} = \frac{ac}{ad} = \frac{c}{d}$$

7. If $\dfrac{a}{b} + \dfrac{e}{f} = \dfrac{c}{d} + \dfrac{e}{f}$, then $\dfrac{af + be}{bf} = \dfrac{cf + de}{df}$

Then $df(af + be) = bf(cf + de)$.   Hence $adf^2 + bdef = bcf^2 + bdef$

Therefore $adf^2 = bcf^2$, $ad = bc$, and $\dfrac{a}{b} = \dfrac{c}{d}$

(113) 1. $\dfrac{9}{10}$ **3.** $\dfrac{17}{15}$ **5.** $\dfrac{17}{36}$ **7.** $\dfrac{5}{24}$ **9.** $\dfrac{7}{12}$

11.

13.

15.

17.

19.

21.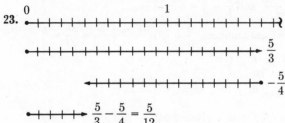

23.

$$25. \quad \frac{a}{b} = \frac{ad}{bd} = (ad)\left(\frac{1}{bd}\right) \quad \frac{c}{d} = \frac{bc}{bd} = (bc)\left(\frac{1}{bd}\right)$$

$$\frac{a}{b} + \frac{c}{d} = (ad)\left(\frac{1}{bd}\right) + (bc)\left(\frac{1}{bd}\right) = (ad + bc)\left(\frac{1}{bd}\right) = \frac{ad + bc}{bd}$$

27.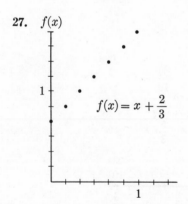

$$f(x) = x + \frac{2}{3}$$

(114) **1.** $\dfrac{1}{3} + \dfrac{1}{2 \cdot 3} = \dfrac{2}{2 \cdot 3} + \dfrac{1}{2 \cdot 3} = \dfrac{2 + 1}{2 \cdot 3} = \dfrac{3}{6} = \dfrac{1}{2}$

3. $\dfrac{3}{2} + \dfrac{5}{2 \cdot 3} = \dfrac{3 \cdot 3}{2 \cdot 3} + \dfrac{5}{2 \cdot 3} = \dfrac{3 \cdot 3 + 5}{2 \cdot 3} = \dfrac{14}{6} = 2\dfrac{1}{3}$

5. $\dfrac{3}{2 \cdot 5} + \dfrac{4}{3 \cdot 5} = \dfrac{3 \cdot 3}{2 \cdot 3 \cdot 5} + \dfrac{2 \cdot 4}{2 \cdot 3 \cdot 5} = \dfrac{3 \cdot 3 + 2 \cdot 4}{2 \cdot 3 \cdot 5} = \dfrac{17}{30}$

7. $\dfrac{5}{2^2 \cdot 3} + \dfrac{7}{2 \cdot 3^2} = \dfrac{3 \cdot 5}{2^2 \cdot 3^2} + \dfrac{2 \cdot 7}{2^2 \cdot 3^2} = \dfrac{3 \cdot 5 + 2 \cdot 7}{2^2 \cdot 3^2} = \dfrac{29}{36}$

9. $\dfrac{13}{3 \cdot 5} - \dfrac{11}{2^3 \cdot 3} = \dfrac{2^3 \cdot 13}{2^3 \cdot 3 \cdot 5} - \dfrac{5 \cdot 11}{2^3 \cdot 3 \cdot 5} = \dfrac{2^3 \cdot 13 - 5 \cdot 11}{2^3 \cdot 3 \cdot 5} = \dfrac{49}{120}$

11. $\dfrac{4}{3} - \dfrac{7}{3^2} = \dfrac{3 \cdot 4}{3^2} - \dfrac{7}{3^2} = \dfrac{3 \cdot 4 - 7}{3^2} = \dfrac{5}{9}$

13. $\dfrac{7}{3 \cdot 5} + \dfrac{5}{2^2 \cdot 3} + \dfrac{11}{2 \cdot 3^2} = \dfrac{2^2 \cdot 3 \cdot 7 + 3 \cdot 5^2 + 2 \cdot 5 \cdot 11}{2^2 \cdot 3^2 \cdot 5} = \dfrac{269}{180}$

15. $\dfrac{3}{2} + \dfrac{5}{2^3} - \dfrac{7}{2^4} = \dfrac{2^3 \cdot 3 + 2 \cdot 5 - 7}{2^4} = \dfrac{27}{16} = 1\dfrac{11}{16}$

17. $\dfrac{A}{B} + \dfrac{C}{D} + \dfrac{E}{F} = \dfrac{ADF}{BDF} + \dfrac{BCF}{BDF} + \dfrac{BDE}{BDF} = \dfrac{ADF + BCF + BDE}{BDF}$

19. $\dfrac{x+1}{x}$ **21.** $\dfrac{y+x}{y}$ **23.** $\dfrac{x-1}{x}$ **25.** $\dfrac{xz+1}{x}$ **27.** $\dfrac{yz+x}{y}$

29. $\dfrac{uy - vx}{vy}$ **31.** $\dfrac{x+1}{x^2}$ **33.** $\dfrac{z + xy}{xz}$

(115)   1. $5\dfrac{1}{6}$ **3.** $1\dfrac{7}{12}$ **5.** $14\dfrac{7}{10}$ **7.** $3\dfrac{13}{16}$ **9.** $1\dfrac{1}{4}$ **11. a.** $\dfrac{1}{2}$ **b.** $\dfrac{3}{4}$ **c.** $\dfrac{7}{8}$ **d.** $\dfrac{15}{16}$ **e.** $\dfrac{31}{32}$

13. a. $\dfrac{1}{2}$ **b.** $\dfrac{2}{3}$ **c.** $\dfrac{3}{4}$ **d.** $\dfrac{4}{5}$ **e.** $\dfrac{5}{6}$

(116)   1. $1\dfrac{1}{3}$ **3.** $\dfrac{1}{10}$ **5.** $\dfrac{7}{24}$ **7.** not defined   **9.** $2\dfrac{1}{3}$ **11.** $\dfrac{1}{3}$ **13.** $\dfrac{2}{15}$ **15.** not defined

17. $\dfrac{1}{18}$ **19.** $\dfrac{2}{15}$ **21.** $6\dfrac{7}{40}$ **23.** not defined   **25.** $x = \dfrac{3}{5} + \dfrac{7}{8}$

27. $\left(\dfrac{4}{5} + \dfrac{5}{12}\right) - \left(\dfrac{4}{5} - \dfrac{5}{12}\right) = x$ **29.** $x = \dfrac{7}{16} + \left(1 - \dfrac{7}{16}\right)$ **31.** $5\dfrac{2}{3} - x = 3$

33. $x - 2\dfrac{1}{3} = 1\dfrac{1}{5}$ **35.** $x - 1\dfrac{1}{2} = 1\dfrac{2}{5} - \dfrac{3}{4}$ **37.** $\dfrac{3}{5} - \dfrac{3}{7} = x$ **39.** $x - 1\dfrac{3}{5} = 3\dfrac{3}{4}$

41. $\left(2\dfrac{1}{3} + 3\dfrac{1}{2}\right) + 3\dfrac{1}{2} = x$

(117)   1. $<$ **3.** $=$ **5.** $<$ **7.** $>$ **9.** $>$ **11.** $=$ **13.** $=$ **15.** $<$

(118)   1. a. If $a > b$ and $b > c$ then natural numbers y_1 and y_2 exist such that $a = b + y_1$ and $b = c + y_2$. Hence, by substitution, $a = (c + y_2) + y_1$ and $a = c + (y_2 + y_1)$ by the associative law. But $y_2 + y_1$ is some natural number y because of closure for addition. Therefore $a > c$.
   b. Similar to **a**.
   3. a. If $a > b$ there exists a natural number y such that $a = b + y$. Then for $c \neq 0$ we have $ac = (b + y)c$ since multiplication is well defined. Then $ac = bc + yc$ by the distributive law. yc is a natural number since multiplication is closed for natural numbers. Therefore $ac > bc$.
   b. Similar to **a**.
   5. a. By the trichotomy principle $a > b$, $a = b$, or $a < b$. If $a = b$, and $c \neq 0$ then $ac = bc$ since multiplication is well defined, but this contradicts $ac > bc$. If $a < b$ and $c \neq 0$ then $ac < bc$ by problem 3, but this also contradicts $ac > bc$. Hence if $ac > bc$ and $c \neq 0$, then $a > b$.   **b.** Similar to **a**.

(119)   1. $\{8, 9\}$ **3.** $\{10, 20, 30\}$ **5.** $\{11, 12, 13, 14\}$ **7.** $\{15, 16, 17, 18\}$
   9. $\{41, 43, 47\}$ **11.** $\{1, 9, 25, 49\}$ **13.** $\{2, 3, 5, 6, 7, 8\}$

(120)   1. $\{21, 22, 23, 24\}$ **3.** $\{20, 21, 22, 23, 24\}$ **5.** $\{21, 22, 23, 24, 25\}$
   7. $\{20, 21, 22, 23, 24, 25\}$ **9.** $\{1, 2, 3\}$ **11.** $\{\ \}$ **13.** $\{11, 13, 14\}$
   15. $\{30, 45, 60, 75\}$ **17.** $\{2, 4, 6, 8, 10, 12, 14, 16, 18\}$ **19.** $\{8, 16\}$
   21. $\{3, 4, 5, 6\}$ **23.** $\{7, 8, 9\}$ **25.** $\{15, 18\}$ **27.** $\{4, 5, 6, 7\}$

(121) **1.** If $\dfrac{a}{b} < \dfrac{a}{c}$, then $ac < ab$. Since a cannot be zero, $c < b$ or $b > c$.

      3. <   **5.** >   **7.** =   **9.** <   **11.** >   **13.** <   **15.** <   **17.** >   **19.** =   **21.** <

      23. a. <   **b.** >   **25. a.** $\dfrac{2}{11}, \dfrac{6}{11}, \dfrac{8}{11}, \dfrac{9}{11}$ **b.** $\dfrac{7}{9}, \dfrac{7}{8}, \dfrac{7}{6}, \dfrac{7}{5}, \dfrac{7}{3}$ **c.** $\dfrac{9}{8}, \dfrac{9}{7}, \dfrac{9}{6}, \dfrac{9}{4}, \dfrac{10}{4}, \dfrac{11}{4}$

          d. $\dfrac{8}{7}, \dfrac{8}{6}, \dfrac{8}{5}, \dfrac{9}{5}, \dfrac{10}{5}, \dfrac{11}{5}, \dfrac{11}{4}, \dfrac{11}{3}, \dfrac{11}{2}$ **e.** $\dfrac{5}{4}, \dfrac{4}{3}, \dfrac{3}{2}, \dfrac{2}{1}$ **f.** $\dfrac{1}{4}, \dfrac{3}{8}, \dfrac{7}{16}, \dfrac{15}{32}$

(122) **1.** 13   **3.** 11   **5.** 19   **7.** 6   **9.** 6   **11.** 56

(123) **1. a.** $\dfrac{4}{5} < \dfrac{49}{60} < \dfrac{5}{6}$ **b.** If $\dfrac{a}{b} < \dfrac{c}{d}$ then $ad < bc$. Hence $abd < b^2c$ and

        $2abd < abd + b^2c$, or $a(2bd) < b(ad + bc)$. Therefore $\dfrac{a}{b} < \dfrac{ad + bc}{2bd}$

        Also if $ad < bc$ then $ad^2 < bcd$ $ad^2 + bcd < 2bcd$ and $d(ad + bc) < c(2bd)$.

        Therefore $\dfrac{ad + bc}{2bd} < \dfrac{c}{d}$ **c.** $\dfrac{49}{60} - \dfrac{4}{5} = \dfrac{1}{60} = \dfrac{5}{6} - \dfrac{49}{60}$

      3. a. $\dfrac{4}{5} < \dfrac{23}{28} < \dfrac{5}{6}$ **b.** If $\dfrac{a}{b} < \dfrac{c}{d}$ then $ad < bc$. Then $and < bnc$,

        $amb + and < amb + bnc$, $a(mb + nd) < b(ma + nc)$, $\dfrac{a}{b} < \dfrac{ma + nc}{mb + nd}$

        Also if $ad < bc$, then $dma < cmb$, $dma + dnc < cmb + cnd$,

        $d(ma + nc) < c(mb + nd)$, $\dfrac{ma + nc}{mb + nc} < \dfrac{c}{d}$

      5. $\dfrac{2}{3} < \dfrac{17}{24} < \dfrac{3}{4}$, $\dfrac{2}{3} < \dfrac{25}{36} < \dfrac{13}{18} < \dfrac{3}{4}$, $\dfrac{2}{3} < \dfrac{11}{16} < \dfrac{17}{24} < \dfrac{35}{48} < \dfrac{3}{4}$ **7.** $\dfrac{4}{8} < \dfrac{4}{7} < \dfrac{4}{6}$

(124) **1. a.** $0 \le n < 5$, $[0, 5)$, $\{0, 1, 2, 3, 4\}$.   **b.** $0 < n < 3$, $(0, 3)$, $\{1, 2\}$

        c. $0 \le n < 1$, $[0, 1)$, $\{0\}$ **d.** $2 < n < 5$, $(2, 5)$, $\{3, 4\}$

      3. a. $0 < x \le 5$, $(0, 5]$

        b. $0 < x < 2$ or $3 \le x \le 6$, $(0, 2)$ or $[3 \ 6]$

        c. $1 < x \le 6$, $(1, 6]$

        d. $1 < x < 2$, $(1, 2)$

        e. ∅

        f. $3 \le x \le 5$, $[3, 5]$

        g. $0 < x \le 1$, $(0, 1]$

        h. $2 \le x \le 5$, $[2, 5]$

        i. $0 < x < 2$, $(0, 2)$

        j. $3 \le x \le 6$, $[3, 6]$

        k. $1 < x < 3$, $(1, 3)$

l. $5 < x \le 6$, $(5, 6]$ 0 1 2 3 4 5 6

m. $2 \le x < 8$, $[2, 8)$ 0 1 2 3 4 5 6 7 8

n. $0 < x \le 1$ or $5 < x < 8$, $(0, 1]$ or $(5, 8)$ 0 1 2 3 4 5 6 7 8

o. $0 < x < 3$ or $6 < x < 8$, $(0, 3)$ or $(6, 8)$ 0 1 2 3 4 5 6 7 8

p. $5 < x < 8$, $(5. 8)$ 0 1 2 3 4 5 6 7 8

q. $0 < x \le 1$ or $2 \le x < 8$, $(0, 1]$, $[2, 8)$ 0 1 2 3 4 5 6 7 8

r. $0 < x \le 6$, $(0, 6]$ 0 1 2 3 4 5 6

s. $1 < x < 2$ or $3 \le x \le 5$, $(1, 2)$ or $[3, 5]$ 0 1 2 3 4 5

t. $0 x \le 1$ or $6 < x < 8$, $(0, 1]$ or $(6, 8)$ 0 1 2 3 4 5 6 7 8

(125) 1. The monotonic law for multiplication of inequalities was given in problem set (118) for natural numbers only. When this has been extended to positive rationals, then $N(y - 2x) > x$ when $N > \dfrac{x}{y - 2x}$, if $y - 2x > 0$.

3. a. $\dfrac{1}{2}, \dfrac{2}{3}, \dfrac{3}{4}, \dfrac{4}{5}, \dfrac{5}{6}$ c. $\dfrac{n}{n + 1} < \dfrac{n + 1}{(n + 1) + 1}$ since $n^2 + 2n < n^2 + 2n + 1$

   d. $\dfrac{n}{n + 1} < 1$, for all n, since $n < n + 1$ e. If $\dfrac{x}{y} < 1$, then $a_n > \dfrac{x}{y}$ if $n > \dfrac{x}{y - x}$

5. a. $\dfrac{1}{3}, \dfrac{3}{7}, \dfrac{5}{11}, \dfrac{7}{15}, \dfrac{9}{19}$ c. $\dfrac{2n - 3}{4n - 5} < \dfrac{2(n + 1) - 3}{4(n + 1) - 5}$ since $8n^2 - 14n + 3$ is less

   than $8n^2 - 14n + 5$ d. $\dfrac{2n - 3}{4n - 5} < \dfrac{1}{2}$ for all $n > 1$ since $4n - 6 < 4n - 5$

   e. If $\dfrac{x}{y} < \dfrac{1}{2}$ then $a_n > \dfrac{x}{y}$ if $n > \dfrac{3y - 5x}{2y - 4x}$

(126) 1. $\dfrac{10}{2} = 5$ $\dfrac{21}{7} = 3$ $10 = 2 \cdot 5$ $21 = 7 \cdot 3$

   $10 \cdot 21 = (2 \cdot 5)(7 \cdot 3) = (2 \cdot 7)(5 \cdot 3)$ $5 \cdot 3 = \dfrac{10 \cdot 21}{2 \cdot 7}$ $\left(\dfrac{10}{2}\right)\left(\dfrac{21}{7}\right) = \dfrac{10 \cdot 21}{2 \cdot 7}$

3. Let $\dfrac{a}{b} = \dfrac{e}{f}$ so that $af = be$. Now $\left(\dfrac{a}{b}\right)\left(\dfrac{c}{d}\right) = \dfrac{ac}{bd}$

   But $\left(\dfrac{e}{f}\right)\left(\dfrac{c}{d}\right) = \dfrac{ec}{fd} = \dfrac{(ab)(ec)}{(ab)(fd)} = \dfrac{(ac)(be)}{(bd)(af)} = \dfrac{ac}{bd}$

5. If $\left(\dfrac{a}{b}\right)\left(\dfrac{e}{f}\right) = \left(\dfrac{c}{d}\right)\left(\dfrac{e}{f}\right)$ then $\dfrac{ae}{bf} = \dfrac{ce}{df}$, $aedf = bfce$, $(ad)(ef) = (bc)(ef)$, $ad = bc$,

   and $\dfrac{a}{b} = \dfrac{c}{d}$

7. For any natural number c, we have $\dfrac{0}{c} = 0$.

   $\left(\dfrac{a}{b}\right) \cdot 0 = \left(\dfrac{a}{b}\right)\left(\dfrac{0}{c}\right) = \dfrac{a \cdot 0}{bc} = \dfrac{0}{bc} = 0$

9. $\left(\dfrac{a}{b}\right)\left(\dfrac{c}{d}\right) = \dfrac{ac}{bd} = \dfrac{ca}{db} = \left(\dfrac{c}{d}\right)\left(\dfrac{a}{b}\right)$

11. $\dfrac{a}{b}\left(\dfrac{c}{d} + \dfrac{e}{f}\right) = \dfrac{a}{b}\left(\dfrac{cf + de}{df}\right) = \dfrac{a(cf + de)}{b(df)} = \dfrac{acf + ade}{bdf} =$
$\dfrac{acf}{bdf} + \dfrac{ade}{bdf} = \dfrac{ac}{bd} + \dfrac{ae}{bf} = \left(\dfrac{a}{b}\right)\left(\dfrac{c}{d}\right) + \left(\dfrac{a}{b}\right)\left(\dfrac{e}{f}\right)$

(127) 1. a. $\left(\dfrac{5}{6}\right)(18) = (5)\left(\dfrac{1}{6}\right)(18) = (5)\left(\dfrac{18}{6}\right) = (5)(3) = 15$

$\left(\dfrac{5}{6}\right)(18) = \left(\dfrac{1}{6}\right)(5)(18) = \left(\dfrac{1}{6}\right)(90) = \dfrac{90}{6} = 15$

b. $\left(\dfrac{5}{6}\right)(17) = (5)\left(\dfrac{1}{6}\right)(17) = (5)\left(\dfrac{17}{6}\right) = \dfrac{85}{6} = 14\dfrac{1}{6}$

$\left(\dfrac{5}{6}\right)(17) = \left(\dfrac{1}{6}\right)(5)(17) = \left(\dfrac{1}{6}\right)(85) = \dfrac{85}{6} = 14\dfrac{1}{6}$

3. a. 4 b. $4\dfrac{1}{7}$ c. 13 d. $12\dfrac{4}{5}$ e. $\dfrac{2}{3}$ f. $3\dfrac{1}{2}$ g. 15 h. $14\dfrac{2}{7}$ i. 27 j. $10\dfrac{4}{5}$

k. $4\dfrac{1}{5}$ l. $13\dfrac{1}{2}$ m. $\dfrac{8}{55}$ n. $10\dfrac{5}{6}$ o. $\dfrac{9}{25}$ p. 0 q. $\dfrac{3}{8}$ r. 1 s. $\dfrac{15}{77}$ t. $\dfrac{15}{77}$

u. $\dfrac{91}{132}$ v. $1\dfrac{16}{33}$ w. $\dfrac{1}{12}$ x. 9

(128) 1.

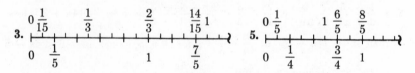

3.

5.

7.

9.

(129) 1.

3.

5. Number line: 0, $\frac{1}{8}$, $\frac{1}{4}$, $\frac{3}{8}$, $\frac{1}{2}$, $\frac{5}{8}$, 1

7. Number line: 0, $\frac{1}{5}$, $\frac{3}{5}$, $1\frac{6}{5}$, $\frac{9}{5}$, $\frac{12}{5}$, 3

9. Number line: 0, $\frac{1}{16}$, $\frac{1}{8}$, $\frac{3}{16}$, $\frac{1}{4}$, $\frac{3}{8}$, $\frac{9}{16}$, $\frac{3}{4}$, $\frac{15}{16}$, 1

11. Number line: 0, $\frac{1}{6}$, $\frac{1}{3}$, $\frac{1}{2}$, $\frac{5}{6}$, 1, $\frac{5}{3}$, $\frac{5}{2}$, $\frac{10}{3}$, $\frac{25}{6}$

13. Number line: 0, $\frac{1}{4y}$, $\frac{1}{2y}$, $\frac{3}{4y}$, $\frac{1}{y}$, $\frac{5}{4y}$

15. Number line: 0, $\frac{a}{3b}$, $\frac{2a}{3b}$, $\frac{a}{b}$, $\frac{4a}{3b}$, $\frac{5a}{3b}$

17. 8 **19.** $\frac{7}{3}$ **21.** $\frac{10}{33}$ **23.** $\frac{20}{3}$ **25.** $\frac{1}{3}$ **27.** $\frac{3}{2}$ **29.** 3 **31.** $\frac{3}{25}$ **33.** $\frac{3x}{5y}$

(130) **1. a.** 32 **b.** 302 **c.** $28\frac{1}{6}$ **d.** 40 **3.** $\frac{5}{6}, \frac{20}{23}$ **5.** $\frac{2}{25}, \frac{13}{150}$ **7.** $0, \frac{3}{4}, 1, \frac{3}{4}, 0$

9. $0, \frac{5}{9}, \frac{8}{9}, 1, \frac{8}{9}, \frac{5}{9}, 0$ **11.** $1, \frac{4}{9}, \frac{1}{9}, 0, \frac{1}{9}, \frac{4}{9}, 1$ **13.** $2, 2\frac{1}{4}, 2\frac{10}{27}, 2\frac{113}{256}$

15. $\frac{1}{4}, \frac{1}{25}, \frac{1}{144}, \frac{1}{841}, \frac{1}{4900}$ **17.** 5 **19.** 13 **21.** 17 **23.** 12 **25.** 10 **27.** 6

29. a. $(8)(3) = 24$ **b.** $(4)\left(\frac{3}{2}\right) = 6$ **c.** $\left(\frac{8}{3}\right)(1) = \frac{8}{3}$ **d.** $(2)\left(\frac{3}{4}\right) = \frac{3}{2}$

e. $\left(\frac{8}{5}\right)\left(\frac{3}{5}\right) = \frac{24}{25}$ **f.** $\left(\frac{4}{3}\right)\left(\frac{1}{2}\right) = \frac{2}{3}$ **31.** 20 **33.** $\frac{20}{3}$ **35.** $\frac{7}{5}$

(131) **1. a.** $\frac{1}{17}$ **b.** $\frac{16}{3}$ **c.** $\frac{2}{11}$ **d.** $\frac{1}{36}$ **e.** $\frac{1}{25}$ **f.** $\frac{12}{17}$ **g.** $\frac{30}{31}$ **h.** $\frac{5}{16}$

3. a. $\frac{22}{35}$ **b.** $\frac{22}{35}$ **c.** $\frac{55}{14}$ **d.** $\frac{55}{14}$ **e.** $\frac{3}{40}$ **f.** $\frac{24}{5}$ **g.** $\frac{1}{28}$ **h.** $\frac{7}{4}$ **i.** $\frac{7}{15}$

j. $\frac{15}{7}$ **k.** $\frac{9}{16}$ **l.** 6 **5.** $\frac{2}{7}, \frac{11}{3}; \frac{3}{11}, \frac{7}{2}; \frac{3}{7}, \frac{11}{2}; \frac{2}{11}, \frac{7}{3}$

(132) **1.** $\frac{8}{15}$ **3.** $\frac{7}{18}$ **5.** $\frac{3}{5}$ **7.** $\frac{3}{25}$ **9.** $\frac{1}{10}$ **11.** 21 **13.** $\frac{3}{8}$ **15.** $\frac{6}{13}$ **17.** $\frac{4}{5}$

19. $\frac{1}{10}$ **21.** 3 **23.** $\frac{33}{25}$ **25.** $\frac{13}{6}$ **27.** $\frac{1}{3}$ **29.** $\frac{4}{13}$ **31.** $\frac{69}{82}$ **33.** $\frac{10}{27}$

35. $\frac{10}{287}$ **37. a.** $\frac{9}{5}$ **b.** $\frac{5}{9}$ **c.** 45 **d.** $\frac{1}{45}$ **e.** $\frac{9}{5}$ **f.** $\frac{5}{9}$ **g.** 45 **h.** $\frac{12}{7}$ **i.** $\frac{12}{7}$ **j.** $\frac{21}{4}$

k. $\frac{21}{4}$ **l.** $\frac{28}{3}$ **m.** $\frac{7}{4}$ **n.** 3 **o.** $\frac{ab}{c}$ **p.** $\frac{ac}{b}$ **q.** $\frac{5}{12}$ **r.** $\frac{16}{15}$

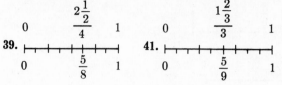

39.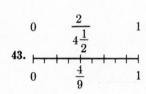

41.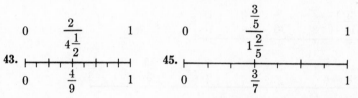

43.

45.

47. If $\dfrac{a}{b} = \dfrac{c}{d}$, then $ad = bc$, $ad = cb$, and $\dfrac{a}{c} = \dfrac{b}{d}$

49. If $\dfrac{a}{b} = \dfrac{a+c}{b+d}$, then $a(b+d) = b(a+c)$, $ab + ad = ba + bc$,

$ab + ad = ab + bc$, $ad = bc$, and $\dfrac{a}{b} = \dfrac{c}{d}$

51. If $\dfrac{a}{b} = \dfrac{c}{d}$, then $ad = bc$, $ad + bd = bc + bd$, $(a+b)d = b(c+d)$, $\dfrac{a+b}{b} = \dfrac{c+d}{d}$

(133) **1.** $\dfrac{2}{5}$ **3.** $\dfrac{2}{3}$ **5.** $\dfrac{5}{4}$ **7.** $\dfrac{10}{3}$ **9.** $\dfrac{6}{7}$ **11.** $\dfrac{21}{20}$ **13.** $\dfrac{7}{3}$ **15.** $\dfrac{8}{21}$ **17.** $\dfrac{10}{7}$ **19.** $\dfrac{1}{8}$

(134) **1.** 9   **3.** 5   **5.** $\dfrac{1}{8}$ **7.** $\dfrac{3}{8}$ **9.** $\dfrac{4}{9}$ **11.** $\dfrac{5}{12}$ **13.** $\dfrac{6}{13}$ **15.** $\dfrac{2}{7}$ **17.** $Q = 12, R = 0$

19. $Q = 5, R = \dfrac{1}{2}$ **21.** $Q = 1, R = \dfrac{5}{24}$ **23.** $Q = 0, R = \dfrac{2}{3}$ **25.** $Q = 2, R = \dfrac{11}{6}$

27. $Q = 5, R = \dfrac{1}{11}$

29. a.   **b.**

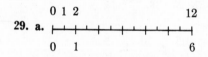 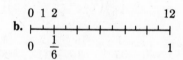

c.

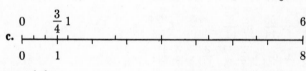

d.

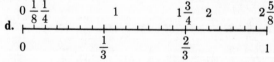

(135) **1. a.**   **b.**   **c.**

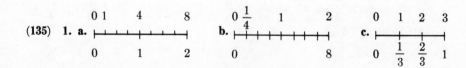

d.

$$0 \quad \tfrac{1}{3} \quad \tfrac{2}{3} \quad 1 \qquad 1\tfrac{2}{3}$$

$$0 \qquad 1 \qquad 2 \quad 2\tfrac{1}{2}$$

3. a.

$$0 \ 1 \ 2 \qquad 5 \qquad\qquad 0 \ \tfrac{1}{5} \ \tfrac{2}{5} \qquad 1 \qquad\qquad 2$$

$$0 \ \tfrac{1}{5} \ \tfrac{2}{5} \qquad 1 \qquad\qquad 0 \qquad 1 \qquad\qquad 5$$

b.

$$0 \ \tfrac{1}{15} \quad \tfrac{1}{5} \quad \tfrac{1}{3} \qquad \tfrac{2}{3} \quad \tfrac{4}{5} \qquad 1 \qquad 0 \qquad \tfrac{1}{3} \qquad \tfrac{2}{3}\ \tfrac{5}{6} \ 1$$

$$0 \qquad \tfrac{1}{6} \qquad\qquad \tfrac{5}{6} \quad 1 \qquad 0 \ \tfrac{1}{5} \qquad \tfrac{4}{5} \ 1$$

c.

$$0 \ \tfrac{1}{15} \quad \tfrac{1}{5} \quad \tfrac{1}{3} \qquad \tfrac{2}{3} \quad \tfrac{4}{5} \qquad 1 \qquad 0 \ \tfrac{1}{5} \qquad \tfrac{4}{5} \ 1 \ \tfrac{6}{5}$$

$$0 \qquad \tfrac{1}{5} \qquad\qquad 1 \quad \tfrac{6}{5} \qquad 0 \qquad \tfrac{1}{3} \quad \tfrac{2}{3} \qquad 1$$

5. 5 **7.** $\tfrac{7}{3}$ **9.** 8 **11.** $\tfrac{4}{5}$ **13.** $\tfrac{3}{2}$ **15.** $\tfrac{4}{11}$ **17.** $\tfrac{5}{7}$ **19.** $\tfrac{1}{3}$

(136) 1. $\tfrac{16}{25}$ **3.** $\tfrac{9}{14}$ **5.** $\tfrac{27}{2}$ **7.** $\tfrac{5}{6}$ **9.** $\tfrac{5}{12}$ **11.** $\tfrac{3}{20}$ **13.** $\tfrac{5}{12}$ **15.** $\tfrac{10}{9}$ **17.** 6 **19.** $\tfrac{27}{40}$

21. $\tfrac{1}{6}$ **23.** 25 **25.** 4 **27.** 25 **29.** $\tfrac{1}{25}$ **31.** $\tfrac{3}{16}$ **33.** $\tfrac{6}{5}$ **35.** $\tfrac{5}{7}$ **37.** $\tfrac{5}{6}$

39. a. 8 **b.** 0 **c.** 52 **d.** 59 **41. a.** 5 **b.** 2 **c.** 1 **d.** 0 **e.** 1

(137) 1. a. $\tfrac{1}{12}, 2, 2$ **b.** $\tfrac{1}{12}, \tfrac{15}{2}, 15$ **c.** $\tfrac{1}{9}, \tfrac{14}{3}, 14$ **d.** $\tfrac{1}{60}, 6, 6$ **e.** $\tfrac{1}{48}, \tfrac{105}{4}, 105$

3. a. $\tfrac{100}{101}$ **b.** $\tfrac{14}{20}$ **c.** $\tfrac{9}{10}$ **d.** $\tfrac{7}{4}$ **e.** $\tfrac{5}{24}$ **f.** $\tfrac{1}{1000}$ **g.** $\tfrac{20}{33}$ **h.** $\tfrac{12}{11}$ **i.** $\tfrac{11}{101}$

5. The new fraction is equivalent to the given fraction.

7. The result is the original number.

9. If $a > 1$, then a and $\dfrac{a}{a-1}$ have the same sum and product.

11. $x = \dfrac{[\ ]}{(\ )}$ **13.** $x = \dfrac{(\ )}{[\ ]}$ **15.** $x = \dfrac{(\ )}{[\ ]}$ **17.** $x = \dfrac{(\ )}{[\ ]}$ **19.** $x = \dfrac{(\ )}{[\ ]}$

21. $x = \dfrac{(\ )}{[\ ]}$ **23.** $\dfrac{20}{\frac{2}{5}} = x,\ x = 50$ **25.** $\dfrac{2\frac{1}{2}}{500} = x,\ x = \dfrac{1}{200}$

27. $x = \left[\dfrac{12}{1\frac{3}{8}}\right],\ x = 8$ **29.** $x = \dfrac{2000}{\frac{2}{5}},\ x = 5000$

(138) **1.** 5 is 10 less than 15.   15 is 10 more than 5.   5 is $\frac{1}{3}$ of 15.   15 is 3 times 5.

3. 12 is 4 less than 16.   16 is 4 more than 12.   12 is $\frac{3}{4}$ of 16.   16 is $1\frac{1}{3}$ times 12.

5. 1 is 6 less than 7.   7 is 6 more than 1.   1 is $\frac{1}{7}$ of 7.   7 is 7 times 1.

7. $\frac{3}{5}$ is $1\frac{1}{5}$ less than $1\frac{4}{5}$. $1\frac{4}{5}$ is $1\frac{1}{5}$ more than $\frac{3}{5}$. $\frac{3}{5}$ is $\frac{1}{3}$ of $1\frac{4}{5}$. $1\frac{4}{5}$ is 3 times $\frac{3}{5}$.

9. $\frac{3}{4}$ is $\frac{1}{4}$ less than 1.   1 is $\frac{1}{4}$ more than $\frac{3}{4}$. $\frac{3}{4}$ is $\frac{3}{4}$ of 1.   1 is $\frac{4}{3}$ times $\frac{3}{4}$.

11. $\frac{7}{8}$ is $4\frac{3}{8}$ less than $5\frac{1}{4}$. $5\frac{1}{4}$ is $4\frac{3}{8}$ more than $\frac{7}{8}$. $\frac{7}{8}$ is $\frac{1}{6}$ of $5\frac{1}{4}$. $5\frac{1}{4}$ is 6 times $\frac{7}{8}$.

(139) **1.** 13 is as much more than 4, as 9 is more than 0.

3. The difference between $2\frac{1}{3}$ and $1\frac{3}{4}$ is the same as that between $\frac{7}{12}$ and 0.

5. The difference comparison of 97 to 25 is the same as that of 100 to 28.

7. $1\frac{1}{4}$ is as much less than 3, as 2 is less than $3\frac{3}{4}$.

9. 35 is as many times 28, as $1\frac{1}{4}$ is times 1.

11. The ratio of 2 to $\frac{3}{4}$, is the same as that of 8 to 3.

(140) **1.** $\frac{5}{4}$ **3.** $\frac{4}{7}$ **5.** $\frac{3}{8}$ **7.** $\frac{3}{4}, \frac{4}{3}$ **9.** $2\frac{2}{3}, \frac{3}{8}$ **11.** $\frac{4}{3}, \frac{3}{4}$ **13.** $\frac{ad}{bc}, \frac{bc}{ad}$

(141) **1.** $x = 1, y = 1\frac{2}{3}$. x is $\frac{2}{3}$ (unit) less than y. x is $\frac{3}{5}$ of y.

3. $x = \frac{3}{5}, y = 1$. x is $\frac{2}{5}$ (unit) less than y. x is $\frac{3}{5}$ of y.

5. $x = 4\frac{1}{2}$ pounds, $y = 7\frac{1}{2}$ pounds. x is 3 pounds less than y. x is $\frac{3}{5}$ of y.

7. $x = \$750, y = \$1250$. x is $\$500$ less than y. x is $\frac{3}{5}$ of y.

(142) **1.** 15 is 10 less than 25, -10, 15 is $\frac{3}{5}$ of 25, $\frac{3}{5}$( ).

3. 1 is $\frac{5}{8}$ more than $\frac{3}{8}$, $+\frac{5}{8}$, 1 is $\frac{8}{3}$ times $\frac{3}{8}, \frac{8}{3}$( ).

5. $\frac{3}{4}$ is $\frac{3}{20}$ more than $\frac{3}{5}$, $+\frac{3}{20}$, $\frac{3}{4}$ is $\frac{5}{4}$ times $\frac{3}{5}, \frac{5}{4}$( ).

(143) **1.** multiplied by 2.   **3.** multiplied by 6.   **5.** multiplied by $\frac{2}{3}$.   **7.** multiplied by 2.

9. decreased by A.   **11.** at least one of the factors is zero.   **13.** less than one.
15. greater than one.   **17.** increased by 5.   **19.** decreased by 7.   **21.** decreased by 3.
23. increased by $3B$.   **25.** multiplied by 5.

(144) **1.** 16   **3.** 12   **5.** 7   **7.** 13   **9.** $6\frac{2}{3}$ **11.** $4\frac{4}{10}$ **13.** $\frac{3}{5}$ **15.** $1\frac{1}{2}$ **17.** $\frac{1}{2}$ **19.** $3\frac{4}{7}$

21. $\dfrac{9000}{7\frac{1}{2}} = \dfrac{x}{1}$, $x = 1200$ **23.** $\dfrac{x}{10} = \dfrac{36}{32}$, $x = 11\frac{1}{4}$ **25.** $\dfrac{1\frac{1}{2}}{10} = \dfrac{x}{24}$, $x = 3\frac{3}{5}$

27. hr   **29.** $\dfrac{\text{lb}}{\text{ft}^2}$ **31.** $\dfrac{\text{ft}^3}{\text{hr}}$ **33.** $\dfrac{\text{gal}}{\text{min}}$ **35.** dollars + dollars = dollars

37. $\dfrac{\text{lb}}{\text{in.}^2} - \dfrac{\text{lb}}{\text{in.}^2} = \dfrac{\text{lb}}{\text{in.}^2}$ **39.** $(\text{hr})\left(\dfrac{\text{mi}}{\text{hr}}\right) = \text{mi}$ **41.** $\text{cans}\left(\dfrac{\text{cents}}{\text{can}} - \dfrac{\text{cents}}{\text{can}}\right) = \text{cents}$

43. $\text{dollars} + \left(\dfrac{\text{dollars}}{\text{month}}\right)\left(\dfrac{\text{months}}{\text{year}}\right)(\text{years}) = \text{dollars}$ **45.** $\dfrac{(\text{bags})\left(\dfrac{\text{lb}}{\text{bag}}\right)}{\text{lb}} = 1(\text{number})$

47. $(\text{gal})\left(\dfrac{\text{mi}}{\text{gal}}\right) - (\text{gal})\left(\dfrac{\text{mi}}{\text{gal}}\right) = \text{mi}$ **49.** $\dfrac{\text{dollars}}{\text{men} - \text{men}} - \dfrac{\text{dollars}}{\text{men}} = \dfrac{\text{dollars}}{\text{men}}$

(145)   **1.** $\{(1, 1), (1, 2), (1, 3), (1, 4), (2, 2), (2, 4), (3, 3), (4, 4)\}$
  3. $\{(1, 1), (1, 2), (1, 3), (1, 4), (2, 1), (2, 3), (3, 1), (3, 2), (3, 4), (4, 1), (4, 3)\}$
  5. $\{(1, 1), (2, 2), (3, 3), (4, 4)\}$ **7.** $\{(1, 3), (2, 4)\}$
  9. $\{(1, 2), (1, 3), (1, 4), (2, 3), (2, 4), (3, 4)\}$
  11. $\{(4, 4), (4, 3), (4, 2), (4, 1), (3, 3), (3, 2), (3, 1), (2, 2), (2, 1), (1, 1)\}$
  13. $\{(4, 4), (4, 3), (3, 3), (3, 2), (2, 2), (2, 1), (1, 1)\}$
  15. $\{(1, 3), (2, 2), (3, 1)\}$ **17.** $\{(1, 2), (2, 4)\}$

(146)   **1.** (1) $\{1, 2, 3, 4\}, \{1, 2, 3, 4\}, \{1, 2, 3, 4\}$.   (5) $\{1, 2, 3, 4\}, \{1, 2, 3, 4\},$
  $\{1, 2, 3, 4\}$.   (7) $\{1, 2\}, \{3, 4\}, \{1, 2, 3, 4\}$.   (15) $\{1, 2, 3\}, \{1, 2, 3\},$
  $\{1, 2, 3\}$.   (17) $\{1, 2\}, \{2, 4\}, \{1, 2, 4\}$.
  3. $5, 7, 15, 17$ **5.** $1; 2; 16; 512; 65,536; 2^{n^2}$

(147)   **1.**
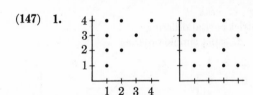

3.
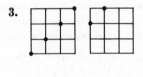

  5.

$$\begin{array}{c} \\ 1 \\ 2 \\ 3 \\ 4 \end{array} \begin{array}{cccc} 1 & 2 & 3 & 4 \\ \left[\begin{array}{cccc} 0 & 1 & 1 & 1 \\ 0 & 0 & 1 & 1 \\ 0 & 0 & 0 & 1 \\ 0 & 0 & 0 & 0 \end{array}\right] & & & \end{array} \begin{bmatrix} 1 & 0 & 0 & 0 \\ 1 & 1 & 0 & 0 \\ 1 & 1 & 1 & 0 \\ 1 & 1 & 1 & 1 \end{bmatrix}$$

  7.
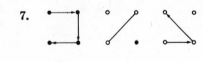

  9.
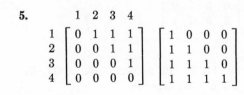

(148)   **1.** (1) R_1, S_3, T_1 (3) R_3, S_1, T_3 (5) R_1, S_1, T_1 (7) R_2, S_2, T_2
  (9) R_2, S_2, T_1, C (11) R_1, S_3, T_1, SC (13) R_1, S_3, T_3
  (15) R_3, S_1, T_1 (17) R_2, S_2, T_2

3. (1) R'_1 or R_2, S_1 or S_2 or S_3, T_1 or T_2, C or SC (The definitions do not distinguish many types for the null relation, but this is no essential loss.)
    (3) R'_1 or R_3, S_3, T_1 (5) R_2, S_2, T_1 or T_2, C (7) R_3, S_3, T_1, C
    (9) R_3, S_3, T_1, C (11) R_2, S_1, T_2, C (13) R_3, S_1, T_3, C (15) R_1, S_3, T_1, SC
5. R_2, S_2, T_1 **7.** R_2, S_2, T_2 **9.** R_2, S_4, T_3 **11.** R_1, S_1, T_1 **13.** R_1, S_4, T_1
15. R_1, S_3, T_3 **17.** R_1, S_1, T_1 **19.** R_2, S_1, T_3

(149.) **1.**   **a.**   **b.**   **c.**   **d.**   **e.**   **f.**   **g.**

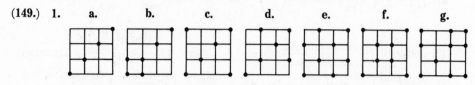

3. (R) $a + b = b + a$, $a - b \sim a - b$. (S) $a - b \sim c - d$, $a + d = b + c$,
$b + c = a + d$, $c + b = d + a$, $c - d \sim a - b$. (T) $a - b \sim c - d$,
$c - d \sim e - f$, $a + d = b + c$, $c + f = d + e$, $a + d + f = b + c + f$,
$b + c + f = b + d + e$, $a + d + f = b + d + e$, $a + f = b + e$, $a - b \sim e - f$.

5. a. $(2, 3)$ **b.** $(1, 4), (2, 1)$ **c.** $(1, 5), (3, 3), (4, 4), (5, 1), (5, 3), (5, 5),$
$(2, 4), (4, 4)$

(150) **1. a.** 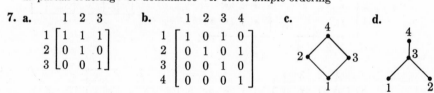 strict simple   **b.** simple

3. a. strict partial   **b.** quasi-ordering   **c.** weak
5. a. simple   **b.** weak ordering   **c.** strict partial ordering
   d. partial ordering   **e.** dominance   **f.** strict simple ordering

7. a.

	1	2	3
1	1	1	1
2	0	1	0
3	0	0	1

b.

	1	2	3	4
1	1	0	1	0
2	0	1	0	1
3	0	0	1	0
4	0	0	0	1

c.   **d.**

(151) **1.** R_1 **3.** R_4 **5.** R_6 **7.** R_2 **9.** R_6 **11.** R_4 **13.** universe   **15.** $\emptyset$ **17.** R_6
19. R_3 **21.** R_1 **23.** R_3 **25.** R_1 **27.** R_1 **29.** universe

31.   **33.**

35. child   **37.** husband   **39.** grandparent   **41.** sibling   **43.** parent
45. maternal grandparent   **47.** grandson   **49.** father-in-law   **51.** child
53. brother   **55.** brother-in-law   **57.** aunt or uncle

(152)   **1.** -10 **3.** $-\dfrac{1}{4}$ **5.** $+50$ **7.** $-\dfrac{3}{5}$ **9.** $+7-2$, or $+5$ **11.** $-7+2$, or -5

13. $-6-4$, or -10 **15.** -21 **17.** $+5$ **19.** -1 **21.** -1 **23.** -1

25. $+40-10$, or $+30$ **27.** $-14-14$, or -28 **29.** $-42+7$ or -35.   **31.** $m-n$

33. $m+n-p$ **35.** $m-n+p$ **37.** $-s-t$ **39.** $a+bc-bd$ **41.** $a-bc-bd$

43. $a+bc+bd$ **45.** $a-bc+bd$ **47.** Reflexive property. Commutativity of addition, and the definition of subtraction. Addition is well defined. Associative property. Commutativity of addition, and the definition of subtraction. Order of operations.

(153)   **1.** See problem 3 of set (149).

3. $[a, b] \oplus [c, d] = [a + c, b + d]; [c, d] \oplus [a, b] = [c + a, d + b]$
$(a + c, b + d) \sim (c + a, d + b); [a + c, b + d] = [c + a, d + b];$
$[a, b] \oplus [c, d] = [c, d] \oplus [a, b].$

5. a. $[x, y] \oplus [a, a] = [x + a, y + a] = [a + x, a + y] = [a, a] \oplus [x, y]$
$(x, y) \sim (a + x, a + y)$ since $x + (a + x) = y + (x + a)$
Hence $[x, y] = [a + x, a + y]$, and $[x, y] \oplus [a, a] = [x, y] = [a, a] \oplus [x, y]$
b. If $[b, c]$ is also an identity for $\oplus$ then $[b, c] + [a, a] = [b, c]$
and $[b, c] + [a, a] = [a, a]$. Hence $[b, c] = [a, a]$.

(154)   **1.** Since $[a, b] = [a', b']$, $a + b' = b + a'$. Since $[c, d] = [c', d']$, $c + d' = d + c'$
These eight equations then follow:

$$c(a + b') = c(b + a') \qquad d(b + a') = d(a + b')$$
$$d'(b + a') = d'(a + b') \qquad c'(a + b') = c'(b + a')$$
$$a(c + d') = a(d + c') \qquad b(d + c') = b(c + d')$$
$$a'(c + d') = a'(d + c') \qquad b'(d + c') = b'(c + d')$$

Adding and using the cancellation laws,
$$(ac + bd) + (a'd' + b'c') = (ad + bc) + (a'c' + b'd')$$
Hence $[ac + bd, ad + bc] = [a'c' + b'd', a'd' + b'c']$
$$[a, b] \odot [c, d] = [a', b'] \odot [c', d']$$

3. $[a, b] \odot ([c, d] \odot [e, f]) = [a, b] \odot [ce + df, cf + de]$
$$= [ace + adf + bcf + bde, acf + ade + bce + bdf]$$
$$= [ace + bde + adf + bcf, acf + bdf + ade + bce]$$
$$= [ac + bd, ad + bc] \odot [e, f] = ([a, b] \odot [c, d]) \odot [e, f]$$

5. a. $[a + 1, a] \odot [b, c] = [ab + b + ac, ac + c + ab] = [b, c]$
b. If $[a + 1, a]$ and $[b, c]$ are both multiplicative identities,
$[a + 1, a] = [a + 1, a] \odot [b, c] = [b, c]$, $[a + 1, a] = [b, c]$

(155)   **1.** $[10, 0]$ **3.** $[10, 0]$ **5.** $[0, 9]$ **7.** $[1, 0]$ **9.** $[0, 2]$ **11.** $[2, 0]$ **13.** $[0, 0]$

15. $[5, 0]$ **17.** $[0, 5]$ **19.** $[5, 0]$ **21.** $[0, 5]$ **23.** $[0, 11]$ **25.** $[8, 0]$ **27.** $[8, 0]$

29. $[5, 0]$ **31.** $[0, 0]$ **33.** $[25, 0]$ **35.** $[0, 0]$ **37.** $[0, 8]$ **39.** $[0, 8]$ **41.** $[8, 0]$

43. $[1, 0]$ **45.** $[0, 1]$ **47.** $[0, 1]$ **49.** $[1, 0]$ **51.** $[1, 0]$ **53.** $[1, 0]$ **55.** $[6, 0]$

57. $[0, 6]$ **59.** $[12, 0]$ **61.** $[0, 12]$ **63.** $[0, 6]$ **65.** $[12, 0]$ **67.** $[0, 12]$ **69.** $[6, 0]$

71. $[0, 0]$ **73.** $[7, 0]$ **75.** $[3, 0]$ **77.** $[30, 0]$ **79.** $[0, 0]$

81. a. $[b + c, a + d]$ **b.** $[a + d, b + c]$

(156)   **1.** 11 **3.** 11 **5.** $3\dfrac{2}{3}$ **7.** 9 **9.** $[0, 3]$ **11.** $[12, 0]$ **13.** $[9, 0]$

(157)   **1.** $[0, m] \odot [0, n] = [mn, 0]$ **3.** $[0, m] \odot [n, 0] = [0, mn]$

5. $[0, m] \oplus [0, n] = [0, m + n]$ **7.** $[m, 0] \oplus [0, m] = [0, 0]$

9. $[0, 1] \odot [n, 0] = [0, n]$

11. $[m, 0] \ominus [n, 0] = [m, 0] \oplus [0, n] = [m, n]$ If $m < n$, $[m, n] = [0, n - m]$

13. $[0, m] \ominus [n, 0] = [0, m] \oplus [0, n] = [0, m + n]$

15. $[0, m] \ominus [0, n] = [0, m] \oplus [n, 0] = [n, m]$. If $m < n$, $[n, m] = [n - m, 0]$

17. $m - n = {}^+m - {}^+n = [m, 0] \ominus [n, 0] = [m, 0] \oplus [0, n] = [m, n]$

(158) **1.** $+11$ **3.** -5 **5.** $+5$ **7.** -11 **9.** -5 **11.** $+5$ **13.** $+10$ **15.** -2 **17.** $+10$

19. $+2$ **21.** -7 **23.** $+7$ **25.** -13 **27.** $+13$ **29.** -7 **31.** $+7$ **33.** $+13$ **35.** -13

37. -4 **39.** $+8$ **41.** 0 **43.** -8 **45.** -2 **47.** $+2$ **49.** -2 **51.** $+12$ **53.** $+4$ **55.** $+17$

(159) **1.** $[2 + (-4)] (+3) + (-1)$ **3.** $[+2 - (-4)] 3 + 1$ **5.** $[+8 + (-5)] (-6 +9)$

7. $(- 8 + 5)(+ 6 - (+9))$ **9.** $(-7)10 + (+5)(-2)$ **11.** $+12(-4) - (-4)3$

13. -7 **15.** 19 **17.** 9 **19.** 9 **21.** -80 **23.** -36 **25.** 13 **27.** -1 **29.** -4

31. 20 **33.** -7 **35.** 2 **37.** $+4$ **39.** $+11$ **41.** $-2, 4, -6, 8, -10$

43. $-1, +3, -6, +10$ **45.** $\{-2, 2\}$ **47.** $\{0\}$ **49.** $\{-1, 0, 1\}$ **51.** $\emptyset$

53. $\{1\}$ **55.** $\{-2\}$ **57.** $\{1, 2, 3\}$ **59.** $\{-3, -2\}$ **61.** $\{1, 2, 3\}$ **63.** $\{0, 1, 2, 3\}$

65. $\{0\}$ **67.** $\{-1, 0, 1\}$.

(160) **1.** $q = 4, r = 5$ **3.** $q = -4, r = 5$ **5.** $q = -5, r = 3$ **7.** $q = 5, r = 3$

9. $q = 7, r = 5$ **11.** $q = -18, r = 14$ **13.** $q = 0, r = 5$ **15.** $q = -1, r = 12$

(161) **1.** Let $\dfrac{-m}{+n} = x$. $-m = (x)(+n)$. $[0, m] = x \odot [n, 0]$. $\left[0, \dfrac{m}{1}\right] = x \odot \left[\dfrac{n}{1}, 0\right]$.

$x = \left[0, \dfrac{m}{n}\right] = -\dfrac{m}{n}$. **3.** $-\dfrac{1}{2}, +\dfrac{1}{4}, -\dfrac{1}{8}, +\dfrac{1}{16}$ **5.** $1, \dfrac{1}{2}, \dfrac{5}{6}, \dfrac{7}{12}$

7. a. 5 **b.** -6 **c.** 25 **d.** -26 **e.** -25 **9. a.** 1 **b.** $\dfrac{3}{4}$ **c.** 1 **d.** $1\dfrac{3}{4}$ **e.** 3

(162) **1.** B **3.** A **5.** B **7.** A **9.** A **11.** B **13.** 15 degrees below zero.

15. $2\dfrac{1}{2}$ hours before noon **17.** a gain of \$75 **19.** 4 miles to the east.

21.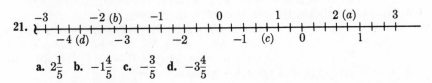

a. $2\dfrac{1}{5}$ **b.** $-1\dfrac{4}{5}$ **c.** $-\dfrac{3}{5}$ **d.** $-3\dfrac{4}{5}$

(163) **1.**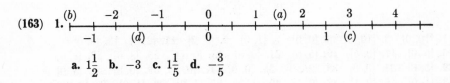

a. $1\dfrac{1}{2}$ **b.** -3 **c.** $1\dfrac{1}{5}$ **d.** $-\dfrac{3}{5}$

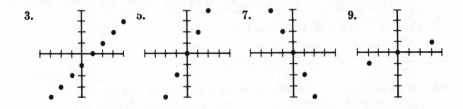

3.   **5.**   **7.**   **9.**

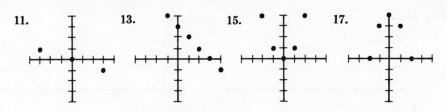

11.   13.   15.   17.

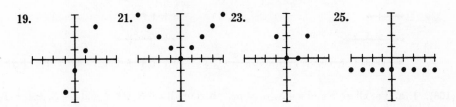

19.   21.   23.   25.

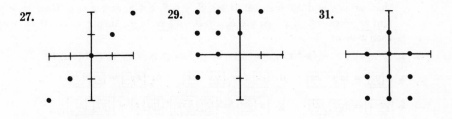

27.   29.   31.

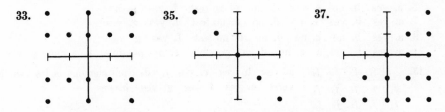

33.   35.   37.

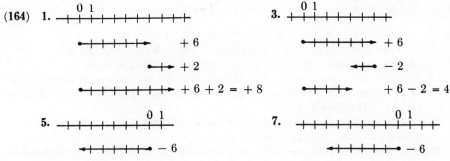

(164) 1.

0 1

+ 6

+ 2

+ 6 + 2 = + 8

3.

0 1

+ 6

− 2

+ 6 − 2 = 4

5.

0 1

− 6

+ 2

− 6 + 2 = − 4

7.

0 1

− 6

− 2

− 6 − 2 = 8

9. #3 11. #1 13. #7 15. #5 17. #1 19. #3 21. #5 23. #7

(165) 1.

3.

5.

7.

(166) 1. a. For all $x \in S$ and $y \in S$, $xy = yx$.   b. For all $x \in S$, $y \in S$, and $z \in S$, $\underline{\underline{xyz}} = \underline{\underline{xyz}}$.

c. For all $x \in S$, $ex = x$ and $xe = x$.   d. For all $x \in S$ there exists $y \in S$ such that $\underline{yx} = e$ and $\underline{xy} = e$.   e. If $x \in S$, $y \in S$, $z \in S$, and $x = y$, then $\underline{xz} = \underline{yz}$ and $\underline{zx} = \underline{zy}$.   f. If $x \in S$, $y \in S$, $z \in S$, and $\underline{xz} = \underline{yz}$, then $x = y$. If $\underline{zx} = \underline{zy}$, then $x = y$.

3. a. $(y \triangle z) * x = (y * x) \triangle (z * x)$ b. $(y * z) \triangle x = (y \triangle x) * (z \triangle x)$

c. $x \boxed{yz} = \boxed{xy} \ \boxed{xz}$ d. $\boxed{yz} x = \boxed{yx} \ \boxed{zx}$ e. $\boxed{xyz} = \boxed{xy} \ \boxed{xz}$

f. $\boxed{yz \ x} = \boxed{yx} \ \boxed{zx}$ g. $x \boxed{yz} = \boxed{xy} \ \boxed{xz}$, $\boxed{yz} x = \boxed{yx} \ \boxed{zx}$

5. a. yes   b. no   c. yes   d. no   e. no test   f. yes   g. no
7. a. yes   b. yes   c. no   d. no   e. no test   f. yes   g. yes
9. a. yes   b. no   c. no   d. no   e. no test   f. yes   g. yes
11. a. yes   b. yes, a c. no   d. not possible   e. not possible   f. $a; c; b$ g. yes

13.

	f_1	f_2	f_3	f_4
f_1	f_1	f_2	f_3	f_4
f_2	f_2	f_1	f_4	f_3
f_3	f_3	f_4	f_1	f_2
f_4	f_4	f_3	f_2	f_1

a. yes   b. yes   c. yes, f_1 d. each element is its own inverse   e. yes   f. yes   g. yes   h. yes

(167) 1. $+1, -1, +2, -2, +3, -3, +4, -4, +6, -6, +12, -12$
3. $ha + ka = (h + k)a$. $h + k$ is an integer. $ha + ka$ is a multiple of a.
5. $(ha)(ka) = (hka)a$. hka is an integer. $(ha)(ka)$ is a multiple of a.
7. $c_1 - c_2 = ab_1 - ab_2 = a(b_1 - b_2)$. $b_1 - b_2$ is an integer. $c_1 - c_2$ is divisible by a.
9. If $a \mid b$, there exists an integer k such that $b = ka$. Then $bc = cka$. ck is an integer.   Therefore $a \mid bc$.
11. If $a \mid b$ and $b \mid c$, there exist integers h and k such that $ah = b$ and $bk = c$. Hence $c = ahk$. hk is an integer. $a \mid c$.
13. The relation is reflexive from (10), transitive from (11), and antisymmetric from (12).
15. If $a \mid b$ and $a \mid c$, there exist integers m and n such that $b = ma$ and $c = na$. $bx = xma$ and $cy = yna$. $bx + cy = xma + yna = a(mx + ny)$. $mx + ny$ is an integer. $a \mid (bx + cy)$.
17. $1 \cdot b = b, 1 \mid b$. $(-1)(-b) = b, -1 \mid b$.
19. If $a \mid b$, there exists an integer k such that $ak = b$. $a + b = a + ak$, $c = a + b = a + ak = a(1 + k)$. $1 + k$ is an integer. $a \mid c$

21. $m \mid (15n + 13)$. $m \mid (3n + 2)$. $m \mid (-5)(3n + 2)$. $m \mid (-15n - 10)$.
$m \mid [(15n + 13) + (-15n - 10)]$. $m \mid 3$. $m > 1$. $m = 3$.

(168) **1.** $a \geq 0, b \geq 0, |a| = a, |b| = b, a + b \geq 0, |a + b| = a + b = |a| + |b|$
$a < 0, b < 0, |a| = -a, |b| = -b$.
   $a + b < 0, |a + b| = -(a + b) = -a - b = |a| + |b|$
$a = 0, b < 0, |a| = a, |b| = -b$.
   $a + b < 0, |a + b| = -a - b = 0 - b = |a| + |b|$
$a < 0, b = 0, |a| = -a, |b| = b$.
   $a + b < 0, |a + b| = -a - b = -a + 0 = |a| + |b|$
$a > 0, b < 0, |a| = a, |b| = -b$.
   If $a + b \geq 0, |a + b| = a + b < a - b = |a| + |b|$
   If $a + b < 0, |a + b| = -a - b < a - b = |a| + |b|$
$a < 0, b > 0, |a| = -a, |b| = b$.
   If $a + b \geq 0, |a + b| = a + b < -a + b = |a| + |b|$
   If $a + b < 0, |a + b| = -a - b < -a + b = |a| + |b|$
3. $(9, 25) = 1 = 4 \cdot 25 - 11 \cdot 9 = 13 \cdot 25 - 36 \cdot 9$
5. $(29, 13) = 1 = 9 \cdot 13 - 4 \cdot 29 = 38 \cdot 13 - 17 \cdot 29$
7. $(8, 13) = 1 = 5 \cdot 8 - 3 \cdot 13 = 18 \cdot 8 - 11 \cdot 13$
9. $(10, 6) = 2 = 2 \cdot 6 - 10 = 7 \cdot 6 - 4 \cdot 10$
11. $(180, 66) = 6$
13. $871 = 13 \cdot 67, 1139 = 17 \cdot 67$
15. $(15, 21, 35) = 1 = 36 \cdot 21 - 48 \cdot 15 - 1 \cdot 35$
17. $(78696, 19332) = 36 = 212(78696) - 863(19332)$
19. $104, 195, 8$
21. $3 \cdot 5 - 2 \cdot 7 = 1, 3 \cdot 25 - 2 \cdot 35 = 5$

(169) **1.** 0, 3, 6 **3.** 2, 5 **5.** 1, 4, 6 **7.** 4, **9.** 5 **11.** 6 **13.** 3, 4 **15.** no solution
17. 3, 4; 2, 10 **19.** 5, 7; 2, 12 **21.** 3, 4; 2, 10 **23.** 2, 4; 3, 9

(170) **1.** 5, 7, 8, 4, 2, 1, 5, 7, 8, 4 **3.** 1 **9.** 1

(171) **1. a.** 6, 6, 3, 11 **b.** 7, 0, 3, 0 **c.** 8, 8, 0, 11 **d.** 1, 4, 1, 6
3. a. 3 **b.** 1 **c.** 8 **d.** 2 **e.** 0 **f.** 5 **g.** $487 = 121 \cdot 4 + 3 = 81 \cdot 6 + 1$,
$7763 = 705 \cdot 11 + 8 = 597 \cdot 13 + 2 = 1109 \cdot 7 = 862 \cdot 9 + 5$
5. a. 11101 **b.** 110101 **c.** 2211 **d.** 11102

(172) **1.** $[a] + [b] = [a + b] = [b + a] = [b] + [a]$
3. $([a] \cdot [b]) \cdot [c] = [a \cdot b] \cdot [c] = [(a \cdot b) \cdot c] = [a \cdot (b \cdot c)] = [a] \cdot [bc] = [a] \cdot ([b] \cdot [c])$.
5. $[a] + [0] = [a + 0] = [a] = [0 + a] = [0] + [a]$
7. $[a] \cdot ([b] + [c]) = [a] \cdot [b + c] = [a(b + c)] = [ab + ac] =$
$[ab] + [ac] = [a] \cdot [b] + [a] \cdot [c]$.

9.

+	0	1
0	0	1
1	1	0

·	0	1
0	0	0
1	0	1

Let zero correspond to the even numbers, and one to the odd numbers.

11. Days of the week **13.** Hours of the day.

(173) **1. a.** $\overline{0}, \overline{4}, \overline{3}, \overline{2}, \overline{1}$ **b.** $\overline{1}, \overline{3}, \overline{2}, \overline{4}$ **3.** $\overline{2} \cdot_6 \overline{3} = 0$, or $\overline{4} \cdot_6 \overline{3} = 0$
5. a. $\overline{1}$ **b.** $\overline{0}$ **c.** $\overline{6}$ **d.** $\overline{2}$ **e.** not defined **f.** not defined **g.** $\overline{6}$ **h.** $\overline{6}$ **i.** $\overline{2}$ **j.** $\overline{3}$
7. a. 2 **b.** 6 **c.** 2 **d.** 4 **e.** 1 **f.** 0 **g.** 2 **h.** 1, 6 **i.** 2, 5 **j.** no solution
   k. 3, 4 **l.** 3, 5, 6 **m.** 4 **n.** 2, 5 **o.** 0
9. a. 3 **b.** no solution **c.** 1, 3, 5 **d.** 0, 3 **e.** 2, 4 **f.** no solution

(174)   **1.** $\dfrac{1}{11}$ **3.** $\dfrac{2}{7}$ **5.** $\dfrac{1}{8}$ **7.** 9   **9.** $\dfrac{1}{12}$ **11.** -5 **13.** $\dfrac{1}{25}$ **15.** 64   **17.** $\dfrac{9}{64}$ **19.** $\dfrac{2}{5}$

      21. $\dfrac{4}{3}$ **23.** $\dfrac{3}{8}$ **25.** -32 **27.** 81   **29.** -81

(175)   **1.** $6(10)^1 + 3(10)^0$ **3.** $6(10)^0 + 3(10)^{-1}$ **5.** $6(10)^{-1} + 3(10)^{-2}$

      7. $0(10)^{-1} + 6(10)^{-2} + 3(10)^{-3}$ **9.** $6(10)^{-1} + 0(10)^{-2} + 3(10)^{-3}$

     11. $6(10)^0 + 0(10)^{-1} + 3(10)^{-2}$ **13.** $0(10)^{-1} + 1(10)^{-2} + 2(10)^{-3} + 5(10)^{-4}$

     15. $9(10)^0 + 9(10)^{-1} + 9(10)^{-2}$ **17.** $1(10)^0 + 4(10)^{-1} + 1(10)^{-2} + 4(10)^{-3}$

     19. $3(10)^0 + 1(10)^{-1} + 4(10)^{-2} + 1(10)^{-3} + 6(10)^{-4}$ **21.** $3(5)^0 + 4(5)^{-1}$

     23. $0(3)^{-1} + 2(3)^{-2}$ **25.** $8(12)^1 + 7(12)^0 + 11(12)^{-1} + 5(12)^{-2}$

     27. $1(2)^1 + 1(2)^0 + 0(2)^{-1} + 1(2)^{-2} + 0(2)^{-3} + 1(2)^{-4}$

     29. $2(10)^{-1} + 5(10)^{-2},\; 2\left(\dfrac{1}{10}\right)^1 + 5\left(\dfrac{1}{10}\right)^2$

     31. $0(5)^{-1} + 1(5)^{-2} + 2(5)^{-3},\; 0\left(\dfrac{1}{5}\right)^1 + 1\left(\dfrac{1}{5}\right)^2 + 2\left(\dfrac{1}{5}\right)^3$

     33. $5(8)^{-1} + 5(8)^{-2} + 5(8)^{-3},\; 5\left(\dfrac{1}{8}\right)^1 + 5\left(\dfrac{1}{8}\right)^2 + 5\left(\dfrac{1}{8}\right)^3$

     35. $1(2)^{-1} + 0(2)^{-2} + 1(2)^{-3} + 1(2)^{-4},\; 1\left(\dfrac{1}{2}\right)^1 + 0\left(\dfrac{1}{2}\right)^2 + 1\left(\dfrac{1}{2}\right)^3 + 1\left(\dfrac{1}{2}\right)^4$

(176)   **1.** $\dfrac{63}{1},\dfrac{63}{10},\dfrac{63}{100},\dfrac{63}{1000},\dfrac{603}{1000},\dfrac{603}{100},\dfrac{125}{10000},\dfrac{999}{100},\dfrac{1414}{1000},\dfrac{31416}{10000}.$

     3. $254(10)^{-2}, 5(10)^{-3}, 101(10)^{-2}, 7(10)^0, 314(10)^{-2}, 333(10)^{-3}, 1732(10)^{-3},$
        $3937(10)^{-2}, 27182(10)^{-4}, 7854(10)^{-4}$

     5. $34(10)^{-1}_{(five)}, 2(10)^{-2}_{(three)}, 87e5(10)^{-2}_{(twelve)}, 110101(10)^{-100}_{(two)}$

     7. a. 25.   **b.** 2.5   **c.** .025   **9.** $.123_{(five)}$ **11.** $11.101_{(two)}$

(177)   **1. a.** 6.1   **b.** .0164   **c.** 80.4   **d.** 720.   **e.** .0688   **f.** .080   **g.** .74   **h.** .34

     3. a. 4.34   **b.** 9.45   **c.** 130.   **d.** 5360   **e.** .0789   **f.** .00020   **g.** .03   **h.** 238.

     i. 7.07

(178)   **1.** 92,000; 92,200; 92,150   **3.** 31,000; 31,400; 31,420

     5. 43,000; 43,000; 43,000   **7.** 110,000; 107,000; 107,100

     9. 990,000; 989,000; 989,400   **11.** 18.; 17.5; 17.54   **13.** 6.1; 6.08; 6.080

     15. .050; .0500; _____   **17.** .0014; .00145; .001450   **19.** .11; .108; .1080

(179)   **1. a.** $3.71(10)^5$ **b.** $9.4(10)^{-4}$ **c.** $1.1(10)^7$ **d.** $2.3(10)^{-2}$ **e.** $6.0(10)^{-2}$

     f. $1(10)^2$ **g.** $1.487(10)^6$ **h.** $3.89(10)^{-5}$

     3. a. .00056   **b.** .604   **c.** 290000.   **d.** .0766   **e.** 30,000,000

     f. 1070.   **g.** 5,000,000   **h.** 5,000,000

     5. a. $5.34(10)^4$ **b.** $9.1(10)^{-3}$ **c.** $6.183(10)^1$ **d.** $8.46(10)^{-1}$ **e.** $2.4(10)^{-5}$

     f. $8.31(10)$ **g.** $5.14(10)^4$ **h.** $5.14(10)$

     7. a. $32(10)^{-2}$ **b.** $7(10)^{-4}$ **c.** $153(10)$ **d.** $14(10)^{-5}$ **e.** $860(10)^{-4}$

     f. $2753(10)^{-1}$ **g.** $3700(10)^{-1}$ **h.** $3982(10)^{-2}$

     9. a. $210(10)^{-2}, 305(10)^{-2}$ **b.** $732(10)^{-2}, 400(10)^{-2}$ **c.** $9,200(10)^{-3}, 3,175(10)^{-3}$

     d. $300(10)^{-4}, 70(10)^{-4}$

(180)   **1. a.** 8.9; 8.9   **b.** .627; .6   **c.** 9.2871; 9.29   **d.** 13.21; 13.21   **e.** .0459; .0459

     f. 42.13; 42.   **g.** 20.498; 20.5   **h.** 272.57; 272.6

     3. a. 4.81; 5.   **b.** .0665; .067   **c.** $-.007; -.007$

     5. a. $+2$ **b.** $+.2$ **c.** $-.47$ **d.** $-.0045$

(181)   **1.** 102.   **3.** .240   **5.** 584.   **7.** 7.44   **9.** .171   **11.** .00383   **13.** 26,400.
 15. 43.1   **17.** .00389   **19.** .0371   **21.** $4(10) \cdot 2 = 80$; 74.34; 74.
 23. $6(10)^{-1} \cdot 5(10) = 30$; 30.683; 31.   **25.** $8(10)^{-1} \cdot 3(10)^{-1} = .24$; .23936; .24
 27. $8(10)^{-2} \cdot 7(10)^{-3} = .00056$; .000567; .0006
 29. $6(10)^{-1} = .6$; .554785; .555   **31.** $1(10) = 10$; 10.682; 10.

(182)   **1.** 2.6   **3.** 5.84   **5.** 94.3   **7.** .27

(183)   **1.** 3.   **3.** .2   **5.** 4.   **7.** 4.   **9.** .3   **11.** 3.   **13.** 700   **15.** .001   **17.** .0306
 19. 55.8   **21.** .0557   **23.** 797.   **25.** 2.6   **27.** 5.84   **29.** 94.3   **31.** .4375   **33.** 430

(184)   **1. a.** 125, .375   **b.** 5, .55   **c.** 4, .28   **d.** 625, .6875   **e.** 3125, .15625
 f. 125, 1.375   **g.** 8, .152
 3. .9375   **5.** .4875   **7.** 2.625   **9.** $.101_{(two)}$ **11.** $.22_{(four)}$ **13.** $.44_{(six)}$
 15. $.6_{(eight)}$ **17.** $.201_{(three)}$ **19.** .4, .43, .429, .4, .43, .429
 21. .2, .22, .222, .2, .22, .222   **23.** .1, .06, .065, .06, .065, .0645
 25. 1.7, 1.71, 1.714, 2., 1.7, 1.71   **27.** 1.8, 1.79, 1.786, 2., 1.8, 1.79
 29. .1, .08, .078, .08, .078, .0784   **31.** $.223_{(four)}$ **33.** $.334_{(five)}$
 35. $.0121_{(three)}$ **37.** $.632_{(eight)}$

(185)   **1. a.** $.74_{(eight)}$ **b.** $.5343_{(six)}$ **c.** $.e3_{(twelve)}$ **3. a.** $\dfrac{19}{27}$ **b.** $\dfrac{54}{625}$ **c.** $\dfrac{63}{64}$

 7. a. $7\dfrac{5}{9}, \dfrac{68}{9}$ **b.** $30\dfrac{9}{16}, \dfrac{489}{16}$ **c.** $3\dfrac{29}{125}, \dfrac{404}{125}$ **d.** $5\dfrac{3}{8}, \dfrac{43}{8}$

(186)   **1.** $.\overline{6}$ **3.** $2.\overline{3}$ **5.** $.\overline{135}$ **7.** $.\overline{076923}$ **9.** $.\overline{4}$ **11.** $.\overline{25}$ **13.** $.\overline{005}$ **15.** $.41\overline{6}$
 17. $.0\overline{7}$ **19.** $\dfrac{4}{33}$ **21.** $\dfrac{11}{90}$ **23.** $\dfrac{34}{3,330}$ **25.** $\dfrac{21578}{49500}$ **27.** $\dfrac{7}{999}$

 29. a. $\dfrac{71}{33}$ **b.** $\dfrac{71}{33}$ **31. a.** $.\overline{53}_{(nine)}$ **b.** $.\overline{3}_{(six)}$ **c.** $.3_{(five)}$ **d.** $.\overline{21}_{(four)}$ **e.** $.\overline{1210}_{(three)}$

 33. a. $\dfrac{1}{16}$ **b.** $\dfrac{11}{24}$ **35.** $.\overline{39}$ $.3\overline{9}$ $.\overline{41}$ $.4\overline{1}$

(187)   **1. a.** 18   **b.** .0055   **c.** $\dfrac{11}{32}$ **3.** 8   **5.** 1   **7.** $\dfrac{2}{15}$ **9.** 1.11   **11.** .509   **13.** 0

(188)   **1.** $\bar{y} = -1, \bar{x} = 1464$.   **3. a.** $c\bar{x}$ **b.** $\bar{x} + k$ **5.** 83   **7.** 2.8

(189)   **1.** 4   **3.** $\dfrac{2}{5}$ **5.** 21   **7.** 48   **9.** $\dfrac{9}{8}$ **11.** .82   **13.** 14.0   **15.** .3   **17.** 40   **19.** 81

 21. .09   **23.** 150   **25.** $c = \dfrac{24 - 9}{24}, c = \dfrac{5}{8}$ **27.** $28 = \dfrac{2}{3} p, p = 42$

 29. $120,000 = \dfrac{4}{5} G, G = 150,000$

(190)   **1.** $\dfrac{7}{20}$, 35%   **3.** 1.75, 175%   **5.** $\dfrac{13}{400}$, .0325   **7.** $\dfrac{31}{250}$, $12\dfrac{2}{5}\%$ **9.** .0075, $\dfrac{3}{4}\%$

 11. $\dfrac{1}{400}$, .0025   **13.** 34   **15.** 84   **17.** $62\dfrac{1}{2}\%$ **19.** $162\dfrac{1}{2}\%$ **21.** 140   **23.** 78
 25. 40%   **27.** 26   **29.** 1.10   **31.** 150%

(191)   **1. a.** What is 40% of 85?   **b.** $x = (.40)(85)$
 3. a. What is 140% of 60?   **b.** $x = (1.40)(60)$
 5. a. 60 is what percent of 96?   **b.** $60 = (x)(96)$
 7. a. 143 is what percent of 88?   **b.** $143 = (x)(88)$
 9. a. 119 is 85% of what number?   **b.** $119 = (.85)(x)$

11. a. 104 is $133\frac{1}{3}\%$ of what number?   **b.** $104 = \left(\frac{4}{3}\right)(x)$

13. a. 39 is how many percent less than 65? $65 - 39 = (x)(65)$

15. a. What number is 80% less than 130? $x = 130 - (.80)(130)$

17. a. 1.54 is 40% more than what number? $1.54 = x + (.40)(x)$

19. a. 9,210 is how many percent more than 3,684? $9,210 - 3,684 = (x)(3,684)$

21. $x = 16.8$.   What number is 80% less than 84?

23. $x = 45$.   What number is 25% more than 36?

25. $x = 80$.   56 is 30% less than what number?

27. $x = 70$.   77 is 10% more than what number?

29. $x = 15.4\%$.   75 is how many percent more than 65?

31. $61.88   **33. a.** $5,940   **b.** $5,940   **35.** 15%

37. 4 grams of salt, 76 grams of water   **39.** 25%

(192) **1. a.** .05; .12; 12%   **b.** .05; .012; 1.2%   **c.** .005; .012; 1.2%   **d.** .005; .12; 12%
     e. .005; .012; 1.2%   **f.** .0005; .0012; .12%   **g.** .005; .016; 1.6%
     h. .0005; .016; 1.6%   **i.** .0005; .0077; .77%   **j.** .0005; .00077; .007%

(193) **1.** 15   **3.** 91   **5.** 165   **7.** $\frac{33}{35}$

(194) **1. a.** -1 **b.** $\frac{1}{4}$ **c.** $-\frac{1}{25}$ **d.** $\frac{1}{144}$ **e.** $-\frac{1}{841}$ **f.** $\frac{1}{4,900}$

     3. a. -1 **b.** $\frac{1}{16}$ **c.** $-\frac{1}{289}$ **5. a.** $-\frac{3}{4}$ **b.** $\frac{1}{9}$ **c.** $-\frac{3}{196}$

     7. a. $-.04$ **b.** .25   **c.** $-.0119$ **d.** .0164   **e.** $-.000604$ **f.** .002225

     9. a. $\frac{1}{4}$ **b.** $-\frac{7}{64}$ **c.** $\frac{17}{256}$ **d.** $-\frac{727}{16,384}$

(195) **1.** $\frac{4}{9}$ **3.** $\frac{7}{33}$ **5.** $\frac{1}{9}$ **7.** $\frac{41}{333}$ **9.** .123   **11.** .826   **13.** .312   **15.** .0102   **17.** 1.65
     19. 1.54   **21.** .4, .48, .496, .4992, .49984

(196) **1.** 121, 144, 169, 196   **3.** 1, 4, 9, 16, 25, 36   **5.** 13.23   **7.** 12.37   **9.** 14.56
     11. 60.83   **13.** 21.64   **15.** 19.18

(197) **1.** 17.32   **3.** 54.77   **5.** 173.2   **7.** .1732   **9.** .05477   **11.** .5477   **13.** 91.10   **15.** 28.
     17. .64   **19.** 520   **21.** .02   **23.** 78.

(198) **1.** 13.78   **3.** 23.73   **5.** .7503   **7.** .04870   **9.** 615.2   **11.** 2.10   **13.** .710
     15. 2.87, $2\frac{3}{4}$ **17.** .771, $\frac{25}{32}$

(199) **1. a.** 3   **b.** 9   **c.** 27   **d.** 81   **e.** 243   **3. a.** 5   **b.** 1   **c.** $\frac{1}{5}$ **d.** $\frac{1}{25}$ **e.** $\frac{1}{125}$

     5. $\frac{1}{16}$ **7.** $\frac{1}{64}$ **9.** .1   **11.** $\frac{1}{13}$ **13.** $\frac{1}{2}$ **15.** 4   **17.** 3   **19.** 6

(200) **1.** D; A_4; A_4; cancellation law for addition.
     3. A_5; A_5; cancellation law for addition.
     5. M_5; M_4; cancellation law for multiplication.
     7. D; A_5; problem 1; A_5; cancellation law for addition.
        $ab + (-a)b = (a + (-a))b = 0 \cdot b = 0.$ $ab + -(ab) = 0.$
        $-(ab) = (-a)b.$ D; A_5; problem 1; A_5; cancellation law for addition.
     9. M_3; M_2; M_2; M_5; M_4; M_5; M_5; cancellation law for multiplication.

(201)   **1.** Definition; A_4.   **3.** Definition; problem 5 in set (200); M_4.
        5. Addition is well defined; A_2; A_5; A_4.   **7.** Definition; M_2; M_5; M_4
        9. Definition; problem 10 in set (200); A_2; definition.
        11. Addition is well defined; A_2; A_5, and definition; A_4 and A_3; addition is well defined; definition and A_2; A_5; A_4.
        Addition is well defined; definition and A_3; A_2; A_5; A_4; addition is well defined; definition; A_2; A_5; A_4.
        13. a. $(a - b) + (c - d) = a + (-b) + c + (-d) = a + c + (-b) + (-d) =$
        $a + c + [-(b + d)] = (a + c) - (b + d)$
        Definition; A_2; A_3; problem 10 in set (200); definition.

        b. $\left(\dfrac{a}{b}\right)\left(\dfrac{c}{d}\right) = a \cdot b^{-1} \cdot c \cdot d^{-1} = a \cdot c \cdot b^{-1} \cdot d^{-1} = a \cdot c \cdot (bd)^{-1} = \dfrac{ac}{bd}$

        Definition and M_2; M_3; problem 9 in set (200); definition.

(202)   **1.** M_4; Definition; Example B; Example G; problems 1 and 8 in set (200); Example B, O_3; O_3.   **3.** M_4; problem 2 in set (202); M_4.
        3. M_4; problem 2 in set (202); M_4.
        5. Definition; O_2; problem 7 in set (200); problem 3 in set (200) and Example A.
        7. O_3; M_5; M_5; problem 1 in set (200); problem 5 in set (202); problem 1 in set (202); O_3.

(203)   **1. a.** 180°, 540°, 900°   **b.** 72°, 144°, 216°, 288°   **c.** 60°, 300°, 420°
        d. 30°, 150°, 210°   **e.** 18°, 198°, 414°   **f.** 15°, 285°   **3.** 15°   **5.** 60°

(204)   **1. a.** 12, 8, 10, 24   **b.** 2.4, 3.5, 4.5, 12
        c. 34, 4.5, 3.3, 10.2   **d.** 15, 48, 32, 40
        3. 8.425, $-.001$; 8.482; $-.003$; 8.540, $-.004$; 8.598, $-.004$; 8.656, $-.004$;
        8.713, $-.005$; 8.771, $-.004$; 8.829, $-.003$; 8.886, $-.002$
        5. a. .4022   **b.** .9080   **c.** 8187   **d.** 35.48   **e.** 63

(205)   **1.** 11.5   **3.** 7.5   **5.** 5   **7.** 11

(206)   **7.** $c = 13$ **9.** $b = 24$ **11.** $a = 12$ **13.** $b = .34$ **15.** $a = 141.4$ **17.** $b = .07937$
        19. $\sqrt{50} + \sqrt{41} + \sqrt{13}$ or $5\sqrt{2} + \sqrt{41} + \sqrt{13}$
        21. $\sqrt{5} + \sqrt{74} + \sqrt{17}$
        23. $\sqrt{53} + \sqrt{40} + \sqrt{10} + \sqrt{13}$ or $\sqrt{53} + 3\sqrt{10} + \sqrt{13}$

(207)   **1. a.** 1   **b.** 2   **c.** 1.25   **d.** 1.5   **e.** 1.375   **f.** $1\frac{1}{3}$

        g. $1 < 1.25 < 1\frac{1}{3} < 1.375 < 1.5 < 2$

        3. .784

Index

List of Symbols (Cont.)

References are to pages on which the symbol is introduced, defined, or illustrated.

Symbol	Meaning or Name	Page
$+n$	Addition operator	203
$-n$	Subtraction operator	203
$(\ )^n$	Exponential operator	205
$f \circ g$	Composition of mappings or functions	206
$f(n)$	Notation for functions	218
$\dfrac{a}{b}$	Fraction; numeral for a rational number	232
$a \geq b$	a is greater than or equal to b	267
$a \leq b$	a is less than or equal to b	267
$a \not> b$	a is not greater than b	267
$a \not< b$	a is not less than b	267
$a < b < c$	b is greater than a and less than c	267
$a \doteq b$	a is approximately equal to b	271
$[a, b]$	Closed interval	275
(a, b)	Open interval	275
$(a, b], [a, b)$	Half-open intervals	275
$[a]$	The greatest integer not greater than a	318
$a\,R\,b$	a has relation R to b	342
$a \sim b$	a is equivalent to b	348
$[x]$	Notation for equivalence classes	350
$\breve{R}$	Converse relation	357
R/S	The relative product of relation R and relation S	358
$-1(\ ), -(\ )$	Opposite operators	361